M000092124

Rebugging
your home & garden

A step by step guide to modern pest control

Ruth Troetschler

• Alison Woodworth • Sonja Wilcomer

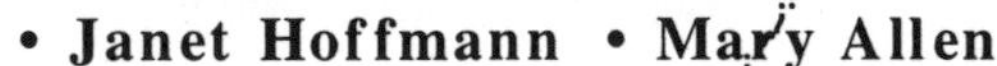
• Janet Hoffmann • Mary Allen

PTF Press, Los Altos

Disclaimer

The information presented in this book accurate to the best of the knowledge of the authors, and is based on research published in the scientific literature. Users should use their own judgement when adopting any of these techniques.

If you wish to apply pesticides, carefully review the information about measuring, dilution, and toxicity presented in the appendix. Most pesticides should be diluted. Apply them as sparingly as possible, and only according to the label. Gloves and other protective clothing should be worn by the applicator. Only selective materials which degrade rapidly can be recommended. Pesticides and all other toxics should be stored in a locked cupboard.

The authors do not guarantee that the current registration status of the pesticides mentioned in this book is accurate, since these change over time. Omission of a registered product, does not imply that is is not appropriate for use, nor does inclusion suggest that we endorse such a product.

Printed in the United States of America on Recycled Paper
by Thomson-Shore, Inc. Dexter, MI 48130

PTF Press, 184 Lockhart Lane, Los Altos, CA 94022

ISBN 0-9648515-0-4 $19.95

Why another pest control book ?

The good information in most pest control books is hidden in a mountain of text. In the back is a chart with a list of pests along one margin, and a list of pesticides along the other. Seemingly *all you need do is find the pest, move over to the pesticide, and voilè you have the answer!* Little is said about the effects of pesticides—possible dangers to you and their potential to contaminate the environment. Even less is suggested about pesticide-resistant pests, or increases in the number of pests.

How IPM helps

We take a different tack. If you adopt the integrated pest management (IPM) suggestions described in this book, you'll discover a different approach to pest control. Obviously you'll still want to avoid serious damage to your plants and your food, but you'll realize you can never eliminate all "pests"—that *many of the animals you may avoid now are really your allies.* A few blemishes or holes in leaves are not necessarily serious. Indeed, you may not even attempt controls until pests exceed predetermined numbers —*economic* or *aesthetic thresholds*— which are known to precede unacceptable damage.

• IPM is a decision making process which will help you determine

- *IF* you need to attempt controls
- *WHEN* you need to intervene
- *WHAT* action to take.

Psychologically it's sometimes easier to do an incorrect *something*, just so you can say, *"I did my best." Perhaps the most difficult decision in IPM may be to do nothing at all!* On the other hand, the word "integrated" is not an accident. *One method* may not be the entire answer. Sometimes several control techniques against a variety of pests are incorporated into an *integrated strategy.*

IPM recognizes and attempts to preserve natural mortality— parasitoids,[1] predators, and diseases that already exist in the environment, by *avoiding routine* application of pesticides and *automatic* cultural strategies which frequently cause problems later on.

• IPM includes common sense ideas which reduce pest success • Varieties which resist diseases or insects • Plant rotation • Removal of damaged plant tissues • Insect traps • Cultural intervention including mulching, flooding, cooling, or heating of the soil • Low-toxic methods to eliminate household insects.

How to begin using our book

A little study will help. You'll begin to recognize pests and their natural enemies. If you learn something about an insect's life style it will be easier to figure out the best time to intervene, since controls are best applied to a susceptible life stage. Several pests may attack the same plant, and their interactions should be taken into account.

We encourage you to use common sense—to try to determine the best way to reach your pest control goals without harm to you or the environment. If you want to find basic controls for a particular pest, or discover something about an insect, check our our step by step diagrams. They should give you the basics. If you want to learn more, read the accompanying text for that topic.

Some basic IPM techniques, such as use of pheromones or beneficial (entomopathogenic) nematodes for insect control are described on special pages. We even tell you how to make your own traps, and which methods are a waste of time and money.

Pesticides may have a role in all this, but they're seldom first choice. You'll be able to choose pesticides carefully—use them sparingly. All things being equal, *the least toxic, most selective available pesticide is best.* We provide pesticide information throughout the book to help you make choices, and information in the appendix will even help you monitor pesticide use in your own community if you choose.

An ideal pesticide should be able to control 'target pests,' but have little effect on natural enemies or other animals and plants. The best choices are not necessarily be the "natural" pesticides mandated by traditional "organic farming." Some of these are neither "least toxic" nor "selective," and their full potential for harm has often not been defined.

You're not left on your own in all this. We explain why some animals and plants are pests, and introduce others that are our allies. We include information about controlling pests on fruit trees and vegetables, and in the house, and take you step by step through the decision processes to utilize IPM. We cover a few plant diseases, and even human diseases which are spread by insects.

It's our hope that after you've used this book for a while you'll even be able to design your own control methods for other pests that may appear.

[1] Minute insects which grow up inside other insects, stopping their development. They are the most valuable natural enemies.

To Gene
thanks for your care and support
during the writing of this book

Cheers to Marcus and Irene
who provided essential
knowhow

Contents

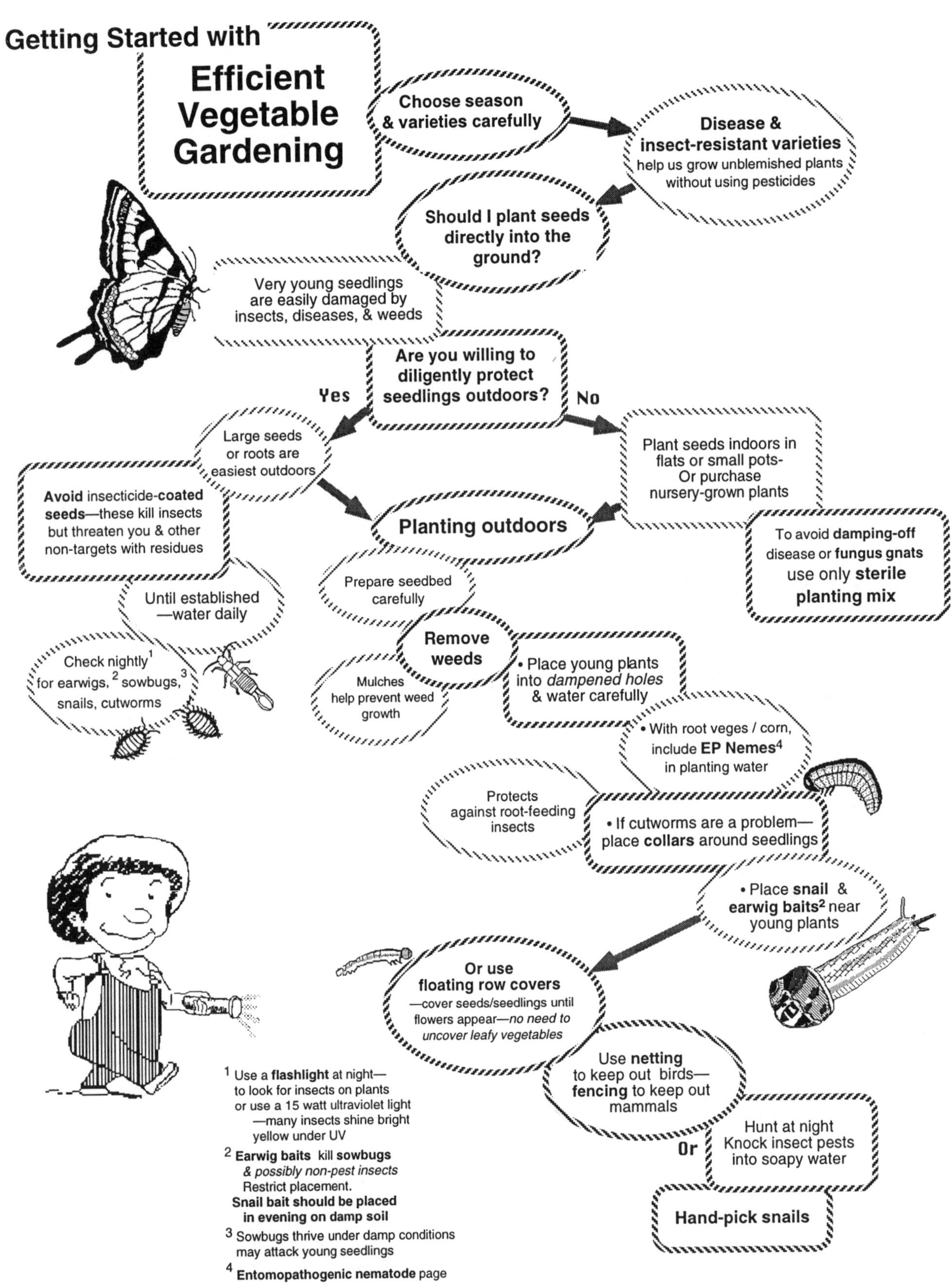
Getting Started with
Efficient Vegetable Gardening
Choose season & varieties carefully
Disease & insect-resistant varieties help us grow unblemished plants without using pesticides
Should I plant seeds directly into the ground?
Very young seedlings are easily damaged by insects, diseases, & weeds
Are you willing to diligently protect seedlings outdoors?
Yes
No
Large seeds or roots are easiest outdoors
Plant seeds indoors in flats or small pots- Or purchase nursery-grown plants
Avoid insecticide-coated seeds—these kill insects but threaten you & other non-targets with residues
Planting outdoors
To avoid damping-off disease or fungus gnats use only sterile planting mix
Until established —water daily
Prepare seedbed carefully
Check nightly1 for earwigs,2 sowbugs,3 snails, cutworms
Remove weeds
Mulches help prevent weed growth
• Place young plants into dampened holes & water carefully
• With root veges / corn, include EP Nemes4 in planting water
Protects against root-feeding insects
• If cutworms are a problem— place collars around seedlings
• Place snail & earwig baits2 near young plants
Or use floating row covers —cover seeds/seedlings until flowers appear—no need to uncover leafy vegetables
Use netting to keep out birds— fencing to keep out mammals
Or
Hunt at night Knock insect pests into soapy water
Hand-pick snails
1 Use a flashlight at night— to look for insects on plants or use a 15 watt ultraviolet light —many insects shine bright yellow under UV
2 Earwig baits kill sowbugs & possibly non-pest insects Restrict placement. Snail bait should be placed in evening on damp soil
3 Sowbugs thrive under damp conditions may attack young seedlings
4 Entomopathogenic nematode page

pest control tools

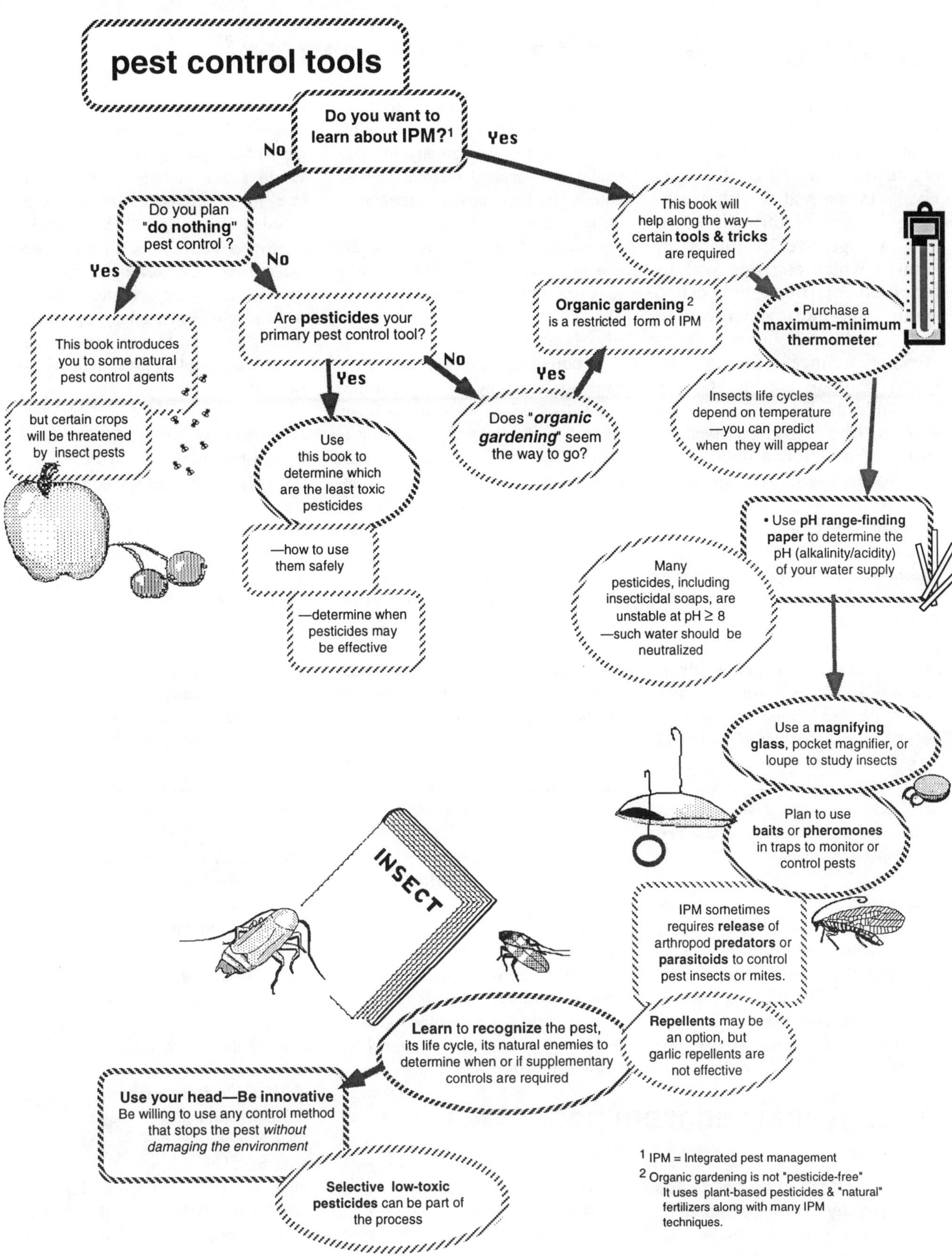

Do you want to learn about IPM?[1]
No
Yes
Do you plan "do nothing" pest control ?
Yes
No
This book introduces you to some natural pest control agents
but certain crops will be threatened by insect pests
Are pesticides your primary pest control tool?
Yes
No
Use this book to determine which are the least toxic pesticides
—how to use them safely
—determine when pesticides may be effective
Does "organic gardening" seem the way to go?
Yes
Organic gardening[2] is a restricted form of IPM
This book will help along the way—certain tools & tricks are required
• Purchase a maximum-minimum thermometer
Insects life cycles depend on temperature —you can predict when they will appear
• Use pH range-finding paper to determine the pH (alkalinity/acidity) of your water supply
Many pesticides, including insecticidal soaps, are unstable at pH ≥ 8 —such water should be neutralized
Use a magnifying glass, pocket magnifier, or loupe to study insects
Plan to use baits or pheromones in traps to monitor or control pests
IPM sometimes requires release of arthropod predators or parasitoids to control pest insects or mites.
INSECT
Repellents may be an option, but garlic repellents are not effective
Learn to recognize the pest, its life cycle, its natural enemies to determine when or if supplementary controls are required
Use your head—Be innovative
Be willing to use any control method that stops the pest without damaging the environment
Selective low-toxic pesticides can be part of the process

[1] IPM = Integrated pest management

[2] Organic gardening is not "pesticide-free" It uses plant-based pesticides & "natural" fertilizers along with many IPM techniques.

How pesticides affect pest control

In a non-human world there would be no such thing as a pest—just millions of different organisms struggling for survival. In the real world, everything is viewed through a human perspective. Plants or animals which compete with us for food or fiber are called "pests", and those which benefit our lifestyle are dubbed "beneficial". Since 75% of the world's animals are insects, it is inevitable that at least a few insects will be considered pests—along with a few mites, ticks, nematodes, snails, and slugs.

Although we've attempted to manipulate our environment since Lucy walked the earth, things didn't get really high tech in insect control until World War II. In 1943 **DDT** was introduced to control the fleas which spread typhus. It was used widely, at first with seemingly unparalleled success. Within two years it was applied in the tropics against houseflies and malaria mosquitoes, again with unprecedented results. *Some even predicted that DDT would eliminate pest insects from the earth!*

Imagine the surprise when *only two years* after its introduction, a few fly and mosquito populations were not being controlled—were *resistant* to the miracle DDT.[1] The shock of this early failure of humankind's "new savior-from-pestilence" initiated the discoveries which we like to call—

Biology learned from pesticides

• Insects stressed by pesticides rapidly become resistant

As soon as new insecticides were introduced **chlordane, dieldren, endrin** —many others—resistance followed close behind. • The more common the pest • The more frequently the pesticides were applied • The higher the dose • The more rapidly resistant populations appeared. *Pesticide resistant populations have been found again and again around the world soon after each new pesticide was introduced.*

• Resistance is a consequence of evolution

Evolution works by the process called **natural selection**. Individuals in any population differ from each other in several ways. If the environment changes—as when a pesticide is applied—some individuals will be susceptible to the change, and die. But usually a few will already have characteristics which enable them to survive in the new environment. In the case of pesticides, a few will have *enzymes* capable of detoxifying the poison, or *coatings* which prevent it from penetrating the body. These resistant individuals survive. In addition, insects in *harborages*—perhaps underground or inside fruits—will be protected. These *survivors become parents of the next generation.*

A few of these survivors may mate with others which have different mechanisms of resistance, so their offspring, live in safe harborages *and* have enzymes to detoxify the pesticide. The next generation would then have even greater resistance. *In rapidly breeding species*, such as mosquitoes and flies, *resistant populations are selected* because many offspring are produced by each resistant female and they, in turn, grow quickly to repeat the process.

If the insecticide dose is concentrated, or the spray is applied frequently over a large area, resistant survivors will be unable to find susceptible mates. Soon most of the population will carry resistant genes, and the pesticide will lose its effectiveness—as has happened again and again.[1] Surprisingly, the trigger need not be from the pesticide itself. Cockroaches from locations which were repeatedly baited with a glucose-containing pesticide showed aversion to the glucose sugar in the bait, enabling them to avoid the pesticide.[2]

To prevent development of resistance any pest controls should be • Used sparingly. Pesticides should be • Specifically applied • At minimum concentrations • To small populations. With this strategy • Most resistance animals will mate with susceptible partners • Resistant strains will be selected slowly. When using pesticides • Treat only obvious problems • Never use routine calendar sprays in anticipation of insect attack • Never increase the recommended dose—both for your own safety, and to decrease the likelihood that resistant population will be selected. *You want susceptible individuals to remain in the population.*

Species with a long life cycle and few offspring, and those small or sedentary populations, remain susceptible longer. But if toxins are applied at frequent high doses over a large area, resistant strains are eventually selected even among long-lived slow breeding species. For example, some populations of the brown garden snail are now metaldehyde-resistant — metaldehyde is the pesticide in snail baits. They became resistant after snail bait was applied frequently, and poisoned animals could find shelter from drying sunshine under a thick groundcover until they recovered.

[1] EPA, 1989, Integrated pest management for turfgrass and ornamentals, p. 26. [2] Environ. Entomol 23: 425-430, 1994.

• Persistent pesticides magnify in food chains

When modern pesticides were first released, few realized that they might harm people or the environment. (After all, DDT had been dusted on thousands of people to kill body lice without apparent harm). No one realized that a persistent DDT metabolite, DDE, was being stored in body fat.

So it's not surprising that observers were initially puzzled when thousands of **robins** were found trembling and dying.[1] Investigators discovered that

• DDT had been sprayed on elms the previous year to control beetles

• Lethal quantities of DDE were stored in the dying robin's brains

• The robin's earthworm diet contained DDE picked up from contaminated leaves.

Later thousands of **grebes** died at Clear Lake—months after another insecticide, DDD, was dumped into the lake to kill larval gnats. Lethal concentrations of DDD were found in the dying grebe's brains. Obviously the robin deaths from pesticides acquired in the environment had not been an isolated incident. How were these massive deaths related to the spraying so long before?

Like a mystery story, the true facts were discovered gradually. Initially chlorinated hydrocarbon pesticides (**organochlorines**)[2] like DDT and DDD were thought to degrade rapidly since they disappeared from water. Then it was verified that these compounds dissolve in oils or waxes in plants, animals, or bottom mud.

Each item in the diet may contain only a minute amount of these organochlorine (**OC**) pesticides. Since they do not degrade easily, they remain in body fat. If they are consumed faster than they are metabolized, the concentration in the body increases over time. Because of this **concentration factor**, top predators obtain a larger dose in their prey than animals which are lower on the food chain.

Thus 5 years after DDD was applied to Clear Lake water, microscopic plankton contained 265 x the original dose, fat of carp and frogs 2500 x, blue gills about 12,500 x, grebes 80,000 x, large mouth bass 75,000 x, and brown bullhead up to 135,000 x. Obviously, DDD was more lethal to grebes than to bullheads, *but what about the fisherman who hooked a bass or a bullhead from that contaminated lake?*

Before governmental restrictions were initiated, biological magnification was responsible for widespread pesticide-based mortality of wildlife. A change to less-persistent insecticides, and an Environmental Protection Agency (EPA) ban of certain persistent OC industrial chemicals such as the polychlorinated biphenyl (PCB) fire retardants, has gradually reduced some releases. But persistent OC pesticides and PCBs are still widespread in the environment and in human fat. They are passed to the next generation through the placenta and in breast milk.

Massive deaths were not the only environmental effects of certain OCs. DDE and dieldrin, for example, interfere with bird reproduction, by causing *egg-shell thinning* and *aberrant reproductive behavior.* Several birds at the top of the food chain—including the Peregrine Falcon, the Bald Eagle, and the Brown Pelican—were declared endangered before DDT and dieldren were banned in the United States—because they had potential to cause cancer, *but not because they threatened birds.*

And, it was many more years before another problem OC—**chlordane**—was banned by the EPA. Many other chlorinated pesticides, including **lindane**, **dicofol**, **endosulfan**, **methoxychlor**, **atrazine**, **captan**, and the **phenoxy herbicides** are still available here, *and DDT and other bad actors are used elsewhere in the world*—still contributing to environmental problems everywhere.

New evidence has demonstrated that individuals with large OC residues in their fat are at greater risk for several cancers and reproductive problems than their less-contaminated fellows. Unfortunately, *even minute residues of persistent chlorinated materials cannot be considered innocuous because of their tendency to magnify in food chains.* (For more information, see Endocrine Disrupters).

• Pesticides create 'Secondary Pests'

Perhaps the most surprising result of the widespread use of these and other broad-spectrum pesticides was an *increase in the total number of pest insects*—the so-called secondary pests present in large enough numbers to cause unacceptable damage to plants, food or fiber. **Mites**, **scales**, and **aphids** are the most common secondary pests, but certain caterpillars almost unheard of before the advent of these insecticides—*Heliothis* and *Spodoptera sp.*—became major pests. Initially it was believed that these "new pests" were aliens. But entomologists soon determined that *they had been present all along, but in much smaller numbers.* What had happened to cause enormous increases in their populations?

---

[1] Carson, R. *Silent spring,* Houghton Mifflin: Boston 21961, 1962. pp. 103-127. [2] Compounds containing chlorine linked to carbon-containing molecules

These *secondary pests are caused by spraying.* Their genesis can be illustrated on cotton—a crop which receives over 50% of U.S. agricultural pesticides. Early on, the **boll weevil** was the major pest of southern cotton. In the 1940s and 50s a series of OCs were used for boll weevil control. As the insect showed resistance to one compound, another was substituted, until by 1958 boll weevils were resistant to all OCs. Insecticides of the **organophosphate** type (OP) were then introduced for weevil control. Almost immediately two pest caterpillars appeared, both in the genus *Heliothis*, the **bollworm** and the **budworm**.

Now the farmers applied an OP to control boll weevils, and a OC to control *Heliothis*. By 1962, *Heliothis* caterpillars were resistant to all OCs, and also to **carbamates (CB)**—the newest pesticide type. At that point only enormous doses of the most toxic OP, **methyl parathion**, could kill the caterpillars. And in 1968 this compound failed as well. Eventually cotton farmers learned to avoid sprays early in the year to allow natural enemies to control *Heliothis.*

This resistance pattern has been repeated many times on many pests on a variety of crops. In studies, scientists even used the **broad-spectrum insecticides** that kill many kinds of insects to create secondary pests *at will.* These experiments were the first to clearly demonstrate the critical importance of **insect biological control**—showing that insect populations are held in check by predators, parasitoids,[1] and diseases.

Potential *secondary pests are naturally resistant to pesticides because they already have enzymes to detoxify plant toxins.* This is especially true of **omnivores**—which eat a diverse group of foods. Most omnivores have enzymes to detoxify several natural plant toxins.

Secondary pests have other origins as well. Sometimes a pesticide tips the nutritional balance in favor of a previously innocuous plant feeder. For instances, when the herbicide **2,4-D** was applied to wheat to eliminate broad-leaved weeds, the nutritional quality of the wheat changed to favor aphid reproduction. **Aphid** populations multiplied more than five times, while at the same time their **ladybird beetle** predators were less effective than before.

• Pesticides are more toxic to natural enemies Predators and parasitoids[1] are easily killed by **contact insecticides**—products that affect insects that touch them. • They are usually more sensitive than are pests because by eating only living organisms, they have had little selective pressure to evolve enzymes to detoxify plant poisons. • Since parasitoids are much smaller than their prey, it obviously takes only a tiny amount of spray to kill them. The larger predators are somewhat less sensitive.

Being higher on the food chain, natural enemies tend to have small populations and a correspondingly small gene pool. • Thus natural enemies acquire pesticide resistance more slowly than animals with larger populations with more genetic variation. • Enemies searching for prey readily contact spray residues, while plant feeders being somewhat sedentary receive a smaller dose. To date, a few predatory mites—natural enemies of plant-feeding mites—and a few generalist insect predators are somewhat resistant to at least one pesticide—but usually less-so than their prey. Most other insect enemies are still readily killed by broad-spectrum contact sprays.

Malathion bait sprays used to eradicate the **Mediterranean Fruit Fly** in central California, provide an example of non-target effects of broad-spectrum sprays. In this application, a high concentration of **malathion** was mixed in a sticky bait which contained protein and sugars. This bait fell as minute droplets with unsprayed space between. It was anticipated that the Medflies would consume the bait, but that non-target animals such as natural enemies would have little contact with the droplets.

In sprayed communities **whitefly** populations exploded within weeks, and caterpillars rapidly defoliated flowers and vegetables throughout the spray zone. The following spring, **scales** were found in previously unheard of numbers and variety. All this suggested that an unusually large population of pests had survived—likely because parasitoids contacted the bait in their wanderings, or were even attracted to the spray. No such outbreaks occurred in adjacent unsprayed areas, and these secondary pest outbreaks subsided within a few months[2] as natural enemy populations recovered.

Effects on some other non-target species were longer lasting. **Katydids** and **tree crickets** apparently ate malathion-laced bait, since their singing ceased abruptly after

[1]Minute insects which grow up inside other insects, stopping their development. [2]Environ. Entomol. 12:1816-1822, 1983

the second spray. These omnivores gradually appeared again in sprayed areas over a period of 5 years. Their slow recovery may be related to the fact that they reproduce only once a year. This experience demonstrates adverse effects possible from a seemingly-selective pesticide application, exacerbated in this case by the enormous area covered by the sprays.

• Pesticides trigger pest resurgence

Even if a spray initially seems effective, it may trigger a tremendous increase in the very pests against which it was applied. Usually toxic, nonselective contact pesticides cause such problems, but even less toxic but broad-spectrum compounds have occasionally caused **pest resurgence** or **pest flarebacks**.

Approximately 1% of arthropod pests have exhibited resurgence, typically following frequent use of non-selective pesticides. Here are examples. • Malayan orchards which were regularly treated with emulsified kerosene, against **citrus blackflies**, contained more citrus blackflies than untreated orchards nearby. • An insecticide application to control aphids was followed within two weeks by the most enormous aphid outbreak ever seen in England. Fortunately when these outbreak-aphids were treated with a **selective insecticide**, which did not affect natural enemies, aphid populations fell to a low level for the remainder of the season. • Use of DDT in an Ontario stream to control blackflies was followed by a dramatic and continuing increase in blackfly numbers. Three years after the first treatment, blackfly populations were 17 times larger than in the pre-treatment period.

There are several possible explanations for pest resurgence. • A few pesticides give a nutritional boost to certain pests • Sometimes spray survivors grow more rapidly due to a lack of competition • But it is now certain that *the primary cause of pest resurgence is the elimination of natural enemies which accompanies spraying.*

Examples abound. • In Southern California, DDT on citrus, upset the balance between ***Cottony cushion scale and its Vedalia* ladybird beetle** predator. Thousands of acres of citrus lost their leaves after the scales became common, and the crop was lost. After DDT was discontinued, cottony-cushion scale was again controlled by the predators. • Predators keep aphids in check in California alfalfa, until malathion applied to kill aphids destroys the major aphid control agents—lady bird beetles and syrphiid flies.

• In a study of the **cyclamen mite** on strawberries, one set of plots were kept free of predators by parathion sprays. In another set, predators were removed by hand. A third group was untreated. In predator-free plots, cyclamen mite populations increased 15 to 35 times, while their numbers decreased in the unsprayed plots. In another experiment, cyclamen mites and their predators were deliberately introduced into 30 strawberry fields. In every case complete biological control of cyclamen mites occurred.

Thus though pesticides are sometimes useful, the timing and selection of materials are very important if these adverse effects are to be avoided. Even the application methods are critical. *Only a small fraction of an aerial spray reaches target insects or plants.* Some spray reaches the ground, but a large fraction evaporates, moves in the clouds and rains down as much as hundreds of miles away. By these means the most volatile pesticides have spread around the world. Residues of DDT and other volatile, persistent OCs have been found everywhere on earth. The herbicides atrazine and alachlor, both suspected human carcinogens[1], have been found in rain far from the farms on which they were applied.

Other sources of pests

• Many pests are imported

A few years ago at U.S. ports of entry 38,461 foreign insects were intercepted during one year—an average of one every 18 minutes. Yet the **cereal leaf beetle**, the **face fly**, and the **Oriental fruit fly** slipped in. Such everyday dramas highlight the fact that many pest insects are imported.

When an insect is introduced into a new land, its natural enemies may be left behind. If environmental factors are favorable, the population of an alien plant-feeding insect without natural enemies can explode. Some familiar alien pest insects are **codling** and **gypsy moths**, the **imported cabbage worm**, **walnut** and **pea aphids**, and **elm bark** and **Japanese beetles**.

If government inspectors detect an immigrant before it spreads widely, eradication may be feasible. That's how the **Mediterranean** (Medfly) and **Oriental fruit flies** have been stopped repeatedly in continental U.S. If eradication fails, containment may limit spread. That may be the strategy if the Medfly is indeed established in Southern California, as some suggest. Currently DNA technologies are being used to determine the origin of the California Medflies.[2] They have dis-

[1]Compounds which cause cancer. [2] Biosci. 43(1):3-6, 1993.

covered that Medflies living in Hawaii and Venezuela belong to one group, and those from Argentina, California, and Guatemala belong to another. Next they will determine if early specimens from California are like those living there now.

Though **gypsy moth** and **Japanese beetle** have been held to the Eastern half of the U.S, alien pests are often established widely before discovery—as was the codling moth and the imported cabbageworm. The ecology or vigor of an alien may preclude eradication—as with the **Africanized honeybee.** Even European honeybees interfere with natural environments. Wild bees are left with less profitable resources because honeybees dominate the richest patches of flowers.[1]

• Other introduced pests

Some introduced pests, thrive in lakes, rivers, and bays—without a chance for control. Some arrived when ships dumped their ballast water in the harbor, others when well meaning humans released them to improve "fishing." **Rabbits, goats, toads, mongeese**, and **birds** introduced here and there as "food sources" or "pest control agents" are often the worst pests of all. The **melaleuca** tree, introduced to dry out mosquito-infected Everglades wetlands, has gone on to crowd out native plants, and now requires extensive control efforts.

• Nature's evolutionary changes

A *native species sometimes can move from its original foods to exploit an abundant agricultural crop.* The **Colorado potato beetle**, the **boll weevil**, and the **cabbage looper** are examples. Usually natural enemies are unable to contain their populations on crops because alternate prey for the natural enemies are not present in a crop monoculture. The **apple maggot**—another changeling—is now not only common in New England apple orchards near its original wild plants, but has been accidentally imported into several western states.

Insects which are able to thrive on plants which synthetize such toxins as tannins or phenols, are usually more resistant to pesticides than those which feed on less toxic plants. These toxins stimulate insect enzymes that detoxify pesticides or inhibit enzymes that activate them. Even certain insect diseases which enter through the gut are less effective on insects feeding on these plants—perhaps for the same reasons.

• Eruptive species

Some insects known as *eruptive species*—e.g. **spruce budworm, California oakworm**, and **western tent caterpillar**—occasionally get ahead of their natural enemies during periods of favorable climate. These three exploit native trees which are usually able to sustain considerable damage without permanent harm. Pesticide applications may interfere with natural control systems in these cases, ultimately causing more harm than good. Although these insects are serious pests at times, they usually have adequate natural controls.

Other adverse effects of pesticide use

Americans apply over two billion pounds of active pesticide ingredients annually at a cost of $7.6 billion. Until recently the pesticide industry didn't worry too much about pest resistance. After all new products would replace those which were no longer effective. Now more than 500 species have developed resistance to one or more pesticide.[2] It takes about ten years, and costs between $35 and $50 million to bring each new pesticide to market—10 times what it cost in the 1970s. When traditional agricultural pesticide strategies are followed, resistance appears rapidly .

Your environment may be contaminated by pesticide movement. *Pesticides can drift from yard to yard.* Minute amounts of of the common insecticides, **diazinon** and **chlorpyrifos**, are now ubiquitous in birdbaths, rivers, streams, sloughs, rain, and fog in concentrations large enough to kill the tiny daphnia water fleas that feed on algae at the bottom of the food chain.[3] **Granular pesticides** pose a particular hazard for birds. Birds ingesting small pebbles or course sand to act as food grinders in their gizzards, are killed when they consume granular pesticides. Granular **carbofuran** is being phased out because it has killed so many birds. Birds can also be harmed by direct contact with pesticides which are absorbed through the skin or ingested by preening contaminated feathers.

The seemingly low-hazard **microencapsulated insecticides**[4] are inadvertently collected by bees along with pollen. These toxic capsules are carried to the nest and kill the brood. Broad-spectrum herbicides— those active against most plants—could completely destroy sensitive populations of endangered plants. Certain persistent herbicides sterilize the soil for years. Any pesticide applied to the soil has potential to leach into the water supply or the nearest river. We seldom take into account that that pesticides threaten fish, birds, mam-

---

[1] BioSci. 43(2): 95-103, 1995. [2]J. Econ. Entomol. 87:293-300, 1994, [3] San Jose Mercury News, 6/19/95. [4] Insecticides placed into minute capsules to lower contact activity to mammals & birds.

proper disposal of these materials, or the run-off from their applications can make the environment uninhabitable for sensitive species which require clear, pollution-free water.

In addition, most of us may not recognize that cleaning compounds are among the most dangerous chemicals in the home environment. For example, in 1992 the State of California found that chlorine bleach, the common household OP insecticide, chlorpyrifos; sulphur dioxide gas, and household ammonia were responsible for the majority of poison accidents.

What is Integrated Pest Management?

Many of us have had little opportunity to learn about insects and other critters and their place in the world. We may have unrealistic expectations— demanding that all insects be eliminated, that plants be completely without blemishes. We may accept hearsay descriptions of "miracle control methods" Some of us may not understand that bees are essential pollinators of vegetables and fruits—that insecticide sprays may kill bees and their beneficial wasp relatives. Lack of pollination is estimated cause about $4 billion in crop losses each year.

You may know someone who is skeptical of the importance of natural or biological controls. They even may have performed experiments similar to those described here, but with different results. This is understandable because such experiments must be performed very carefully. Study plots must be large, and untreated control plots far away from treated plots so that there will be no chance of pesticide drift. This is difficult because pesticides drift a very long way. In addition—a suitable "untreated plot" may not be available. It usually takes a long time for a diverse population of animals to return after large fields are sprayed.

Integrated pest management (IPM) utilizes a combination of techniques which give primary reliance on natural control agents, but may also include use of cultural controls, diseases, resistant cultivars, baits or attractants, release of predators or parasitoids, or judicious use of pesticides.

For example, dust can interfere with natural insect enemies and favor pest insects. Dust on leaves kills predatory mites and favors their prey. Under dry dusty conditions, a weekly rinse of the leaves can help keep pest mites in check.

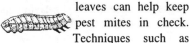

Techniques such as rinsing the foliage with water may seem to be a homespun trick or just common sense, but when used within a framework of common sense pest control, can become part of IPM. Most plants can tolerate a few plant-feeding insects, and the beneficial predators and parasitoids are also found on plants. Use of insecticides in a effort to eliminate all insects will always backfire.

IPM programs should include

• Maximum protection or augmentation of natural enemies • Monitoring of pests and natural enemy populations to determine whether controls are needed. Although some insects can be monitored with traps, most are checked by *counting*. Often the *ratio* of pests to natural enemies will indicate whether pests are a threat. Your pest control decisions may be based on experimentally determined agricultural economic thresholds. In addition, mechanical or cultural method—pruning, cultivating, or changes in soil composition—can be effective and selective means of pest control.

If chemicals seem to be needed
• Treat the most sensitive stages • Use techniques which selectively affect the target pest • Apply only low-toxic, biodegradable materials.

IPM Benefits

A switch to IPM can produce dramatic changes. In agriculture, money saved from reduced pesticide use usually more than pays for pest management specialists and monitoring. The greatest savings occur when pesticides are no longer routinely applied on a calendar basis. Other IPM benefits—fewer secondary pests, fewer resistant and resurgent pests, and lower environmental pollution—are less obvious but even more important. With IPM crops yields often increase as well.

In the diversified and relatively permanent suburban landscape, pest populations tend to be smaller. At home it's relatively easy to remove a problem plant and replace it with a resistant strain, or ignore minor leaf damage.

Still, you will be able to target your pest control efforts and accomplish more for your efforts, when you adopt IPM. You'll know when to let well enough alone, and when to purchase natural enemies. You will use pesticides more selectively and safely, time spray applications for maximum effect. You'll rotate crops, and use cultivation to keep pests off balance. Sometimes killing half the pest population will be the best strategy. It's not easy to change old habits, but this book should help you begin.

Introducing Insects

How about you? Can you distinguish insects from other small creatures? Not to worry, it's actually very easy to focus in on insects.

Adult insects have *three*, distinct *body segments*—head, thorax, and abdomen—with *six slender jointed legs* attached to the thorax. In addition, they have *two antennae*, and most have *compound eyes* (with many segments) and *two pairs of wings*. To confuse the picture, true flies have only one pair of wings, and a few adult insects have no wings at all. Insects are almost unique, in that many of them change form, or *metamorphose*, as they grow and develop.

Thus, immature or **larval insects** do not look like adults. Many larvae possess the six legs and three body segments, but other larvae resemble "worms," and it's these which can be difficult to recognize as insects.

Insect Metamorphosis

Metamorphosis means "to change form". Like their spider, crab, and shrimp relatives, insects shed (molt) the tough outer skin (cuticle)—the **exoskeleton**—as they pass from one developmental stage to the next. The exoskeleton serves both as a supporting skeleton, and protective armor. At each molt, the young insect gets a new tough larger head, and a flexible body, whose skin gradually stretches during subsequent growth until the body finaly matches the head-size just before the next molt. Insects grow larger only during the juvenile period. Some insects—true bugs, cockroaches, grasshoppers, earwigs, dragonflies, and aphids—develop by **incomplete metamorphosis.** Even though their growth stages are divided by molts—in this case egg, nymph, and adult—the young look something like the adults, and they often have a similar life style and diet. There are exceptions. Young cicadas feed underground for 1 to 17 years, but the ephemeral adults emerge in spring, buzz loudly for a few days to attract a mate, and live just long enough to lay eggs. Mayfly adults have even shorter lives. After the long-lived aquatic larva matures, they molt synchronously to adults which fly, mate, and lay eggs during one spring day.

Other insect families develop via **complete metamorphosis**. Bees, wasps, butterflies, moths, beetles, fleas, lacewings, and snakeflies develop this way. In these families the larvae never resemble the adults, and they usually eat different foods and live different lifestyles. Again, some adults are essentially egg-laying machines which live only a few days, while their larvae may grow for months or even years.

Larval identification[2]

Worm-like larvae have a series of segments one behind the other. If you have a "worm" with a distinct head, six legs behind the head, and several other (≤ 5)[1] *pairs* of stubby legs tipped with little hooks, and some segments without legs, you have a *caterpillar*—the larva of a moth or a butterfly. If a similar larva lacks the hooks, but there are stubby legs on each segment, you have a larval sawfly.

If your "worm" has a darkened tough cuticle, 6 legs behind a jawed head, you may have the larva of a snakefly or a beetle. A white keyhole-shaped larvae in a tree burrow is also a beetle. If your larva is white, soft, lethargic worm, with a well-developed head, and no legs, it's probably the offspring of an ant, a wasp, or a bee. While a more active legless "worm", with a pointed head, may be a **maggot**, a larval fly. If you have a tiny active larvae with wire-like legs, it is probably an aphid, scale, psyllid, or, if brightly-colored, a true bug.

After the feeding, growing larval period, insects with complete metamorphosis molt to a quiescent, nonfeeding, "resting" stage known as the **pupa**. (A **chrysalis** is a butterfly pupa, a **cocoon** the silky woven covering which surrounds a moth pupa). Though pupae do not feed, and possess no legs or wings, they *can* move, and they are *not* "resting." The entire insect is being redesigned within—soon to emerge as an entirely different animal—a winged adult.

The changes during insect development are controlled by hormones—**juvenile hormones** and **ecdysone** (molting hormone). Juvenile hormones reign during the larval period, but disappear just before the molt, allowing ecdysone to trigger the molt itself. Since growth is messed up if these hormones are present at the wrong time, several strategies utilize hormone analogues for insect control .

Metamorphosis is very advantageous. It allows insects to pass unfavorable seasons in a resting stage, and grow and thrive during a more favorable period. (The cicada and the mayfly, for example, spend most of their long lives in a relatively safe place—in soil or water, respectively—and only emerge briefly to reproduce.) Metamorphosis also allows insect larvae to utilize different foods and territories than the adults so they do not compete with one another.

Getting insect terms straight

Singular	Plural	Definition	Alternate name
larva	larvae	juvenile insect	caterpillar (butterfly, moth)
			maggot (fly), naiad (aquatic)
		juvenile similar to adult	nymph*
pupa	pupae	quiescent stage	chrysalis (butterfly)
puparium	puparia	encases fly pupa	cocoon (silken / moth)
antenna	antennae	sensory organ at front of adult insect	
cercus	cerci	sensory organ at rear of adult insect	
juvenile hormone		keeps insect in larval stage	JH
eccysone (hormone)		causes insect to molt	molting hormone
exoskeleton	skeleton on the outside (insects have no bones)		
cuticle		protein-chitin "skin" which forms the exoskeleton	

*incomplete metamorphosis only

[1] ≥ = greater or equal to; ≤ = less than or equal to; > = greater than; < = less than than. [2] See also page 15.

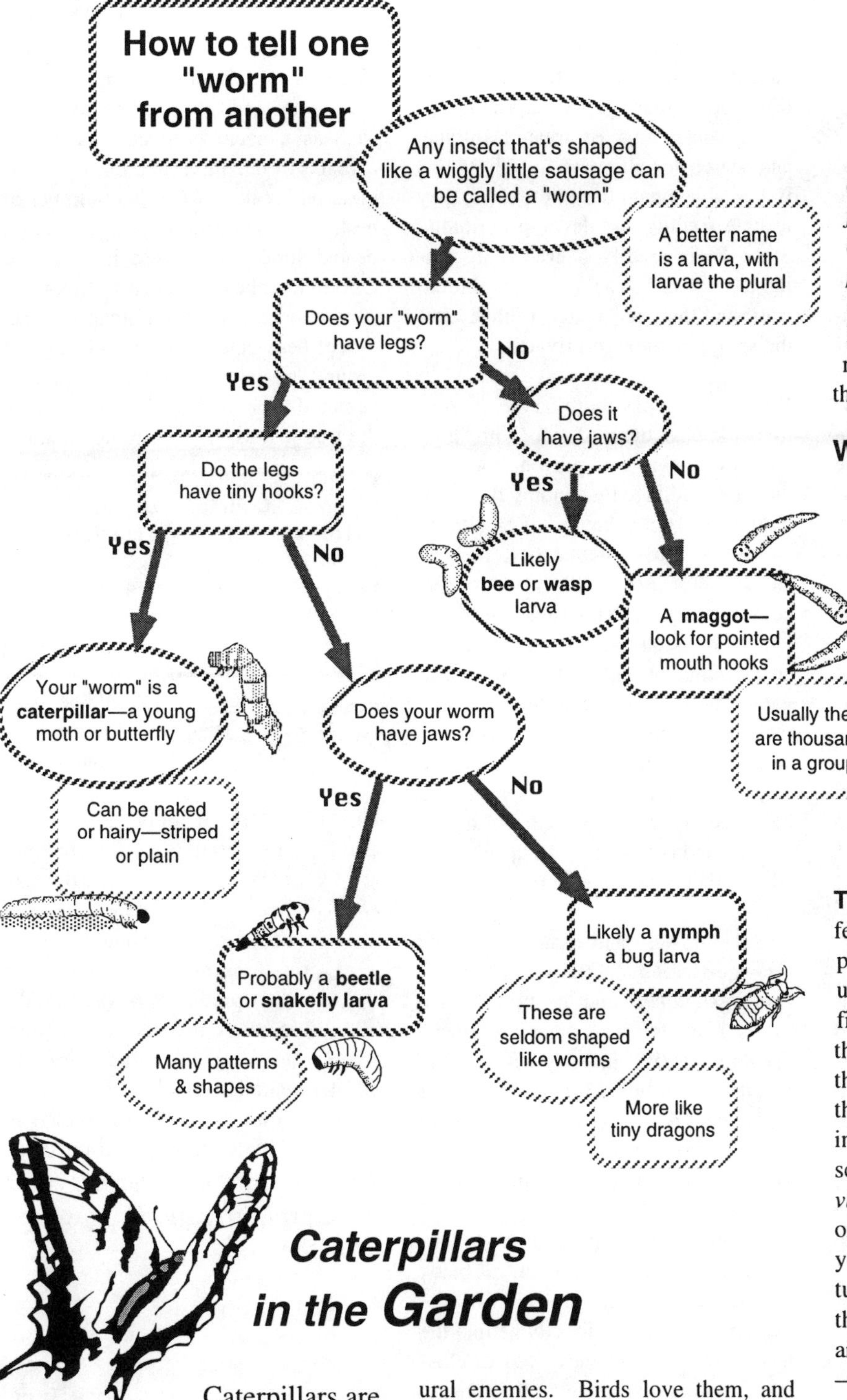
How to tell one "worm" from another
Any insect that's shaped like a wiggly little sausage can be called a "worm"
A better name is a larva, with larvae the plural
Does your "worm" have legs?
Yes
No
Do the legs have tiny hooks?
Does it have jaws?
Yes
No
Likely bee or wasp larva
A maggot— look for pointed mouth hooks
Usually there are thousands in a group
Yes
No
Your "worm" is a caterpillar—a young moth or butterfly
Can be naked or hairy—striped or plain
Does your worm have jaws?
Yes
No
Probably a beetle or snakefly larva
Many patterns & shapes
Likely a nymph a bug larva
These are seldom shaped like worms
More like tiny dragons

Caterpillars in the **Garden**

Caterpillars are immature butterflies or moths—the scaly-winged insects. They hatch as minute "worms"-with-legs, and feed on plants. Like other insects, butterflies and moths have many natural enemies. Birds love them, and their eggs and larvae are captured by spiders, large wasps, lacewings, beetles, ants, predatory bugs, or, they are consumed from within by wasp or fly parasitoids. Because of all these natural enemies, most plants are little damaged by caterpillars. Thus, *before you attempt to control caterpillars, be sure you really have a problem.* If you apply broad-spectrum pesticides—the types that kill may types of organisms—you may kill birds and beneficial insects, thereby causing more harm than good.

Where problems occur

If you grow **cabbage-family plants** —broccoli, cabbage, collards, brussel sprouts —watch for the **cabbage looper** —a green inchworm—or the velvety green, **imported cabbage worm.** Sometimes you can brush off their eggs, or hand pick the larvae, but if caterpillars are eating the valuable central parts, see Crucifers for control suggestions.

Tomato fruits are also attacked by a few pest "worms"—*Heliothis* caterpillars (big holes) or pin worms (minute holes). These caterpillars are difficult to control with sprays because they burrow into the fruit. Fortunately they have many natural enemies. In the unusual case where they are causing serious damage, control is described on the tomato page. *Heliothis virescens* also burrows into geranium or petunia buds, and sometimes the young fruits of beans and squash. Cultural controls don't help much because these, and several other pest moths—armyworm and black cutworm moths —fly in from distant regions. Both *H. virescents* and its relative, the corn ear worm, *Heliocoverpa (Heliothis) zea*, are resistant to broad-spectrum insecticides. See the *Heliothis* and corn pages for control suggestions.

If you have **apple trees**—see **codling moth**. If you have trouble with other caterpillars on fruit trees —see fruit tree profiles and the **borer** page. Entomopathogenic (beneficial) nematodes can be injected into borer holes.

Oaks in California are occasionally defoliated by the **California Oakworm** (moth) *(Phryganidia californica).* These larvae overwinter on live oaks. In early April look for tiny (1/4-1/3 inch) naked caterpillars. If more than 15 are present on 25 shoots, the tree may be defoliated this year. If you find these numbers, use Bt spray when a majority of the larvae just begin to feed on the edges of the leaves. During the second generation which is active in July, count caterpillars on both deciduous and evergreen oaks. Use the same threshold to determine if spray is needed.

In the Eastern U.S. the **Gypsy Moth**, *Lymantria dispar,* has been a problem for a long time. Now, an aggressive strain—the Asian gypsy Moth which differs, in that the the female can fly—has been imported into the Pacific Northwest. (Gypsy moths are easily transported because their egg clusters are deposited in hidden places such as wood piles, or the bottom of trailers or automobiles.) When these eggs hatch, each larva climbs to the top of a tree, and wafts on a strand of web into the breezes, sailing away like a gypsy to distant places.

Gypsy moth caterpillars sometimes defoliate entire forests because their natural enemy component in this country does not provide adequate control. In order to control these larvae, ***Bacillus thuringiensis*** (**Bt**), the bacterial disease of caterpillars, is sometimes sprayed on infested forests. These sprays have not always provided adequate control. Recently researchers discovered that gypsy moth larvae avoid consuming Bt treated foliage, and search for alternate food.[1] If this is available even after a few days, they resume feeding and develop normally. Since Bt is readily degraded in sunlight, treated larvae may be able to wait, and then eat treated foliage after the sprays become inactivated.

If you have gypsy moth larvae on your trees, knock them down with high pressure water, and prevent their return to the foliage by banding the trunk with wide sticky bands. Long term, encourage birds—nuthatches, titmice, chickadees, and small woodpeckers consume the overwintering eggs.[2] Alternately, encourage your town or other government entity to spray with gypsy moth nuclear polyhedrosis virus (see *How diseases control insects).* One of the most predicative ways to monitor whether sprays will be needed is to band the tree with burlap and count eggs or pupae which are hidden beneath the bands.[3]

In midwest and eastern U.S. the **Orange-striped Oakworm** *(Anistota senatoria)* and its close relatives may defoliate oaks or other deciduous trees. In early summer the females lay about 500 eggs in one mass under a leaf. Oaks can withstand a loss of 25% of their foliage but more eventually cause the tree to decline.

The caterpillars, which have 6 longitudinal orange stripes on a black ground can be recognized by the *curved orange horn* directly behind the head. When small they feed in clusters, but later disperse over the foliage. Obviously it would be best to remove the eggs before they hatch, but the young larvae feeding together on the lower leaves are obvious and easy to spray with Bt.

If defoliation seems imminent, spray with a another pesticide, such as a neem product. Avoid the carbaryl or diazinon used during a Virginia outbreak,[3] where the number of pests increased year by year despite repeated sprays with these insecticides. Only when they switched to less toxic compounds, did the outbreak decline. Since these caterpillars crawl into the ground to pupate, entomopathogenic nematodes applied to the soil beneath the tree just as the caterpillars mature, should be helpful in controlling future outbreaks.

OSO 25% Threshold[4]

Tree size (ft)	# egg clusters
16	1
24	4
30	7
40	9

In general, if only a few caterpillars are present, ignore them—but keep your eyes open. *Sprays are more efficient when the larvae are still small.* Since Bt should not directly harm you, your pets, or insect predators or parasitoids, it is often the spray of choice when caterpillar problems arise. Bt usually degrades rapidly in open situations, but may persist up to 30 days in forests.[5] Be selective and careful. *Those beautiful butterflies start as caterpillars, and Bt zaps them too.*

1 Environ Entomol 24" 755-761, 1995. 2 Environ. Entomol. 24: 571-575, 1995, 3Environ. Entomol. 24: 193-203, 1995. 4J Econ Enomol 83:2044-2049, 1990. J. Econ Enomol 86:1512-1515, 1993, 5 Environ Entomol 24:288-297, 1995.

Are ants pests ?

Most of us recognize ants—even have *strong feelings about them.* After all, *we've been told for years that these little wingless insects are the ultimate pests*—worthy of persistent insecticide sprays throughout the house and garden. We may be reacting to the shear numbers, know little about them, and care less that they're often important insect predators.

Ants *are* numerous *and* intimate. After all they live in colonies. Each colony has one or more queens and their female offspring—the workers. The workers do just that—work at caring for the young, collecting food, digging and maintaining the nest. No doubt you've occasionally disturbed an ant nest, and seen workers carrying little white "eggs"—they're really transporting precious larvae[1] and pupae[1] to safety.

How to recognize ants

Ants can be recognized by a narrow 'waist' sporting an upward 'bump' (the node), a large rounded abdomen, and *elbowed antennae.*

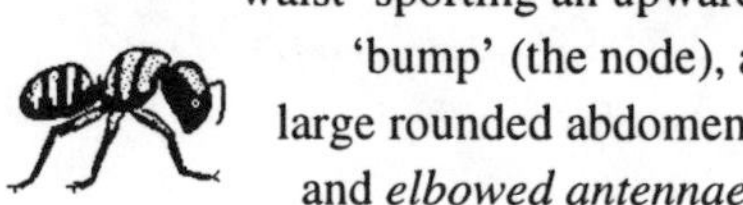

Most ants are wingless, but groups of winged reproductives emerge once or twice a year. Ant wings are shorter than the body, and their forewings are larger than their hindwings—unlike the elongated equal-sized wings of the larger termites. With some ant reproductives, a large virgin queen is surrounded by a cluster of smaller pursuing males, but with other species of ants large numbers of tiny winged ants seem to fill the air.

Pheromones control ant behavior

As each ant walks along, it occasionally touches the tip of its abdomen to the ground, releasing a droplet of 'trail' pheromone. (A pheromone is an odor-producing chemical). Worker ants travel in columns following this colony trail pheromone. They follow the pheromone to food or back to the nest. Other pheromones excreted by the queen keep the workers sterile, and govern the development of the winged males and females. Pheromones from larvae initiate still other behaviors of colony members. Some ants respond to alarm pheromones. You might even say that the ant's pheromone glands control their lives.

Household Ants

A major indoor ant in the U.S. is the imported **Argentine ant**, *Iridomytrmex humilis.* These little dark ants come inside seeking shelter and food—usually sweets, but sometimes pet foods. Argentine ants, and most other household ants should not be considered serious pests. They're best dealt with as shown on our diagram.

There *are* two serious ant pests in the U.S.—the imported fire ant and the Pharaoh's ant. The Pharaoh ant *(Monomorium pharaonis)*—originally from the land of the Pharaohs—is a minute blond ant that inhabits buildings. Now common in Europe, Pharaoh's ants have established beachheads in southeastern U.S. They can be a major problem in hospitals where they contaminate wounds and spread disease. Fortunately certain low-toxic baits containing analogs[2] of an insect juvenile hormone[1], or non-repellant toxicants can eliminate Pharaoh's ant.

Our largest household ants are **carpenter ants**, *Camponotus sp.* These relative giants may be more than half an inch in length. They construct their nests by excavating holes in damp wood. (You can help prevent both carpenter ants and damp wood rots, by eliminating moisture in house walls). Carpenter ant tunnels may alarm you, but they seldom threaten the structures, except for those of houses built in forested areas where main colonies are common and they are likely to extend a satellite colony into the house.

Though carpenter ants look ferocious, they do not bite or sting. They eat sweets and the flesh of other insects. In that, they are representative of many ants—a combination of insect predator, scavenger, and sweet lover—obviously not too pesky but maybe not welcome indoors. If they do get in, caulk all openings and follow our directions for control. On the other hand, the **imported fire ants**, *Solenopsis invicta* ad *S. richteri,* cannot be tolerated in a typical suburban setting because of their painful sting, even though they are ferocious and effective caterpillar predators.

How ants fit in

Ants are most abundant in the tropics where they make up as much as one half of the total weight of insects. They are less common in temperate lands, but are influential wherever they are found—which is almost everywhere. Ants influence other insects because they have abundant, stable, populations and diverse eating habits. In addition to being insect predators,

---

[1]See, introducing insects, pg 14, [2] Synthetic compound that is similar in structure or activity to another. *Trade name

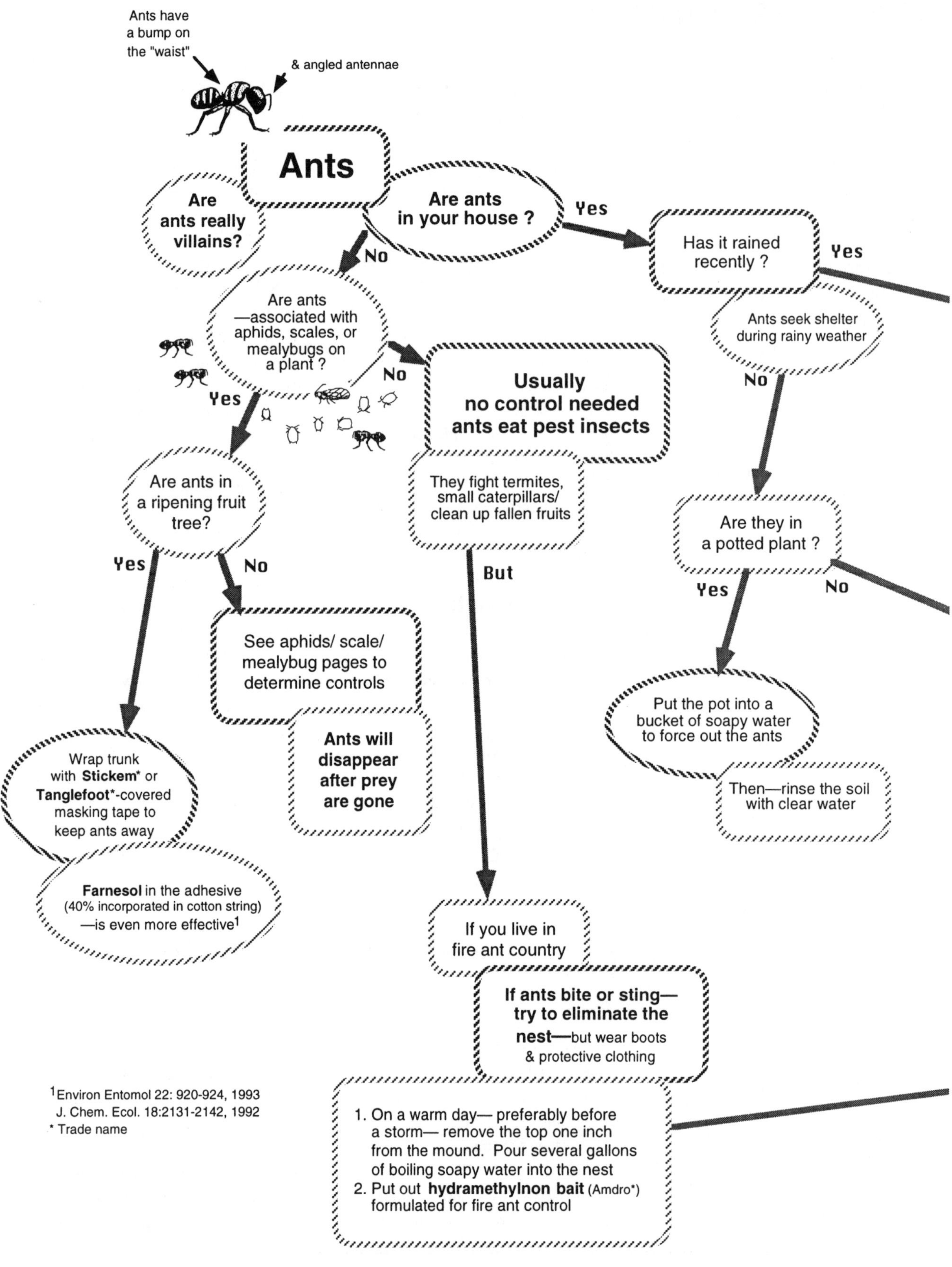

Ants have
a bump on
the "waist"
& angled antennae
Ants
Are ants really villains?
Are ants in your house ?
Yes
No
Has it rained recently ?
Yes
Ants seek shelter during rainy weather
No
Are ants —associated with aphids, scales, or mealybugs on a plant ?
Yes
No
Usually no control needed ants eat pest insects
They fight termites, small caterpillars/ clean up fallen fruits
But
Are ants in a ripening fruit tree?
Yes
No
See aphids/ scale/ mealybug pages to determine controls
Ants will disappear after prey are gone
Wrap trunk with Stickem* or Tanglefoot*-covered masking tape to keep ants away
Farnesol in the adhesive (40% incorporated in cotton string) —is even more effective1
Are they in a potted plant ?
Yes
No
Put the pot into a bucket of soapy water to force out the ants
Then—rinse the soil with clear water
If you live in fire ant country
If ants bite or sting— try to eliminate the nest—but wear boots & protective clothing
1. On a warm day— preferably before a storm— remove the top one inch from the mound. Pour several gallons of boiling soapy water into the nest
2. Put out hydramethylnon bait (Amdro*) formulated for fire ant control
1Environ Entomol 22: 920-924, 1993
J. Chem. Ecol. 18:2131-2142, 1992
* Trade name

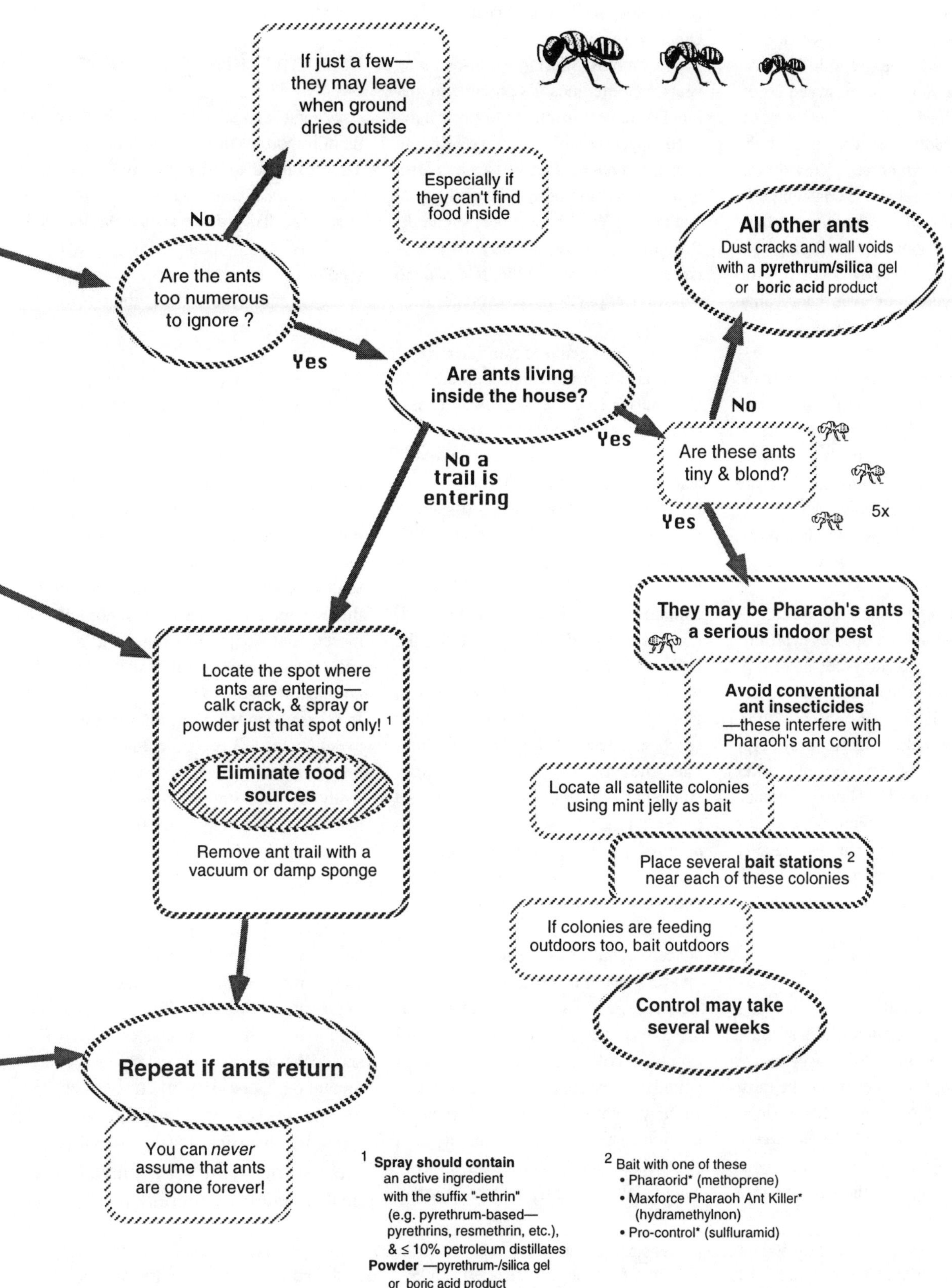
If just a few—
they may leave
when ground
dries outside
Especially if
they can't find
food inside
No
Are the ants
too numerous
to ignore ?
Yes
All other ants
Dust cracks and wall voids
with a pyrethrum/silica gel
or boric acid product
Are ants living
inside the house?
No
Yes
Are these ants
tiny & blond?
No a
trail is
entering
Yes
5x
They may be Pharaoh's ants
a serious indoor pest
Avoid conventional
ant insecticides
—these interfere with
Pharaoh's ant control
Locate all satellite colonies
using mint jelly as bait
Place several bait stations 2
near each of these colonies
If colonies are feeding
outdoors too, bait outdoors
Control may take
several weeks
Locate the spot where
ants are entering—
calk crack, & spray or
powder just that spot only! 1
Eliminate food
sources
Remove ant trail with a
vacuum or damp sponge
Repeat if ants return
You can never
assume that ants
are gone forever!

[1] **Spray should contain** an active ingredient with the suffix "-ethrin" (e.g. pyrethrum-based—pyrethrins, resmethrin, etc.), & ≤ 10% petroleum distillates
Powder —pyrethrum-/silica gel or boric acid product

[2] Bait with one of these
- Pharaorid* (methoprene)
- Maxforce Pharaoh Ant Killer* (hydramethylnon)
- Pro-control* (sulfluramid)

ants also pollinate plants when they visit blossoms. Ants improve the soil and help recycle nutrients when they dig their nests in the ground. Harvester ants store and consume weed seeds. A few ants feed on living plants, occasionally spreading plant diseases in the process. Ants which are primarily important insect predators, consume other foods as well. To support their large stable populations during unfavorable seasons, they often rely on insect honeydew[1] or even cannibalize their own brood.

Most ants do not harm large animals, although fire ants respond to disturbances with a fiery sting, and occasionally attack young birds and mammals. The most formidable ants are tropical army ants which attack and consume helpless mammals, birds, reptiles, and insects as a way of life.

In stable habitats such as forests or prairies, several ant species with different life styles form a mosaic of separate colonies. Small ants can be important predators of insect eggs. Larger species seek larger prey, typically disregarding the foods of smaller species. Some ants enslave other ants, requiring them to do their work. Most of us are not aware that ants readily consume young caterpillars—though because of their size, its not surprising that larger caterpillars often escape. Ants also capture larval and adult Colorado potato beetles, and leaf miners are a tasty ant tidbit. Aggressive ants with large colonies make the most effective insect predators. It's estimated that a typical nest of the **European forest ant**, *Formica polyctena,* consumes about eight million insects in a single year. Of these, 80-93% are could be described as "pest" insects. Other *Formica* ants help suppress gypsy moths during non-outbreak years.[2] Sometimes it's possible to manipulate the environment to favor a desired species. It's even possible to augment a native species to aid control of a troublesome pest. The pear psylla is a pest in Washington pear orchards. Recently, a native ant, ***Formica neoclara,*** was successfully released to control pear psylla in these orchards.[3]

The fire ant genus *Solenopsis* also contains important insect predators. Our **native fire ant**, *S. geminata,* was observed to remove 98% of the maize weevils from corn, and is also an avid weed seed eater.
The imported fire ants also attack many plant feeding insects and their eggs, and the maggot larvae of cattle-biting flies. Imported fire ants are common in southern U.S. and spreading westward. Beginning in 1957, the U.S. government spent about $200 million trying to eradicate *S. invicta* with persistent insecticides—without success. These efforts not only polluted the environment with toxic carcinogens, but *inadvertently hastened their spread by killing their competitors.* Efforts to import and establish imported fire ant natural enemies offer the best chance for control. In South America, a microsporidium *(Thelohania solenopsae)* is an important natural enemy.[4] Because new research[5] has demonstrated *S. invicta* has value as an insect control agent—a colony consumes about 14 pounds of insects per acre per week—we may want to preserve and enhance them in certain situations. In any case chemicals are recommended only where control is essential—as in urban areas where their stings cannot be tolerated.

Important insect enemies

Ants have characteristics which make them important insect natural enemies. They respond to prey density because *they remain abundant even when prey is scarce.* To prevent starvation, they store food—including insects and seeds—use honeydew as a source of energy, and cannibalize their own brood when prey is scarce.

Obviously, *if ants are to succeed as predators in the home garden, you can't follow the dogma that all ants are pests.* There are ways to intervene when necessary without destroying entire colonies. If ants are tending aphids, whiteflies, or scales on a sensitive plant, control these plant feeders with superior oil, insecticidal soap, or even WiltPruf* anti-transpirant,[6] or put a sticky band around the plant to keep ants at bay. In other situations, remember that honeydew helps to keep ant colonies—and other insect enemies—strong and ready to attack important plant feeding insects. A few aphids on the groundcover, sturdy plants, or weeds can be a bonus.

Avoid using pesticides around your house foundation to "eliminate ants and other vermin." Ants attack termites and seek shelter from the heat, cold, and wet under houses. They should be no problem as long as they remain outdoors. If you find several species of ants around your garden, rejoice. It probably means that you've achieved a healthy ecology there.

---

[1]Sweet substance excreted by plant-sucking insects. [2] Environ. Entomol. 23:870-877, 1994. [3]Agric. Entomol. 9:37-39, 1992. [4]Envrion. Entomol 24: 1328-1332, 1995. [5]Environ. Entomol 24: 387-391, 1995. [6] Substance which prevents transpiration—evaporation from plant surfaces

Bees and wasps

Are you afraid of bees and wasps because of their stings? You're not alone. Many of us fear bees and wasps. But we hope you'll learn to tolerate, even appreciate *Hymenopterans,* insects with stingers, because the membrane-winged order of insects is essential to human endeavors, and critical to proper functioning of the natural world.

How bees live

Bees have four clear wings, a well defined—but not thin—waist, a robust body, usually covered with hair. In bees and large wasps—the *stinger* or *ovipositor*—an egg-laying structure, functions both as defense weapon and an egg laying tool. Worker honeybees (infertile females) do not lay eggs, and the barbs on the stinger remain in the wound, eventually causing death of the stinging honeybee. The males, or drones, develop from unfertilized eggs. Their sole function is to mate with young queens. Obviously, they do not possess the modified ovipositor we call a stinger.

Kinds of bees—Most of us think of *honeybees* as the only bees, but there are thousands of others. Among them, *bumble bees*, *solitary bees*, and large black, shiny *carpenter bees* are common garden visitors. You may have noticed the circular holes cut from leaves by *leafcutter bees.* Only a few bees—honeybees and bumble bees—live together in large social colonies, though carpenter bees may dig their wooden tunnels in close proximity to one another.

Most solitary bees dig nest holes in the ground, burrow into wood, or construct cells of resin or mud, each of which holds a single baby—the larva. Many solitary bees visit only one or a few flower species, though others are valuable crop pollinators. The life span of the most specialized bees is limited by the blooming season of these particular plants, and *many of these plants would disappear if their pollinator bees were eliminated.*

Bees pollinate flowers—When bees visit flowers to collect pollen and nectar for their young, they pollinate (fertilize) the blossoms they visit. Pollination is essential to the reproduction of these plants. Though some other plants are wind pollinated, most flowering plants are pollinated by insects, usually bees, flies, and beetles. (A few plants are pollinated by birds or bats). Without bees there would be fewer apples, berries, oranges, pumpkins and watermelons to name a few. When you find that most fruits fall off, its likely that bees did not pollinate the flowers. This can occur when the weather is too cool, too rainy, or too hot for insects to be out and about. It can also occur if bees are missing.

In the United States honeybees are currently being decimated by two species of parasitic mites. **Varroa** mites suck blood from both immature and adult honeybees. **Tracheal mites** live inside bee's trachae, and eventually block air flow. Beekeepers are using several chemicals to reduce parasitic mite populations in their hives, but wild honeybees are declining rapidly. Many other strains of honeybees around the world are *behaviorally* resistant to these parasites, and natural selection being what it is, European honeybees which avoid these mites will eventually appear as well, but this may take several years. Meanwhile crop pollination is seriously impacted.

Bee life cycle—Only **honeybees** form large colonies in which one queen lays all the eggs, and the characteristics of her offspring are largely determined by the diet they receive as they are growing up. Each legless, helpless bee larva is fed by infertile worker bees. Larvae destined to be queens are fed only a 'royal jelly' secreted by worker glands. Larvae which are fed honey and pollen after the first three days grow up to be female workers which gather pollen and nectar, build waxen cells, make honey, care for the queen, feed larvae and drones.

When weather is favorable and honey stores are ample, the workers begin to feed royal jelly to a few queen larvae. These virgin queens emerge, and leave to mate with drones from other hives. When the first young queen successfully returns after mating, she kills all remaining queen larvae. Soon the young queen and half of the workers fly away to form a new colony.

Solitary bees do not work this way. Each female provisions a cell with pollen, lays an egg nearby, and closes the cell. The solitary larva feeds on its own. Honey bees feed their larvae individually until they mature, then close the cell with wax. When a larva of either type matures, it molts to the pupal stage—which may last days or months. Eventually a young adult bee gnaws it way out of its waxen, clay, or wooden cell.

Africanized Bees—Pessimists believe that Africanized (killer) bees will doom backyard bee-keeping, and seriously threaten U.S. commercial bee industry. (The African strain was accidentally released many years ago in Brazil during breeding experiments designed to improve honeybee efficiency in the tropics. They gradually spread northward until they reached Texas in October, 1990). There, public policy no longer thinks of honeybees as "good guys". Swarms are being exterminated on sight. Such an attitude can threaten our food supply.

Africanized (AHB) drones behave differently than EHB drones. They easily invade new hives, and the workers accept them without conflict. Young queens of both strains mate preferentially with AHB drones—maybe because these are more readily avail-

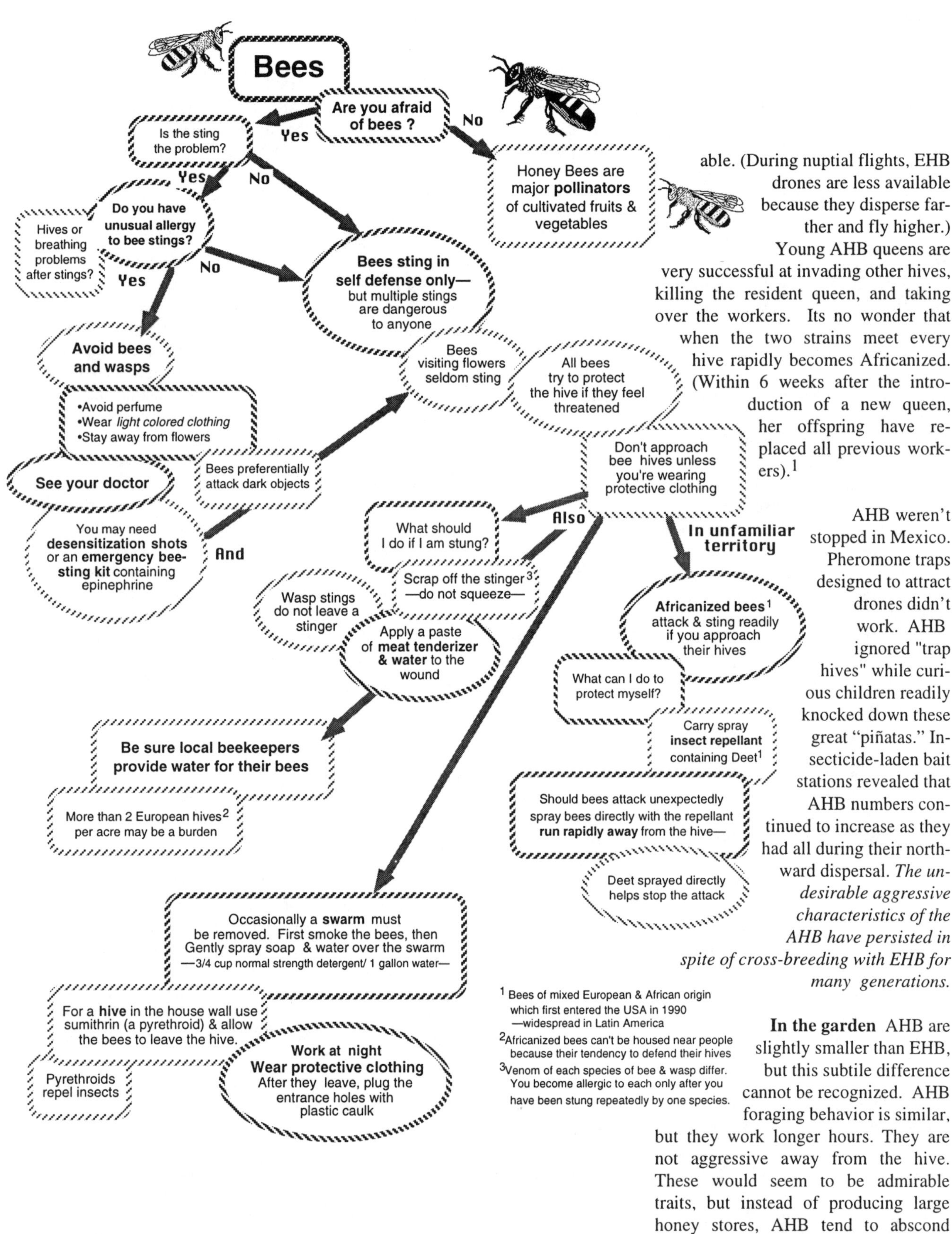

Bees
Are you afraid of bees ?
Yes
No
Is the sting the problem?
Yes
No
Do you have unusual allergy to bee stings?
Hives or breathing problems after stings?
Yes
No
Avoid bees and wasps
•Avoid perfume
•Wear light colored clothing
•Stay away from flowers
See your doctor
You may need desensitization shots or an emergency bee-sting kit containing epinephrine
And
Bees preferentially attack dark objects
Honey Bees are major pollinators of cultivated fruits & vegetables
Bees sting in self defense only— but multiple stings are dangerous to anyone
Bees visiting flowers seldom sting
All bees try to protect the hive if they feel threatened
Don't approach bee hives unless you're wearing protective clothing
Also
In unfamiliar territory
What should I do if I am stung?
Scrap off the stinger3 —do not squeeze—
Wasp stings do not leave a stinger
Apply a paste of meat tenderizer & water to the wound
Be sure local beekeepers provide water for their bees
More than 2 European hives2 per acre may be a burden
Africanized bees1 attack & sting readily if you approach their hives
What can I do to protect myself?
Carry spray insect repellant containing Deet1
Should bees attack unexpectedly spray bees directly with the repellant run rapidly away from the hive—
Deet sprayed directly helps stop the attack
Occasionally a swarm must be removed. First smoke the bees, then Gently spray soap & water over the swarm —3/4 cup normal strength detergent/ 1 gallon water—
For a hive in the house wall use sumithrin (a pyrethroid) & allow the bees to leave the hive.
Pyrethroids repel insects
Work at night
Wear protective clothing
After they leave, plug the entrance holes with plastic caulk

able. (During nuptial flights, EHB drones are less available because they disperse farther and fly higher.) Young AHB queens are very successful at invading other hives, killing the resident queen, and taking over the workers. Its no wonder that when the two strains meet every hive rapidly becomes Africanized. (Within 6 weeks after the introduction of a new queen, her offspring have replaced all previous workers).[1]

AHB weren't stopped in Mexico. Pheromone traps designed to attract drones didn't work. AHB ignored "trap hives" while curious children readily knocked down these great "piñatas." Insecticide-laden bait stations revealed that AHB numbers continued to increase as they had all during their northward dispersal. *The undesirable aggressive characteristics of the AHB have persisted in spite of cross-breeding with EHB for many generations.*

[1] Bees of mixed European & African origin which first entered the USA in 1990 —widespread in Latin America

[2] Africanized bees can't be housed near people because their tendency to defend their hives

[3] Venom of each species of bee & wasp differ. You become allergic to each only after you have been stung repeatedly by one species.

In the garden AHB are slightly smaller than EHB, but this subtile difference cannot be recognized. AHB foraging behavior is similar, but they work longer hours. They are not aggressive away from the hive. These would seem to be admirable traits, but instead of producing large honey stores, AHB tend to abscond

[1] Cal. Agric. 48(2):6, 1994.

(move out) to start a new colony just as honey stores begin to accumulate. The Africans seem to be pre-programed for rapid reproduction and long-distance dispersal They're happy with a smaller hive—about 5.5 gallon size compared to 10-20 gallon volume for the Europeans. AHB may not be able to survive cold temperatures. Most researchers believe that they will thrive in the sunbelt and along the coasts, move north during spring into the mid latitudes, and be excluded by cold from the far north.

AHB are not more venomous than their European counterpart, but they *are more likely to sting near the hive.* They are also *very sensitive* to loud noises such as power mowers and chain saws. A disturbed honeybee releases an alarm pheromone which alerts other colony members. Near the hive, AHB respond to this pheromone in enormous numbers, while the response of the European strain is more subdued. Successful AHB beekeepers place hives far from outside disturbances, wear more protective clothing, and use more smoke to calm their charges than EHB beekeepers. Many care for the hives at night. AHB will follow a threatening person or animal *as far as a quarter mile. If they attack you, your best defense is to run to shelter as rapidly as possible. Do not stop, and do not attempt to hide. Run!* In one successful incident, a man using a tractor retreated under a tarp until the bees dispersed. An insect repellent (DEET) spray will temporarily slow the attack.

Since each state differs as to laws concerning venomous insect management, it might be well for you to find out the laws in your situation. *Texas*, where the AHB first entered the U.S. *makes citizens legally responsible for the behavior of stinging insects on their own property.* [2]

One scientist has recommend that we import the sweeter-natured mountain honeybee (MHB) to replace the EHB. This subspecies has remained separate in Africa in spite of the AHB. MHB might buffer the other two subspecies, or even successfully replace the EHB. Others believe that we can prevent AHB from taking over by excluding foreign queens, and regularly requeen the hives with artificially inseminated EHB queens. We might even be able to breed EHB with different drone behavior, and select for AHB with slower response behaviors. Unfortunately, it may be too late or impossible to accomplish any of these proposals.

Some individuals are taking a different tack. The **blue orchard bee** on almonds and the **alfalfa leafcutting bee** on alfalfa are alternate pollinators. In order to utilize these bees, the grower should supply nesting blocks—wooden blocks containing many 6 inch deep holes, which are 1/4 inch in diameter. These blocks should be placed in a sunny location near the crop. Others are looking to **bumble bees** as pollinators for fruits and nuts. Bumble bees have much smaller colonies than honeybees, and their colonies start anew each spring. Two companies have short-circuited this life cycle to rent and sell bumblebee colonies.[3]

Wasps—the unknown secret

Do you consider wasps to be a problem? Surprisingly, *you won't go far wrong if you believe that all wasps are helpful to human interests.* Most wasps are natural enemies of other insects, though we know of one genus of wasps, *Megastigmus sp,* that feeds on the seeds of roses. Wasps range in size from minute mini-wasp *parasitoids*—which lay their eggs inside a variety of insects (aphids, insect eggs, caterpillars)—to the giant tarantula hawk wasps which feed tarantula spiders to their young. Wasps look like bees with a thinner waist, and no hair on a slender body. *All insects with yellow and black stripes are not wasps, and wasps do not all have stripes.* A wasp may have stripes, or be solid black, yellow, metallic green, or even red.

Vespid wasps—Only a few colonial (Vespid) wasps have the large populations and behaviors typical of 'pests'. The major 'pest wasps' are the familiar striped yellow and black *'yellow-jackets'*. And even yellowjackets are insect predators which like other Vespids live in colonies. In early spring a young queen constructs a few cells to to raise her larvae. When these first offspring mature, she serves as the colony egg-laying machine, and her progeny do the work. Such a colony may increase to 14,000 cells by fall. The larvae in each of these cells is fed chewed-up meat—usually caterpillars and other insects. In one study,[4] wasps removed 90% of the *Heliothis* staked out in an oak-hickory forest in Arkansas. The authors concluded that wasps efficiently removed caterpillars before other predators even found them. Still, it's no wonder that by late summer yellowjackets come to your picnic table seeking meat as they try to feed all these baby wasps! In temperate climates, these colonies die-out over the winter, but occasionally in mild winter areas they become perennial, with several queens.

Vespid wasps build nests of paper, made by combining plant fibers with saliva. Most are a light strong, insulated, structures which hang from a single stalk. The nests of *hornets* are large, round and hive-like. Those of the valuable and mild-mannered *Polistes wasps* which contain only a few cells, are often found under eaves. Yellowjackets may not be a problem when they fit their nest into an aban-

[2]Amer. Bee J. 133(6):399, 1993. [3]See sources [4] Ecol. Entomol. 13:81-86, 1988.

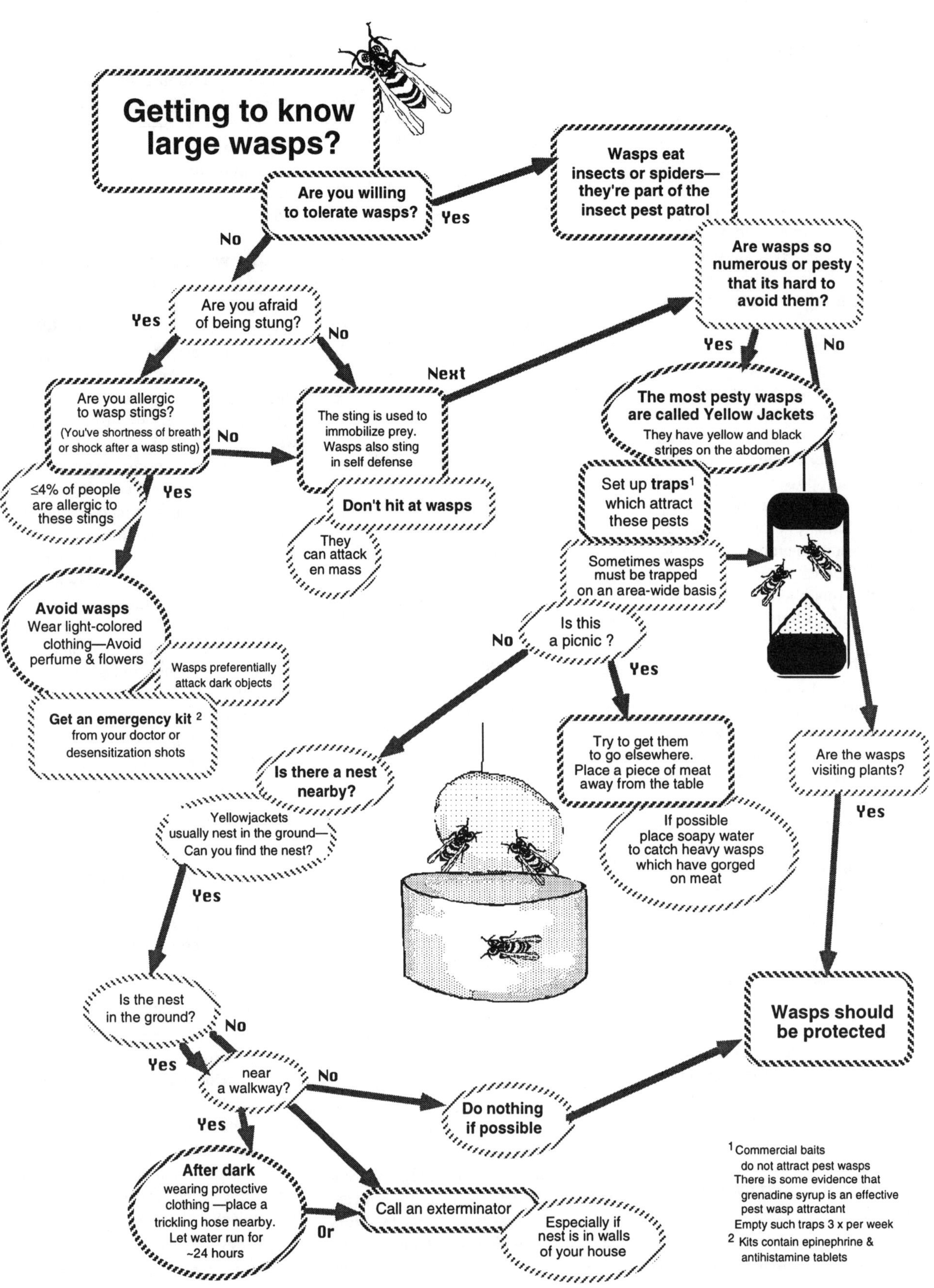

Getting to know large wasps?
Are you willing to tolerate wasps?
Yes
Wasps eat insects or spiders—they're part of the insect pest patrol
No
Are you afraid of being stung?
Yes
No
Are you allergic to wasp stings?
(You've shortness of breath or shock after a wasp sting)
No
≤4% of people are allergic to these stings
Yes
The sting is used to immobilize prey. Wasps also sting in self defense
Next
Don't hit at wasps
They can attack en mass
Avoid wasps
Wear light-colored clothing—Avoid perfume & flowers
Wasps preferentially attack dark objects
Get an emergency kit 2 from your doctor or desensitization shots
Are wasps so numerous or pesty that its hard to avoid them?
Yes
No
The most pesty wasps are called Yellow Jackets
They have yellow and black stripes on the abdomen
Set up traps1 which attract these pests
Sometimes wasps must be trapped on an area-wide basis
Is this a picnic ?
No
Yes
Try to get them to go elsewhere. Place a piece of meat away from the table
If possible place soapy water to catch heavy wasps which have gorged on meat
Are the wasps visiting plants?
Yes
Is there a nest nearby?
Yellowjackets usually nest in the ground—Can you find the nest?
Yes
Is the nest in the ground?
No
Yes
near a walkway?
No
Yes
Do nothing if possible
Wasps should be protected
After dark
wearing protective clothing —place a trickling hose nearby. Let water run for ~24 hours
Or
Call an exterminator
Especially if nest is in walls of your house

[1] Commercial baits do not attract pest wasps
There is some evidence that grenadine syrup is an effective pest wasp attractant
Empty such traps 3 x per week

[2] Kits contain epinephrine & antihistamine tablets

doned rodent burrow, but they are less welcome when they nest in house walls. All large wasps can sting repeatedly with barbless stingers. They use their sting to subdue prey—food for their offspring. Solitary wasps put a prey animal into an individual cell and lay an egg nearby. The Vespid wasps chew the meat before feeding it to the larvae. Wasps are not usually aggressive unless they are disturbed. Don't hit at colonial wasps except in an emergency, because they may release an alarm pheromone which excites their nest mates to come to the rescue.

Insect Stings

In the U.S. each year ≈100,000 people are stung by insects—47% yellowjackets, 20% other wasps, 27% honeybees, and 6% bumblebees. The venom of bees is not the same as that of wasps, and sensitivity to each is expressed separately. Though <1% of us are allergic to these toxins, everyone will experience pain, & most respond with inflammation, swelling, and itching. These symptoms can be relieved with a cool compress, followed by an antihistamine ointment. Should a more serious alergic reaction appear, use an oral antihistamine such a benadryl or chlortrimeton. If breathing is affected (anaphylactic shock) go to the emergency room immediately.

These venoms are rather toxic—the LD_{50}[2] of honey-bees being ≈3mg/kg[3]—similar to that of very toxic pesticides. Only a tiny amount is injected by the insect—147µg[4] for the European honeybee, and 94µg for the Africanized honeybee. In order to be killed, a typical adult would have to receive >1000 stings. Those who receive so many stings suffer muscle & blood cell break down and a drop in blood pressure, both of which cause kidney failure.

Solitary wasps— many solitary wasps build a chain of cells in hidden places such as hollow plant stems. The *mud dauber* or *potter wasps* construct single cells of mud, others dig a tunnel under ground. Solitary wasps provision each of their larvae with paralyzed insect prey. These larvae mature in days or weeks. Some then wait—sometimes through the winter—when all are ready to emerge synchronously as the new spring generation.

Structures—houses, patios, driveways, even lawns, cover potential nest sites for ground-nesting bees and wasps. When clearing "brush" we eliminate nest sites for stem nesters. Seemingly "safe" encapsulated spray particles are transported along with pollen to wipe out entire honeybee hives. If we can minimize some of these changes we will protect predator-prey, pollinator-plant interactions in our gardens. Habitat diversity is the key.

Miniwasps

A few tiny wasps feed on plants. For example, each **gall wasp** oviposits in a single host. Chemicals excreted from its developing larva trigger the plant to form a distinctive gall on leaves or stems—a source of food for the larva. These galls are diagnostic of these wasps, but do not seriously harm the host plants.

Most of the common **parasitoid miniwasps**, neither sting nor subdue prey. Instead they use their stinger=ovipositor to pierce an insect egg, aphid, caterpillar, or other host, and *deposit eggs within.* Some feed on the blood which leaks from such wounds. They are also sustained by nectar and pollen produced by small flowers of clovers, daisy or carrot families, or the honeydew excreted by aphids or other sucking insects. When they hatch, most parasitoid larvae mature within the prey, but some emerge and complete development outside the host body.

Other parasitoid miniwasps paralyze their hosts by stinging, and their larvae feed from the outside. These typically prey on concealed or partially concealed larvae or pupae. Though many parasitoids are solitary, such that with one larva consumes one host, large hosts may sustain many parasitoids. Either more than one egg is laid, or a developing egg divides into multiple clones.

When looking for prey, parasitoids hone in on odors—**kairomones**—released from prey feces, from plants, or released as injured plants respond to the saliva of insect feeders. Each prey insect or plant yields a different kairomone. These complex odors are detected by the wasp's antennae.[1]

Each plant-feeding insect has parasitoid enemies—minute wasps or flies. Most insect populations are kept in check by this array of natural enemies. Since each attacks only one or a few hosts, parasitoids provide selective natural insect control. *Indeed when parasitoids are eliminated by broad-spectrum insecticides, pest insect populations often explode.* Try to protect and nourish the parasitoids in your garden.

Classical biological control

Plant-feeders are easily transported in fruits or plants from one country to another. With natural enemies left behind, these aliens often become intolerable pests. In response, government entomologists search for parasitoids or predators in the native lands of these pests. These parasitoids or predators are carefully studied to assure that they are not diseased or injurious to beneficials. If all goes well, the selected natural enemies are released in an effort to control the imported pest. Climate has an all im-

[1] Scient. Amer. 3/93, 100-106. [2] Lethal dose in 50% of an experimental population. [3]Milligrams/kilogram body weight.
[4]1 microgram = 1 millionth of a gram

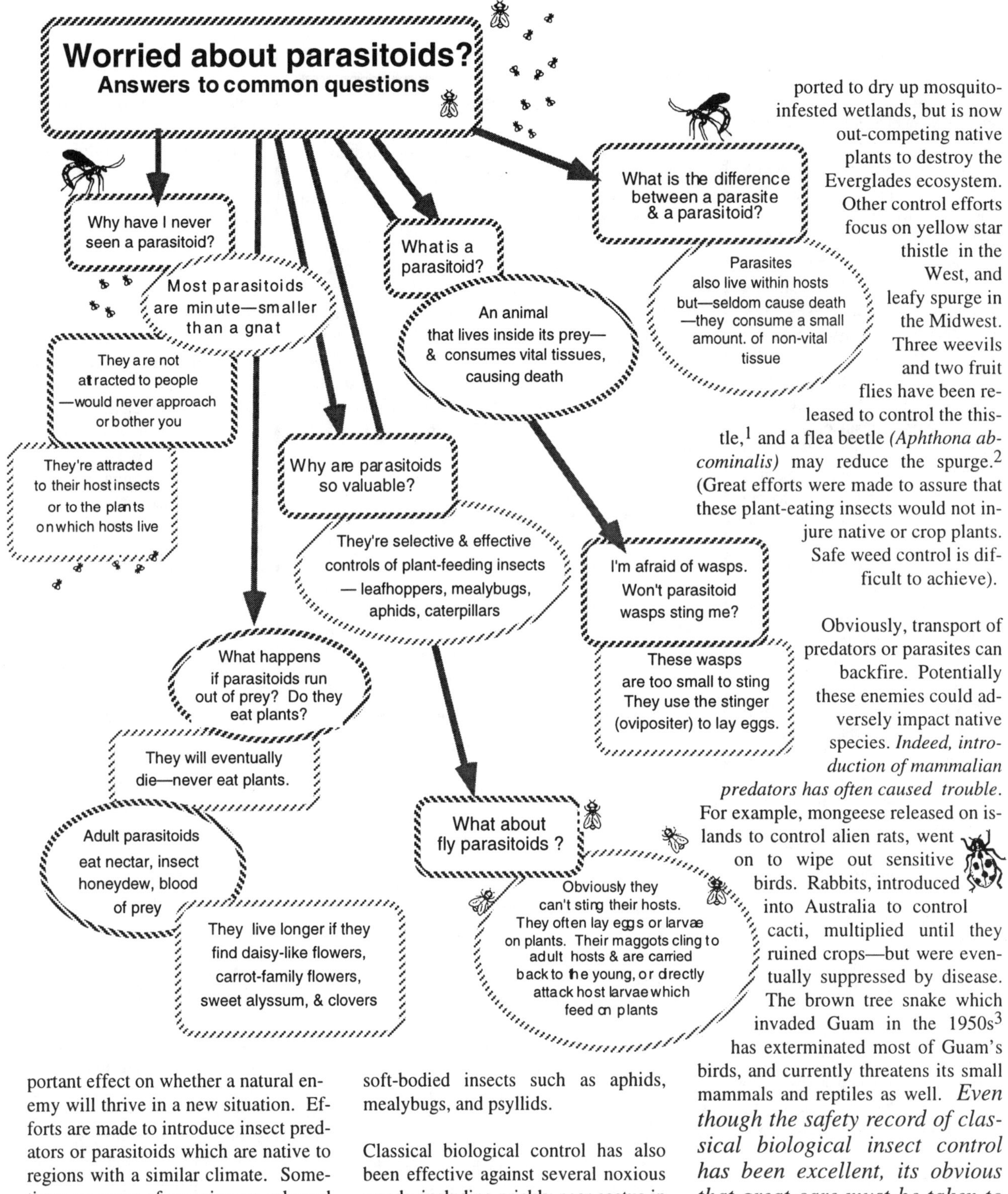
Worried about parasitoids?
Answers to common questions
Why have I never seen a parasitoid?
Most parasitoids are minute—smaller than a gnat
They are not attracted to people —would never approach or bother you
They're attracted to their host insects or to the plants on which hosts live
What is a parasitoid?
An animal that lives inside its prey— & consumes vital tissues, causing death
What is the difference between a parasite & a parasitoid?
Parasites also live within hosts but—seldom cause death —they consume a small amount. of non-vital tissue
Why are parasitoids so valuable?
They're selective & effective controls of plant-feeding insects — leafhoppers, mealybugs, aphids, caterpillars
I'm afraid of wasps. Won't parasitoid wasps sting me?
These wasps are too small to sting They use the stinger (ovipositer) to lay eggs.
What happens if parasitoids run out of prey? Do they eat plants?
They will eventually die—never eat plants.
Adult parasitoids eat nectar, insect honeydew, blood of prey
They live longer if they find daisy-like flowers, carrot-family flowers, sweet alyssum, & clovers
What about fly parasitoids ?
Obviously they can't sting their hosts. They often lay eggs or larvae on plants. Their maggots cling to adult hosts & are carried back to the young, or directly attack host larvae which feed on plants

portant effect on whether a natural enemy will thrive in a new situation. Efforts are made to introduce insect predators or parasitoids which are native to regions with a similar climate. Sometimes an array of enemies are released so their combined efforts will suppress the pest. This system of introduction of beneficial insects—**classical bio-log-ical control**—has been remarkably successful, in suppressing alien soft-bodied insects such as aphids, mealybugs, and psyllids.

Classical biological control has also been effective against several noxious weeds, including prickly pear cactus in India and Australia, and Kalamath weed on U.S. rangelands. Australian weevils may soon be released to control the melaleuca tree in Everglades National Park. Melaleuca was imported to dry up mosquito-infested wetlands, but is now out-competing native plants to destroy the Everglades ecosystem. Other control efforts focus on yellow star thistle in the West, and leafy spurge in the Midwest. Three weevils and two fruit flies have been released to control the thistle,[1] and a flea beetle *(Aphthona abcominalis)* may reduce the spurge.[2] (Great efforts were made to assure that these plant-eating insects would not injure native or crop plants. Safe weed control is difficult to achieve).

Obviously, transport of predators or parasites can backfire. Potentially these enemies could adversely impact native species. *Indeed, introduction of mammalian predators has often caused trouble.* For example, mongeese released on islands to control alien rats, went on to wipe out sensitive birds. Rabbits, introduced into Australia to control cacti, multiplied until they ruined crops—but were eventually suppressed by disease. The brown tree snake which invaded Guam in the 1950s[3] has exterminated most of Guam's birds, and currently threatens its small mammals and reptiles as well. *Even though the safety record of classical biological insect control has been excellent, its obvious that great care must be taken to pre-evaluate the potential effects of each such effort.*

[1] IPM Pract. 15(3): 6-7, 1993. [2] Environ. Entomol. 24; 720-723, 1995. [3] Ecol. 68: 660-668, 1987.

Getting to know more insects

Some of our most attractive insects have transparent wings. Many of these are predators or parasitoids of other insects, so its important to recognize, protect, and distinguish them from problem insects.

Dragonflies & Damselflies

Most of us recognize the *Odonata*, or tooth-jawed dragonflies and damselflies. Dragonflies hold their wings straight to the side. The slender damselflies fold their's at a 45° angle over the body. Their superb flying abilities and efficient eyesight enable these large predators to snatch gnats, mosquitoes and flies from the air. You may have spotted dragonflies hovering near the permanent ponds where their eggs are laid, but they sometimes stray far afield to hunt insects in woodlands or meadows.

The juvenile stages of dragonflies and damselflies—nymphs or naiads—are also predators. The smaller nymphs and naiads consume mosquito wigglers or other aquatic insect larvae, but as they grow larger dragonfly naiads are able to capture small fish or tadpoles. They themselves are prey of bigger fish. *These naiads, like other water-dwelling beneficials, are easily killed when broad-spectrum pesticides are added to the water to kill mosquito or blackfly larvae.*

Fortunately we know of additional natural controls for water-dwelling pests so broad-spectrum pesticides are not needed. Garden pools or artificial lakes can be stocked annually with mosquito fish to reduce mosquito wiggler populations. (Native fish do the same in natural lakes). Alternately, *Bacillus thuringiensis israelensis* (Bti)—a bacterial disease of aquatic flies—can be added to suppress these pest mosquito larvae without harming other water-dwellers.

Nerve-winged insects

All life stages of the swivel-necked **snakeflies** are predators, as are most other Neuropteran (nerve-winged) insects. The wingless, slender, dark brown snakefly larvae—reported to live under bark—run rapidly backward or forward when out in the open. Its triangular head reveals which end is the "proper" front.

In western U.S., adult snakeflies are common in spring. They are active in the daytime searching plants for small soft bodied insects—aphids, caterpillars, mealybugs, etc. Their four transparent roof-like wings—marked with a dark spot near the tip—can carry them rapidly from plant to plant.

The **mantidfly** is a rare large Neuropteran which resembles a preying mantis. These ferocious-looking adults are predators, and their larvae are parasites in the nests of spiders, wasps or bees. Near streams other large neuropterans—similar in appearance to lacewings (see below)—are common. These *dobsonflies* and *alderflies* are more than an inch in length. Their larvae are stream-dwelling predators.

Because **lacewings** mimic leaves or twigs, and they are active only at night, you may not realize that they even exist, let alone that they are valuable insect predators. Brown lacewings are active in cool weather, while green lacewings favor warmer seasons. The adults feed on honeydew or pollen. Their offspring attack insects. The adults are attracted to plants which release two volatile kairmones (signals). One is the honeydew excreted by aphids, whiteflies, leafhoppers, or mealybugs. The other is a terpene released by plants which are prey of these sucking insects. The lacewing's fierce voracious hook-mouthed "*aphid lion*" larva are major predators of these plant feeders. When a cover crop is grown, lacewings are usually present and laying eggs on the foliage.

Green lacewings are available commercially for insect control. In early spring, place cards covered with lacewing eggs near aphid or mealybug prey. *Be sure to keep ants away with a sticky barrier or they may eat the eggs.* It's best to wait until a few aphid lions begin to hatch before you release them outside. To achieve control in greenhouses, place these cards monthly. Alternately, a honeydew mimic—a mixture of sugar plus dried yeast powder in water—can be sprayed on infested plants to attract lacewing adults. Parasitoids will usually control these Homopteran pests later in the season.

Homopterans

A loud metallic buzzing sound as you walk through the woods is a clue that adult **cicadas** are present. These large (same-winged) insects look like a giant version of their **aphid** and **leafhopper** relatives. The buzzing courtship song emanates from a large drum-like membrane on the abdomen of adult males. The noise is believed to attract females for mating.

During their short adult life span, cicadas suck juices from trees or shrubs, and oviposit into slits in tree branches. The newly hatched larvae drop to the ground, dig in, and suck sap from rootlets for the extended one to 17 year larval period. This all sounds as if cicadas would be horrible pests, but they seem to cause few adverse affects to their host plants, and controls are never attempted.

The similar feeding of aphids and leafhoppers, on the other hand, can cause serious plant damage from feeding, toxins, or diseases. Though they are often controlled by natural enemies, artificial controls are sometimes required.

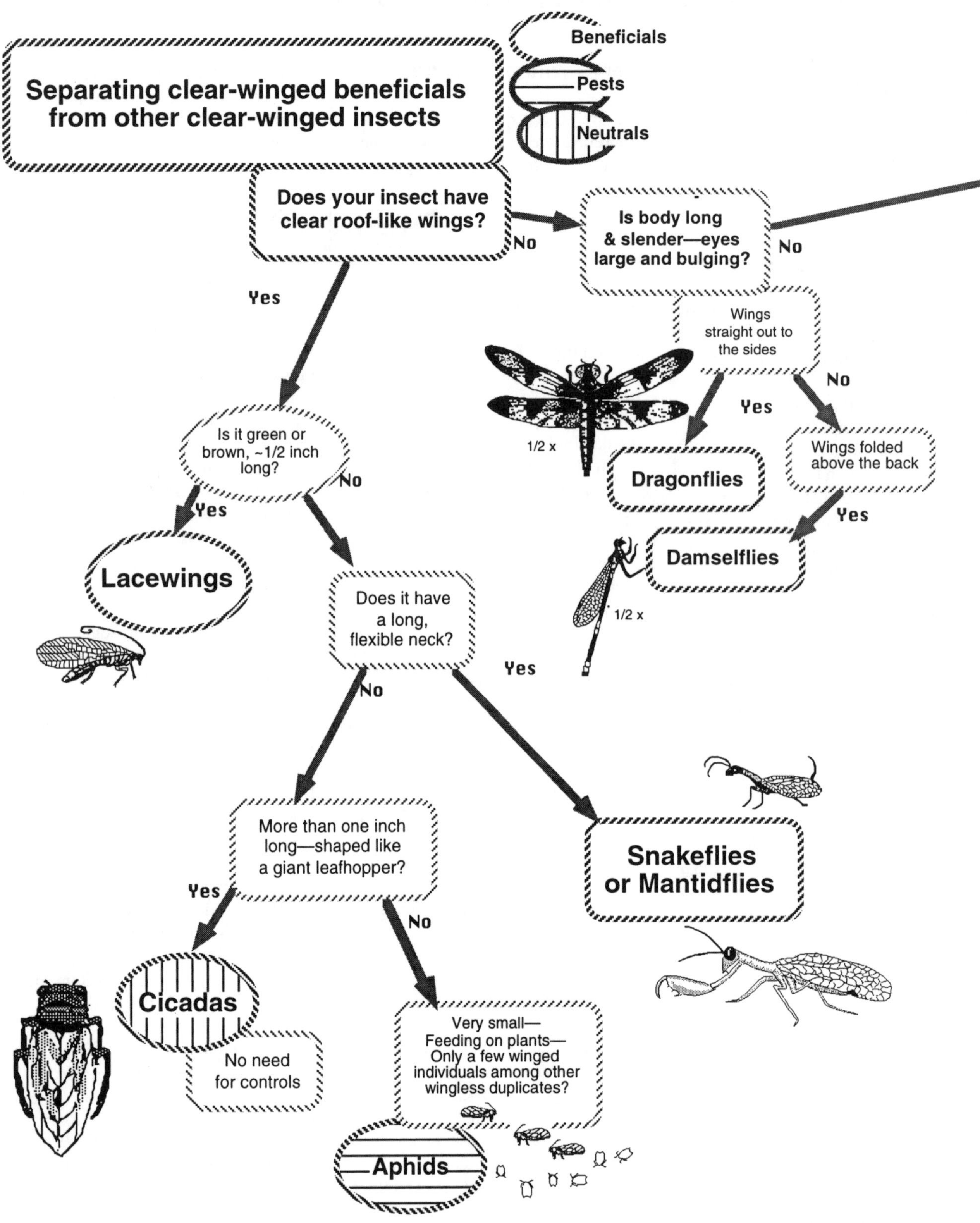
Separating clear-winged beneficials from other clear-winged insects
Beneficials
Pests
Neutrals
Does your insect have clear roof-like wings?
No
Is body long & slender—eyes large and bulging?
No
Yes
Wings straight out to the sides
Yes
No
Dragonflies
1/2 x
Wings folded above the back
Yes
Damselflies
1/2 x
Is it green or brown, ~1/2 inch long?
Yes
No
Lacewings
Does it have a long, flexible neck?
Yes
No
Snakeflies or Mantidflies
More than one inch long—shaped like a giant leafhopper?
Yes
No
Cicadas
No need for controls
Very small—Feeding on plants—Only a few winged individuals among other wingless duplicates?
Aphids

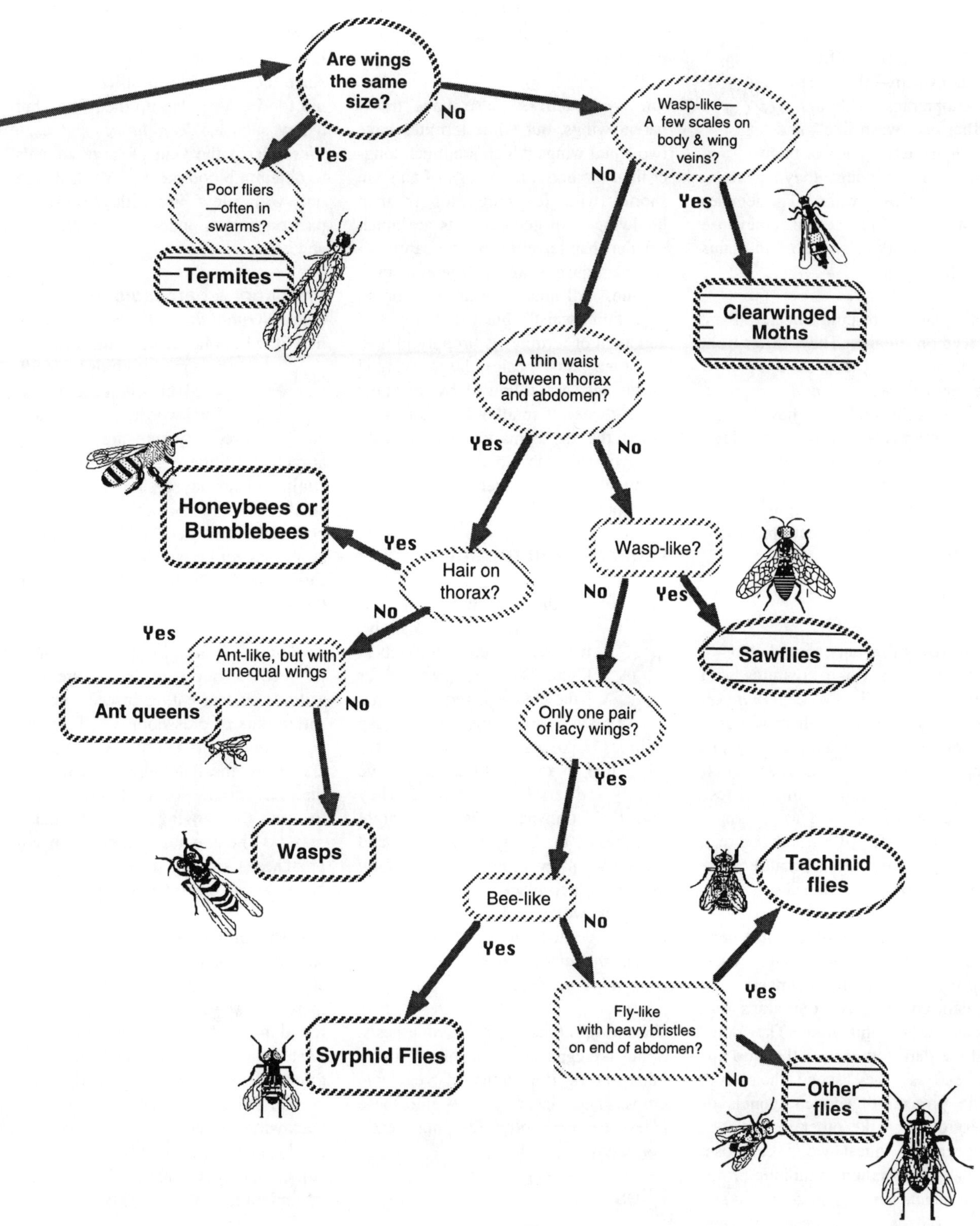
Are wings the same size?
No
Yes
Poor fliers —often in swarms?
Termites
Wasp-like— A few scales on body & wing veins?
No
Yes
Clearwinged Moths
A thin waist between thorax and abdomen?
Yes
No
Honeybees or Bumblebees
Yes
Hair on thorax?
No
Yes
Ant-like, but with unequal wings
Ant queens
No
Wasps
Wasp-like?
No
Yes
Sawflies
Only one pair of lacy wings?
Yes
Bee-like
No
Yes
Syrphid Flies
Fly-like with heavy bristles on end of abdomen?
Yes
Tachinid flies
No
Other flies

Sawflies

Sawflies are different from bees and wasps—the other Hymenopterans. Although sawflies *are* "wasp-like", and they *do* have two pairs of membranous unequal wings, they lack the diagnostic "wasp" waist. The females are called sawflies because they use their ovipositors to saw slits in plants to lay their eggs.

Sawfly larvae resemble caterpillars, and feed on foliage. They differ from caterpillars in that they have a pair of false legs *on each abdominal segment.* True caterpillars always have a few central segments which lack legs. Groups of sawfly larvae feeding on plants, can cause serious damage. Since they're not true caterpillars, they are not affected by the caterpillar disease, Bt.

Termites

We all recognize ants, right? No we don't. Large ant-like creatures with broad waists are likely to be *termite reproductives.* If you see them walking, some of their fellows are probably still flying weakly about on four equal-sized enormous gauzy wings. These wings drop off as soon as a termite couple pairs off. (It's good *they* can recognize who's who, because male and female look alike to us.)

Each couple searches for suitable dead wood to begin a new colony. Their offspring—the colony members—are not dark-colored like the kings and queens, but soft and white. They don't need the dark pigment or the hard cuticle because they spend their lives within protective wooden tunnels or underground. Like other insects, termites cannot digest wood cellulose, but their gut contains symbiotic protozoans which can. The termites and these protozoa share these nutrients. The termite workers pass the protozoans to each juvenile. Most termites have small heads, but a few big-headed soldiers with enormous pigmented jaws guard the colony from predators.

Ant reproductives also have transparent wings, but while termites have two equal wings which are much longer than the body, the wings of ants are shorter with forewings longer than hindwings. In general, ants are much smaller than termites, but be careful—some ant queens are as large as a small termite. All ants have an little bump on a thin "waist", but the thorax and abdomen of termites is broadly joined. In some ant species large winged queen ants are followed by an enormous cluster of small ardent suitors, in others the air seems to be filled with tiny winged ants which appear to be identical. You'll never see ants walking around in pairs.

Clearwinged moths

Most of us think of moths as delta winged, scaly-winged drab creatures that come to lights at night. We're not prepared for the clear-winged moths that are almost perfect wasp mimics. Like wasps, clearwing moths are active in the daytime, and move rapidly and jerkily over foliage. They fold their transparent wings straight back beside the body as wasps do, and sport a wasp's warning colors in shiny metallic blue, black, yellow, or red. But they won't fool you if you look closely, because *they have a broad waist, and a usually a few scales on wing veins and legs.*

Clearwing moths can be terrible pests. Some lay eggs on the trunks of trees, other attack the stems of vegetable crops. Their larvae burrow into these plants to feed, often causing death. For controls, see 'borers'.

Flies

Since flies have one pair of transparent wings and one pair of knob-like halteres, they're fittingly called *Diptera*—two-winged insects. (The halteres function in equilibrium). All flies have lapping or piercing mouthparts, since they are able to utilize only liquid food. Most lap up their food, but a few such as *deer, horse,* and *horn flies* pierce the skin of large animals to obtain a blood meal. We deal here only with a few flies with greatest impact on human endeavors—both good and bad.

Predatory & parasitoid flies

Most *Syrphid flies*—hover flies—look like little bees hovering in the air near flowers. Syrphids typically feed on pollen and nectar. Buckwheat, phacelia, and sweet alyssum are especially attractive to these important syrphid adults. They lay their eggs near the small insect prey—mites and soft-bodied insects—relished by their predatory maggot larvae. They're most active in areas which are sheltered from the wind.

Tachinid flies are also pollen and nectar feeders, but their larvae are parasitoids of leaf-eating insects such as caterpillars or grasshoppers. They deposit eggs or larvae on leaves or flowers where the hatchlings borrow into their prey. (One species has the ability to hear the singing of field cricket prey.[1] The female tachinid then approaches a singing male and deposits larvae which burrow into the cricket.)

The streamlined adult *robber* and *stiletto flies* snatch adult insects from the air; while their larvae capture insects in rotten wood or underground. The round hairy *bee flies* visit (and pollinate) flowers as they suck up nectar through an elongate beak-like proboscis. Their larvae are parasitoids of burrowing insects. The giant mosquito-like, *crane flies* are also insect predators, but their larvae feed underground on the roots of grasses.

Plant-feeding flies

Certain small flies, known as **Tephretid fruit flies**, have attractive and distinctive dark patterns on their wings. Familiar Tephritids include *Mediterranean, Caribbean, Oriental, Mexican, Cherry, Walnut Husk, Apple,* and *Melon Fruit Flies.* Tephritid fruit flies lay their eggs inside fruits which are developing on the plant. Their feeding larvae burrow through the fruit. (The apple fruit fly is commonly called the apple maggot). All pupate in the soil.

Fruits infested with larval fruit flies have been carried around the world. Fruit raised in infested areas, such as Hawaii, is often treated with insecticides before and after harvest to achieve quality fruit and keep the flies from spreading further. In addition, several introduced parasitoids provide partial control. Parasitoids can be raised and repeatedly released to augment these natural controls. In addition, sterile flies are often released to mate with the wild population and reduce their reproduction.

In restricted areas such as small islands, poison bait stations containing methyl eugenol, a powerful attractant for the Oriental Fruit Fly, has enabled elimination of this pest. Such a technique requires careful analysis to assure that this attractant does not exterminate non-target insects which may be attracted to the bait. To prevent further spread of these flies and other pest insects, *travelers should never transport backyard fruits from areas where fruit flies live.* Although all Tephritids may seem harmful to human interests, think again. Gall-forming fruit flies which attack Diffuse and Spotted Knapweed have been released in the U.S. to augment the control of these imported weeds.

Other tiny flies—sometimes called fruit flies in biology classes—are better designated *vinegar flies* or *Drosophila.* Their larvae feed on yeasts and bacteria in spoiling fruits. They often pupate on the fruits. If you find these flies in the house throw the fruit in an outside garbage can or the compost pile. Protect other fruits from the flies until they disappear.

The name *fungus gnat* suggests that these little flies grow up eating fungi. Now we know that they also relish seedlings and may harbor diseases which spread from their fecal droppings. To prevent problems from fungus gnats, always use sterilized soil for seedling propagation. If fungus gnats appear on indoor plants, flood the pot with the Bt H-14 product, Gnatrol*. Fungus gnats are widespread outdoors, and may cause the decline over time of *Trifolium* clovers since they preferentially attack clover seedlings.[2] On clover, use the entomopathogenic nematode, *Tetradonema plicans,* or a predacious mite, *Hypoaspis miles*[3] for control. (Scatter the mites over the soil at 5-8 mites per square foot of bed).

Root maggots —If you've ever grown **onions**, **carrots**, or **cole crops** you may have found maggots gnawing on the roots. These have such common names as the Onion, Cabbage, Turnip, Seed corn, Carnation, or Turnip Maggots *(Delia sp.)*, or Carrot Rust Fly *(Psila rosea).* All cause more trouble in the northern half of the U.S. and Canada than they do further south. The response has usually been to treat the soil with toxins. These maggots are now widely resistant to insecticides, natural enemies have been eliminated, and soil and water contaminated.

Since these flies spend the winter in puparia in the soil, *susceptible crops should never be planted in the same site two years in a row.* Several IPM tactics can help prevent damage. • Use yellow sticky traps placed 10 feet apart around the edge of the plot to watch for the appearance of adult flies. Place the traps oriented toward the north at the top of the crop canopy. Check them at 5 day intervals. The threshold for carrot rust fly is 1 fly per trap. You may find it easier to • Cover vegetables with row covers, or cover the soil tightly around each plant with garden fabric to prevent egg laying. Those with larger plots can surround the entire bed with a 4 foot vertical nylon barrier fence, with a 1/2 inch nylon overhang to trap incoming flies in the apex.[4] In warm weather, entomopathogenic nematodes in planting water will help control root maggots.

Several advanced flies—those that resemble house flies—are dubbed **filth flies** because they serve on the garbage detail. The larvae of *fleshflies* and *blowflies* consume animal carcasses. *Housefly, hornfly,* and *blowfly* larvae feed on animal wastes or decaying plant material. Filth flies are useful, but not welcome near human food or inside homes. Keep them out of the house with screens and rapidly clean up these wastes to prevent breeding.

Blood-feeding flies

Some adult flies are adapted to feed on blood. Appropriately, the most feared are *mosquitoes*, and the *sand* and *tsetse flies* of the tropics which vector[5] dangerous diseases. Obviously, *blackflies, horseflies, deerflies,* and *hornflies* are not fun to have around either. As befits the diversity of insect lifestyles, the larvae of horse and deerflies live in polluted water, blackfly larvae cling to stones in rushing streams, and hornflies seek out fresh manure to lay their eggs. Fortunately, you can *use insect repellents and netting to prevent bites* from these human adult predators, but understanding and management of their larvae is the key to keeping their populations under control.

---

[1]Nat. Hist. 103(7): 49-50, 1994. [2]J. Econ Entomol 86:420-423, 1993. [3]Environ Entomol 22 : 246-253, 1993; J. Invert. Pathol. 62:79-86, 1993; Biocontrol Sci. & Tech. 3::285-293, 1993. [4] IPM Pract. 15(4):12, 1994. [5] Carry & transmit disease organisms

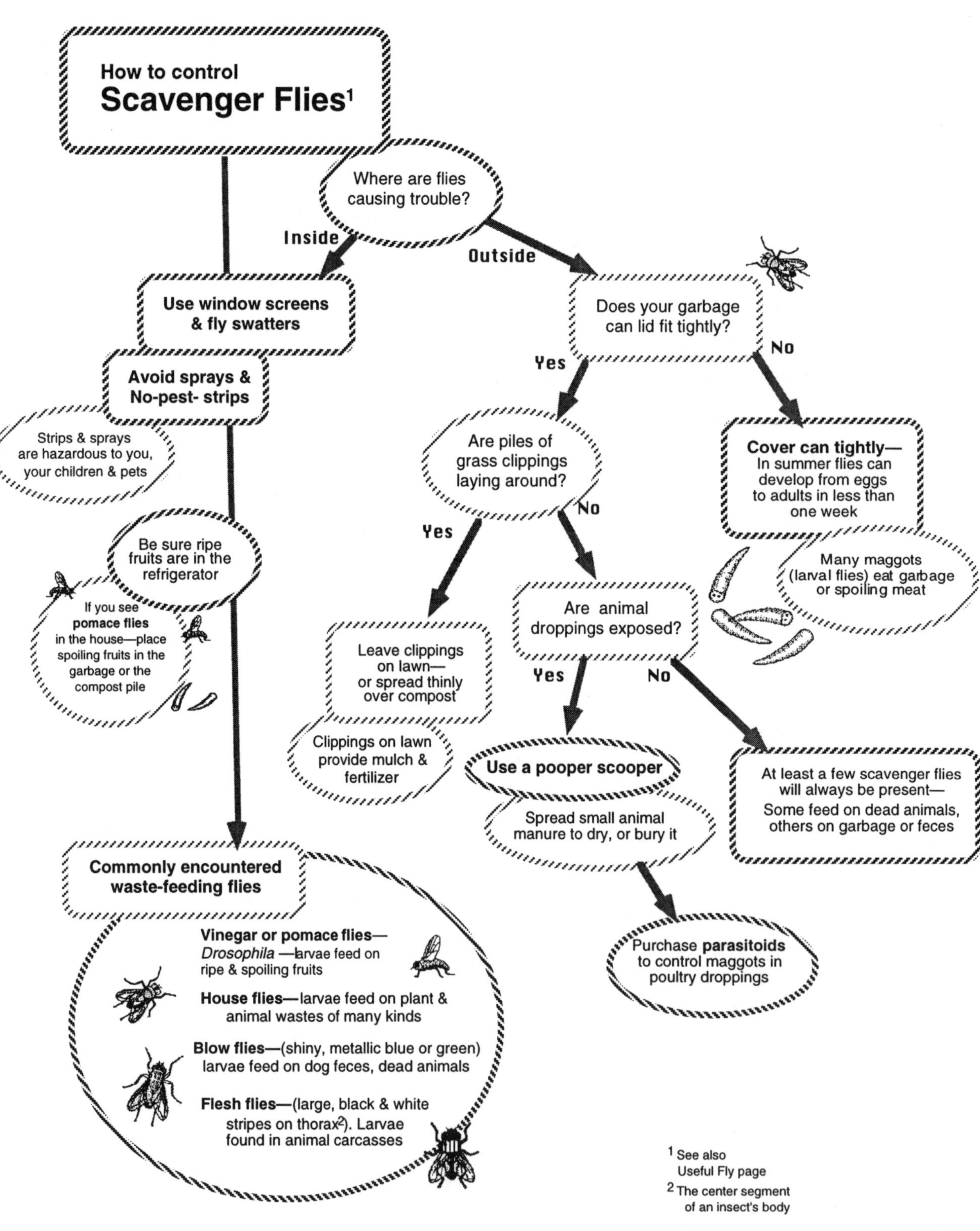
How to control
Scavenger Flies[1]
Where are flies causing trouble?
Inside
Outside
Use window screens & fly swatters
Avoid sprays & No-pest- strips
Strips & sprays are hazardous to you, your children & pets
Be sure ripe fruits are in the refrigerator
If you see pomace flies in the house—place spoiling fruits in the garbage or the compost pile
Commonly encountered waste-feeding flies
Vinegar or pomace flies—Drosophila —larvae feed on ripe & spoiling fruits
House flies—larvae feed on plant & animal wastes of many kinds
Blow flies—(shiny, metallic blue or green) larvae feed on dog feces, dead animals
Flesh flies—(large, black & white stripes on thorax[2]). Larvae found in animal carcasses
Does your garbage can lid fit tightly?
Yes
No
Are piles of grass clippings laying around?
Yes
No
Leave clippings on lawn— or spread thinly over compost
Clippings on lawn provide mulch & fertilizer
Are animal droppings exposed?
Yes
No
Use a pooper scooper
Spread small animal manure to dry, or bury it
Purchase parasitoids to control maggots in poultry droppings
At least a few scavenger flies will always be present— Some feed on dead animals, others on garbage or feces
Cover can tightly— In summer flies can develop from eggs to adults in less than one week
Many maggots (larval flies) eat garbage or spoiling meat

[1] See also Useful Fly page

[2] The center segment of an insect's body

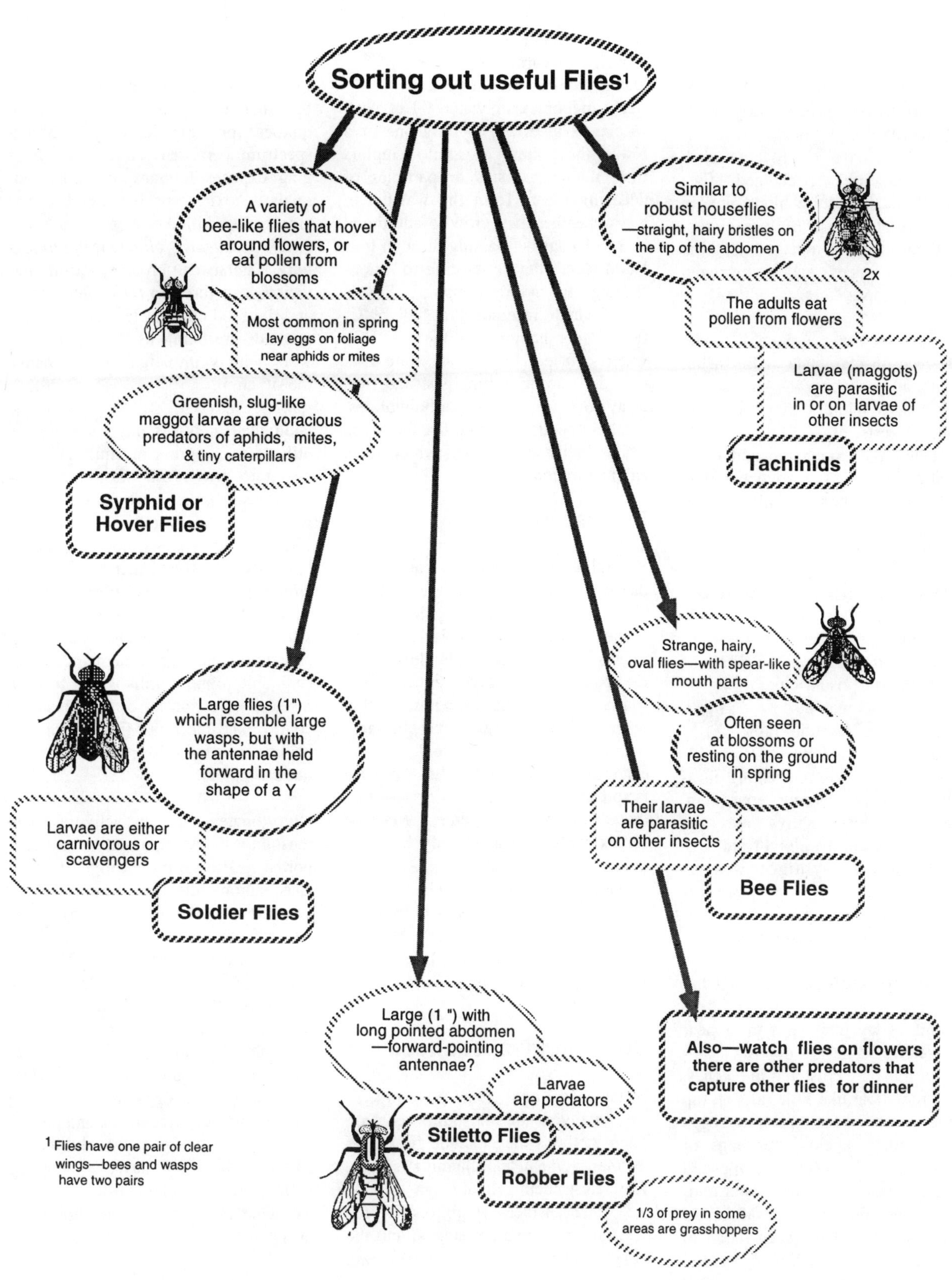
Sorting out useful Flies[1]
A variety of bee-like flies that hover around flowers, or eat pollen from blossoms
Most common in spring lay eggs on foliage near aphids or mites
Greenish, slug-like maggot larvae are voracious predators of aphids, mites, & tiny caterpillars
Syrphid or Hover Flies
Similar to robust houseflies —straight, hairy bristles on the tip of the abdomen
2x
The adults eat pollen from flowers
Larvae (maggots) are parasitic in or on larvae of other insects
Tachinids
Large flies (1") which resemble large wasps, but with the antennae held forward in the shape of a Y
Larvae are either carnivorous or scavengers
Soldier Flies
Strange, hairy, oval flies—with spear-like mouth parts
Often seen at blossoms or resting on the ground in spring
Their larvae are parasitic on other insects
Bee Flies
Large (1 ") with long pointed abdomen —forward-pointing antennae?
Larvae are predators
Stiletto Flies
Robber Flies
1/3 of prey in some areas are grasshoppers
Also—watch flies on flowers there are other predators that capture other flies for dinner

[1] Flies have one pair of clear wings—bees and wasps have two pairs

Mosquitoes

At best mosquitoes are an annoyance, with whiny voice and vicious bites. But they're more than annoying when they vector[1] diseases.

Mosquitoes are specialized flies whose females require blood protein for egg development. Both sexes sustain themselves on nectar and other sweet plant juices, and a few even pollinate plants.

Each species has a unique lifestyle. Most feed on mammals or birds, but amphibians and reptiles are sometimes hosts. While a few are found in deep forests, others thrive only in the open. We expect mosquitoes to bite at night, but a few are active during daylight hours. Only careful study would enable you to sort out the ecology of a particular species.

How mosquitoes find you

Female mosquitoes seek body warmth and carbon dioxide from the breath of their hosts, but visual clues and other odors may also be a factor. The ultrasound traps that are purported to attract them are a hoax (see unmasking ultrasound). After piercing your skin, mosquitoes inject saliva into the wound to prevent the blood from clotting. The saliva may trigger welts or itching, but any allergic response often declines in people who have prolonged exposure to mosquito bites.

Life cycle based on water

Mosquitoes lay their eggs in or near still water. Some are deposited singly, but most are clustered in batches, which may float like little rafts on top of the water. Most mosquito eggs hatch rather quickly, but eggs of flood-water species—oviposited above the water line—must wait until rising water floods them. Mosquito larvae (wigglers) have been found in temporary ponds, lakes, marshes, and water-filled hollow trees, as well as in carnivorous plants, old tires and tin cans, in fresh and brackish water. But each species is restricted to only one or a few of these sites. Mosquito wigglers filter microorganisms or particles of decaying plants from the water. In warm weather they grow to adulthood in 3 to 10 days— passing through four larval stages before molting to a non-feeding, but mobile pupal stage which resembles a fat comma hanging at the water surface. In a couple more days the adult mosquito emerges, and flies away to feed on plant carbohydrates. It takes few days before the female is ready for the blood meal which fuels egg maturation.

Disease vectors

Several mosquito species can harbor disease organisms that are injected along with their saliva. Mosquito-borne diseases include malaria—which infects millions of people throughout the world—yellow fever, encephalitis, filariasis (sleeping sickness), dog heartworm, and dengue fever, to name but a few. (See individual diseases elsewhere in this book). Each disease is spread by only a few insects—often those from a single genus. Malaria, for example, is spread only by mosquitoes in the genus *Anophales.* Most diseases—including the virus which causes AIDS—*are not* spread by mosquitoes (or any other insect) because they cannot live and multiply in the insect body or survive in the insect's salivary glands.

Controlling mosquitoes

Usually local or regional governments are involved in mosquito control. Their methods may include flood water management and chemical sprays. The safest chemicals are light *oils* on the water surface which restrict the breathing of immature stages, and the insect growth regulator, *methoprene,* which prevents normal larval maturation in both mosquitoes and flies. Questionable chemical control methods include fogging for adult mosquitoes or application of broad-spectrum persistent larvicides. Fogging exposes humans and other animals to toxins, and beneficial insects are readily killed. *Pest insect outbreaks frequently follow mosquito fogging.* Persistent broad-spectrum larvicides can threaten the water supply and the food chains. If these outdated methods are being used in your area, work with your neighbors to change the situation.

Biological controls are increasingly utilized to suppress mosquitoes. The mosquito disease *Bacillus thuringiensis israelensis* (Bti) provides excellent wiggler control. (This disease also controls larval blackflies and gnats, but does not effect other insects). *Bacillus sphaericus* is most effective against *Culex species* which are resistant to most chemicals. Some fungi and entomopathogenic nematodes (microscopic round worms which feed on insects) offer promise for mosquito control, and mosquito fish, hydra, and backswimmers—are predators of mosquito wigglers.

Unfortunately, human activities help mosquitoes. Mosquitoes were transported to Hawaii in the bilge of ships. Used automobile tires from Asia are suspected in the introduction of the Asian Tiger Mosquito, *Aedes albopictus,* into southern U.S.[2] This potential disease carrier is out-competing *A. aegypti,* the yellow fever mosquito, to live in small containers. Obviously you can't depend only on the government for mosquito control. Mosquitoes lay their eggs in cans, vases, tank bromeliads, tree holes, and garden ponds. These should be eliminated, emptied every few days, or supplied with mosquito biocontrols so they won't be the source of neighborhood mosquitoes.

---

[1]Carry & transmit disease organisms. [2]Amer Entomol. Fall, 1993. p 163-172.

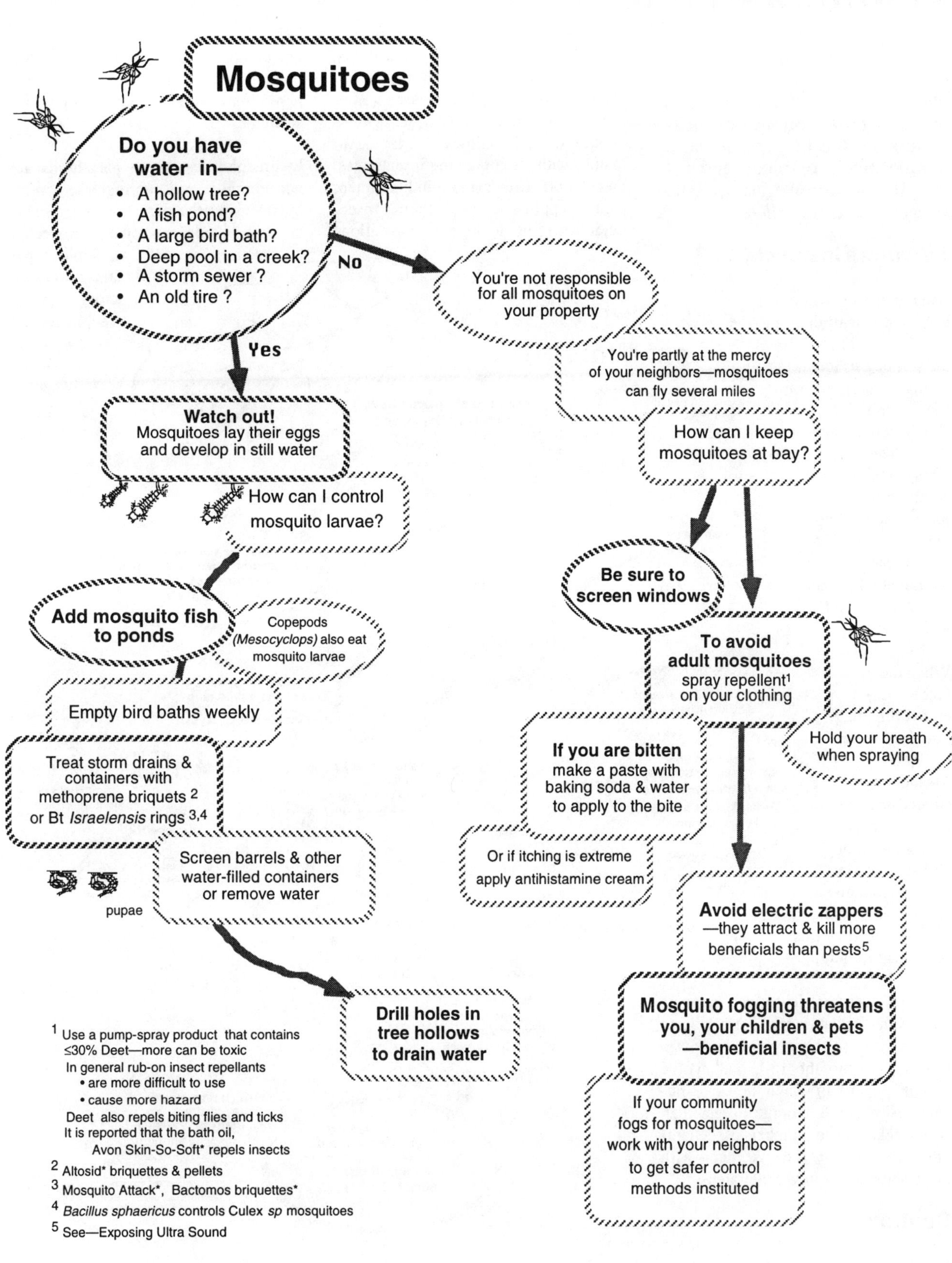
Mosquitoes
Do you have water in—
• A hollow tree?
• A fish pond?
• A large bird bath?
• Deep pool in a creek?
• A storm sewer ?
• An old tire ?
No
You're not responsible for all mosquitoes on your property
You're partly at the mercy of your neighbors—mosquitoes can fly several miles
How can I keep mosquitoes at bay?
Be sure to screen windows
To avoid adult mosquitoes spray repellent1 on your clothing
Hold your breath when spraying
If you are bitten make a paste with baking soda & water to apply to the bite
Or if itching is extreme apply antihistamine cream
Avoid electric zappers —they attract & kill more beneficials than pests5
Mosquito fogging threatens you, your children & pets —beneficial insects
If your community fogs for mosquitoes— work with your neighbors to get safer control methods instituted
Yes
Watch out! Mosquitoes lay their eggs and develop in still water
How can I control mosquito larvae?
Add mosquito fish to ponds
Copepods (Mesocyclops) also eat mosquito larvae
Empty bird baths weekly
Treat storm drains & containers with methoprene briquets 2 or Bt Israelensis rings 3,4
Screen barrels & other water-filled containers or remove water
pupae
Drill holes in tree hollows to drain water

1 Use a pump-spray product that contains ≤30% Deet—more can be toxic
In general rub-on insect repellants
• are more difficult to use
• cause more hazard
Deet also repels biting flies and ticks
It is reported that the bath oil, Avon Skin-So-Soft* repels insects

2 Altosid* briquettes & pellets

3 Mosquito Attack*, Bactomos briquettes*

4 *Bacillus sphaericus* controls Culex *sp* mosquitoes

5 See—Exposing Ultra Sound

Leafmining flies

Leafminer larvae are specialized to feed and live within leaf blades. Some are caterpillars, but the most troublesome leafminers are the maggot larvae of minute black, or black and yellow flies—especially the serpentine leafminer, *Liriomyza trifolii.*

Liriomyza life cycle

After spending winter underground, leafminer pupae develop into adults as the soil begins to warm in spring. Emerging young flies search for a suitable host plant and future mates. The female punctures a leaf with her ovipositor, and both feed on the juices that well up in the wound. Within a day the pair mates and the female deposits her eggs just under the leaf surface.

When the eggs hatch a few days later, the tiny maggots feed within the leaf. Meandering silvery lines in tomato, spinach, squash, or chrysanthemum leaves—to name a few—delineate the tunnels produced by this larval leaf mining.

In warm weather, leafminer maggots mature in about a week, cut a hole to escape, drop to the ground, burrow a few inches into the soil, and evolve into the puparia in which they soon pupate. New adults emerge in less than two weeks. The number of generations depend on the weather—with more generations in warmer areas.

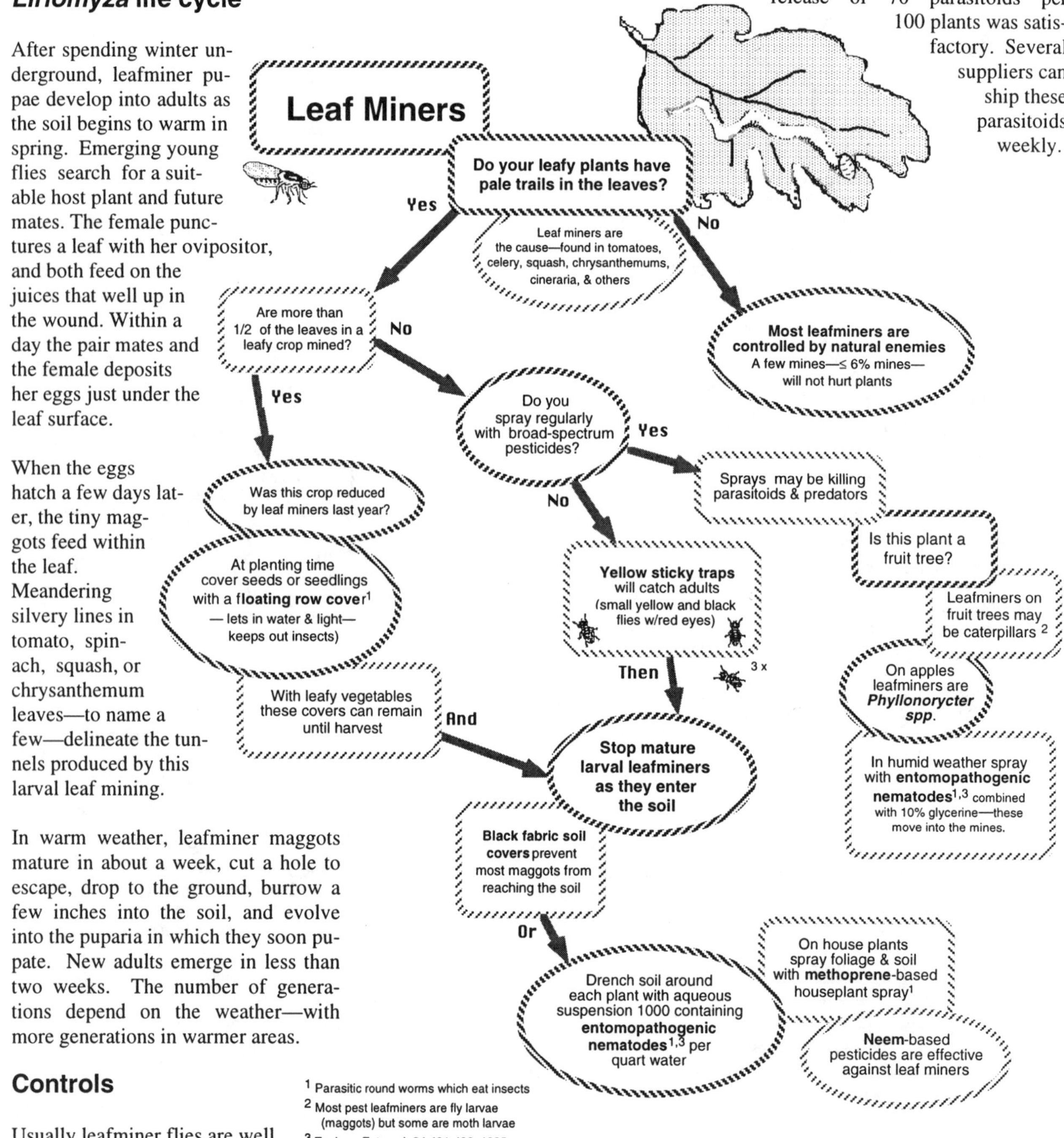
Leaf Miners
Do your leafy plants have pale trails in the leaves?
Yes
No
Leaf miners are the cause—found in tomatoes, celery, squash, chrysanthemums, cineraria, & others
Most leafminers are controlled by natural enemies
A few mines—≤ 6% mines—will not hurt plants
Are more than 1/2 of the leaves in a leafy crop mined?
No
Yes
Do you spray regularly with broad-spectrum pesticides?
Yes
No
Sprays may be killing parasitoids & predators
Is this plant a fruit tree?
Leafminers on fruit trees may be caterpillars 2
On apples leafminers are *Phyllonorycter spp.*
In humid weather spray with **entomopathogenic nematodes**1,3 combined with 10% glycerine—these move into the mines.
Was this crop reduced by leaf miners last year?
At planting time cover seeds or seedlings with a **floating row cover**1 — lets in water & light—keeps out insects)
With leafy vegetables these covers can remain until harvest
And
Yellow sticky traps will catch adults (small yellow and black flies w/red eyes)
3 x
Then
Stop mature larval leafminers as they enter the soil
Black fabric soil covers prevent most maggots from reaching the soil
Or
Drench soil around each plant with aqueous suspension 1000 containing **entomopathogenic nematodes**1,3 per quart water
On house plants spray foliage & soil with **methoprene**-based houseplant spray1
Neem-based pesticides are effective against leaf miners
1 Parasitic round worms which eat insects
2 Most pest leafminers are fly larvae (maggots) but some are moth larvae
3 Environ. Entomol. 24:431-436, 1995. (500,000 per quart)

Controls

Usually leafminer flies are well controlled by mini-wasp parasitoids, so a few mines are nothing to worry about—particularly if they are on non-food leaves. However, because their cryptic lifestyle allows the larvae to mature without contacting insecticides, their short life cycle, and frequent sprays applied against them, insecticide-resistant leafminer populations are common. More selective control methods such as the barriers described here are more selective than insecticides.

In greenhouses where parasitoids are not common, you can increase control by releasing the parasitoid *Digliyphus begini.* In one experiment[1] a weekly release of 70 parasitoids per 100 plants was satisfactory. Several suppliers can ship these parasitoids weekly.

---

[1]Environ. Entomol. 22:1217-1233, 1993.

Beetles

Beetles are famous for fantastic variety—perhaps greater than that of any other group of animals. Nonetheless beetles are easily recognized by distinctive hardened forewings—elytra—which meet along a straight line in the center of the back. Thin membranous underwings allow beetles to fly even though the rigid elytra slow their flight. Beetles belong to the Coleoptera (sheath winged insects).

Beetle lifestyle

All beetles develop by complete metamorphosis,[1] passing through egg, larva, pupa, and adult stages. All have jaws and chew their food. The larvae seldom look or behave like beetle adults. They are so diverse, that it is impossible to generalize about beetle-larval appearance or life style characteristics, though several select the same foods as the adults. Lady beetles, for example, eat aphids throughout life; rove beetle larvae and adults are also predators.

Many beetles eat plants. Some larvae tunnel into wood, others consume succulent leaves. Asparagus and some flea beetles and their young feed on the same plants side by side. **Japanese** and **June beetle** larvae—white grubs—gnaw roots of grasses and other plants, while the adults of these scarab beetles choose flowers or fruits. The names carrion, dung, tiger, and whirlygig beetles suggest the diversity of beetle life styles. Just think of any life style niche and likely a beetle is there to fill it.

Leaf beetles

Several beetles feed on leaves in both the larval and adult stages. The **Elm leaf beetle** *(Pyrrhalta luteola)* is a typical example. The small olive green adults have black stripes along the sides of each forewing. The youngest larvae are black, but other instars are yellowish with dark stripes along each side. American elms are most susceptible, Siberian elms slightly less so, and Chinese elms mostly resist their feeding. Elm trees which are heavily infested with ELBs year after year, may eventually die.

ELBs were accidentally introduced into the United States from Europe in the nineteenth century. Like many other alien pests, ELB populations are not usually controlled naturally, even though scientists have released several parasitoids. The larvae of a small tachinid fly and several parasitic wasps feed on larvae or eggs.

In the north, ELB has two generations per year—three or more generations mature in the south. The adults overwinter in sheltered places, appearing in spring just in time to feed and lay eggs on young succulent foliage. The larvae skeletonize the underside of leaves during three larval instars. At maturity, they crawl down the trunk to pupate on the surface of the ground or in bark crevices. Young emerging adults return to the recovering foliage to repeat the cycle.

Elms are often sprayed with insecticides to control these leaf feeders. If you understand the their life cycle, you can use selective methods for control. The bacterial disease, *Bt tenebrionis,* is effective against ELB larvae, but does not kill their natural enemies. If your city helps control ELB, let them know of the control strategies described on the ELB page.

Cucumber beetles

There are several cucumber beetles in the U.S. The adults feed on not only cucumbers, but also on melons, beans, peas, pumpkins and squash—plants which contain curcubitacin. All cucumber beetles are about 1/4 inch long and live underground in the larval stage, but their appearance, food plants, and home ranges differ.

The **southern spotted cucumber beetle**—or southern corn rootworm— *(Diabrotica undecimpunctata howardi)* with 11 black spots on yellow-green forewings, is almost identical in appearance to the **western twelve-spotted cucumber beetle** *(D. undecimpunctata undecimpunctata).* Beside the fact that the southern spotted lives east of the Rockies, and the western, west of these mountains, you should notice that the southern spotted cucumber beetle has yellow on its antennae; while the antennae of the western twelve spotted are black. The larvae of these species may not cause serious damage to the roots of your corn because they feed on roots of several species. This may explain why a hairy vetch cover crop before corn is linked to reduced corn production. One study showed that spotted cucumber beetles lay eggs in damp soil about 1/2 inch from sprouting corn. In addition, spotted cucumber beetle feeding on vegetables can cause serious damage. A tachinid fly partially controls cucumber beetle larvae.

Larvae of two other cucumber beetles feed *exclusively* on the roots of corn. They are the yellow-green **northern corn rootworm** *(D. longicornis)* of north central U.S., and the black striped yellow-green **western corn rootworm** *(D. virgifera virgifera)* of the eastern plains states. Eggs deposited near corn roots in fall, hatch the following spring, or, after a one year diapause. If another crop is planted in these plots, hatching root worm larvae die. *The best protection against these cucumber beetles is to rotate corn* (move the plot where

[1] See page 14.

corn is planted) *on a three year cycle.*

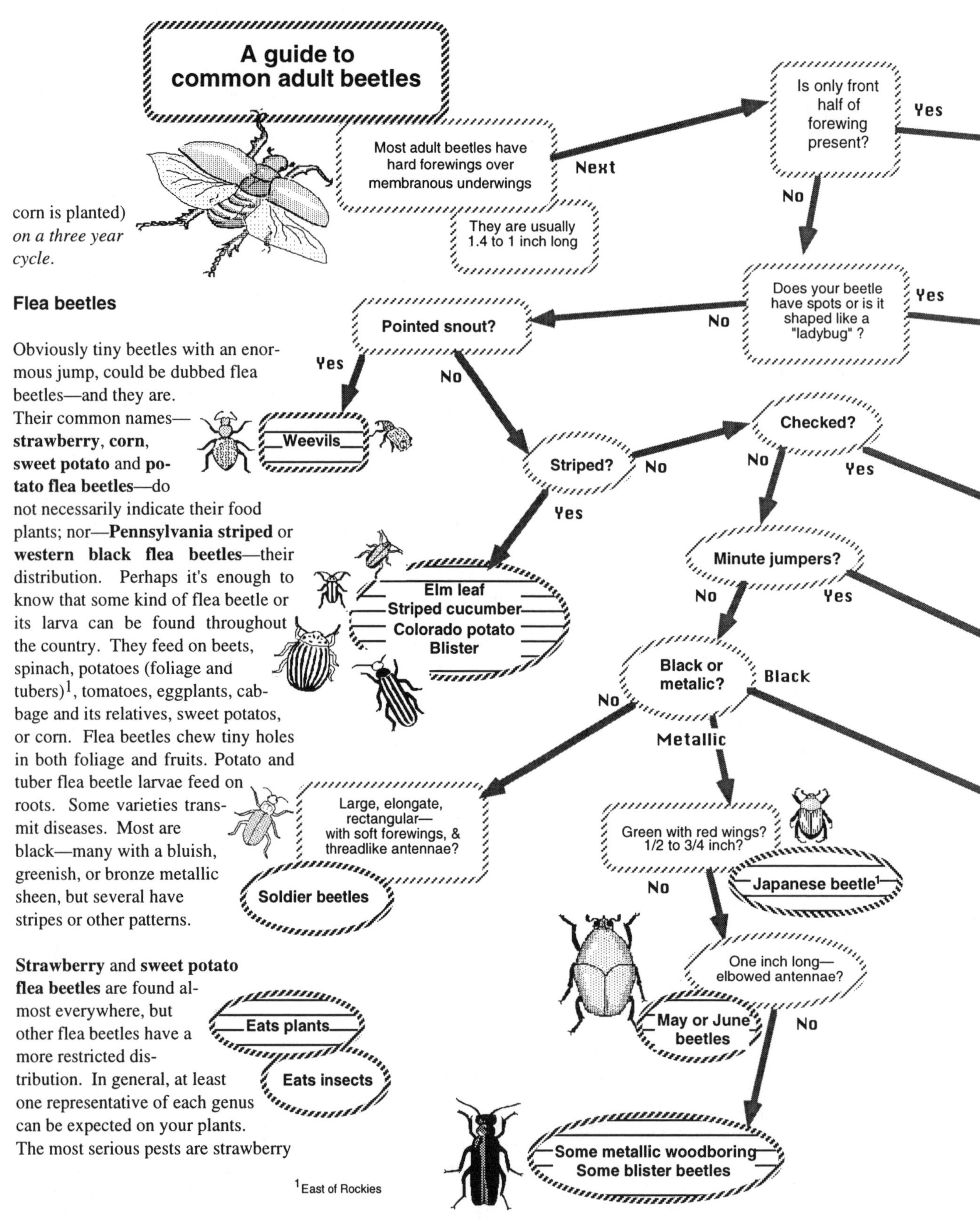

A guide to common adult beetles
Most adult beetles have hard forewings over membranous underwings
They are usually 1.4 to 1 inch long
Next
Is only front half of forewing present?
Yes
No
Does your beetle have spots or is it shaped like a "ladybug" ?
Yes
No
Pointed snout?
Yes
Weevils
No
Striped?
Yes
Elm leaf
Striped cucumber
Colorado potato
Blister
No
Checked?
Yes
No
Minute jumpers?
Yes
No
Black or metalic?
Black
No
Large, elongate, rectangular— with soft forewings, & threadlike antennae?
Soldier beetles
Metallic
Green with red wings? 1/2 to 3/4 inch?
Japanese beetle1
No
One inch long— elbowed antennae?
May or June beetles
No
Some metallic woodboring
Some blister beetles
Eats plants
Eats insects
1 East of Rockies

Flea beetles

Obviously tiny beetles with an enormous jump, could be dubbed flea beetles—and they are. Their common names—**strawberry**, **corn**, **sweet potato** and **potato flea beetles**—do not necessarily indicate their food plants; nor—**Pennsylvania striped** or **western black flea beetles**—their distribution. Perhaps it's enough to know that some kind of flea beetle or its larva can be found throughout the country. They feed on beets, spinach, potatoes (foliage and tubers)[1], tomatoes, eggplants, cabbage and its relatives, sweet potatos, or corn. Flea beetles chew tiny holes in both foliage and fruits. Potato and tuber flea beetle larvae feed on roots. Some varieties transmit diseases. Most are black—many with a bluish, greenish, or bronze metallic sheen, but several have stripes or other patterns.

Strawberry and **sweet potato flea beetles** are found almost everywhere, but other flea beetles have a more restricted distribution. In general, at least one representative of each genus can be expected on your plants. The most serious pests are strawberry

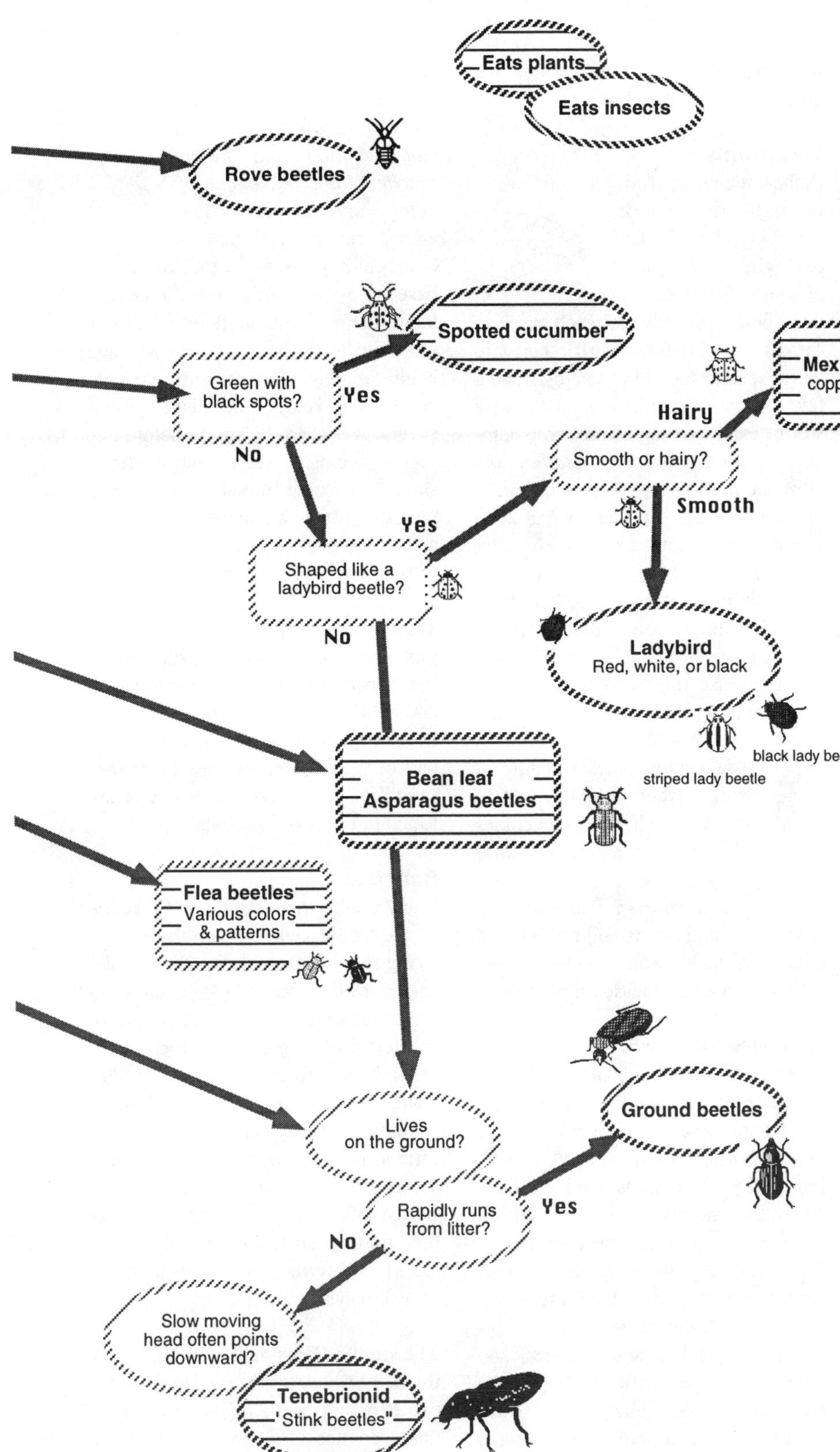
Eats plants
Eats insects
Rove beetles
Spotted cucumber
Green with black spots?
Yes
No
Mexican bean
copper colored
Hairy
Smooth or hairy?
Smooth
Yes
Shaped like a ladybird beetle?
No
Ladybird
Red, white, or black
black lady beetle
striped lady beetle
Bean leaf
Asparagus beetles
Flea beetles
Various colors
& patterns
Ground beetles
Lives on the ground?
Rapidly runs from litter?
Yes
No
Slow moving head often points downward?
Tenebrionid
'Stink beetles"

flea beetle *(Atica ignita)*, potato flea beetles *(Epitrix sp)*—on potatoes, eggplants, tomatoes, sweet potato and corn flea beetles *(Chaezocnema sp.)*—on corn, sweetpotato, or raspberry. See the flea beetle page for more details.

Occasionally flea beetles and other leaf-feeding insects can work to our advantage. The **ragwort flea beetle** and the **cinnabar moth** have been introduced in the Pacific Northwest, to help control the alien tansy ragwort.

Scarab beetles

Scarab beetles have distinctive elbowed antennae with club-like tips made up of three or more lamellae (leaves). Scarab beetles are very common. The numerous species have diverse lifestyles. Many feed on dung or other waste products such as decaying plant or animal tissues. *We are concerned here with those those larvae— white grubs—which live under-ground and feed on roots of grasses or other plants.*

These soil-dwelling scarab beetles are medium to large in size. Their long-lived larvae, white grubs, do extensive damage to the roots of grasses and other plants. The adults of these species eat plants too. Adult **rose chafer beetles** injure flowers and foliage of roses and grapes; and the fruits of peaches and other soft fruits. The even larger **May** or **June beetles**—over 100 species—also chafer beetles —come to lights at night. The adults

[1] J. Econ. Entomol. 87:1683-1688, 1994

at night. The adults chew foliage or flowers. Their larvae take three years to mature, eating roots all the while.

The imported **Japanese beetle** (JB) is a very serious pest in Eastern United States. JB adults eat the foliage and fruits of grape, apple, cherry, plum, peach, and berries, as well as vegetables and flowers. Their larvae thrive on grass roots, causing extensive damage to lawns. The major recommendation for Japanese and other root-feeding scarab beetle control has traditionally been soil application of a product containing **milky spore disease** for control of these white grubs. In the laboratory, at least this disease effects all of these soil-dwelling scarab beetle larva. Recent reports question the effectiveness of the available milky spore disease products. Fortunately, certain **entomopathogenic nematodes**—*Steinernema glaseri*—have proved to be more effective than toxic chemicals for white grub control,[1] and excellent formulations are now available commercially. See entomopathogenic nematodes for more information.

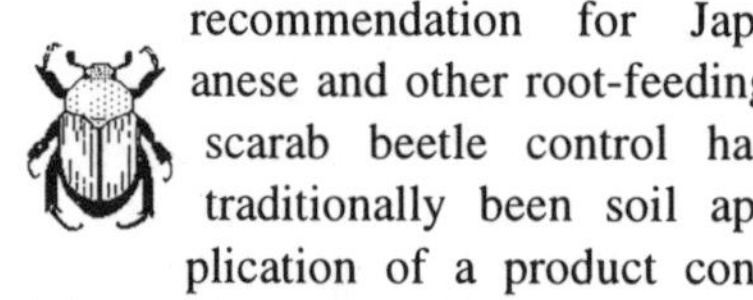

Unfortunately, JB fly readily from place to place, so larval control does not always prevent appearance of adults on your fruits. The JB adults can be trapped with pheromone traps. Other fruit-feeding scarabs can be captured in fruit-baited traps. Some people question the value of trapping, believing that the traps attract more beetles than would appear otherwise. It may be best to put out traps only after adults appear. In one golf course study[2] many more JB were captured when the top of the pheromone trap was mounted on a large plastic garbage can than when it was screwed onto the normal small jar. JB traps were also more successful when they were placed about a foot above the ground.

Wireworms

Rather than confining their feeding to fibrous roots, the shiny, hard-bodied, tan "wire-worm" larvae of some click beetles bore into fleshy vegetables such as carrots and potatoes. (Still other wire worm species feed in rotten logs, and a few are insect predators). Pest wire worms can cause significant crop damage. Fortunately, *crop rotation and parasitic nematodes can provide satisfactory control.* If you've had wire worm on your potatoes in the past, dip potato starts into a neem solution, or spray the product on the soil of other vegetable beds soon after planting seeds or seedlings. Keep soil evenly moist because entomopathogenic nematodes are dormant in cold or dry soil.

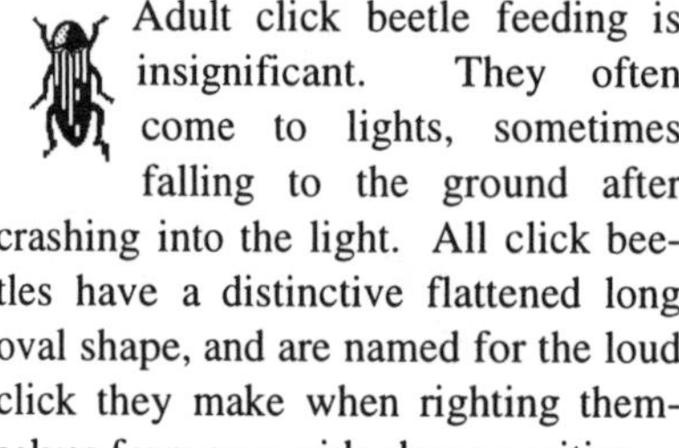

Adult click beetle feeding is insignificant. They often come to lights, sometimes falling to the ground after crashing into the light. All click beetles have a distinctive flattened long oval shape, and are named for the loud click they make when righting themselves from an upside-down position.

Root weevils

Weevils belong to a distinctive family of beetles which are also called snout beetles because their mandibles are found at the end of an elongated snout. Practically all weevils feed on plant materials, and many of their legless grub-like larvae infest nuts, twigs etc. The larvae of ***Otiorhynchinae* root weevils** feed on the roots of a wide variety of garden ornamentals and vegetables, as well a pears, berries, and citrus. The quarter inch long adults are hard-bodied, black or brown, flightless and nocturnal. Their snout is shorter that that of most weevils—they're called short-nosed weevils—*but that doesn't stop them from cutting out round notches from the edges of petals and leaves.* The adults spend the daylight hours hiding in soil crevices at the base of plants. After dark it usually takes them about an hour to slowly climb up to the leaves or flowers and begin feeding. There is only one generation per year. The adults eat for several weeks in the spring before egg laying begins. Adult control efforts should be concentrated in this spring period. Larval can be treated with parasitic nematodes from late spring through early fall.

The names of some of these root weevils are **black vine weevil, strawberry root weevil, fuller rose weevil,** and **white fringed beetle.** The white fringed beetle is a pest in the Eastern part of the country, and the fuller rose weevil in the West. The others are found throughout the country.

Bark beetles

Many conifers are damaged by beetle larvae feeding just beneath the bark of living trees. Other beetles feed on decaying wood after trees have died. In most situations proper cultural care of conifers will help the trees themselves resist beetle feeding. If a tree dies from a bark beetle infestation, it should be rapidly removed to prevent further beetle breeding. Trees which die from other causes (snags) are a source of food and living space for hole nesting birds and should be protected unless they threaten structures or walkways.

The smaller European elm bark beetle *(Scolytus multristriatus)* and the native elm bark beetle *(Hylurgopinus rufipes)* do not seriously damage elms,

---

[1] J. Econ. Entomol. I 87:1014-1021, 1994. [2] J. Econ. Entomol. 87: 775-780, 1994.

but spread fatal **Dutch elm disease.** *Insecticide sprays to control the beetles will not control the disease.* Only rapid removal of elm trees infested with Dutch elm disease, and burial or chipping of the wood can slow the spread. Several hybrid elms resist the disease.

Predatory beetles

Lady beetles

We're sure that you already know that "ladybugs" or ladybeetles are "good guys". More than almost any other insect they have received good press. Because some of them hibernate through the winter in groups, they are relatively easy to capture and market for pest control—even in local nurseries. This is helpful because most lady bird beetles provide excellent control of aphids and mealybugs and other soft-bodied insects and mites. If you release them where an aphid or whitefly problem, they'll likely stick around to feed. Be careful though not to treat these plants with insecticides or fungicides. These chemicals can kill these helpful beneficials.

You may not recognize all lady beetles. They're not only red with spots, but solid red, black, or white. *They are never green, however.* (The green spotted beetles are cucumber beetles, and they are plant feeders). The lady beetle relatives, **alfalfa lady beetle** and the **Mexican bean beetle**, are plant feeders. MBB are pests in south central and eastern U.S. Studies have shown that they cause problems under inadequate cultural conditions such as too much shade, or too little water which slow growth of bean plants. Natural enemies are available to release for their control.

Soldier & checkered beetles

Never assume that a conspicuous beetle on your flowers must mean trouble. Though never common, the straight-sided soldier and colorful checkered beetles are important insect predators. They are often seen on flowers where they supplement their diet with nectar and pollen. Soldier beetles feed on aphids, and the eggs and larvae of pest beetles, grasshoppers, and butterflies and moths. Most checkered beetle larvae are important in the control of larval bark beetles.

Ground beetles

Ground beetle habits are varied, with some searching trees, others underground, and most on the ground surface. Individual ground beetles are important enemies of insects, but some of the largest eat snails and slugs. One species lives in the intertidal zone of Southern California, and an electric green European searcher has been imported to control gypsy moth caterpillars.

Carabid ground beetles are valuable in orchards where they attack overwintering codling moths which seek shelter in soil or bark crevices. They are also important enemies of the armyworms which are sporadic pests of corn and other cereal crops in Eastern north America.

Most ground beetles are black with parallel ridges on the back. They run away rapidly when their litter shelters are disturbed during the daytime. They do best where diverse ground covers are grow because these provide shelter. If you have a compost pile, ground beetles will be part of the fauna living there.

Rove beetles

Among unusual beetles, are rove beetles which lack a large elytra (forewing) so that their segmented abdomens are visible below stubby wings. Some rove beetles are important predators of insects, but others feed on decaying plant materials or fungi. Rove beetles are inconspicuous because they are seldom seen on flowers or leaves and most are black and quite small. Their larvae live in the same habitats as the adults. We've seen them in compost piles. Several attack the fly and beetle larvae which feed on carrion. One parasitic rove beetle attacks cabbage maggots. Other species search for caterpillars such as armyworms on crops. The red spider mite destroyer consumes two-spotted spider mites. The large imported **Devils Coach Horse**, *Ocypus olens,* a predator of the brown garden snail, requires the same moist climate as the snails themselves.

There are other beetle predators which may come your way. The familiar **fireflies**—adults and larvae—are predaceous on snails, slugs, and insect larvae. Most U.S. species live east of the Rockies in areas of high humidity. **Blister beetle** adults eat plants but all known larvae are predators on on grasshopper eggs and larvae of wild bees.

Most predatory beetles are more effective in situations where habitats are relatively undisturbed, such as orchards or no-till gardens. They benefit from leaf litter. They are killed by cultivation and pesticide use.

Beetles that live part of their life in the soil

Can often be controlled by Entomopathogenic Nematodes[1]

Or

scarb beetle larvae may also be suppressed by **milky-spore disease** [2]

Control takes >one year

Masked chafer Beetles
Cyclocephala immaculata & *C. borealis*
1/2 inch pale brown adults do not feed
White grub larvae eat grass roots

Rose chafer
Larvae at roots of grass in sandy soil
Adults on fruits, flowers, vegetables

Japanese beetle
250 host plants
Larvae grass roots 3 years

May & June beetles
Larvae eat grass, vegetable roots
Adults attracted to fruit
E of Rockies

Black vine (root weevils)
Larvae feed on roots of berries, Rhododendron, small fruits, many others.
Adults notch leaves & petals of shrubs & flowers

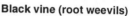

- **Rotate crops—**
- In fall and spring incorporate **entomopathogenic nematodes** into soil beneath affected plants
- After dark, the flightless adults can be knocked from plants into **soapy water**—repeat twice for best effect

Wire Worms-Click Beetles[3]
Live 2-3 years as larvae which feed on roots of grass, potatoes, onions, legumes, carrots
Plow in summer—rotate crops
avoid planting vegetables after grass

Elm Leaf Beetle
Pyrrhalia luteola
Yellowish, with black margins around wings
Adults & larvae skeletonize elm leaves

Beetle Bts help control larvae
—Tree trunk treatment can prevent pupation

Details described on ELB page

[1] Entomopathogenic nematodes applied annually on warm moist soil at a time when pest larvae are active (see pest life cycle & entomopathogenic nematode page)

[2] Now reported to be quite ineffective

[3] See also wire worm page

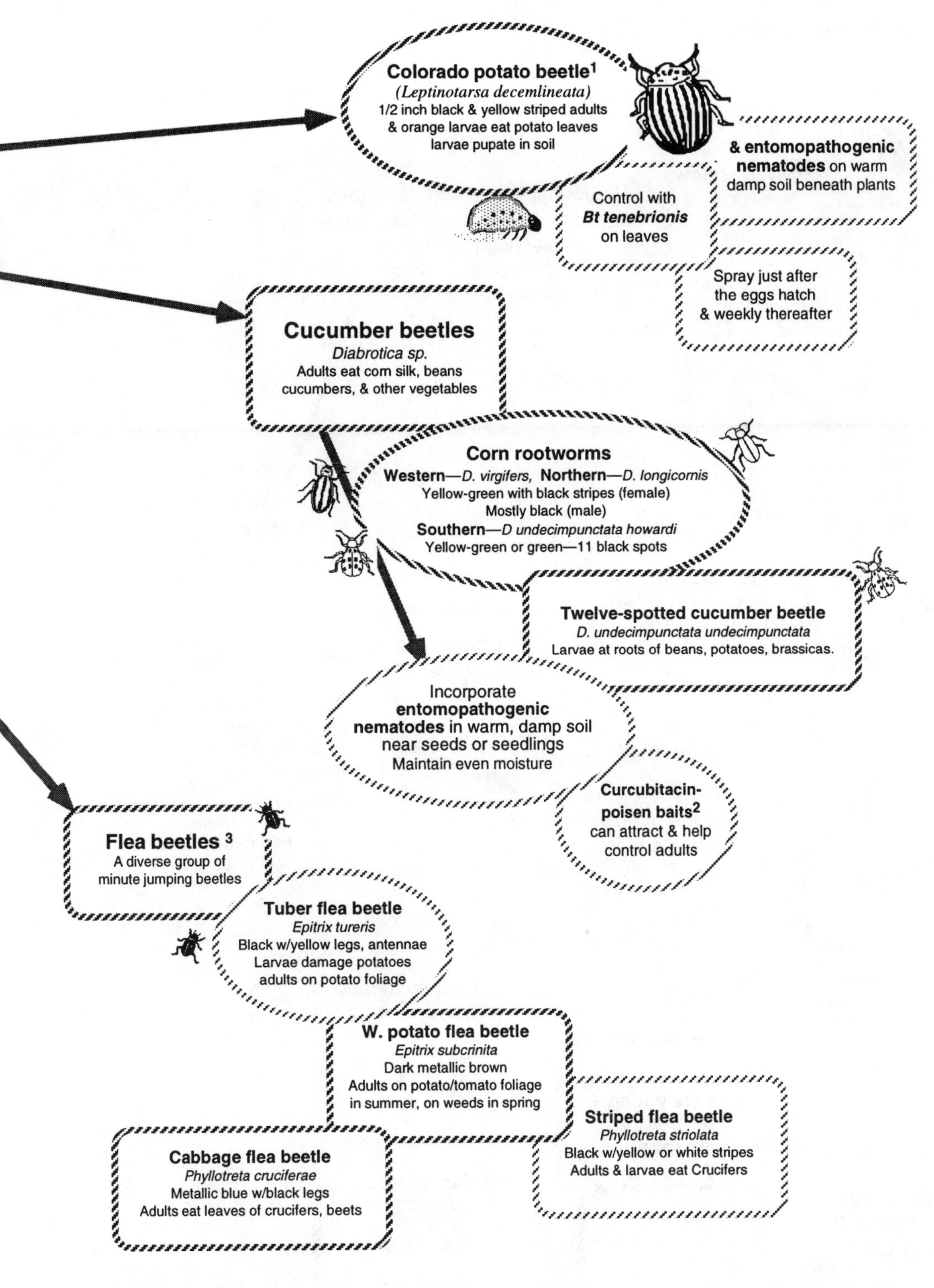

Colorado potato beetle[1]
(Leptinotarsa decemlineata)
1/2 inch black & yellow striped adults
& orange larvae eat potato leaves
larvae pupate in soil
& entomopathogenic nematodes on warm damp soil beneath plants
Control with Bt tenebrionis on leaves
Spray just after the eggs hatch & weekly thereafter
Cucumber beetles
Diabrotica sp.
Adults eat corn silk, beans cucumbers, & other vegetables
Corn rootworms
Western—D. virgifers, Northern—D. longicornis
Yellow-green with black stripes (female)
Mostly black (male)
Southern—D undecimpunctata howardi
Yellow-green or green—11 black spots
Twelve-spotted cucumber beetle
D. undecimpunctata undecimpunctata
Larvae at roots of beans, potatoes, brassicas.
Incorporate entomopathogenic nematodes in warm, damp soil near seeds or seedlings
Maintain even moisture
Curcubitacin-poisen baits[2] can attract & help control adults
Flea beetles [3]
A diverse group of minute jumping beetles
Tuber flea beetle
Epitrix tureris
Black w/yellow legs, antennae
Larvae damage potatoes
adults on potato foliage
W. potato flea beetle
Epitrix subcrinita
Dark metallic brown
Adults on potato/tomato foliage
in summer, on weeds in spring
Striped flea beetle
Phyllotreta striolata
Black w/yellow or white stripes
Adults & larvae eat Crucifers
Cabbage flea beetle
Phyllotreta cruciferae
Metallic blue w/black legs
Adults eat leaves of crucifers, beets

1 See also colorado potato beetle page

2 Adios*, see also corn

3 See also flea beetle page

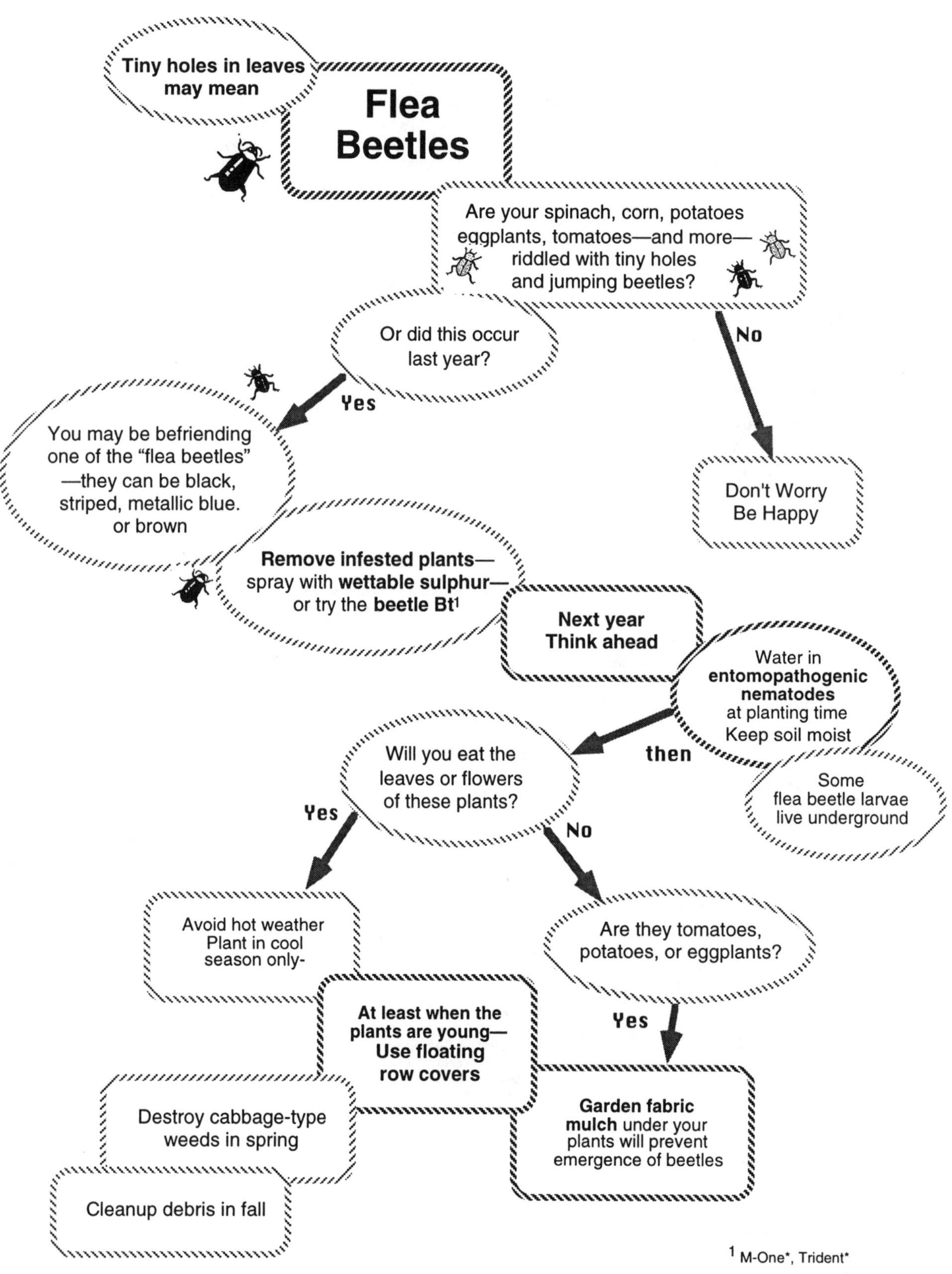
Tiny holes in leaves may mean
Flea Beetles
Are your spinach, corn, potatoes eggplants, tomatoes—and more—riddled with tiny holes and jumping beetles?
Or did this occur last year?
No
Don't Worry Be Happy
Yes
You may be befriending one of the "flea beetles" —they can be black, striped, metallic blue. or brown
Remove infested plants—spray with wettable sulphur—or try the beetle Bt1
Next year Think ahead
Water in entomopathogenic nematodes at planting time Keep soil moist
Some flea beetle larvae live underground
then
Will you eat the leaves or flowers of these plants?
Yes
Avoid hot weather Plant in cool season only-
At least when the plants are young—Use floating row covers
Destroy cabbage-type weeds in spring
Cleanup debris in fall
No
Are they tomatoes, potatoes, or eggplants?
Yes
Garden fabric mulch under your plants will prevent emergence of beetles

[1] M-One*, Trident*

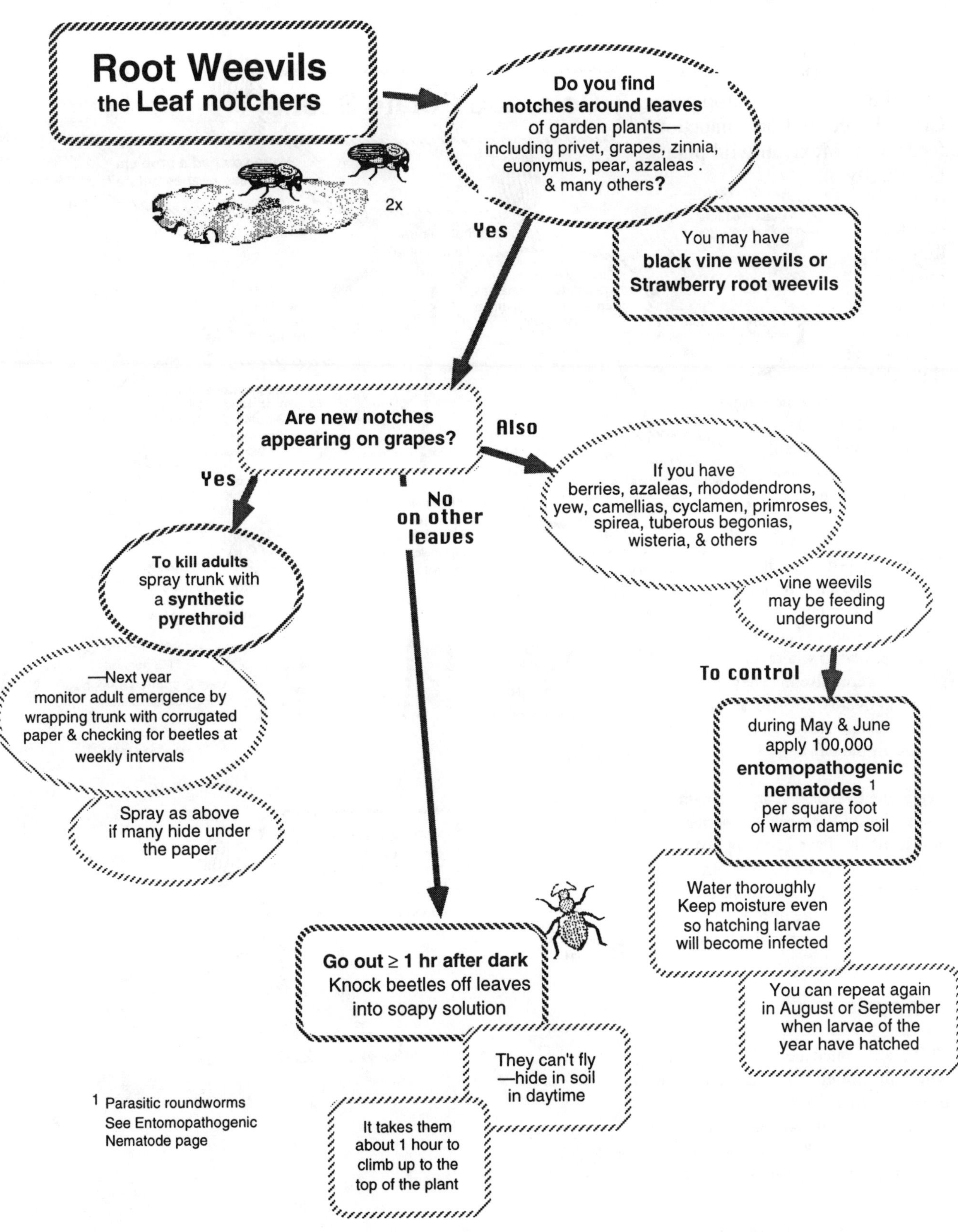
Root Weevils
the Leaf notchers
2x
Do you find
notches around leaves
of garden plants—
including privet, grapes, zinnia,
euonymus, pear, azaleas .
& many others?
Yes
You may have
black vine weevils or
Strawberry root weevils
Are new notches
appearing on grapes?
Also
Yes
No
on other
leaves
If you have
berries, azaleas, rhododendrons,
yew, camellias, cyclamen, primroses,
spirea, tuberous begonias,
wisteria, & others
vine weevils
may be feeding
underground
To control
during May & June
apply 100,000
entomopathogenic
nematodes 1
per square foot
of warm damp soil
Water thoroughly
Keep moisture even
so hatching larvae
will become infected
You can repeat again
in August or September
when larvae of the
year have hatched
To kill adults
spray trunk with
a synthetic
pyrethroid
—Next year
monitor adult emergence by
wrapping trunk with corrugated
paper & checking for beetles at
weekly intervals
Spray as above
if many hide under
the paper
Go out ≥ 1 hr after dark
Knock beetles off leaves
into soapy solution
They can't fly
—hide in soil
in daytime
It takes them
about 1 hour to
climb up to the
top of the plant

1 Parasitic roundworms
See Entomopathogenic
Nematode page

Colorado potato beetle background

The Colorado potato beetle is *a* Chrysomelid (leaf-feeding) beetle. Like many other crop pests, CPB started out as innocuous feeders on Mexican wild plants. Eventually, they expanded their range, moving north from Mexico to south-central U.S., feeding on wild nightshades—the family to which potatoes and tomatoes belong. When potatoes became a major crop in the mid 1800's, the U.S. strain moved over to the abundant potato —though the Mexican race still prefers the original wild plants. This new CPB strain expanded rapidly eastward wherever potatoes were raised. They now thrive all over North America (except California and Nevada), and most of the rest of the world.

Beginning over 100 years ago with arsenic-based Paris green, a series of insecticides have been applied in efforts to control CPB. Not surprisingly, many CPB populations are now resistant to one or more insecticides. This is a particular problem in northeastern U.S.

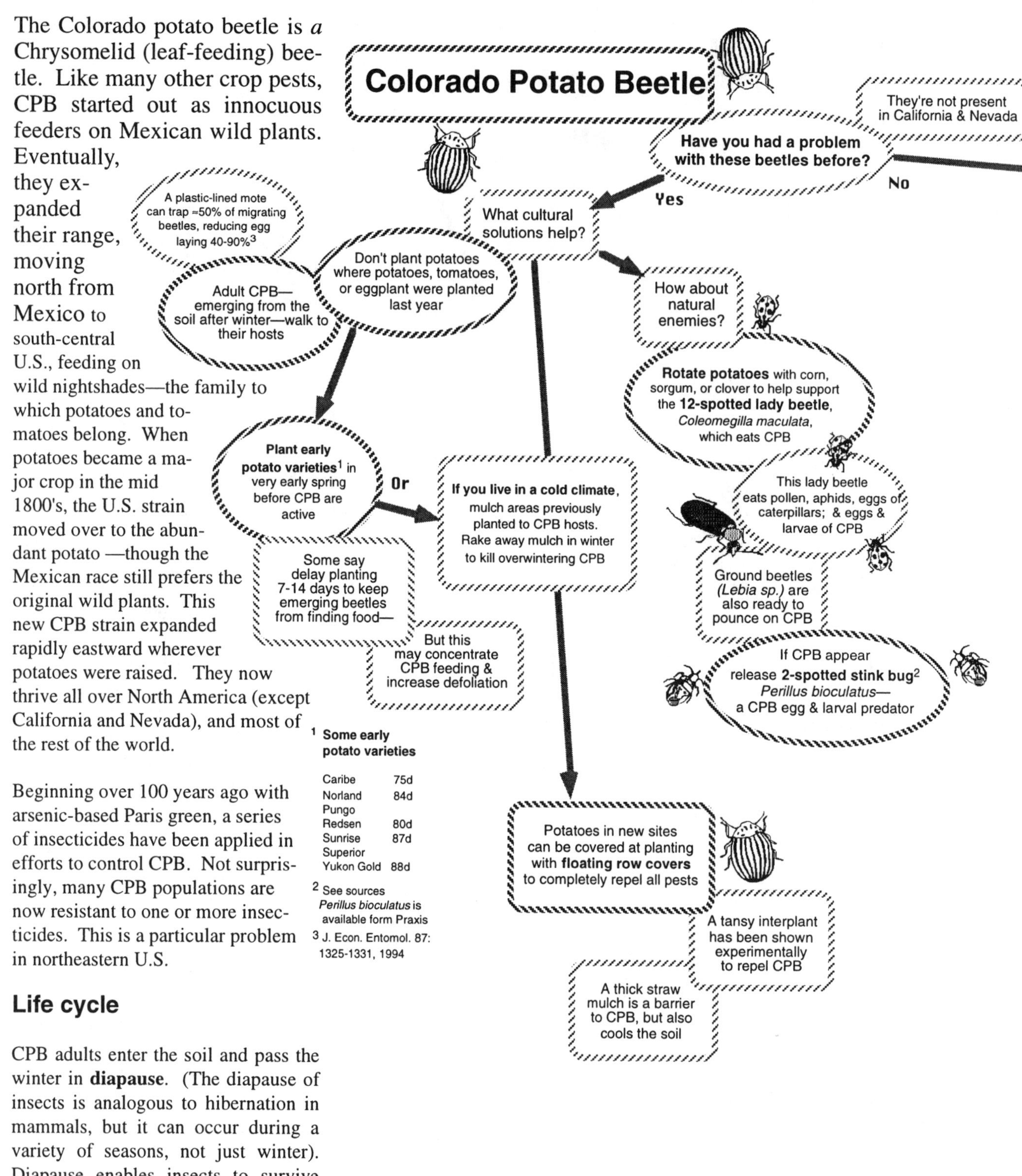

Colorado Potato Beetle
They're not present in California & Nevada
Have you had a problem with these beetles before?
No
Yes
What cultural solutions help?
A plastic-lined mote can trap ≈50% of migrating beetles, reducing egg laying 40-90%3
Don't plant potatoes where potatoes, tomatoes, or eggplant were planted last year
Adult CPB—emerging from the soil after winter—walk to their hosts
How about natural enemies?
Rotate potatoes with corn, sorgum, or clover to help support the 12-spotted lady beetle, Coleomegilla maculata, which eats CPB
This lady beetle eats pollen, aphids, eggs of caterpillars; & eggs & larvae of CPB
Ground beetles (Lebia sp.) are also ready to pounce on CPB
If CPB appear release 2-spotted stink bug2 Perillus bioculatus—a CPB egg & larval predator
Plant early potato varieties1 in very early spring before CPB are active
Or
If you live in a cold climate, mulch areas previously planted to CPB hosts. Rake away mulch in winter to kill overwintering CPB
Some say delay planting 7-14 days to keep emerging beetles from finding food—
But this may concentrate CPB feeding & increase defoliation
1 Some early potato varieties
Caribe 75d
Norland 84d
Pungo
Redsen 80d
Sunrise 87d
Superior
Yukon Gold 88d
2 See sources Perillus bioculatus is available form Praxis
3 J. Econ. Entomol. 87: 1325-1331, 1994
Potatoes in new sites can be covered at planting with floating row covers to completely repel all pests
A tansy interplant has been shown experimentally to repel CPB
A thick straw mulch is a barrier to CPB, but also cools the soil

Life cycle

CPB adults enter the soil and pass the winter in **diapause**. (The diapause of insects is analogous to hibernation in mammals, but it can occur during a variety of seasons, not just winter). Diapause enables insects to survive

[1]Canad. Entomol.122:175-177.1990

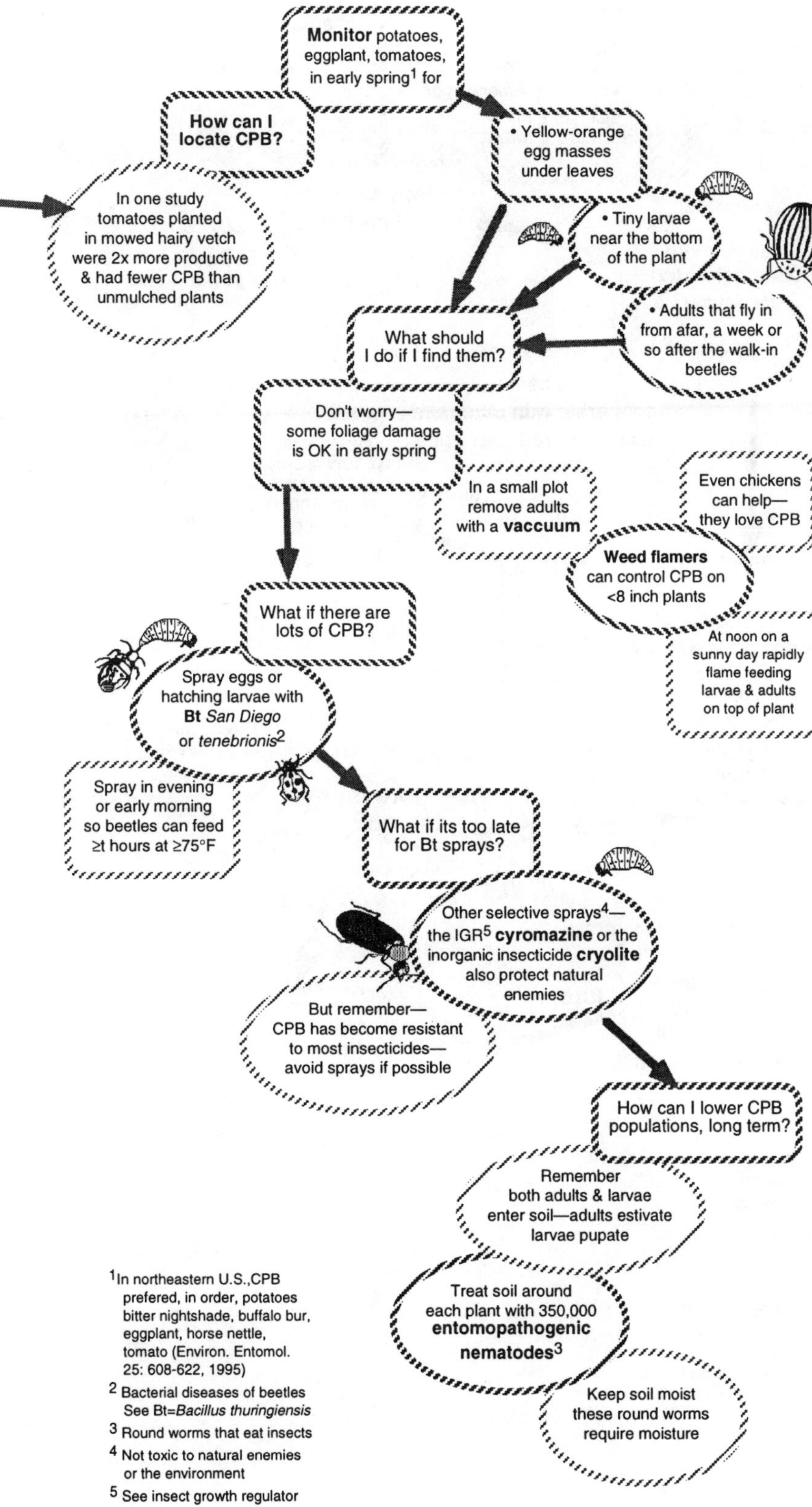
Monitor potatoes, eggplant, tomatoes, in early spring1 for
How can I locate CPB?
• Yellow-orange egg masses under leaves
In one study tomatoes planted in mowed hairy vetch were 2x more productive & had fewer CPB than unmulched plants
• Tiny larvae near the bottom of the plant
What should I do if I find them?
• Adults that fly in from afar, a week or so after the walk-in beetles
Don't worry— some foliage damage is OK in early spring
In a small plot remove adults with a vaccuum
Even chickens can help— they love CPB
Weed flamers can control CPB on <8 inch plants
What if there are lots of CPB?
At noon on a sunny day rapidly flame feeding larvae & adults on top of plant
Spray eggs or hatching larvae with Bt San Diego or tenebrionis2
Spray in evening or early morning so beetles can feed ≥t hours at ≥75°F
What if its too late for Bt sprays?
Other selective sprays4— the IGR5 cyromazine or the inorganic insecticide cryolite also protect natural enemies
But remember— CPB has become resistant to most insecticides— avoid sprays if possible
How can I lower CPB populations, long term?
Remember both adults & larvae enter soil—adults estivate larvae pupate
Treat soil around each plant with 350,000 entomopathogenic nematodes3
Keep soil moist these round worms require moisture
1In northeastern U.S.,CPB prefered, in order, potatoes bitter nightshade, buffalo bur, eggplant, horse nettle, tomato (Environ. Entomol. 25: 608-622, 1995)
2 Bacterial diseases of beetles See Bt=Bacillus thuringiensis
3 Round worms that eat insects
4 Not toxic to natural enemies or the environment
5 See insect growth regulator

unfavorable seasons. In the case of CPB, the 'winter diapause' can occasionally extend as long as three years.[1]

In late spring CPB adults begin to emerge from the soil. They seem to appear after rain, and the emergence period is prolonged during dry years. These young CPB adults walk along the ground in search of food. If they find the right plants, they feed and begin to lay eggs. Not to much happens even after the eggs hatch because most damage only occurs after the larvae reach their last instar (last growth period). In this last instar both feeding and growth is enormous. CPB larvae take about a month to reach this damaging size.

Fortunately vigorously growing potato vines tolerate considerable leaf feeding. They are most sensitive to defoliation during the first few weeks of seedling growth, and during very hot or cold weather. They are less sensitive after bloom begins.

If you plant early potatoes, they will be well grown when CPB adults emerge from winter diapause, and your crop may have begun to bloom before they begin to lay clusters of lemon-yellow eggs under the leaves.

Plant potatoes in a well-mulched plot well away from last year's crop. Remove the CPB's preferred weeds listed in our chart, or use them as a trap crop which you can destroy along with the beetles. (Mulches, a plastic-lined trench around the field, and crop rotation will help prevent CPB from finding the crop).[1] Winter wheat or hay covercrops between this year's plot and previous potatoes also deter colonization.[2] CPB eggs and young larvae are attacked by parasitoids and some of the predators shown here. Hard rain washes eggs and young larvae onto the soil. You can even simulate rain with a *water spray.* Later as the mature larvae enter the soil to pupate, zap them with entomopathogenic nematodes.

1 J. Econ. Entomol. 83: 1982-1987, 1990

2 J. Econl. Entomol. 87:723-729, 1994

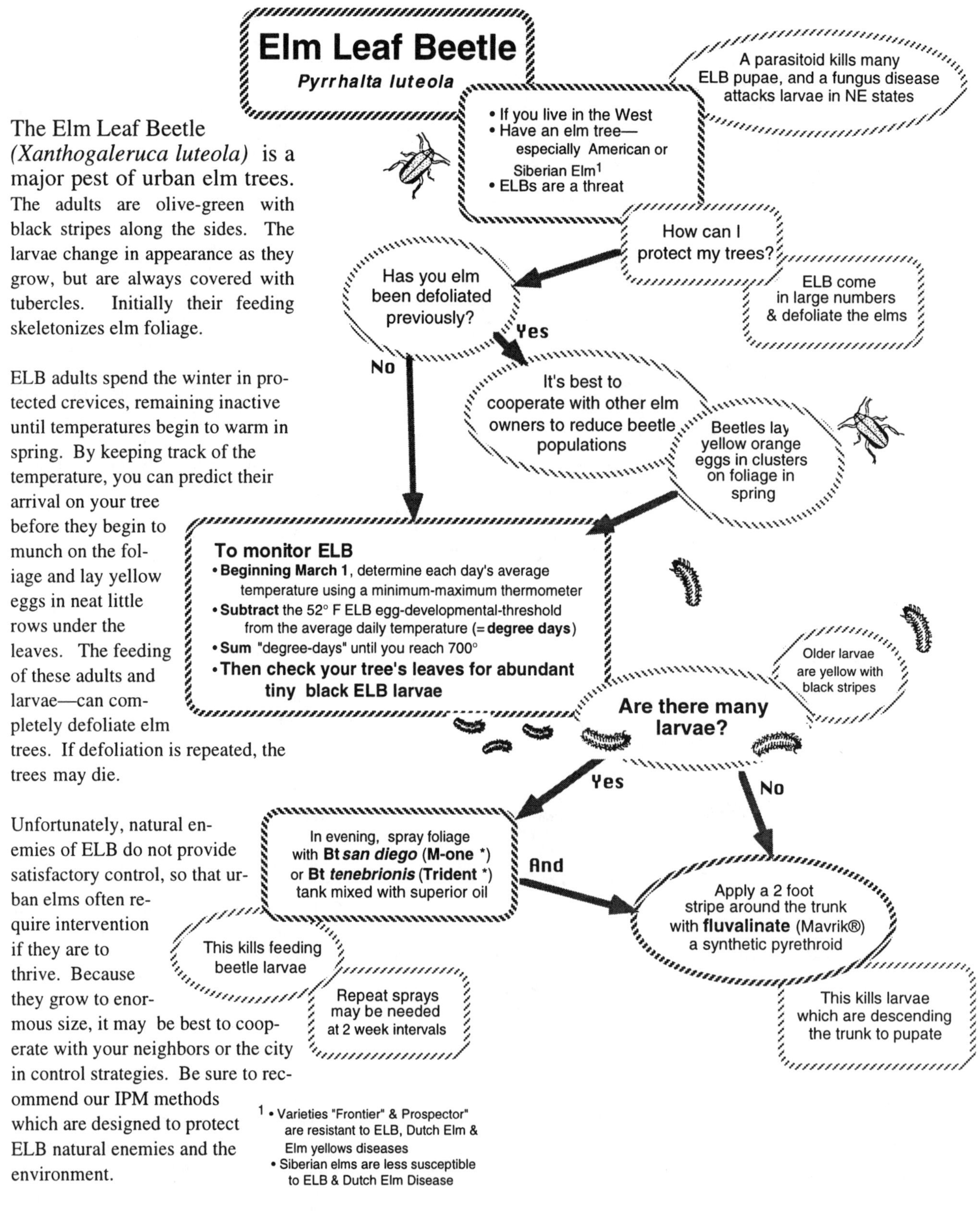
Elm Leaf Beetle
Pyrrhalta luteola
• If you live in the West
• Have an elm tree— especially American or Siberian Elm[1]
• ELBs are a threat
A parasitoid kills many ELB pupae, and a fungus disease attacks larvae in NE states
How can I protect my trees?
ELB come in large numbers & defoliate the elms
Has you elm been defoliated previously?
Yes
No
It's best to cooperate with other elm owners to reduce beetle populations
Beetles lay yellow orange eggs in clusters on foliage in spring
To monitor ELB
• Beginning March 1, determine each day's average temperature using a minimum-maximum thermometer
• Subtract the 52° F ELB egg-developmental-threshold from the average daily temperature (= degree days)
• Sum "degree-days" until you reach 700°
• Then check your tree's leaves for abundant tiny black ELB larvae
Older larvae are yellow with black stripes
Are there many larvae?
Yes
No
In evening, spray foliage with Bt san diego (M-one *) or Bt tenebrionis (Trident *) tank mixed with superior oil
And
Apply a 2 foot stripe around the trunk with fluvalinate (Mavrik®) a synthetic pyrethroid
This kills feeding beetle larvae
Repeat sprays may be needed at 2 week intervals
This kills larvae which are descending the trunk to pupate

The Elm Leaf Beetle (*Xanthogaleruca luteola)* is a major pest of urban elm trees. The adults are olive-green with black stripes along the sides. The larvae change in appearance as they grow, but are always covered with tubercles. Initially their feeding skeletonizes elm foliage.

ELB adults spend the winter in protected crevices, remaining inactive until temperatures begin to warm in spring. By keeping track of the temperature, you can predict their arrival on your tree before they begin to munch on the foliage and lay yellow eggs in neat little rows under the leaves. The feeding of these adults and larvae—can completely defoliate elm trees. If defoliation is repeated, the trees may die.

Unfortunately, natural enemies of ELB do not provide satisfactory control, so that urban elms often require intervention if they are to thrive. Because they grow to enormous size, it may be best to cooperate with your neighbors or the city in control strategies. Be sure to recommend our IPM methods which are designed to protect ELB natural enemies and the environment.

[1] • Varieties "Frontier" & Prospector" are resistant to ELB, Dutch Elm & Elm yellows diseases
• Siberian elms are less susceptible to ELB & Dutch Elm Disease

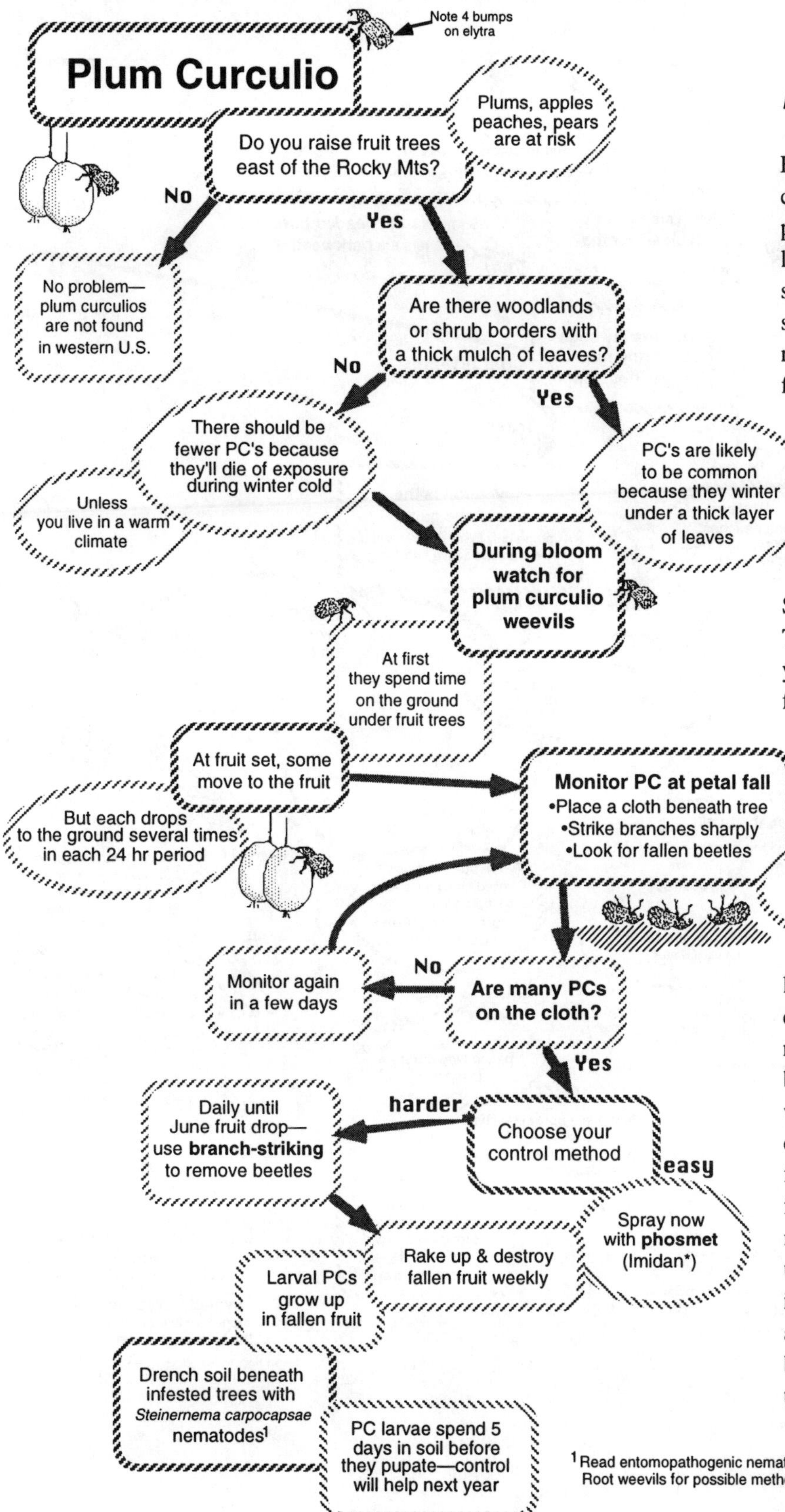
Note 4 bumps on elytra
Plum Curculio
Plums, apples peaches, pears are at risk
Do you raise fruit trees east of the Rocky Mts?
No
Yes
No problem—plum curculios are not found in western U.S.
Are there woodlands or shrub borders with a thick mulch of leaves?
No
Yes
There should be fewer PC's because they'll die of exposure during winter cold
Unless you live in a warm climate
PC's are likely to be common because they winter under a thick layer of leaves
During bloom watch for plum curculio weevils
At first they spend time on the ground under fruit trees
At fruit set, some move to the fruit
But each drops to the ground several times in each 24 hr period
Monitor PC at petal fall
•Place a cloth beneath tree
•Strike branches sharply
•Look for fallen beetles
Dump PCs into a bucket of soapy water
Monitor again in a few days
No
Are many PCs on the cloth?
Yes
harder
Daily until June fruit drop—use branch-striking to remove beetles
Choose your control method
easy
Spray now with phosmet (Imidan*)
Rake up & destroy fallen fruit weekly
Larval PCs grow up in fallen fruit
Drench soil beneath infested trees with Steinernema carpocapsae nematodes1
PC larvae spend 5 days in soil before they pupate—control will help next year
1 Read entomopathogenic nematodes Root weevils for possible methods

Plum Curculio

East of the Rocky mountains, plum curculio beetles are pests of apples, pears, peaches and plums. After wintering in leaf litter, the adults fly to host trees on humid spring days near apple blossom time—specifically when the average temperature reaches 60° to 65°F for three days, or 75° for 2 days. Obviously, you can predict this first spring invasion by recording maximum/minimum temperatures daily, adding the total, and dividing by 2 to get the average. When these activity threshold temperatures occur, immediately spread a tarp under your tree. Sharply strike the branches with a hose. The beetles will fall—playing dead—and you just dump them into soapy water before they move. Their populations will be highest if you live near a wooded area which will shelter them during winter.

If you find more than a few, you can spray with phosmet (Imidan*) now, or wait until time to spray for codling moth in a week or two. For plum curculio you must use phosmet, because ryania codling moth spray does not affect beetles. Be alert for crescent-shaped wounds on the fruits later in the season—evidence that curculios are present. If you find more than a few, destroy these infested fruits, and repeat the branch-striking method, or, spray again with phosmet. At the same time apply the **entomopathogenic nematodes** to the soils beneath the tree as described under Root Weevils. These beneficial nematodes are effective against these weevils in laboratory experiments, so should be able to to reduce the number of plum curculios coming to your tree next year. Fall cleanup of leaves will help eliminate both apple scab spores and shelter for overwintering adult plum curculios, though some may winter in nearby wooded areas .

Borer basics

Fruit and ornamental trees and some vegetables, are attacked by borers—usually the larvae of clear-winged moths or beetles. Weakened trees are most susceptible, so to avoid them it is important to maintain plant health and avoid injury to the bark.

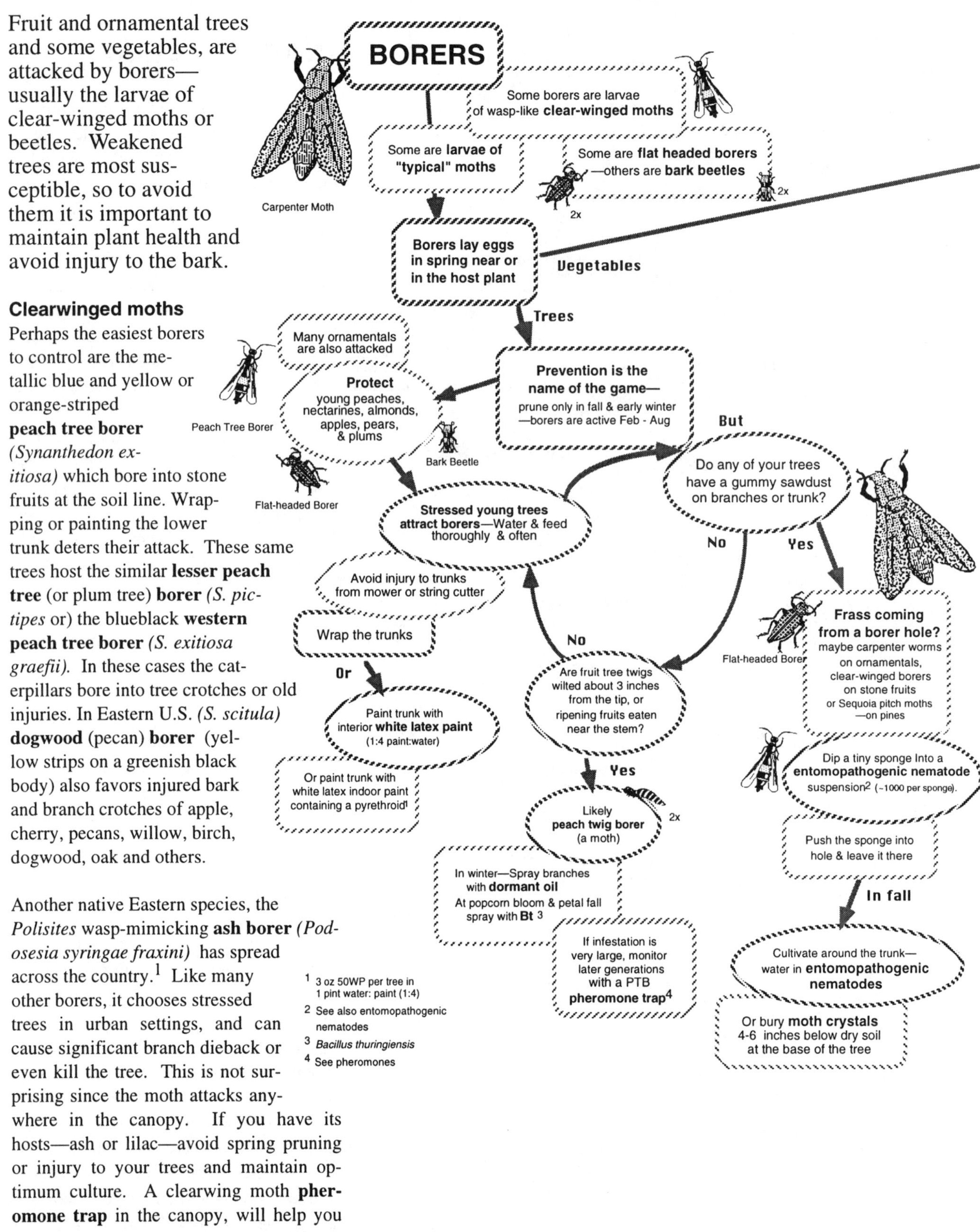

BORERS
Carpenter Moth
Some borers are larvae of wasp-like **clear-winged moths**
Some are **larvae of "typical" moths**
Some are **flat headed borers** —others are **bark beetles**
2x
2x
Borers lay eggs in spring near or in the host plant
Vegetables
Trees
Many ornamentals are also attacked
Peach Tree Borer
Protect young peaches, nectarines, almonds, apples, pears, & plums
Bark Beetle
Flat-headed Borer
Prevention is the name of the game—
prune only in fall & early winter —borers are active Feb - Aug
But
Do any of your trees have a gummy sawdust on branches or trunk?
No
Yes
Stressed young trees attract borers—Water & feed thoroughly & often
Avoid injury to trunks from mower or string cutter
Wrap the trunks
Or
Paint trunk with interior **white latex paint** (1:4 paint:water)
Or paint trunk with white latex indoor paint containing a pyrethroid[1]
No
Are fruit tree twigs wilted about 3 inches from the tip, or ripening fruits eaten near the stem?
Yes
Likely **peach twig borer** (a moth)
2x
In winter—Spray branches with **dormant oil**
At popcorn bloom & petal fall spray with **Bt** [3]
If infestation is very large, monitor later generations with a PTB **pheromone trap**[4]
Frass coming from a borer hole? maybe carpenter worms on ornamentals, clear-winged borers on stone fruits or Sequoia pitch moths —on pines
Flat-headed Borer
Dip a tiny sponge Into a **entomopathogenic nematode** suspension[2] (~1000 per sponge).
Push the sponge into hole & leave it there
In fall
Cultivate around the trunk—water in **entomopathogenic nematodes**
Or bury **moth crystals** 4-6 inches below dry soil at the base of the tree
1 3 oz 50WP per tree in 1 pint water: paint (1:4)
2 See also entomopathogenic nematodes
3 *Bacillus thuringiensis*
4 See pheromones

Clearwinged moths

Perhaps the easiest borers to control are the metallic blue and yellow or orange-striped **peach tree borer** *(Synanthedon exitiosa)* which bore into stone fruits at the soil line. Wrapping or painting the lower trunk deters their attack. These same trees host the similar **lesser peach tree** (or plum tree) **borer** *(S. pictipes* or) the blueblack **western peach tree borer** *(S. exitiosa graefii)*. In these cases the caterpillars bore into tree crotches or old injuries. In Eastern U.S. *(S. scitula)* **dogwood** (pecan) **borer** (yellow strips on a greenish black body) also favors injured bark and branch crotches of apple, cherry, pecans, willow, birch, dogwood, oak and others.

Another native Eastern species, the *Polisites* wasp-mimicking **ash borer** *(Podosesia syringae fraxini)* has spread across the country.[1] Like many other borers, it chooses stressed trees in urban settings, and can cause significant branch dieback or even kill the tree. This is not surprising since the moth attacks anywhere in the canopy. If you have its hosts—ash or lilac—avoid spring pruning or injury to your trees and maintain optimum culture. A clearwing moth **pheromone trap** in the canopy, will help you

[1] Calif. Agri. 45(5):32-33, 1991 [2]Modesto ash is subject to serious disease problems

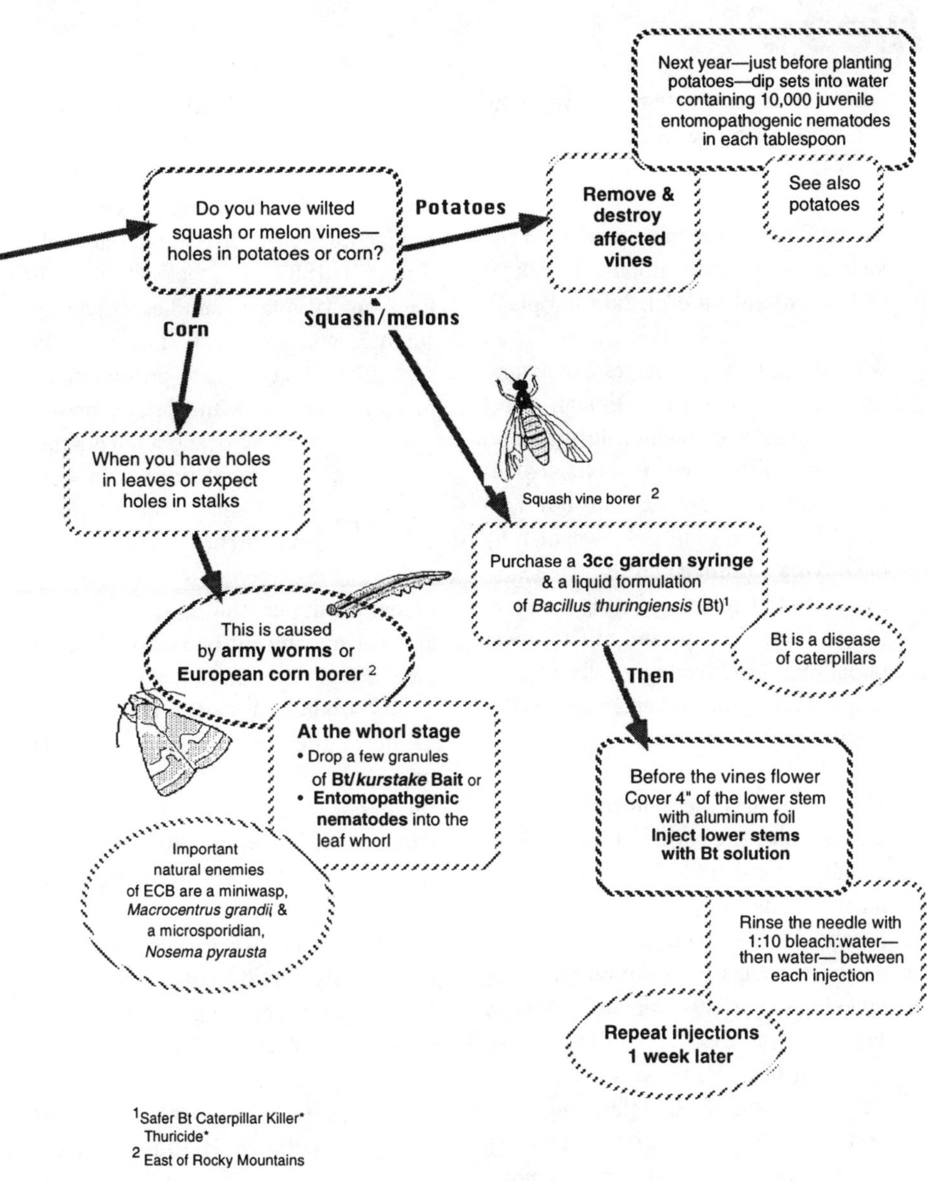
Next year—just before planting potatoes—dip sets into water containing 10,000 juvenile entomopathogenic nematodes in each tablespoon
Do you have wilted squash or melon vines—holes in potatoes or corn?
Potatoes
Remove & destroy affected vines
See also potatoes
Corn
Squash/melons
When you have holes in leaves or expect holes in stalks
Squash vine borer 2
Purchase a 3cc garden syringe & a liquid formulation of Bacillus thuringiensis (Bt)1
Bt is a disease of caterpillars
This is caused by army worms or European corn borer 2
Then
At the whorl stage
• Drop a few granules of Bt/kurstake Bait or
• Entomopathgenic nematodes into the leaf whorl
Before the vines flower Cover 4" of the lower stem with aluminum foil Inject lower stems with Bt solution
Important natural enemies of ECB are a miniwasp, Macrocentrus grandii & a microsporidian, Nosema pyrausta
Rinse the needle with 1:10 bleach:water—then water— between each injection
Repeat injections 1 week later

[1]Safer Bt Caterpillar Killer* Thuricide*
[2]East of Rocky Mountains

determine when sprays should be applied—a week or so after the first moth is found. Though chlorpyriphos is usually recommended, this product is not appropriate for IPM. Follow our directions for safer controls. Be aware that Arizona and Modesto ash may be resistant to clearwing moth attacks. Watch also for the yellow with black striped ***Paranthrene spp.*** clear-winged moths which look like the yellow and black wasps they mimic. They include *P. simulans* on oak and elm in Eastern U.S., *P. asilipenns,* the **oak clearwing moth**, and *P. robiniae,* the **western poplar clearwing moth.**

Other moth borers

Some moths that bore do not have clear wings. The larva of the giant mottled-grey **carpenter moth** *(Prionoxiptus robiniae* requires 3-4 years to mature in elm, ash, locust, fig, or oak. Though the carpenter moth seldom kills the tree, it can cause unsightly damage. Fortunately, the holes it makes are so large that it's easy to inject entomopathogenic nematodes into the burrows. The grayish **American plum borer**, *Ruophera semifuneralis*, lays it eggs in crotches of young, injured, or weakened almond, apple, peach, London plane, walnut, poplar, and others. If necessary, they and other borers with similar habits can be suppressed with the pesticide-plus-paint system described in the chart. Paint should cover the trunk up to the secondary scaffold branches. This method will kill many non-target insects so use it only in an emergency situation.

Boring Beetles

Woodboring beetles also attack weakened trees. The most common such beetles in urban areas are the tiny black alien **shot hole borer** *(Scolytus rugulosus)* and ***Chrysobothris*** **flat-headed borers—apple tree** *(C. femorata)* and **Pacific** *(C. malis),* which bore into injured or sunburned bark. You can prevent their access to your trees by wrapping or painting the trunk of young trees and optimizing the culture of all specimens. If the beetles do appear, remove injured branches and chip the wood to destroy the beetle larvae.

The **small European elm bark beetle** *(Scolytus multistriatus)*—though not a serious pest itself—transports the spores of **Dutch elm disease** *(Ceratostomella ulmi.).* Several elm species resist this conducting-system disease, but American elms are readily killed. Spraying for the beetles is polluting and not effective in preventing spread of the disease. The only way to slow the spread of DED is to promptly removed diseased elms, and burn or bury the wood to kill the fungus. *Do not use or transport elm wood which has been obtained from dead or dying trees.* Hybrid elms are available which resist DED.

Whither whiteflies ?

Whiteflies are minute (~1 mm) insects with white powdery roof-like wings that fly up when you jostle an affected plant. Since they're related to leaf hoppers and aphids, the 'fly' suffix is obviously misleading. Like their relatives, they suck plant juices.

Until a few years ago, home gardeners could almost assume that problem whiteflies were **greenhouse whiteflies** *(Trialeurodes vaporariorum).* This was the only problem species was this one even although it is controlled in warm weather by miniwasp parasitoids *(Encarsia formosa).* Unfortunately in cool weather, the whiteflies can keep ahead of the parasitoids.

Whitefly lifestyles

Look beneath leaves for the juvenile stages. An distinctive feature of all tiny scale-like sedentary whitefly nymphs, is a fringe, or covering of wax which projects from a whitish or yellowish translucent or black oval body. *The pattern of wax is unique to each species allowing species recognition* (eg., greenhouse whitefly nymphs appear as flattened whitish translucent ovals surrounded by a sparse translucent spiny fringe, while the dome-like pupae are covered with scattered translucent spines.)

All whitefly nymphs, except newly-hatched crawlers, are permanately attached to the leaves. Their heavy feeding can cause yellowing and drying of leaves, and their honeydew exudate coats the foliage and nourishes a sooty mold fungus which blackens leaves, preventing photosynthesis. Nymphs can take weeks to mature—the length of time depending on temperature and species. Eventually they molt to non-feeding pupae. After the adults emerge, the female lays about 300 eggs during her lifetime of several weeks.

There is more than one generation per year, so several developmental stages can be present on each infested plant. Although severe weather can be lethal, whiteflies of all four stages can and do overwinter on plants—though most are nymphs or pupae during cold weather. IPM control strategies include • Interrupting the developmental cycle during cold weather by destroying infested crops • Eliminating weed hosts • Using selective sprays such as soaps and oils to lower populations • Covering newly planted crops with spun polyester and • Releasing natural enemies.

Most whiteflies are controlled by parasitoids and predators. (Look closely for dark parasitoids inside the translucent whitefly nymphs). You can purchase a miniwasp, *Encarsia formosa,* for release during outbreaks of greenhouse or sweetpotato *(Bemisia tabaci)* whiteflies. Avoid the broad spectrum insecticides which kill these valuable natural enemies, and are quite ineffective against whitefly nymphs and pupae. If supplementary whitefly controls are needed, it's important to use the selective methods suggested here.

Pest whiteflies

Most of the more than 1200 whitefly species feed on one or a few woody perennials. However eight species attack both herbaceous and woody hosts—including lettuce, cantaloupe, squash, tomato, cotton, pumpkin, potato, broccoli, cabbage, dahlia, geranium, poinsettia, cotton, fuchsia, rose, toyon, and coffeeberry. *These eight have unusual potential to form pest outbreaks, even though they are potentially controlled by natural enemies.* Several whiteflies have caused serious problems in recent years.

The alien **ash whitefly** *(Siphoninus phillyreae)* was discovered in California in 1987. It attacks shrubs and trees in 10 plant families. During summer and early fall, this whitefly seriously damaged ash, pomegranate, pear, and apple; with apricot, privet, and pyrocantha having minor populations. In winter it moved on to citrus and toyon. Its nymphs were recognized by a waxy bloom on the central upper surface of an oval translucent body. (The pupae have a waxy bloom, plus a rim of tiny 'beads' around a roundish body). Fortunately after government scientists imported and released two ash whitefly parasitoids, *Encarsia inaron* and *Clitostethus arcuatus,* the pest was rapidly controlled the following year.

The European **sweetpotato = tobacco whitefly** has dispersed throughout the U.S. after sneaking into Florida at the turn of the century. Initially it was not a serious pest. Then in 1986 in Florida, pesticide-resistant populations of a 'poinsettia or B strain' erupted. Beginning in 1988, the strain was common on peanuts in the south. Next it was linked to spread of viral diseases—**squash silverleaf** on squash and cabbage, and **tomato irregular** which prevents normal ripening of tomatoes. In 1991, in Arizona and California desert sunbelt fields, an enormous population of this whitefly spread diseases to vegetable and melon crops.

This new pesticide-resistant whitefly reproduced very rapidly—egg to adult in ~16 summer days. It differed from the less resistant, less virulent strain of the sweetpotato whitefly originally present in California which did not vector diseases. *But this new whitefly appeared to be identical to sweetpotato whitefly.* Adults have yellowish bodies, and the translucent balloon-like nymphs lack a waxy fringe. Recently sophisticated studies have shown this outlaw to be a new species—dubbed the **silverleaf whitefly**[1] *(B. argentifolii)*[2] because of its ability to spread silverleaf disease. It's proteins differ from those of the sweetpotato whitefly, and it will not mate with this species. Finally scientists have located a patch of wax along the edge at 10 and 2 o'clock on silverleaf nymphs which enables us to to distinguish them from sweetpotato whitefly nymphs in the field.[2]

Viruses spread by silverleaf whitefly are **infectious yellows** (on lettuce, melons, cantaloupe, carrot, cucumber, sunflower, broccoli, squash, and sugarbeet); **cotton leaf crumple** (on cotton, beans, and mallow= cheeseweed), and **silverleaf** and **squash leaf curl**—on beans, squash, and melons. Fall vegetables are most affected. The larvae acquire these viruses from diseased plants, and the young adults transmit it when they move on to new hosts. This pesticide-resistant whitefly has been found only in areas with warm climates. In Hawaii, it attacks papaya, taro, and plumeria. It is not known whether it will move to cooler regions. Its origin is unknown.

Silverleaf Whitefly-Transmitted Diseases

Virus Name	Host Crops	Location	Symptoms
Bean golden mosiac	legumes	FL	yellow mosaic
Cabbage virus	cabbage	FL	chlorosis, stunting
Cotton leaf crumple	cotton, bean	AR, CA	distorted leaf, mosaic
Lettuce infectious yellows	lettuce, melon, carrot squash, watermelon	AR, CA, TX	chlorosis, stunting, some reddish leaves
Squash leaf curl	squash, watermelon mosaic	AZ, CA	leaf curl, yellow
Tx pepper virus	pepper, tomato	TX	mild mosaic
Tomato mottle	tomato	FL	yellow mottle, stunting
Tomato calico	tomato	AZ	yellow mottle, leaf curl

Based on Amer. Veg. Grower 9/93, p 22H

A black lady beetle *(Delphastus pusillus)* can be released to increase natural controls. This beetle consumes large numbers of white-fly eggs and larvae during outbreaks, but cannot wipe out a whitefly population because it cannot lay eggs until it has consumed many whitefly eggs.[3] [It is a predator of other whitefly species, and of two-spotted spider mite *(Tetranychus urticae)* and broad mite *(Polyphagotarsonemus latus)*] In addition several native parasitoids may be helpful against silverleaf whitefly. In Florida, *E. nigricephala* and *E. transvena* provided excellent control on peanuts.[4]

A rapid search for new chemicals has turned up an soil-applied nicotine analogue[5] known as imidacloprid (Admire*). Since all required tests have not been completed on this product, the EPA has granted a special exemption for certain crops in California, Texas, and Arizona. Imidacloprid is applied to the soil during planting, and translocates through the plant to the foliage where it paralyses the muscles of sucking insects such as whiteflies and aphids. In this application it is not toxic to beneficials, but the product may persist in the soil. If it is applied to the foliage, it kills beneficials. Because of resistance buildup, no toxic can be expected to control such a rapidly breeding species for long.

Other problem whiteflies

The **bandedwinged whitefly** *(Tralearodes acutilonea),* reported on 140 crops, including tomato, eggplant, okra, sweet potato; sometimes erupts to pest status. It also vectors diseases. Its winter hosts include common nightshade and cocklebur. Whiteflies on citrus include **woolly whitefly** *(Aleurothrixtu floccosus)* whose wax-covered nymphs resemble non-moving wooly aphids, **citrus whitefly** *(Dialeurodes citri)* with flat, oval transparent, fringeless nymphs which exhibit a raised 'segmented animal' on top, and the **bayberry whitefly** *(Parabemisia myricae)* whose translucent oval young are distinguished by two black 'eye spots' and no fringe. Finally, the **redbanded whitefly** *(Trialeurodes sp.)* is associated with avocado. The adults have red bands on their wings; the flat, black, oval larvae are surrounded by an upward-curling white fringe.

Populations of any of these potential pests could explode if broad-spectrum pesticides are repeatedly applied to their hosts.

[1]Sci. 259:74-77, 1993. [2]Cal Agri. 48(3):4, 1994. [3]J. Econ Entomol 86: 322-329, 1994. [4] Environ, Entomol. 23: 1203-1210, 1994. [5]Synthetic compound with comparable biological effects to the original

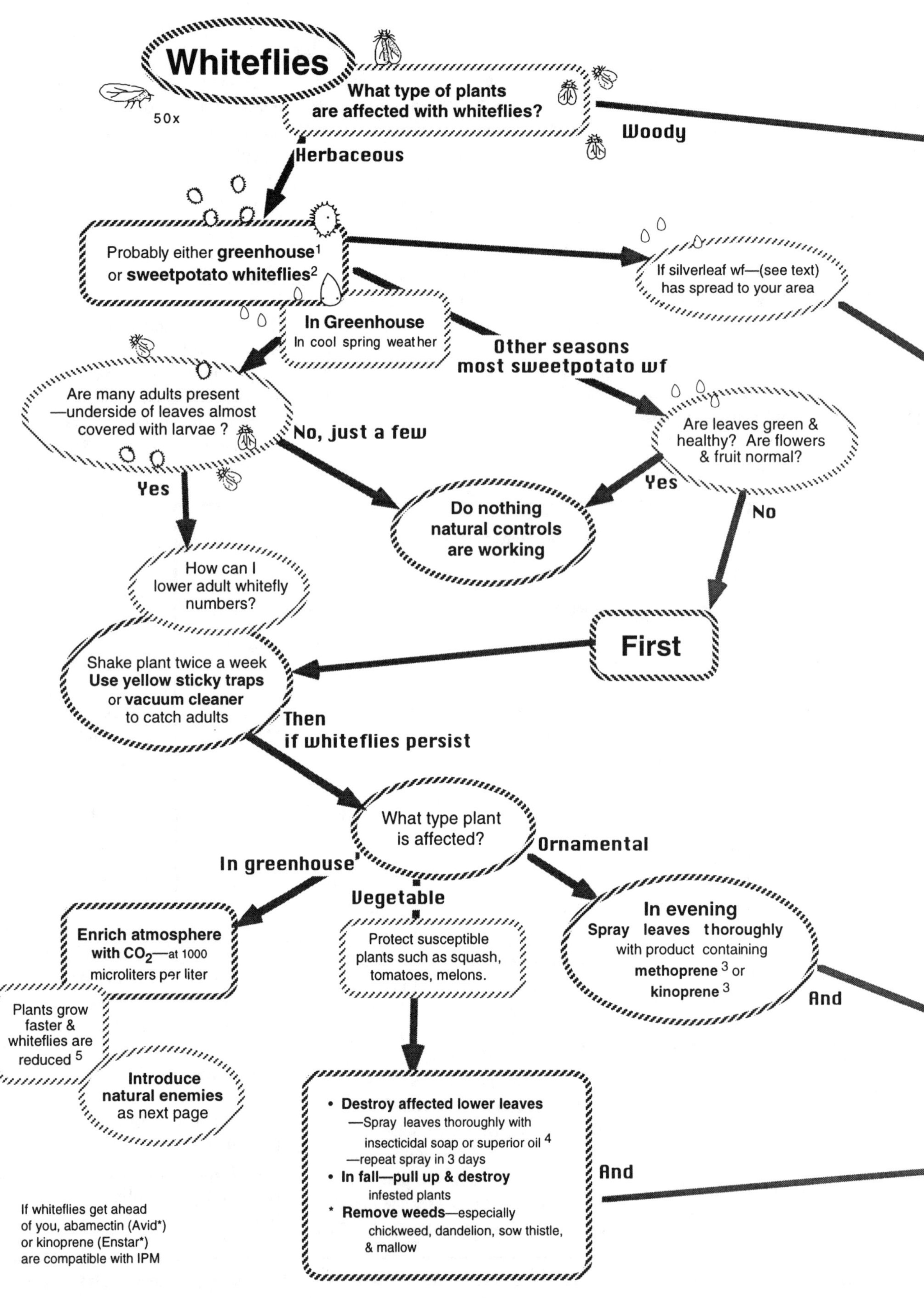
Whiteflies
50x
What type of plants are affected with whiteflies?
Woody
Herbaceous
Probably either greenhouse[1] or sweetpotato whiteflies[2]
If silverleaf wf—(see text) has spread to your area
In Greenhouse
In cool spring weather
Other seasons most sweetpotato wf
Are many adults present —underside of leaves almost covered with larvae ?
No, just a few
Are leaves green & healthy? Are flowers & fruit normal?
Yes
Yes
No
Do nothing natural controls are working
How can I lower adult whitefly numbers?
First
Shake plant twice a week
Use yellow sticky traps
or vacuum cleaner
to catch adults
Then
if whiteflies persist
What type plant is affected?
In greenhouse
Ornamental
Vegetable
Enrich atmosphere with CO2—at 1000 microliters per liter
Plants grow faster & whiteflies are reduced 5
Introduce natural enemies as next page
Protect susceptible plants such as squash, tomatoes, melons.
In evening
Spray leaves thoroughly with product containing methoprene 3 or kinoprene 3
And
• Destroy affected lower leaves
—Spray leaves thoroughly with insecticidal soap or superior oil 4
—repeat spray in 3 days
• In fall—pull up & destroy infested plants
* Remove weeds—especially chickweed, dandelion, sow thistle, & mallow
And

If whiteflies get ahead of you, abamectin (Avid*) or kinoprene (Enstar*) are compatible with IPM

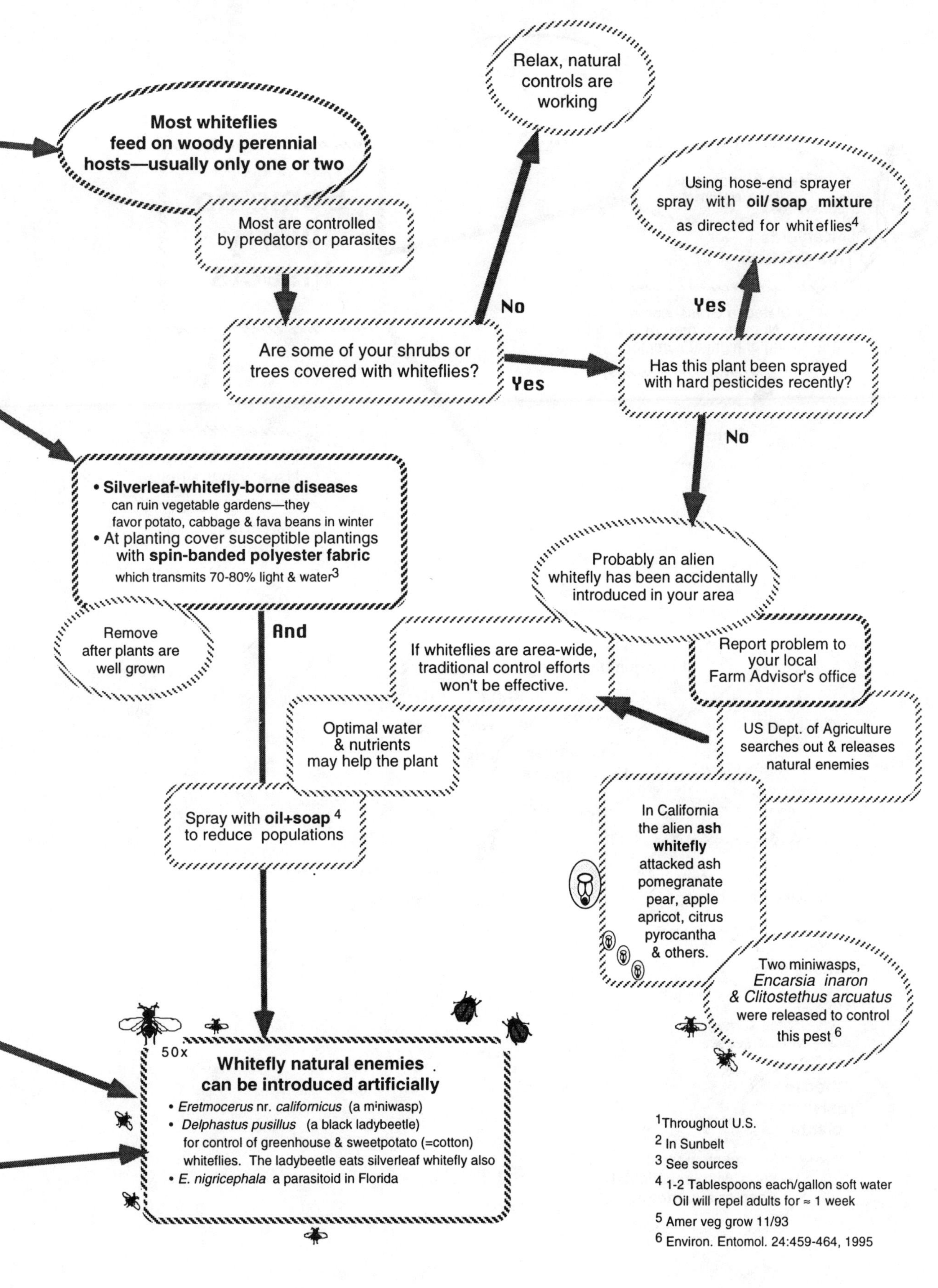

Relax, natural controls are working
Most whiteflies feed on woody perennial hosts—usually only one or two
Using hose-end sprayer spray with oil/soap mixture as directed for whiteflies4
Most are controlled by predators or parasites
No
Yes
Are some of your shrubs or trees covered with whiteflies?
Yes
Has this plant been sprayed with hard pesticides recently?
No
• Silverleaf-whitefly-borne diseases can ruin vegetable gardens—they favor potato, cabbage & fava beans in winter
• At planting cover susceptible plantings with spin-banded polyester fabric which transmits 70-80% light & water3
Probably an alien whitefly has been accidentally introduced in your area
Remove after plants are well grown
And
If whiteflies are area-wide, traditional control efforts won't be effective.
Report problem to your local Farm Advisor's office
Optimal water & nutrients may help the plant
US Dept. of Agriculture searches out & releases natural enemies
Spray with oil+soap 4 to reduce populations
In California the alien ash whitefly attacked ash pomegranate pear, apple apricot, citrus pyrocantha & others.
Two miniwasps, Encarsia inaron & Clitostethus arcuatus were released to control this pest 6
50x
Whitefly natural enemies can be introduced artificially
• Eretmocerus nr. californicus (a miniwasp)
• Delphastus pusillus (a black ladybeetle) for control of greenhouse & sweetpotato (=cotton) whiteflies. The ladybeetle eats silverleaf whitefly also
• E. nigricephala a parasitoid in Florida

[1] Throughout U.S.

[2] In Sunbelt

[3] See sources

[4] 1-2 Tablespoons each/gallon soft water
Oil will repel adults for ≈ 1 week

[5] Amer veg grow 11/93

[6] Environ. Entomol. 24:459-464, 1995

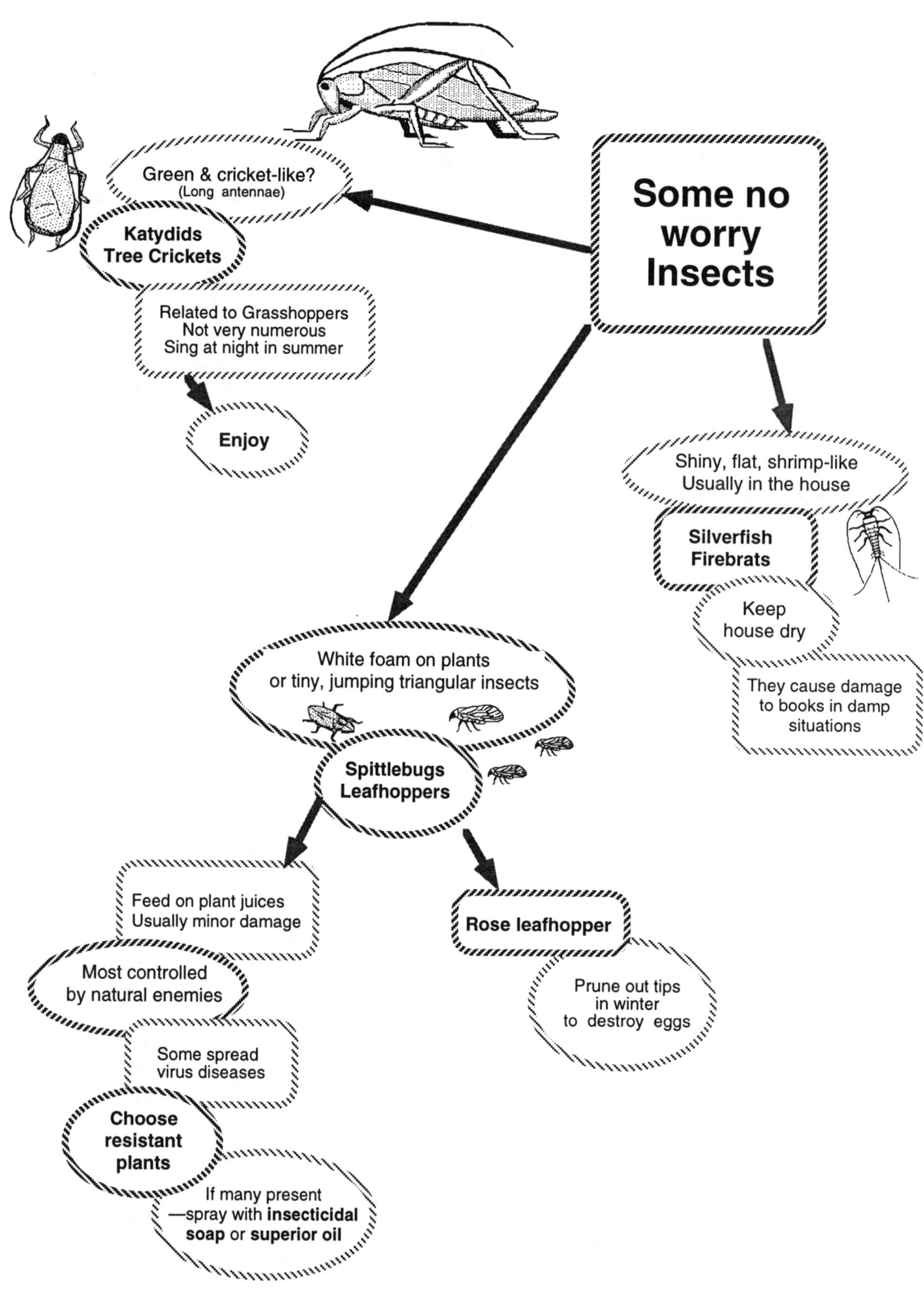
Some no worry Insects
Green & cricket-like?
(Long antennae)
Katydids
Tree Crickets
Related to Grasshoppers
Not very numerous
Sing at night in summer
Enjoy
Shiny, flat, shrimp-like
Usually in the house
Silverfish
Firebrats
Keep
house dry
They cause damage
to books in damp
situations
White foam on plants
or tiny, jumping triangular insects
Spittlebugs
Leafhoppers
Feed on plant juices
Usually minor damage
Most controlled
by natural enemies
Some spread
virus diseases
Choose
resistant
plants
If many present
—spray with insecticidal
soap or superior oil
Rose leafhopper
Prune out tips
in winter
to destroy eggs

A little about aphids

Aphids are minute (1-3 mm) insects that suck sap from, leaves twigs, or roots. They, along with scales, whiteflies, leafhoppers and other plant-sucking insects with roof-like wings belong to the order Homoptera—uniform winged insects. In the spring aphids multiply rapidly. In many gardens aphids are not a problem, however, because predatory and parasitic insects thrive on aphids, and these begin to arrive just as the aphids get crowded.

Aphid's Lifestyle

There are many species of aphids, each with a complex life cycle. Fortunately you need not know all the details to keep them under reasonable control. It *is* important to know that *most spend the winter in the egg stage.* These eggs are hidden in bark crevices or under bud scales. *In spring winged females* hatch and rapidly *disperse* to their favorite host plants—anything from roses and apples or plums, to beans, or even conifers—where they begin to feed and reproduce. Each kind of aphid has its own array of plants.

These spring aphids do not lay eggs. Instead, they give birth to live offspring—several every day. The first offspring may also have wings, but usually a group of wingless clones cluster around the mother. As they feed on the sap, they utilize the important nutrients, and excrete most of the fluids and some of the sugars as a sweet, sticky *honeydew* which may drip down to cover the plant, or sometimes the car or sidewalk beneath. Occasionally a blackish sooty mold colonizes this honeydew. This mold does not directly harm the plant, but it is unsightly, and it cuts down on light, blocking the photosynthesis which enables plants to produce food. Some other insects love this honeydew. Mini-wasp parasitoids and adult lacewings and other beneficials are sustained by honeydew. But ants may gather honeydew, and, at the same time protect the aphids from their predators and parasitoids. If ants and aphids occur together, it's important to keep the ants off the plant, or control the aphids artificially.

If the aphids continue feeding undeterred by natural enemies until the population is crowded, a few develop into winged adults which disperse to "greener pastures". As the season progresses the hardening of the maturing leaves and changes in natural plant toxins slow aphid reproduction and maturation. Finally, as the days shorten in fall, aphids produce males and females which mate and lay overwintering eggs.

Aphids differ widely in appearance and lifestyle. They may be black, green, gold, pinkish, or covered with a white, waxy coating (woolly aphids). Some infest only one plant, others move from one host to another, and a few feed on a wide variety of plants. In many cases aphid's piercing-sucking strategy produces little obvious plant damage, but sometimes their feeding results in yellowing, curling, or stunting of leaves or decline of the plant itself. A few problem aphids transmit diseases which cause far more damage than aphid feeding alone.

How Aphids Get Ahead

Several factors tip the balance toward aphid success. • Ants and broad-spectrum pesticides kill their natural enemies • Alien aphids from foreign lands reproduce rapidly in absence of specific natural enemies. (The government often responds by introducing the natural parasitoid enemies of alien aphids). This **classical biological control**, has been successful in suppressing the alien walnut aphid. • Unhealthy or stressed plants are nutritionally favorable to aphids. Sun-loving plants in shade, too much water or nitrogen fertilizer, cause plants to respond with lush floppy growth. Obviously, you can tip the balance away from aphids by avoiding such pitfalls.

Aphid Controls

Obviously, the easiest control strategy is to rely on aphid natural enemies. If these are not sufficient in your situation, aphids are easily killed by *surfactants*[1]—insecticidal **fatty acid soaps** and **light oils**—which cause insects to lose water. (**Dormant oils** have similar activity on overwintering aphid eggs). Since these surfactants are not toxic, they may be a better choice than insecticides that kill anything that touches them—**contact insecticides**.

Since soaps and oils have no such residual action, they must be sprayed directly on insects to cause death. Thus surfactants do not kill insects which arrive after the spraying—though oils are somewhat repellent. On the other hand, most conventional insecticides have contact activity at least for a few days, killing insects that walk across them. These broad spectrum materials readily kill natural enemies, too, triggering pest upsets. Barriers, such as **floating row covers**, may be the best way to keep aphids off plants, especially when they may transmit diseases. Any of these solutions is much better than repeated pesticide sprays.

The **cotton aphid**, *Aphis gossypii,* doesn't limit its feeding to cotton. It is also found on watermelon, eggplant, cucumber, Chinese melon, zucchini, and cheese weed.[1] Because the cotton aphid and the **green peach aphid**

[1] Any substance which reduces the surface tension between water & another imcompatable liquid such as oil. Soap, a surfactant, allows oil to disperse in water. Surfactants remove the water-resistant coating on an insect's body.

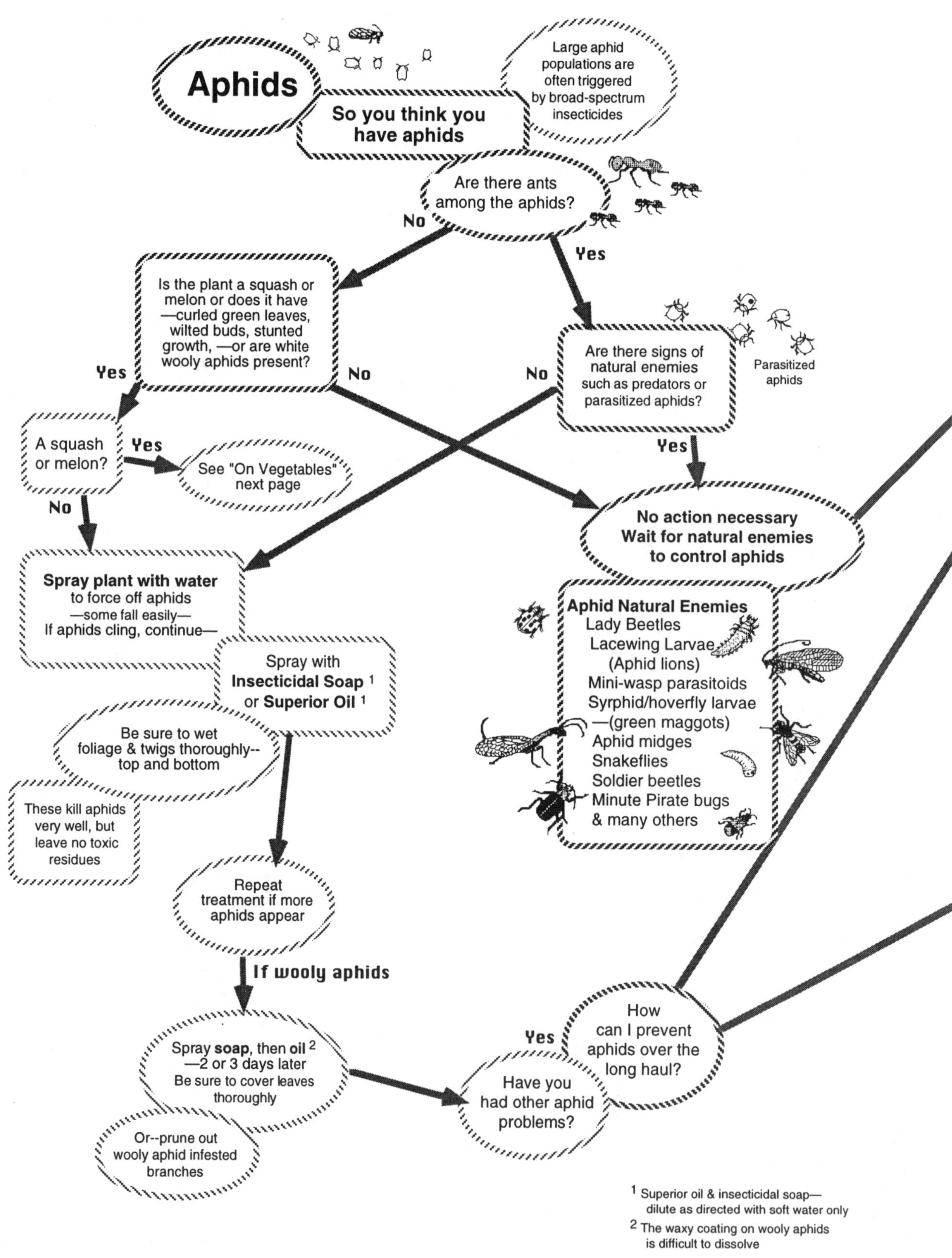
Aphids
So you think you have aphids
Large aphid populations are often triggered by broad-spectrum insecticides
Are there ants among the aphids?
No
Yes
Is the plant a squash or melon or does it have —curled green leaves, wilted buds, stunted growth, —or are white wooly aphids present?
Yes
No
Are there signs of natural enemies such as predators or parasitized aphids?
Parasitized aphids
No
Yes
A squash or melon?
Yes
See "On Vegetables" next page
No
No action necessary Wait for natural enemies to control aphids
Spray plant with water to force off aphids —some fall easily— If aphids cling, continue—
Spray with Insecticidal Soap 1 or Superior Oil 1
Be sure to wet foliage & twigs thoroughly-- top and bottom
These kill aphids very well, but leave no toxic residues
Aphid Natural Enemies
Lady Beetles
Lacewing Larvae (Aphid lions)
Mini-wasp parasitoids
Syrphid/hoverfly larvae —(green maggots)
Aphid midges
Snakeflies
Soldier beetles
Minute Pirate bugs
& many others
Repeat treatment if more aphids appear
If wooly aphids
Spray soap, then oil 2 —2 or 3 days later Be sure to cover leaves thoroughly
Or--prune out wooly aphid infested branches
Have you had other aphid problems?
Yes
How can I prevent aphids over the long haul?
1 Superior oil & insecticidal soap— dilute as directed with soft water only
2 The waxy coating on wooly aphids is difficult to dissolve

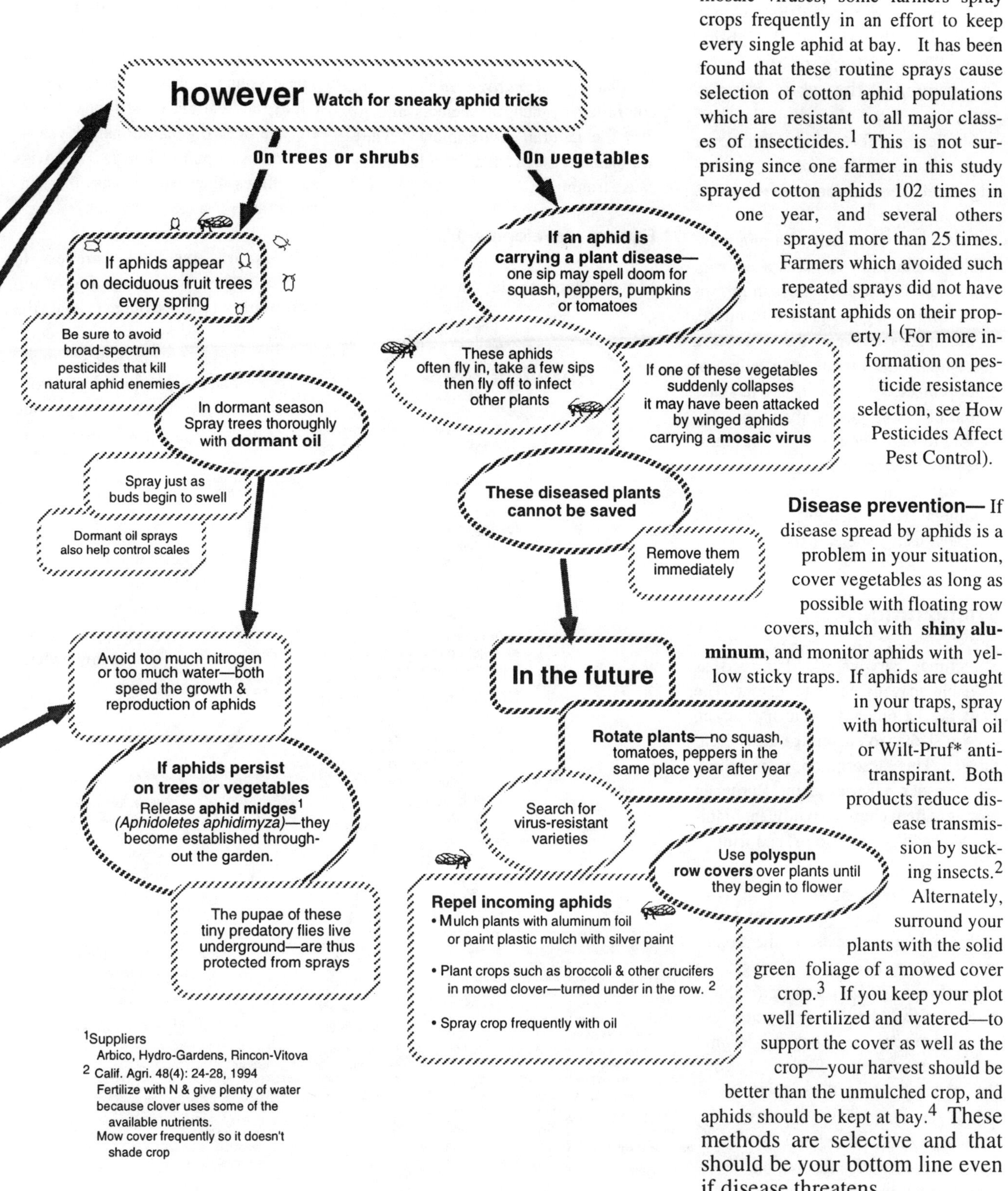

however Watch for sneaky aphid tricks
On trees or shrubs
On vegetables
If aphids appear on deciduous fruit trees every spring
Be sure to avoid broad-spectrum pesticides that kill natural aphid enemies
In dormant season Spray trees thoroughly with dormant oil
Spray just as buds begin to swell
Dormant oil sprays also help control scales
Avoid too much nitrogen or too much water—both speed the growth & reproduction of aphids
If aphids persist on trees or vegetables
Release aphid midges[1] (Aphidoletes aphidimyza)—they become established throughout the garden.
The pupae of these tiny predatory flies live underground—are thus protected from sprays
If an aphid is carrying a plant disease—one sip may spell doom for squash, peppers, pumpkins or tomatoes
These aphids often fly in, take a few sips then fly off to infect other plants
If one of these vegetables suddenly collapses it may have been attacked by winged aphids carrying a mosaic virus
These diseased plants cannot be saved
Remove them immediately
In the future
Rotate plants—no squash, tomatoes, peppers in the same place year after year
Search for virus-resistant varieties
Use polyspun row covers over plants until they begin to flower
Repel incoming aphids
• Mulch plants with aluminum foil or paint plastic mulch with silver paint
• Plant crops such as broccoli & other crucifers in mowed clover—turned under in the row. 2
• Spray crop frequently with oil
[1]Suppliers
Arbico, Hydro-Gardens, Rincon-Vitova
2 Calif. Agri. 48(4): 24-28, 1994
Fertilize with N & give plenty of water because clover uses some of the available nutrients.
Mow cover frequently so it doesn't shade crop

(Myzus persicae) carries several plant mosaic viruses, some farmers spray crops frequently in an effort to keep every single aphid at bay. It has been found that these routine sprays cause selection of cotton aphid populations which are resistant to all major classes of insecticides.[1] This is not surprising since one farmer in this study sprayed cotton aphids 102 times in one year, and several others sprayed more than 25 times. Farmers which avoided such repeated sprays did not have resistant aphids on their property.[1] (For more information on pesticide resistance selection, see How Pesticides Affect Pest Control).

Disease prevention— If disease spread by aphids is a problem in your situation, cover vegetables as long as possible with floating row covers, mulch with **shiny aluminum**, and monitor aphids with yellow sticky traps. If aphids are caught in your traps, spray with horticultural oil or Wilt-Pruf* antitranspirant. Both products reduce disease transmission by sucking insects.[2] Alternately, surround your plants with the solid green foliage of a mowed cover crop.[3] If you keep your plot well fertilized and watered—to support the cover as well as the crop—your harvest should be better than the unmulched crop, and aphids should be kept at bay.[4] These methods are selective and that should be your bottom line even if disease threatens.

1 J. Econ. Entomol. 87: 293-300, 1994. 2 Plant Dis. 77:915-918. 1993. 3For more information, see tomatoes. 4Cal. Agri.48 (4): 24-28, 1994.

Earwigs

Earwigs are flattened inch-long dark brown insects with obvious pincers at the end of the abdomen. They belong to the order *Dermoptera*—the skin winged insects. Even though their short stubby leathery fore-wings often cover large membranous hind-wings, earwigs rarely fly, and some are wingless.

Earwigs are nocturnal. During daylight, the common **European earwig,** *(Forticula auricularia)* hides in groups in the hollow legs of garden furniture, in the spaces between the coils of a hose, under the boards of a fence, or other protected places. If they're shaken out of hiding places, they run away rapidly to find a new refuge. At nightfall, they emerge to chew on decaying vegetation, ripening fruit, and new seedlings. Keep then out of your fruit trees by using sticky banding on the trunk.

Friend or foe?

Sometimes earwigs are described as valuable scavengers or predators. The Park Seed Company even markets an earwig shelter to encourage these creatures! This description is puzzling, since in our experience the European earwig often causes significant damage to seedlings, blossoms, and fruit.

The alien **ring-legged earwig** *(Euborellia annulipes)* is reported to eat both plants and insects. In the Southeastern states two other earwigs, the **striped earwig** *(Labidura riparia)* and *E cicticollis,* have a reputation as valuable predators. They thrive under warm, moist conditions. If you live in areas where these species exist, you may want to protect earwigs. On the other hand, if you observe earwigs feeding on your plants at night, you may need to control them—at least in mild-weather areas where they thrive. *You must judge for yourself whether they are a serious threat to your garden.*

Populations of *native earwigs* are controlled by natural enemies and fit into the natural environment. They are seldom seen and should never cause trouble.

Earwig development

Female earwigs lay a clutch of about 20 eggs in a hidden safe place—perhaps beneath a rock—and protect them until they hatch and the nymphs are partially grown. These young look like small wingless adults, and eat the same foods. There are one or two generations per year—depending upon climate. Earwigs sometimes hibernate, or pass the winter in the egg stage.

Earwigs are essentially harmless to people, though they can inflict a nip from either end—evidence that the posterior forceps are not just decoration. An earwig's tough, leathery exoskeleton(skin) seems to provide protection from drying and mechanical damage, but the fact that they rest in sheltered places suggests that preservation of moisture may be important in their survival. In any case, they will die if you dump them into soapy water.

Earwigs

Earwigs are slender wingless, brown insects (10-15 mm) with pincers in the rear.

In the daytime they hide in crevices—hunt at night for decaying plants, seedlings, or soft-bodied insects

Have you seen feeding damage to seedings, tender fruits, or vegetables?

No — Yes

After dark, look for earwigs on damaged plants or flowers

Are large numbers of earwigs present ?

Yes — No

Do you live in south-eastern U.S.?

No — Yes

You likely have **European earwigs**, *Forticula auricularia*

On several nights
Knock earwigs from plants into soapy water—or
Earwigs will hide in **damp folded newspaper**
After a few days shake them into soapy water

Place tuna can filled with cooking oil or sprinkle **earwig/sowbug bait**[1] near seedlings & bedding plants

Restrict bait placement

Protect fruits/veges by enclosing them in old panty hose

You may have striped earwigs, *Labidura riparia*, in your garden—these are important predators of caterpillars

they do best at about 86° F so look for them on warm nights

Search for another cause for the damage

On flowers & foliage—could be caterpillars, root weevils, snails & slugs
On seedlings—could be cutworms

Avoid combination pesticides which attempt to kill both snails & insects
You should be selective

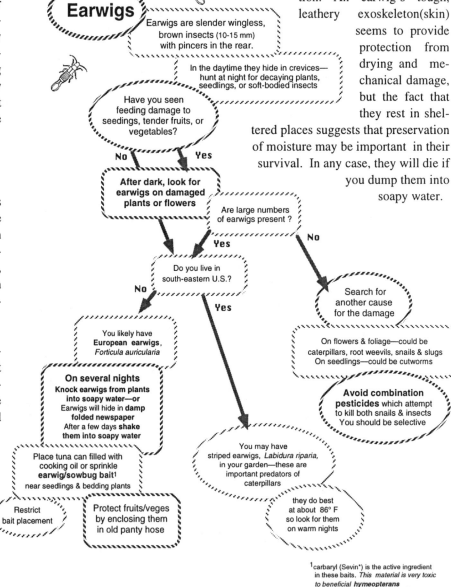

[1]carbaryl (Sevin®) is the active ingredient in these baits. ***This material is very toxic to beneficial hymeopterans***
This bran-based bait also attracts important predators such as **ground beetles**[2]

[2] Environ Entomol 20:1285-1294, 1991

Getting to know 'true bugs'

Even though we all call insects "bugs" at times, *all insects are not bugs,* and obviously not all bugs are insects. *True bugs* are a select group of insects with several easily recognized features. They are the Heteroptera —different-winged insects. Some call them *Hemiptera,* half-winged insects because adult bugs have unusual fore wings which are half hard and opaque, half thin and membranous. When folded these wings usually appear to form an X on the insect's back. *Most adult bugs can be recognized by this distinctive X.*

A bug's *mouth acts like a flexible straw* enabling them to eat only liquid food. Some plant-feeding bugs use this remarkable "straw" to penetrate tough leaves; seeds by others. Some predatory bugs pierce the epidermis of other insects to feed on their blood, and a few bugs even partake of the blood of mammals or birds.

In general, most bugs are flattened insects which move rapidly on long legs. Like grasshoppers and cockroaches, bugs develop via incomplete metamorphosis. This means that baby bugs (nymphs) look like smaller versions of their parents—but with incomplete wings. As nymphs grow, and molt, the wing buds become larger and larger. Sometimes the wing-bud colors contrast against a brightly colored abdomen.

Bug life styles

Plant Feeding Bugs—Some of the most common bugs in the garden are **tarnished plant bugs**, *Lygus sp,—L. lineolaris, L. hesperius—*which belong to the bug family Miridae. *Lygus* bugs migrate into the garden from weedy fields, and seldom cause trouble unless you use the broad-spectrum pesticides which kill their natural enemies. They may cause damage to strawberries or other fruits. If they cause trouble, try mowing nearby weeds—usually *Geranium sp.* are lygus' weedy hosts. If you see them in the garden before bloom, release big-eyed bugs to aid control. Watch also for **shield bugs.** These smooth green or tan shield-shaped bugs feed on vegetables or fruits.

In the northwest the **mullein bug**, *Campylomma verbasci,* formerly common only on mullein has begun to attack tiny apple fruits just after petal fall; perhaps another case of an insect moving to a new abundant food plant.

Many bugs are red and black. These include the **harlequin** (shield) **bug** *(Murgantia histrionica),* which favors cabbages, the slender **milkweed bugs**, and the look-alike **boxelder bug** *(Boisea trivittata),* which are innocuous feeders on weedy plants or forest trees. No need to be alarmed if hordes of boxelder bugs appear in fall—they're looking for a dry

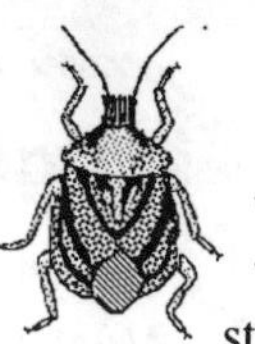

warm place to spend the winter, and they neither sting nor bite.

Predatory bugs—In the garden, look for the shield-shaped specimens known as shield bugs. Though some of the smooth green or tan shield bugs feed on vegetables or fruits, but the rough, brownish shield bugs—**rough stink bugs-**—are predators which capture caterpillars and other soft insects. One of these, the **spined soldier bug** *(Posisus maculiventris)* is commercially available (Garden's Alive) to help control plant-feeding beetle larvae. Many other predatory bugs are aquatic, but **big-eyed bugs**, **pirate bugs**, **damsel bugs**, **assassin bugs** and **ambush bugs** live on plants. They relish insect eggs and small larvae—but unfortunately not only those of plant-feeding insects. Recently it was discovered that both big-eyed and damsel bugs are major predators on eggs and larvae of important aphid predators, the green lacewings.[1]

The **insidious pirate bug** *(Orius insidiosus)—*of Eastern U.S.—and the **minute pirate bug** *(O. tristicolor)—*a native of the west—are commercially-available to control flower thrips and other pests on several crops, including potatoes, tomatoes, corn, and strawberries. They eat pollen of several plants, and capture pests as they do so.

Most **ambush bugs** move slowly over foliage looking for prey to capture with their mantid-like raptorial forelegs. Insect prey are quickly snatched up and subdued by a powerful venom injected through the beak before be-

Complete vs Incomplete Metamorphosis[2]

Among insects which have "complete metamorphosis" the adults usually live a different lifestyle from their young. Caterpillars, for example, eat leaves or fruits, whereas moths and butterflies sip nectar, or live without feeding. In bugs, as is typical of insects with incomplete metamorphosis, the adults fill the same niche as the nymphs. The nymphs of predatory adult bugs are also predators, and the plant-feeding bugs follow a similar pattern.

---

[1] Cal. Agri. 47(5): 7-9, 1993. [2]See more on metamorphosis page 14.

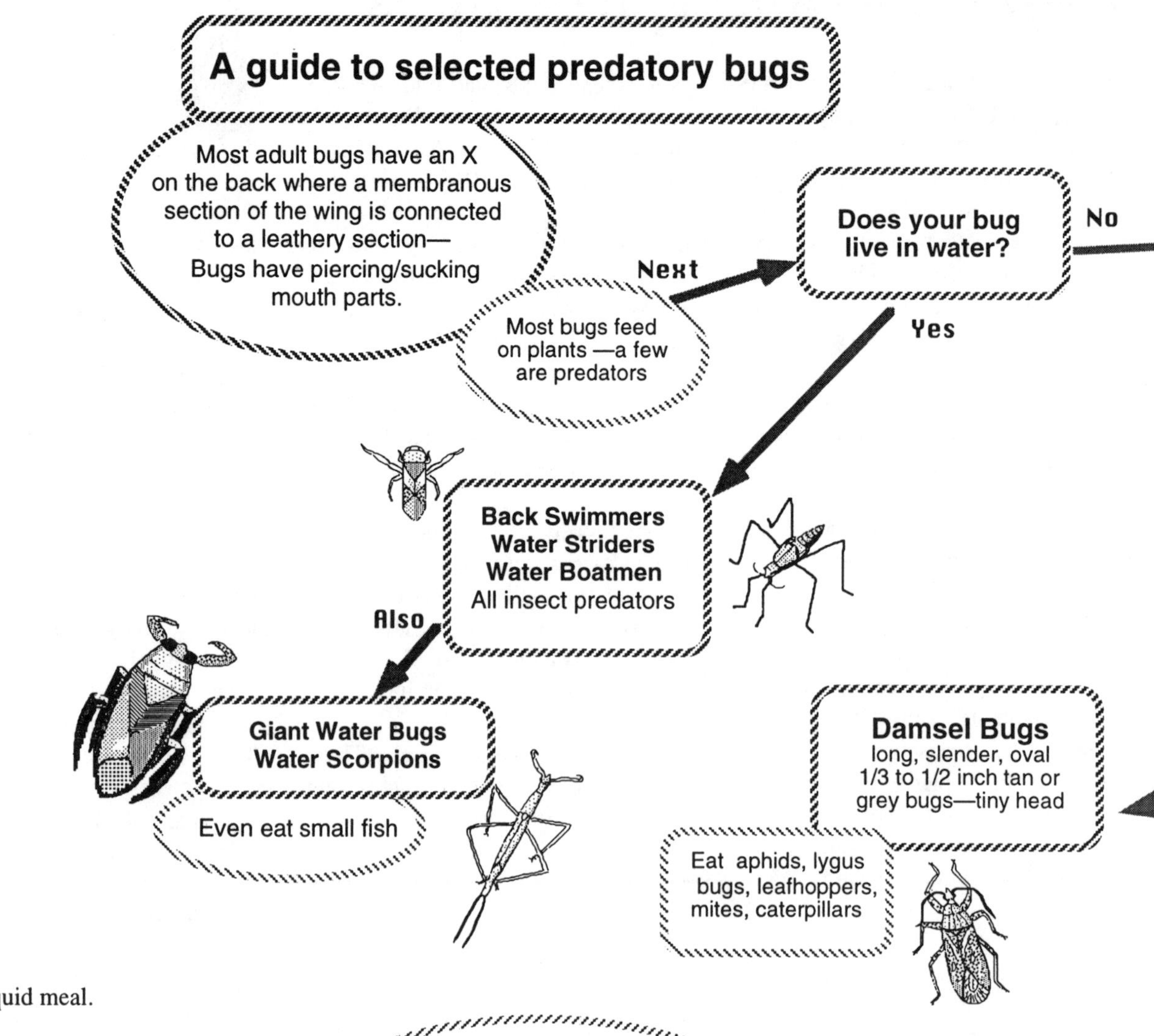
A guide to selected predatory bugs
Most adult bugs have an X on the back where a membranous section of the wing is connected to a leathery section— Bugs have piercing/sucking mouth parts.
Next
Most bugs feed on plants —a few are predators
Does your bug live in water?
No
Yes
Back Swimmers
Water Striders
Water Boatmen
All insect predators
Also
Giant Water Bugs
Water Scorpions
Even eat small fish
Damsel Bugs
long, slender, oval 1/3 to 1/2 inch tan or grey bugs—tiny head
Eat aphids, lygus bugs, leafhoppers, mites, caterpillars
Large (1/2 to 1 inch) bugs
w/ striped border around a pear-shaped body
Front legs—"raptorial" Head—small
Eyes—large & bead-like
A few species suck blood at night from sleeping mammals Many are important insect predators
Assassin Bugs

coming a liquid meal.

One group of ambush bugs—residents the U.S., Mexico, Central and especially Brazil—suck the blood of sleeping mammals. Some of these transmit Chagas disease.[1] If you live or visit these regions, it is very important to use mosquito netting in suspect areas, and window screens in hotels to protect against these and other nocturnal insects which transmit diseases there. For more on these insects, see Chagas disease.

Protecting predators

Most of us are unfamiliar with the important bug predators discussed here. Though never very common, damsel bugs and rough stink bugs help control certain caterpillars and

[1] Acute symptoms of Chagas disease include fever, indigestion, inability to eat, and swollen glands or liver which can last for weeks of months. About 10% of the victims die if the disease invades the brain or the heart. Eventually, as the immune system suppresses the infection, the disease enters a chronic phase. Serious chronic symptoms develop over several years, and include heart failure and or gastrointestinal malfunction.

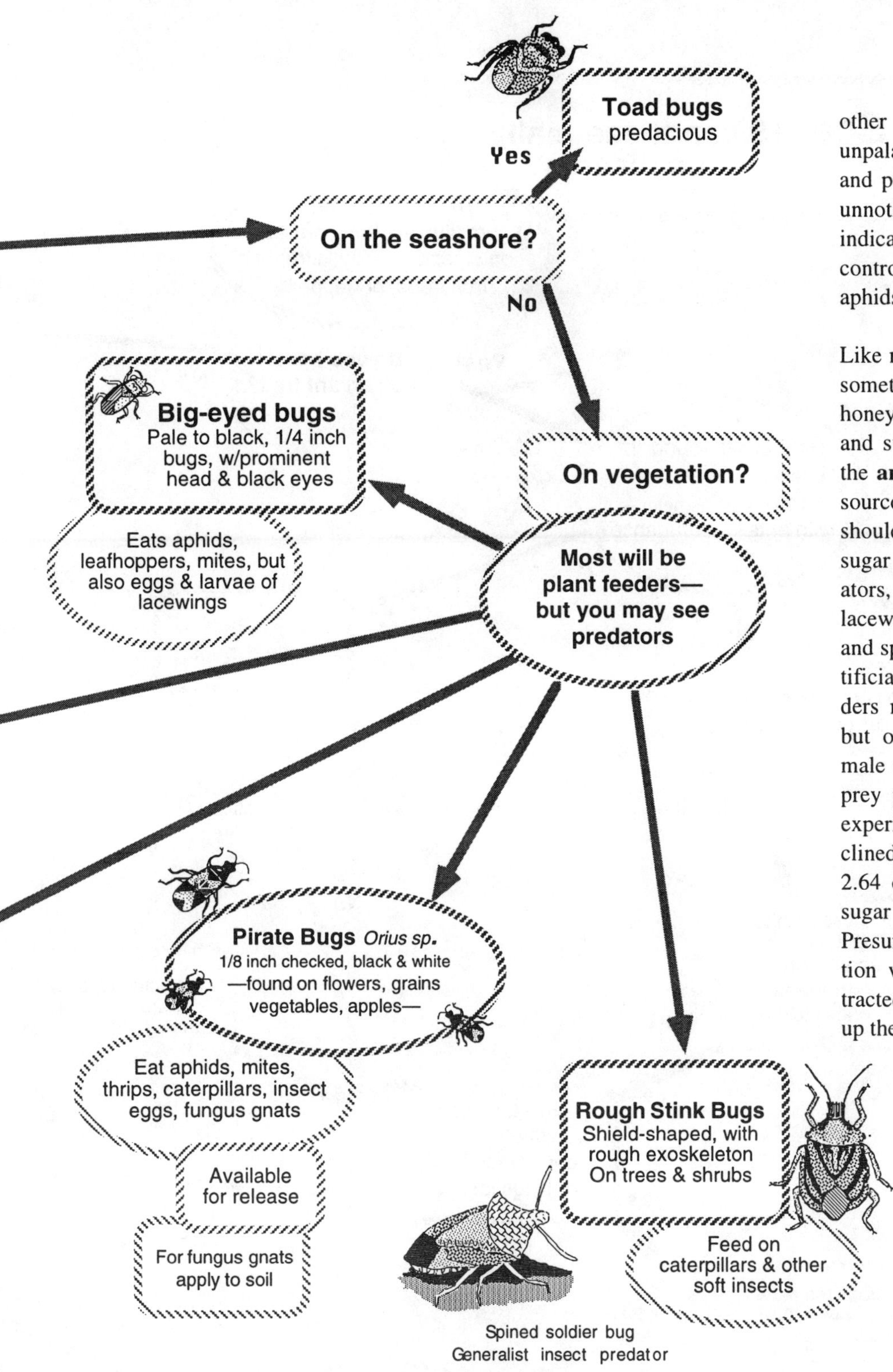
Toad bugs
predacious
Yes
On the seashore?
No
Big-eyed bugs
Pale to black, 1/4 inch bugs, w/prominent head & black eyes
Eats aphids, leafhoppers, mites, but also eggs & larvae of lacewings
On vegetation?
Most will be plant feeders—but you may see predators
Pirate Bugs Orius sp.
1/8 inch checked, black & white —found on flowers, grains vegetables, apples—
Eat aphids, mites, thrips, caterpillars, insect eggs, fungus gnats
Available for release
For fungus gnats apply to soil
Rough Stink Bugs
Shield-shaped, with rough exoskeleton
On trees & shrubs
Feed on caterpillars & other soft insects

Spined soldier bug
Generalist insect predator

other plant-feeding insects which are unpalatable to birds. The big-eyed and pirate bugs are so small as to go unnoticed by most of us, but research indicates that they are very important control agents on tiny but damaging aphids, mites, and insect eggs.

Like many other predators, these bugs sometimes take a sip of honeydew. If honeydew is scarce you can attract and sustain them by applying one of the **artificial honeydews** listed in the sources. The most effective of these should contain both a protein and a sugar source. In addition to bug predators, other beneficial insects—lacewings, lady beetles, syrphiid flies and spiders—are attracted by these artificial honeydews.[2] The idea that spiders might eat nectar seems foreign, but one study [3] found that at least male crab spiders utilize nectar when prey populations are scarce. In this experiment, pea aphid populations declined immediately after sprays of 2.64 ounces wheast and 1.76 ounces sugar in 1 quart water were applied. Presumably a mixed predator population which included crab spiders attracted by the wheast mixture, cleaned up the aphids.

[2] Environ. Entomol 22:1392-1401, 1993. [3] Nat. Hist. 102(10): 59-64, 1993.

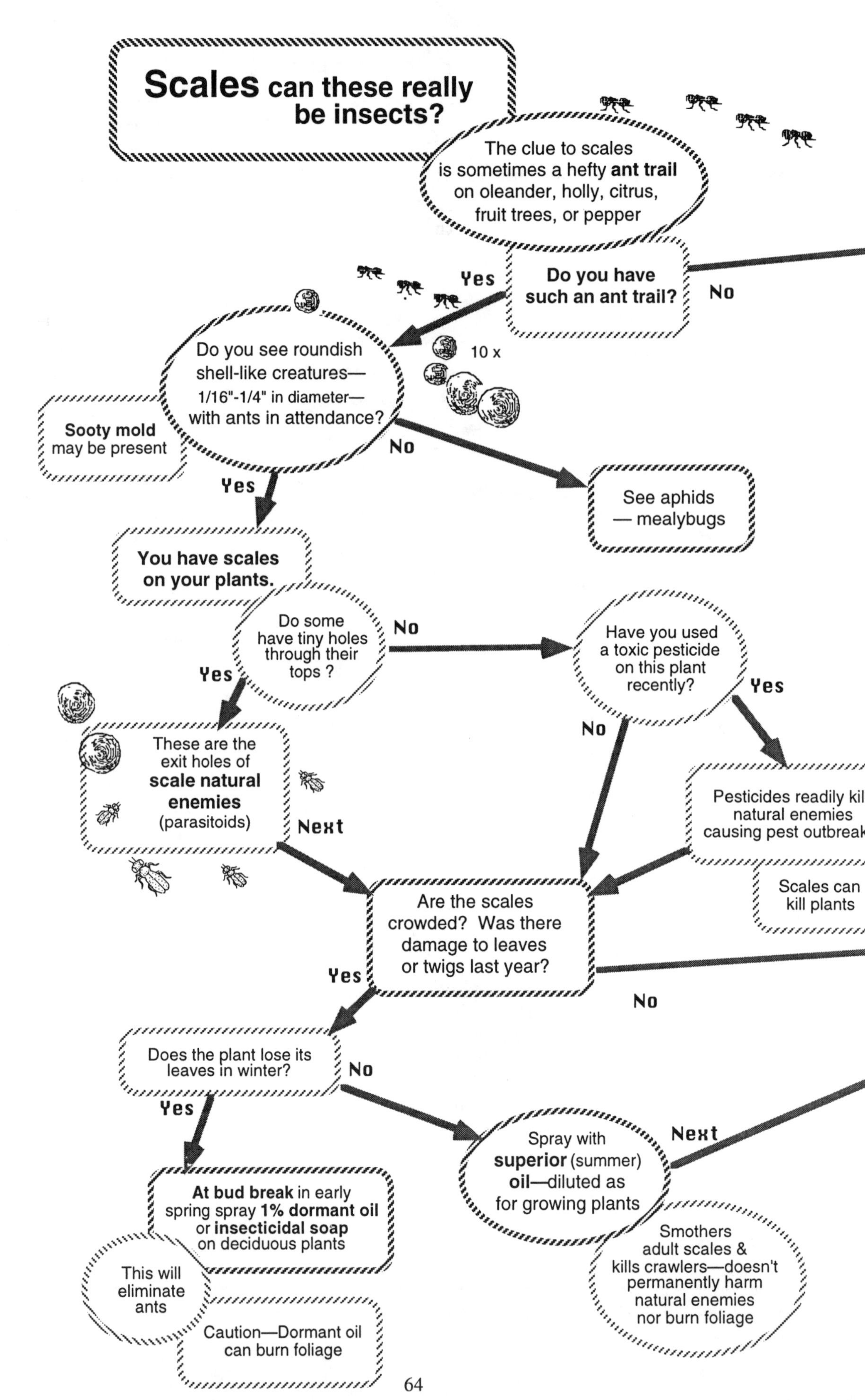
Scales can these really be insects?
The clue to scales is sometimes a hefty ant trail on oleander, holly, citrus, fruit trees, or pepper
Do you have such an ant trail?
Yes
No
Do you see roundish shell-like creatures— 1/16"-1/4" in diameter— with ants in attendance?
10 x
Sooty mold may be present
No
See aphids — mealybugs
Yes
You have scales on your plants.
Do some have tiny holes through their tops ?
No
Have you used a toxic pesticide on this plant recently?
Yes
These are the exit holes of scale natural enemies (parasitoids)
No
Yes
Pesticides readily kill natural enemies causing pest outbreaks
Scales can kill plants
Next
Are the scales crowded? Was there damage to leaves or twigs last year?
Yes
No
Does the plant lose its leaves in winter?
No
Yes
At bud break in early spring spray 1% dormant oil or insecticidal soap on deciduous plants
This will eliminate ants
Caution—Dormant oil can burn foliage
Spray with superior (summer) oil—diluted as for growing plants
Next
Smothers adult scales & kills crawlers—doesn't permanently harm natural enemies nor burn foliage

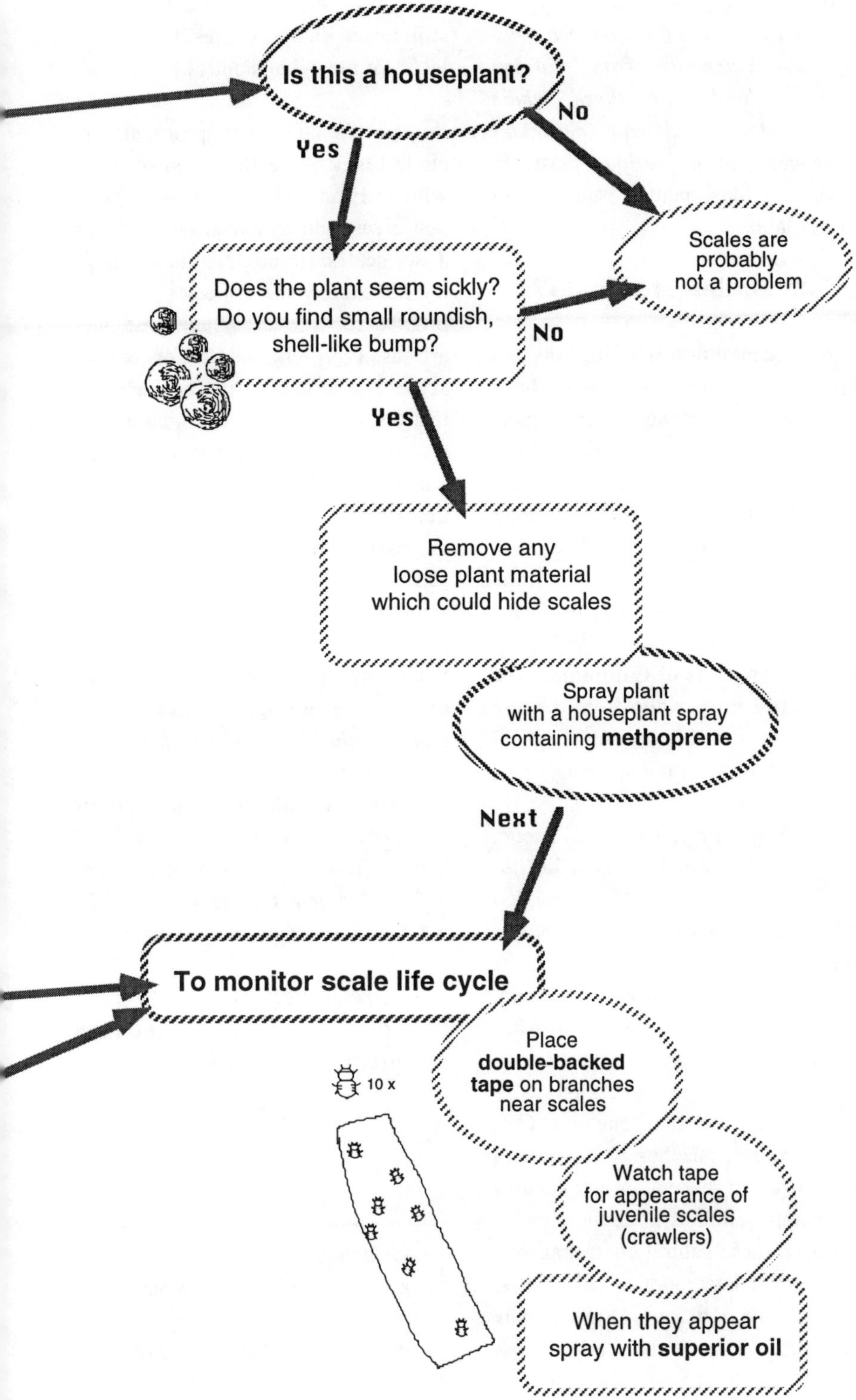

Scale insects

The amazing scale insects seem to break all the rules of insect morphology. They lack the typical insect body parts—head, thorax, abdomen, and have no wings or obvious legs either. At first glance, many scales seem not to be alive at all. Yet, if not alive, why are ants so interested? And, what's that sticky material covering their host plants?

Scale development

Scale insects (scales, for short) belong to the insect order Homoptera (same wing) because they suck plant juices like other homopterans, and male scales (if present) resemble their aphid relatives—but with only one pair of transparent roof-like wings. Scale males have all the usual insect body parts, and more—a long spikey stylet protrudes from the tip of their abdomen. (You didn't know about scale males, did you?)

Its no wonder that you didn't know about male scales. Anything so tiny that spends most of its life growing under a little scale, has to be obscure. They're only out and about at mating time, and since they don't feed, soon disappear.

It's female scales which cause all the trouble. They also spend their adult life under a protective cover (armored type), or secrete a cover as part of the body itself (soft

Is this a houseplant?
No
Scales are probably not a problem
Yes
Does the plant seem sickly? Do you find small roundish, shell-like bump?
No
Yes
Remove any loose plant material which could hide scales
Spray plant with a houseplant spray containing **methoprene**
Next
To monitor scale life cycle
Place **double-backed tape** on branches near scales
10 x
Watch tape for appearance of juvenile scales (crawlers)
When they appear spray with **superior oil**

type). Most female scales look like little bumps on the host plants—but a few are covered with a fluffy, waxy coating which makes them difficult to distinguish from wooly aphids or mealybugs.

Scale lifestyle

Although most adult female scales—except for the fluffy-coated types—can't move, a scale's life style is similar to that of other insects. Scales suck fluids through filamentous mouth parts inserted into plants. After mating—the male comes to them—they lay eggs or bear live young. Then they die, with the scaly shell serving as a protective cover for the developing offspring.

Most scales have only one generation each year, but in warmer areas a few have two or even three generations. Dormant periods differ from species to species, as well. Some scales overwinter as immature females, others in the egg stage, or as nymphs.

Scale nymphs, or *crawlers*, have obvious legs, and no scale covering. They move about the plant, often feeding on leaves, before "settling" on woody stems as adulthood approaches. (A few species feed, then settle on fruits or leaves.) When feeding, many scales exude a sticky "honeydew" which is attractive to ants.

Many scales are distributed nationwide, others have more restricted ranges. All are preyed on by a variety of natural enemies—mini-wasp parasitoids and lady beetles are typical *Usually scales introduced accidentally from foreign lands, or those which which are sprayed with pesticides sometimes become serious pests.* In these situations natural enemies are not available.

Which scales are pests?

Such accidental pest introductions and experiments with pesticides have helped to demonstrate the true value of insect natural enemies in the *Biology learned from pesticides* essay. (page 8-13). In 1868 the **cottony cushion scale** *(Icerya purchasi)* was discovered the U.S. for the first time. This scale feeds on a variety of plants, but by 1886 it was rapidly destroying the citrus orchards of California. The trees were snowy white from the egg cases of this creature, and chemical control efforts were not working.

Fortunately, a ladybird beetle, the black and red **vedalia** *(Rodolia (Vedalia) cardinalis)* and a **parasitic fly** *(Cryptocaetum iceryae)* were successfully transported from Australia by ship, and introduced here. After only two years, this enormous scale infestation was successfully controlled by these natural enemies. Cottony cushion scale has never been a problem again, except in a few cases where application of toxic insecticides destroyed these natural control agents. [A few years later, another lady beetle, the mealybug destroyer *(Cryptolaemus montrouzieri),* was similarly transported from Australia to control mealybugs on citrus. These are still raised in insectaries for release for mealybug control.]

Some of the most likely pest scales include **black scale** *(Saissetia oleae)*—with an H on its back—in coastal sunbelt areas, and **oyster-shell**[1] and **San Jose**[2] **scales**, (throughout the country), but almost any scale species may be a problem at times. Where pesticides are used on citrus, **California red scale**[3] is a serious pest. There are now many scale populations which are resistant to organophosphate and carbamate insecticides.[4] Obviously pesticide use should be restricted as much as possible to avoid these upsets, and selective methods and materials chosen if available.

Scales are most easily controlled during the crawler stage, so *scale-infested plants should be monitored for crawlers in the spring before they settle and multiply.* Usually deciduous plants can be sprayed with dormant oil at bud break. Fortunately oils smother scales without leaving toxic residues or killing natural enemies that contact it.

Oils are an effective, and ecologically desirable control chemical for scales.

---

1 *Lepidosaphes ulmi,*

2 *Quadraspidiothhus perniciosus*

3 *Aonidiella aurantii,*

4 J. Econ. Entomo. 87: 1046-1057, 1994.

Thrips

Thrips are tiny—so small that you've likely never seen one—that's why we've dubbed them "rapidly moving threads". Even though thrips adults have folded wings—with fringed edges, no less—without visual aids all stages appear to be wingless. Like most small delicate insects, thrips are consumed by so many predators that they're seldom a problem.

But once in a while—when plants are water stressed, for example—or other cultural things are favorable to thrips or unfavorable to their enemies, there can be trouble. Likewise, should a new thrips species be accidentally introduced without its natural enemies, thrips will probably cause damage. However, thrips are most likely to be regarded as pests • when pesticide sprays have killed off their predators, or, • they are spreading diseases—such as the **tomato spotted wilt virus (TSWV)**—to vegetables.

Where thrips are found

Although there are about 700 thrips species in the United States, it's seldom easy to locate them. During the spring and summer, they usually hang out within leaf and flower buds, though occasionally you can see them scurrying around on blossoms. (Most adult thrips spend the winter on weeds). They feed by scraping the plant surface, causing the sap to ooze. This damage causes light-colored streaks or splotches on leaves, or brownish curled edges on petals and shoots. Sometimes the most obvious evidence of thrips is the *tiny black specks which are left behind when they defecate.* Here we highlight those thrips species which may cause trouble in your garden.

The champion pest thrips is called **onion thrips** *(Thrips tabaci),* an obvious understatement when you learn that it has been found on cabbage, peas, cucumbers, beans, beets, tomatoes, squash, celery, carrots, melons, asparagus, and a variety of weeds. Its feeding tends to retard leaf development, and sometimes growth of the entire plant, and it also transmits TSWV. In winter it may be lurking on stored onions its favorite host.

Flower thrips *(Frankliniella tritici)* are the most widespread thrips in the U.S. Hardly a flower is without a few of these. Fortunately, they don't cause too much trouble—usually. But watch for them on their favorite white flowers—roses or peonies. Its relative, the **Western flower thrips** *(F. occidentalis),* common in the south and west, likewise relishes many flowering plants. Surprisingly, it is beneficial as a spider mite predator, but is also a TSWV vector. [The **tobacco thrips** *(F. fusca)* is the third TSWV vector].

Sometimes weed control helps reduce thrips in winter or very early spring, but later in the season thrips from destroyed weeds move over to other species such as your vegetables or fruits. Since thrips may transport TSWV each spring from infected weeds to vegetables, if disease has been a problem, try to cover sensitive seedlings as long as possible, and follow the other suggestions in our diagram.

Thrips are much more likely to attack stressed plants, so water and nutrients should be optimum. They also attack new growth, so pruning should be selective. Under conditions of high humidity—greenhouse thrips *(Heliothrips haemorroidalis)* may damage a several soft fruits (avocado, citrus, guava, mango, pear, etc.), but it also likes such moisture-loving ornamentals as rhododendron, azalea, fuchsia, dogwood, viburnum and orchids).

Effect of sprays

A native westerner, the **citrus thrips** *(Scirtothrips citri),* sometimes feeds on embryonic oranges and lemons causing scarring around the fruit stem. (This is another example of an endemic insect exploiting to an abundant new host, and attaining pest status). In this case, any damage is superficial. *This unsightly feeding does not affect the flavor or quality of the fruit.* However, because scarred fruit is downgraded commercially, orchardists try to kill citrus thrips with insecticides. This was initially effective, even though these sprays triggered outbreaks of a secondary pest, **citrus red mite**. Now, however, many citrus thrips populations show resistance to these sprays. Thus many thrips sprays do more harm than good. Fortunately, we suggest alternatives.

If you live in Florida you will not be pleased to learn that a new thrips *(Thrips palmi)* is devastating vegetables there. Cover your crops as much as possible, use water and oil sprays, and **light blue sticky traps** to monitor for thrips, and help lower populations until the Federal Government locates and releases natural enemies from its Southeast Asian homeland.

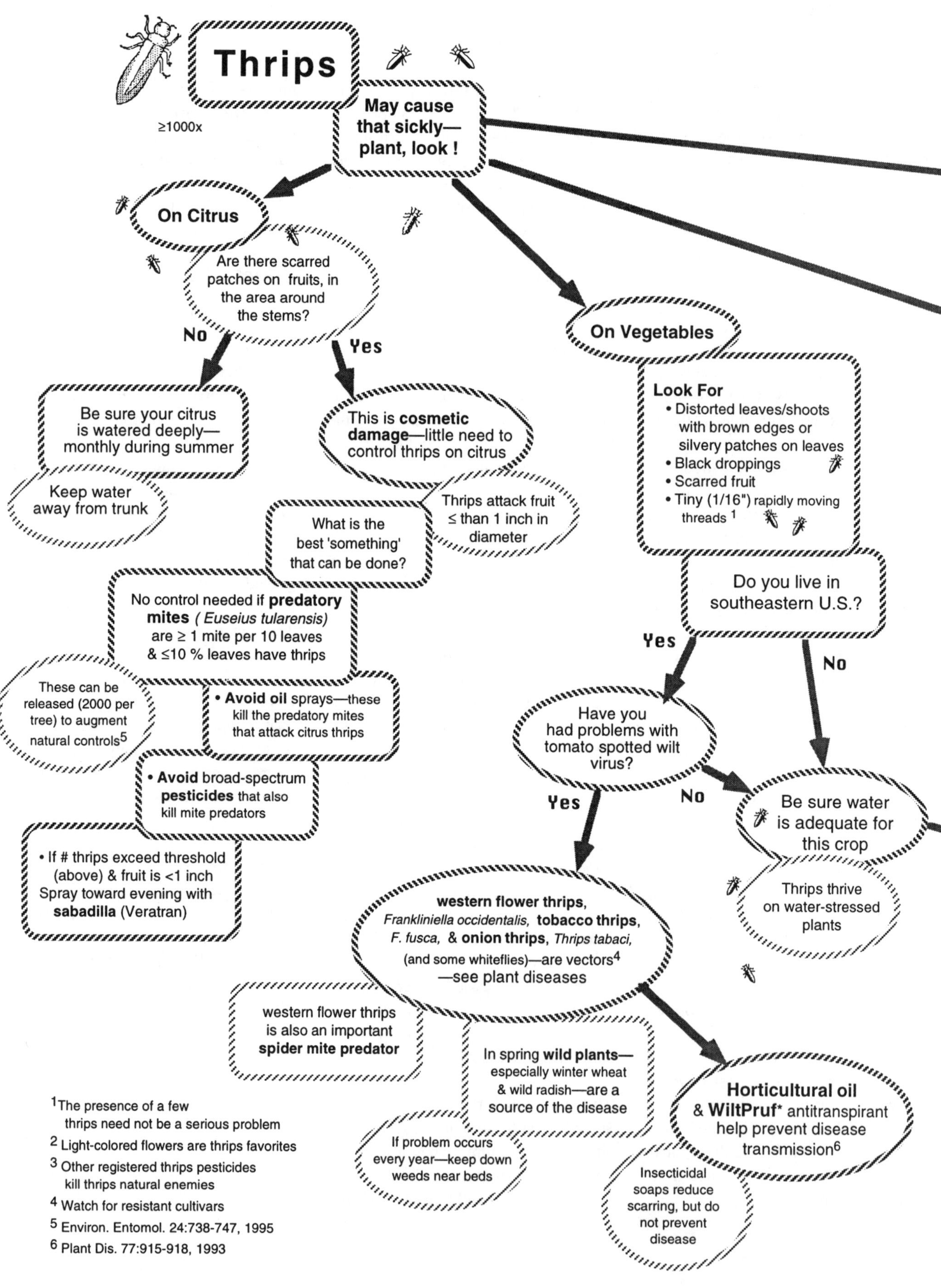

Thrips
≥1000x
May cause that sickly—plant, look !
On Citrus
Are there scarred patches on fruits, in the area around the stems?
No
Yes
Be sure your citrus is watered deeply—monthly during summer
Keep water away from trunk
This is cosmetic damage—little need to control thrips on citrus
Thrips attack fruit ≤ than 1 inch in diameter
What is the best 'something' that can be done?
No control needed if predatory mites (Euseius tularensis) are ≥ 1 mite per 10 leaves & ≤10 % leaves have thrips
These can be released (2000 per tree) to augment natural controls5
• Avoid oil sprays—these kill the predatory mites that attack citrus thrips
• Avoid broad-spectrum pesticides that also kill mite predators
• If # thrips exceed threshold (above) & fruit is <1 inch Spray toward evening with sabadilla (Veratran)
On Vegetables
Look For
• Distorted leaves/shoots with brown edges or silvery patches on leaves
• Black droppings
• Scarred fruit
• Tiny (1/16") rapidly moving threads 1
Do you live in southeastern U.S.?
Yes
No
Have you had problems with tomato spotted wilt virus?
Yes
No
Be sure water is adequate for this crop
Thrips thrive on water-stressed plants
western flower thrips, Frankliniella occidentalis, tobacco thrips, F. fusca, & onion thrips, Thrips tabaci, (and some whiteflies)—are vectors4 —see plant diseases
western flower thrips is also an important spider mite predator
In spring wild plants—especially winter wheat & wild radish—are a source of the disease
If problem occurs every year—keep down weeds near beds
Horticultural oil & WiltPruf* antitranspirant help prevent disease transmission6
Insecticidal soaps reduce scarring, but do not prevent disease

1 The presence of a few thrips need not be a serious problem

2 Light-colored flowers are thrips favorites

3 Other registered thrips pesticides kill thrips natural enemies

4 Watch for resistant cultivars

5 Environ. Entomol. 24:738-747, 1995

6 Plant Dis. 77:915-918, 1993

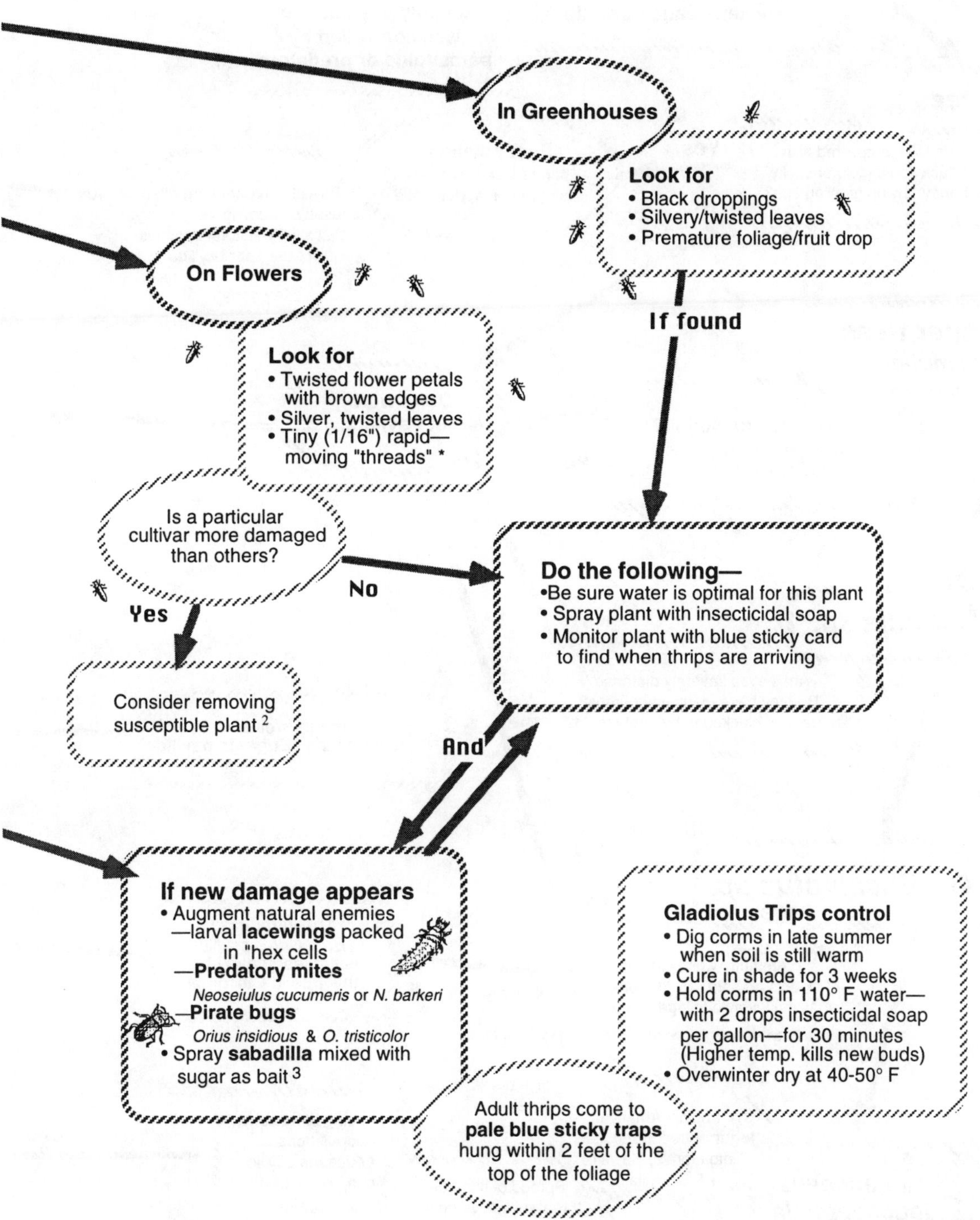
In Greenhouses
Look for
• Black droppings
• Silvery/twisted leaves
• Premature foliage/fruit drop
If found
On Flowers
Look for
• Twisted flower petals with brown edges
• Silver, twisted leaves
• Tiny (1/16") rapid—moving "threads" *
Is a particular cultivar more damaged than others?
No
Yes
Consider removing susceptible plant 2
Do the following—
•Be sure water is optimal for this plant
• Spray plant with insecticidal soap
• Monitor plant with blue sticky card to find when thrips are arriving
And
If new damage appears
• Augment natural enemies
—larval lacewings packed in "hex cells
—Predatory mites
Neoseiulus cucumeris or N. barkeri
—Pirate bugs
Orius insidious & O. tristicolor
• Spray sabadilla mixed with sugar as bait 3
Adult thrips come to pale blue sticky traps hung within 2 feet of the top of the foliage
Gladiolus Trips control
• Dig corms in late summer when soil is still warm
• Cure in shade for 3 weeks
• Hold corms in 110° F water—with 2 drops insecticidal soap per gallon—for 30 minutes (Higher temp. kills new buds)
• Overwinter dry at 40-50° F

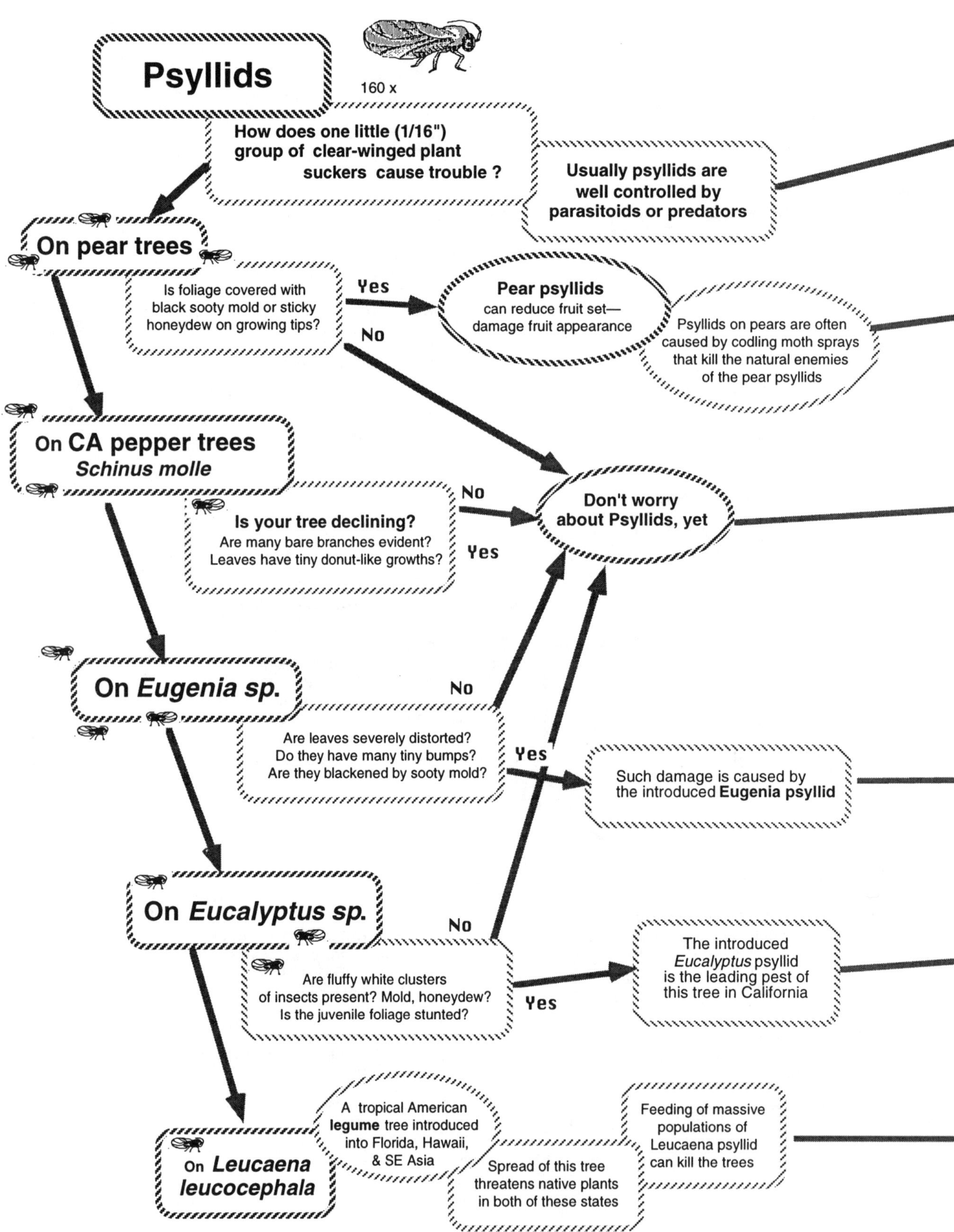

Psyllids
160 x
How does one little (1/16") group of clear-winged plant suckers cause trouble ?
Usually psyllids are well controlled by parasitoids or predators
On pear trees
Is foliage covered with black sooty mold or sticky honeydew on growing tips?
Yes
No
Pear psyllids can reduce fruit set— damage fruit appearance
Psyllids on pears are often caused by codling moth sprays that kill the natural enemies of the pear psyllids
On CA pepper trees Schinus molle
Is your tree declining? Are many bare branches evident? Leaves have tiny donut-like growths?
No
Yes
Don't worry about Psyllids, yet
On Eugenia sp.
No
Are leaves severely distorted? Do they have many tiny bumps? Are they blackened by sooty mold?
Yes
Such damage is caused by the introduced Eugenia psyllid
On Eucalyptus sp.
No
Are fluffy white clusters of insects present? Mold, honeydew? Is the juvenile foliage stunted?
Yes
The introduced Eucalyptus psyllid is the leading pest of this tree in California
On Leucaena leucocephala
A tropical American legume tree introduced into Florida, Hawaii, & SE Asia
Spread of this tree threatens native plants in both of these states
Feeding of massive populations of Leucaena psyllid can kill the trees

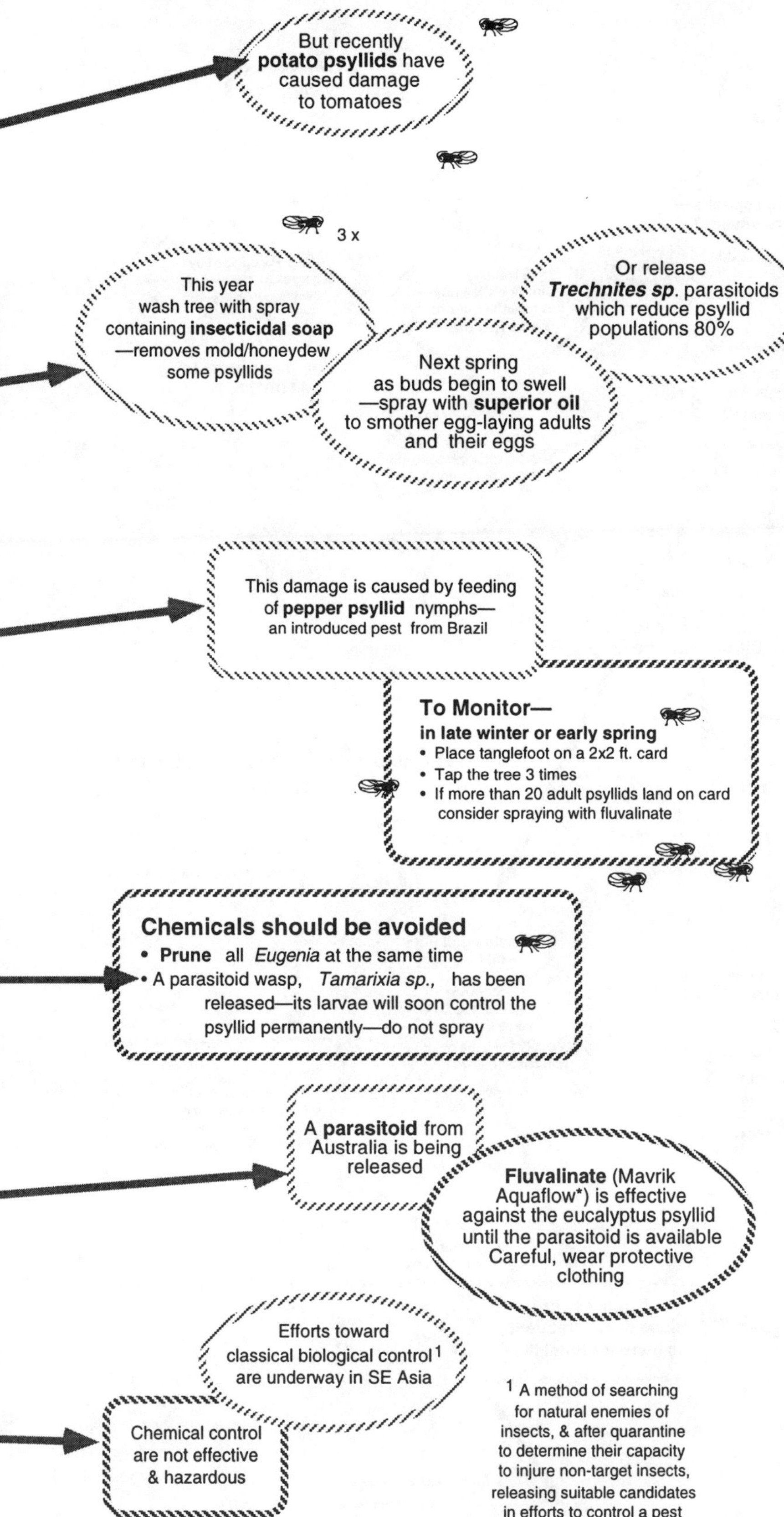
But recently **potato psyllids** have caused damage to tomatoes
3 x
This year wash tree with spray containing **insecticidal soap** —removes mold/honeydew some psyllids
Or release ***Trechnites sp.*** parasitoids which reduce psyllid populations 80%
Next spring as buds begin to swell —spray with **superior oil** to smother egg-laying adults and their eggs
This damage is caused by feeding of **pepper psyllid** nymphs— an introduced pest from Brazil
To Monitor—
in late winter or early spring
• Place tanglefoot on a 2x2 ft. card
• Tap the tree 3 times
• If more than 20 adult psyllids land on card consider spraying with fluvalinate
Chemicals should be avoided
• **Prune** all *Eugenia* at the same time
• A parasitoid wasp, *Tamarixia sp.*, has been released—its larvae will soon control the psyllid permanently—do not spray
A **parasitoid** from Australia is being released
Fluvalinate (Mavrik Aquaflow*) is effective against the eucalyptus psyllid until the parasitoid is available Careful, wear protective clothing
Efforts toward classical biological control[1] are underway in SE Asia
Chemical control are not effective & hazardous
[1] A method of searching for natural enemies of insects, & after quarantine to determine their capacity to injure non-target insects, releasing suitable candidates in efforts to control a pest

Psyllids

Psyllids like aphids, belong to the insect order Homoptera. All Homopteran adults have roof-like wings, and all life stages are sustained by plant juices. Some call psyllids *jumping plant lice* because they have strong jumping legs.

Some psyllid larvae look like a small version of the adults, but others secrete a waxy coating similar to that of wooly aphids or mealybugs. Larval saliva may cause an unsightly leaf curling or gall formation in affected plants. All excrete the sticky honeydew which accompanies the feeding of sap-eating insects. In addition, a few psyllids transmit viral diseases which can cause far more damage than their feeding alone. Each psyllid is restricted to one or a few plant species, and usually their populations are controlled by natural enemies.

Occasionally, as highlighted here, psyllids have been accidentally transported from foreign lands without their all-important natural enemies. These immediately became pests. Only our ability to find parasitoids in their land of origin, have enabled us to control these aliens because their cryptic life-style, and rapid reproduction, makes use of pesticides difficult for routine psyllid control.

Recently, Gary Puterka, a USDA scientist in Ithaca New York, discovered three fungal diseases which control the **pear psyllid**. He found that if these diseases are sprayed onto pear psyllid-infested foliage, the pests die and the diseases become permanately established in the orchard. If you raise pears, watch for these diseases to become available in a commercial product.

In addition to the species described here, psyllids on laurel, hackberry, and a few other shrubs and trees are occasionally a problem.

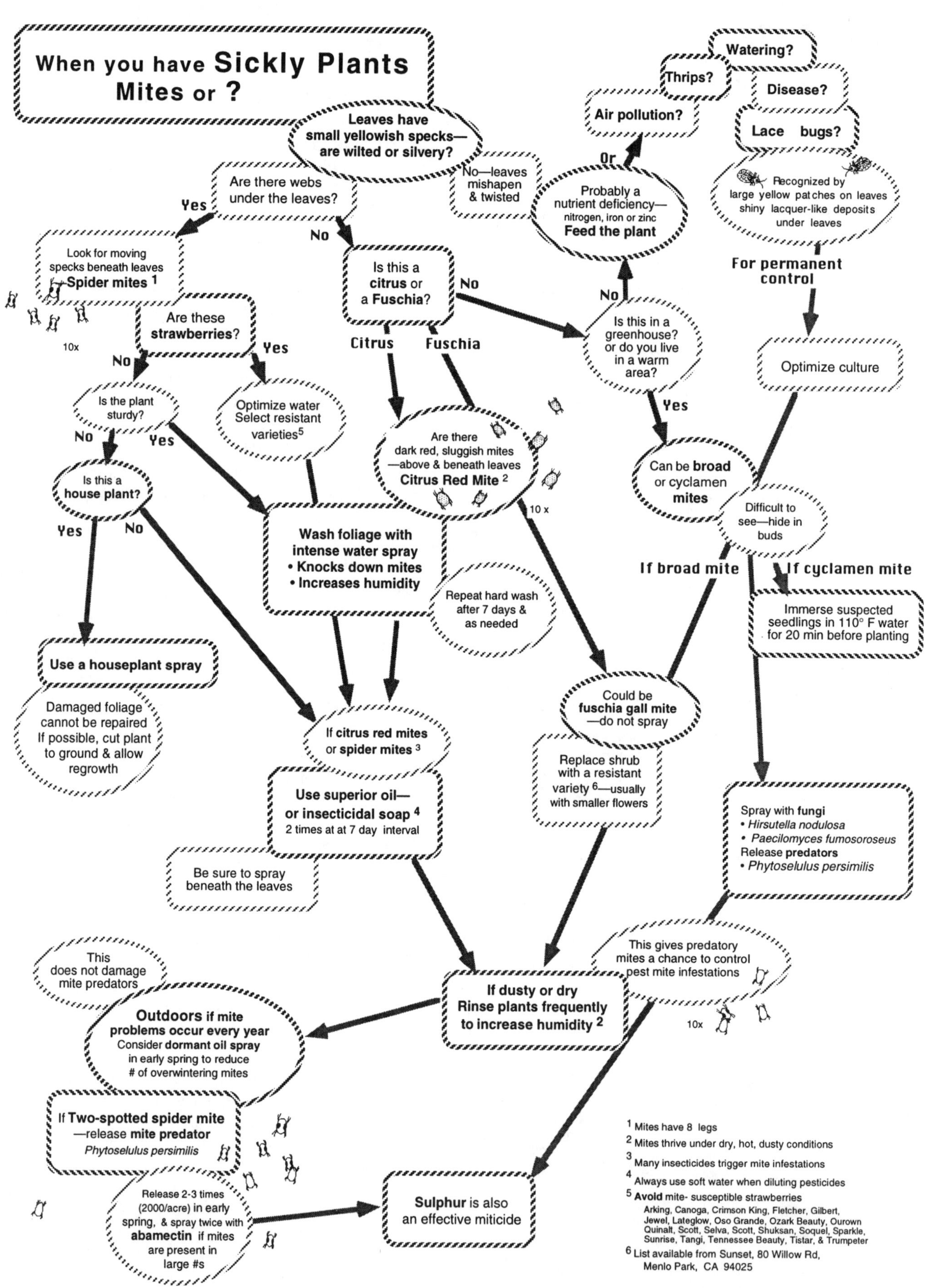
When you have Sickly Plants Mites or ?
Leaves have small yellowish specks—are wilted or silvery?
Are there webs under the leaves?
Yes
No
No—leaves mishapen & twisted
Probably a nutrient deficiency—nitrogen, iron or zinc
Feed the plant
Or
Air pollution?
Thrips?
Watering?
Disease?
Lace bugs?
Recognized by large yellow patches on leaves shiny lacquer-like deposits under leaves
For permanent control
Optimize culture
Look for moving specks beneath leaves
Spider mites 1
10x
Are these strawberries?
No
Yes
Is the plant sturdy?
Optimize water Select resistant varieties5
No
Yes
Is this a house plant?
Yes
No
Is this a citrus or a Fuschia?
No
Citrus
Fuschia
Is this in a greenhouse? or do you live in a warm area?
Yes
Are there dark red, sluggish mites —above & beneath leaves
Citrus Red Mite 2
10 x
Can be broad or cyclamen mites
Difficult to see—hide in buds
If broad mite
If cyclamen mite
Immerse suspected seedlings in 110° F water for 20 min before planting
Wash foliage with intense water spray
• Knocks down mites
• Increases humidity
Repeat hard wash after 7 days & as needed
Use a houseplant spray
Damaged foliage cannot be repaired If possible, cut plant to ground & allow regrowth
If citrus red mites or spider mites 3
Use superior oil—or insecticidal soap 4
2 times at at 7 day interval
Be sure to spray beneath the leaves
Could be fuschia gall mite —do not spray
Replace shrub with a resistant variety 6—usually with smaller flowers
Spray with fungi
• Hirsutella nodulosa
• Paecilomyces fumosoroseus
Release predators
• Phytoselulus persimilis
This gives predatory mites a chance to control pest mite infestations
10x
This does not damage mite predators
If dusty or dry Rinse plants frequently to increase humidity 2
Outdoors if mite problems occur every year
Consider dormant oil spray in early spring to reduce # of overwintering mites
If Two-spotted spider mite —release mite predator
Phytoselulus persimilis
Release 2-3 times (2000/acre) in early spring, & spray twice with abamectin if mites are present in large #s
Sulphur is also an effective miticide

1 Mites have 8 legs

2 Mites thrive under dry, hot, dusty conditions

3 Many insecticides trigger mite infestations

4 Always use soft water when diluting pesticides

5 **Avoid** mite- susceptible strawberries
Arking, Canoga, Crimson King, Fletcher, Gilbert, Jewel, Lateglow, Oso Grande, Ozark Beauty, Ourown Quinalt, Scott, Selva, Scott, Shuksan, Soquel, Sparkle, Sunrise, Tangi, Tennessee Beauty, Tistar, & Trumpeter

6 List available from Sunset, 80 Willow Rd, Menlo Park, CA 94025

Mites

You need a magnifying glass to see that mites have eight legs and two body segments, like spiders. The word mite means tiny, and mites are minute spider relatives—**arachnids** not insects—about the size of the dot at the end of this sentence.

Mites have an enormous variety of life styles. Mites that live in the soil may break down decaying plant material, or feed on insect eggs or larvae. Dust mites survive on damp house dust, mites are found in the hair of mammals or the feathers of birds. Other mites live on plants. *We are concerned here with mites which weaken the food-making capacity of plants by sucking leaf juices.*

Recognizing mite problems

We usually recognize a serious pest mite infestation when pale dots, crinkly edges, or a silvery sheen appear on leaves—when its too late. (Crinkly leaf edges may also be caused by too much or too little water, or excess minerals). You have should search for mites if you have these symptoms.

You'll know you have "spider mites" —e.g. the **Two-spotted Spider Mite**, *Tetranicus urticae,* or the **European Red Mite** (ERM)—if a diffuse webbing covers the lower leaf surface. These webs hold adult mites and their numerous offspring, well above pesticide-treated foliage. Their beautiful green, bead-like eggs are also suspended on this web. Not all plant mites produce webs. Some minute pest mites feed in the crevices of unopened buds, the saliva of others trigger the formation of plant galls. Young mites pass through several life stages, each of which is separated by a molt. The entire growing process may take only about a week in warm weather.

Beneficial mites

Surprisingly, in spite of their small size, certain mites on plants are predators. They thrive on insect and mite eggs, and even attack their plant-feeding mite relatives. You can recognize predatory mites by their relatively large triangular bodies, and their rapid movement. It appears that *predators are largely responsible for keeping pest mite populations under control.* You'll want to preserve these important predators by careful choice of insect control methods.

Plant-feeding mites seldom cause significant damage because so many insect and mite predators eat them. Unfortunately, *when broad-spectrum insecticides are used, mite enemies are killed along with the pests.* Without their natural enemies pest mite populations can easily burgeon to plant-damaging levels. They, themselves, are little affected because they tend to flee the plant when insecticides are applied.[1] Even though several selective miticides are available, costs and environmental pollution increase if they are used to overcome effects of previous broad spectrum pesticide use. The newest, abemectin, is already losing effectiveness in Florida because certain growers applied it as much as 52 times per year.[2]

Because mite predators cannot usually get into houses, selective miticides are sometimes appropriate on house plants—or the plant itself can be replaced. The safest miticide is superior oil. Other miticides include sulphur and certain fungi attack mites. Sometimes beneficial mites are released for pest mite control.

When it was discovered that certain predatory mites had spontaneously become resistant to pesticides, researchers worked to select other pesticide-resistant strains. Currently these are raised commercially for release on crops which are sprayed with broad-spectrum pesticides. These resistant strains make insect control easier, by eliminating the need to use miticides.

The obvious next step has also occurred. A transgenic form of the the predatory mite *Metaseliulus occidentalis,* has been produced which possesses multiple resistance to the insecticides used on strawberries, orchards, and vineyards. This method of developing resistance was cheaper and quicker than conventional genetic selection. Many fear that release of such multiple-resistant natural enemies will save money in the short run, but encourage increased pesticide use over the long term.

Even when no pesticides are applied, the number of natural mite enemies sometimes declines under dry or dusty conditions allowing mite populations to increase. If you suspect these weather conditions are occurring, you can help prevent mite problems by periodically washing down the foliage to remove dust and increase plant humidity.

If you follow our IPM methods, the only other pest mites you may encounter outdoors are **citrus** and **European red mites**. These mites are sometimes pests in orchards because of insecticide sprays. The relatively large citrus red mite is easily visible because it feeds above, as well as below the leaves. Because it produces no protective web, this species is readily removed by a hard water spray. Recently[3] experimenters successfully controlled ERM on apples with 2% superior oil applied at petal fall, and repeated every 2 to 3 weeks if problem mite populations persisted.

---

[1] Environ Entomol 24:226-232, 1995

[2] IPM Practitioner 16(8), 1994.

[3] J. Econ. Entomol. 87:148-161, 1994.

How spiders fit in

Spiders generate weird reactions in people. A few of us admire them, but others scream or even grab the nearest weapon and beat them to death. *We recommend admiration.* Although many of us think of spiders as some different kind of insect, they aren't insects at all, of course, but *arachnids.* (Mites are another arachnid you'll commonly encounter, and *pseudoscorpions* and *scorpions* are also arachnids).

Arachnid characteristics

Arachnids have eight legs, in contrast to an insect's six, and two, rather than three body parts. Like insects, spiders molt several times as they develop from egg to adult, but all stages look like spiders. A spider's body is divided into a cephalothorax (head-thorax), and an unsegmented abdomen. The six to eight eyes, chelicerae (jaws), and legs are located on the cephalothorax. Several silk glands and the gill-like book lungs are located on the abdomen. Indeed, silk is crucial to spiders.

Spider's lifestyle

Spiders are part of our everyday life. They live almost everywhere, and most are harmless to humans. All spiders are primarily predators, though they may eat insect eggs or pollen, or even scavenge dead creatures when the going gets tough.

Appearance gives a clue to spider hunting strategy. The sturdy-legged **jumping spiders** have eight large, front-facing eyes to watch for prey—the sharpest vision in spider-land. They slowly stalk an unsuspecting fly or caterpillar, and after a spectacular leap, deliver the coup de grâce with poison-bearing fangs. The long legged, rapid-running **wolf spiders**, chase their prey at night, while **lynx spiders** fill a similar niche on sunlit foliage.

Some spiders wait in ambush. **Trap door spiders** hide under a lid in a silk-lined burrow until insect prey approaches, while the enormous **tarantula** rushes out of its open hole. Flower-colored **crab spiders** wait motionless on flower petals until an insect comes seeking nectar or pollen then sneaks up and grabs it for dinner.

The most common spider life style is an in-the-web syndrome. Spiders are the only animals other than humans that construct traps. The most familiar webbing spiders are the **orb weavers** of the book, *Charlotte's Web* fame. Almost everyone has seen circular orb webs with a colorful large garden spider suspended in the center. Many web-weaving spiders are named for the shape of their snares. The words **funnel**, **ray**, **cobweb**, and **sheetweb** describe the webs constructed by the spiders of the same names. Each waits until a prey animal becomes entangled into its snare, before running out to paralyze the victim with a well placed bite.

You have probably encountered the silk used to construct these snares in "cobwebs" or glossimer strands across a path. Pound for pound spider silk is said to be stronger than steel wire. "Spider web may be large or small; single-line or multiline; sticky.....or nonsticky—a kaleidoscope of different design for catching insects."[1] Spiders change the strength and elasticity of the strands according to their needs. Silk used to construct the web, is not the same as silk which envelopes their prey. The silk in the center of an orb web is coated with a sticky glue, while a protective waterproof silk is used to cradle the eggs. Even spiders that do not make webs "trail a silk dragline along. Many ....retire to the safety of a silk nest to rest....to molt, and to lay eggs."[1]

After an insect is swathed in silk, a poisonous bite subdues its struggles. Since spiders have no teeth, they must inject digestive fluids into or onto their prey. Eventually the liquefied nutrients are sucked into the spider's stomach. A spider may take hours to digest and eat a small prey item.

Spiders help control insects

Since spiders are found almost everywhere, it should be obvious that they could be important in controlling insects. Indeed, studies suggest that spiders are the major control agents for certain pest insects. You should protect them, if possible, even in the home. Certain spiders may to be specialized to live indoors. The most attractive of these is the shimmering, silvery **cellar spider**, a cobweb spider that may set up housekeeping in a sunny window. The feared **widow spiders** are cobweb spiders which prefer dark closets or holes out of doors. Other indoor spiders may be hunters that prowl after dark. The floor-dwelling **Brown Recluse** is one of these. If you dislike sharing your house with spiders, catch them gently in a tissue, and carry them outdoors, or, if numbers get out of hand use a vacuum cleaner to clean out the spiders and their webs. No need to spray or bomb spiders.

Most spiders you see will be females. After mating female spiders can lay several batches of eggs, fertilizing them with stored sperm. This egg laying takes place throughout the year. Each spider constructs a protective egg sac around her eggs. Sometimes she remains nearby to keep away egg predators, but she may die within a short time. If the weather is cold, the spiderlings may remain inside the sac through the winter. When they do emerge, most disperse by casting a web to the breezes, and sailing away. This spider-flying method is so effective that spiderlings have been found at 10,000 feet, and some of the same spider genera are found all over the world.

---

1 Nat. Hist. 104(3):29-31, 1995

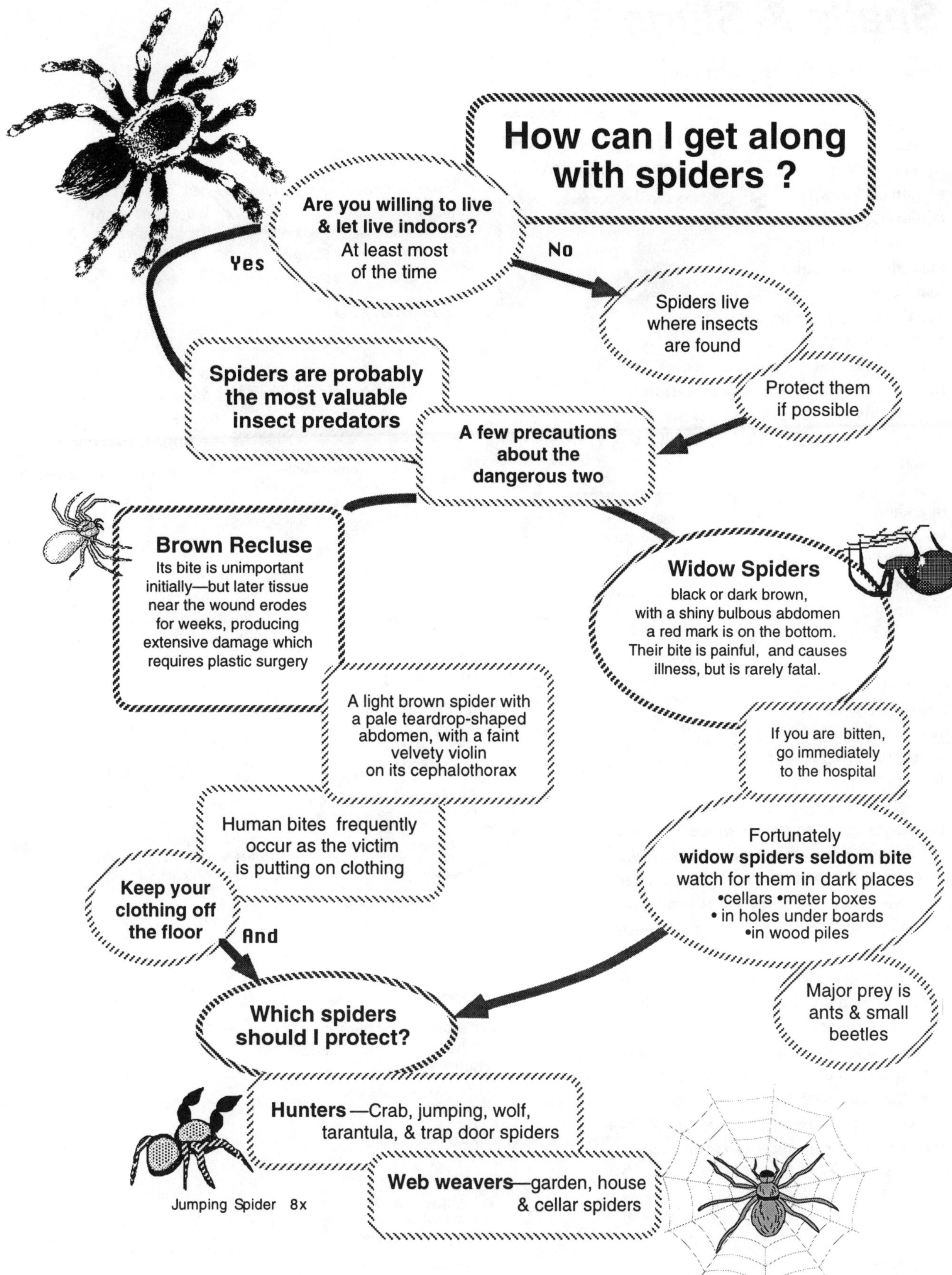
How can I get along with spiders ?
Are you willing to live & let live indoors? At least most of the time
Yes
No
Spiders live where insects are found
Protect them if possible
Spiders are probably the most valuable insect predators
A few precautions about the dangerous two
Brown Recluse
Its bite is unimportant initially—but later tissue near the wound erodes for weeks, producing extensive damage which requires plastic surgery
A light brown spider with a pale teardrop-shaped abdomen, with a faint velvety violin on its cephalothorax
Widow Spiders
black or dark brown, with a shiny bulbous abdomen a red mark is on the bottom. Their bite is painful, and causes illness, but is rarely fatal.
If you are bitten, go immediately to the hospital
Human bites frequently occur as the victim is putting on clothing
Keep your clothing off the floor
And
Fortunately widow spiders seldom bite watch for them in dark places
•cellars •meter boxes
• in holes under boards
•in wood piles
Major prey is ants & small beetles
Which spiders should I protect?
Hunters—Crab, jumping, wolf, tarantula, & trap door spiders
Web weavers—garden, house & cellar spiders
Jumping Spider 8x

Snails & Slugs

Snails and slugs are gastropods—head-footed animals—which belong, along with clams, octopi, and squids, in the group of animals known as *mollusks*. Their main structures are a large muscular, flat, gliding foot-body (which contains internal organs) and a head with two pairs of tentacles which are sensitive to light, touch, and possibly to odors. They eat holes in young green plants, flowers, fallen fruits and decaying leaves with the aid of a rasping file-like radula which serves as teeth.

In addition, snails have a visceral hump encased in a shell. The shell helps protect these moisture-sensitive creatures, and enables them to pass the dry season in exposed places. Slugs, on the other hand, must rest in a moist protected site or risk dehydration.

The major gastropod pests in the U.S. are the imported **brown garden snail,** *Helix aspersa,* in the West and a variety of slugs everywhere, including the **great gray garden slug**, *Limax maximus,* the **greenhouse slug**, *Milax gagates,* and the **gray garden slug**, *Agriolimax reticulatis.* In cold climates at the approach of winter, these burrow up to 10 inches into loose soil. In milder winters snails also rest, but possibly in more exposed sites. In dry, hot seasons, they also stop feeding and seek shelter. In any adverse seasons, the opening of a snail shell is covered by a membrane, the epiphram, which also helps prevent drying.

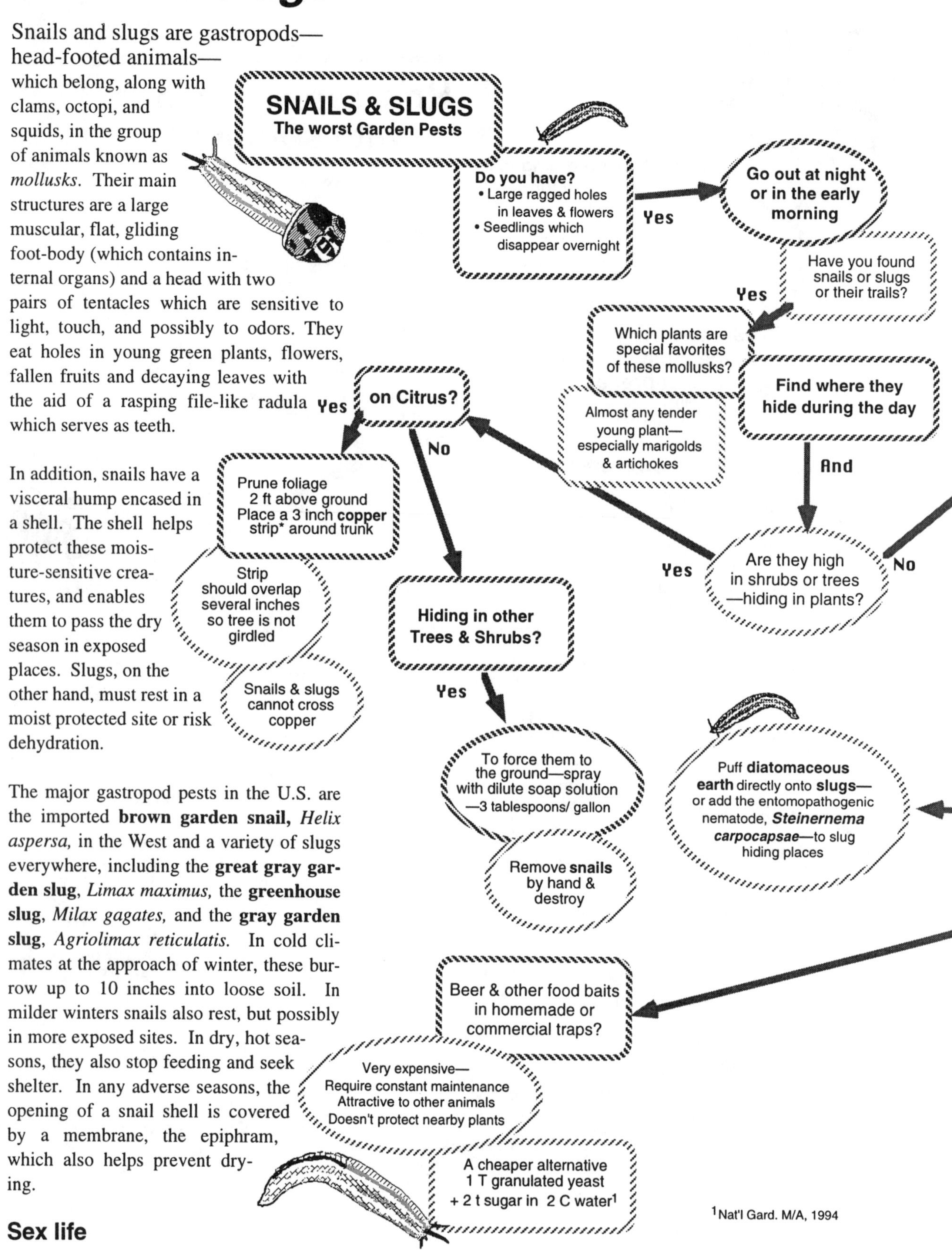

SNAILS & SLUGS
The worst Garden Pests
Do you have?
• Large ragged holes in leaves & flowers
• Seedlings which disappear overnight
Yes
Go out at night or in the early morning
Have you found snails or slugs or their trails?
Yes
Which plants are special favorites of these mollusks?
Almost any tender young plant—especially marigolds & artichokes
Find where they hide during the day
And
Are they high in shrubs or trees —hiding in plants?
Yes
No
on Citrus?
Yes
No
Prune foliage 2 ft above ground Place a 3 inch copper strip* around trunk
Strip should overlap several inches so tree is not girdled
Snails & slugs cannot cross copper
Hiding in other Trees & Shrubs?
Yes
To force them to the ground—spray with dilute soap solution —3 tablespoons/ gallon
Remove snails by hand & destroy
Puff diatomaceous earth directly onto slugs—or add the entomopathogenic nematode, Steinernema carpocapsae—to slug hiding places
Beer & other food baits in homemade or commercial traps?
Very expensive—
Require constant maintenance
Attractive to other animals
Doesn't protect nearby plants
A cheaper alternative
1 T granulated yeast
+ 2 t sugar in 2 C water[1]
[1] Nat'l Gard. M/A, 1994

Sex life

A gastropod's sex life is as different as is

its appearance. All gastropods are *hermaphrodites*—both male and female structures occur in the same animal. When two get together, each serves as both and male and a female a partner. For example, during the mild, moist spring nights when Brown Garden Snail copulations occur, the partners first erect the anterior part of their bodies and slowly and firmly press the foot soles together. Then after each injects a copulatory dart into the other, the actual cross fertilizations occur. As you can imagine all of this takes several hours—at a snail's pace, as it were—and you may find these amorous pairs during your early morning stroll.

Under optimum conditions, a snail lays about 400 eggs per year. Each mating yields about 60 to 80 of the translucent, whitish, tapioca-like progeny. The eggs, which are deposited in a hole in the earth, hatch about 25 days later unless they are consumed by *ants, ground beetles,* or other predators. The delicate young grow very rapidly, maturing in about 6 months. Young snails and slugs are consumed by *rove beetles*, *toads* and *turtles*. Roof rats and some birds relish adult snails. Unfortunately, none of these is enough to protect most gardens from serious damage. You must help control these pests if you wish to have a beautiful garden.

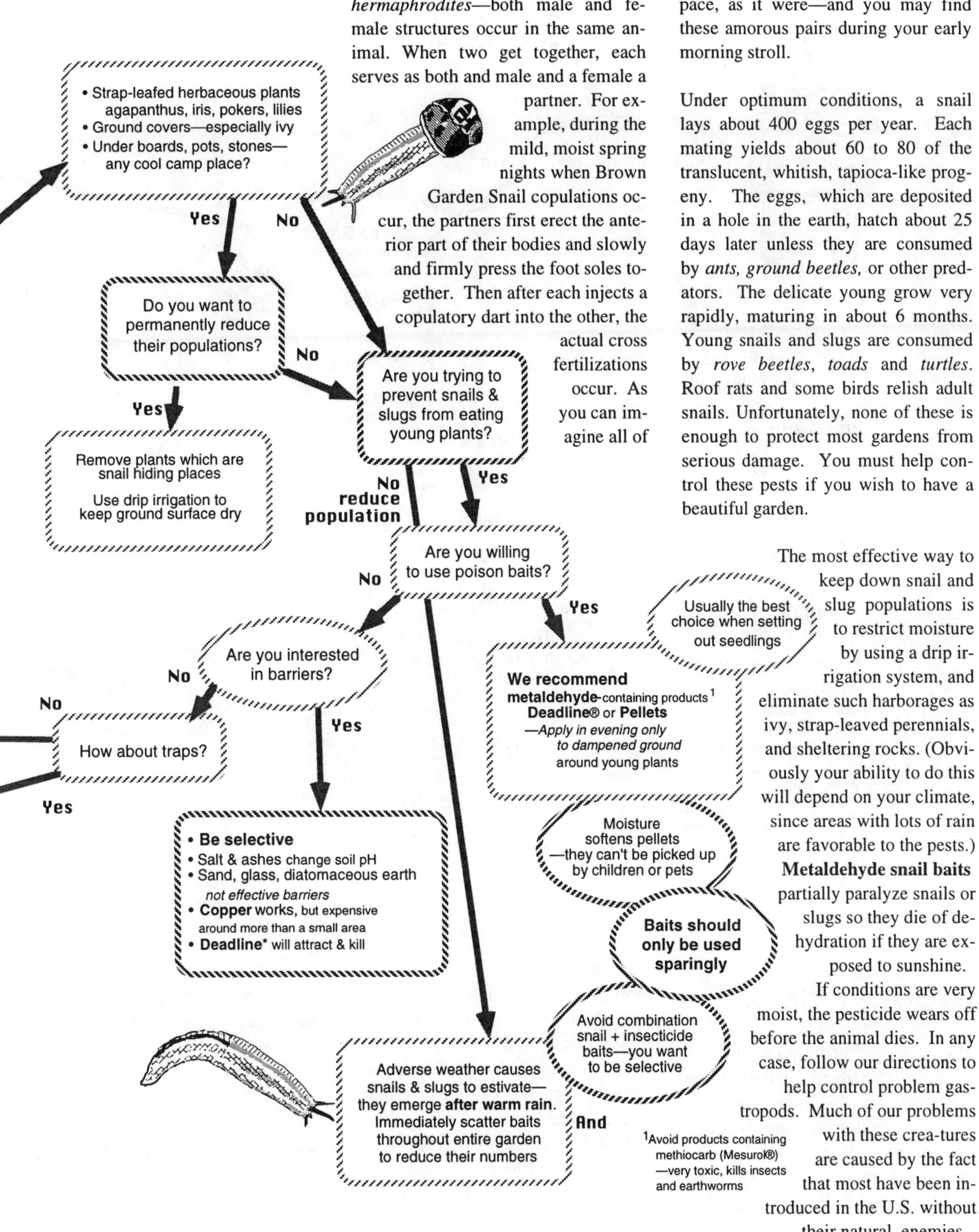

• Strap-leafed herbaceous plants agapanthus, iris, pokers, lilies
• Ground covers—especially ivy
• Under boards, pots, stones—any cool camp place?
Yes
No
Do you want to permanently reduce their populations?
No
Yes
Remove plants which are snail hiding places
Use drip irrigation to keep ground surface dry
Are you trying to prevent snails & slugs from eating young plants?
No reduce population
Yes
Are you willing to use poison baits?
No
Yes
Usually the best choice when setting out seedlings
We recommend metaldehyde-containing products 1 Deadline® or Pellets
—Apply in evening only to dampened ground around young plants
Are you interested in barriers?
No
No
Yes
How about traps?
Yes
• Be selective
• Salt & ashes change soil pH
• Sand, glass, diatomaceous earth not effective barriers
• Copper works, but expensive around more than a small area
• Deadline* will attract & kill
Moisture softens pellets —they can't be picked up by children or pets
Baits should only be used sparingly
Avoid combination snail + insecticide baits—you want to be selective
Adverse weather causes snails & slugs to estivate—they emerge after warm rain. Immediately scatter baits throughout entire garden to reduce their numbers
And
1Avoid products containing methiocarb (Mesurol®) —very toxic, kills insects and earthworms

The most effective way to keep down snail and slug populations is to restrict moisture by using a drip irrigation system, and eliminate such harborages as ivy, strap-leaved perennials, and sheltering rocks. (Obviously your ability to do this will depend on your climate, since areas with lots of rain are favorable to the pests.) **Metaldehyde snail baits** partially paralyze snails or slugs so they die of dehydration if they are exposed to sunshine.

If conditions are very moist, the pesticide wears off before the animal dies. In any case, follow our directions to help control problem gastropods. Much of our problems with these crea-tures are caused by the fact that most have been introduced in the U.S. without their natural enemies.

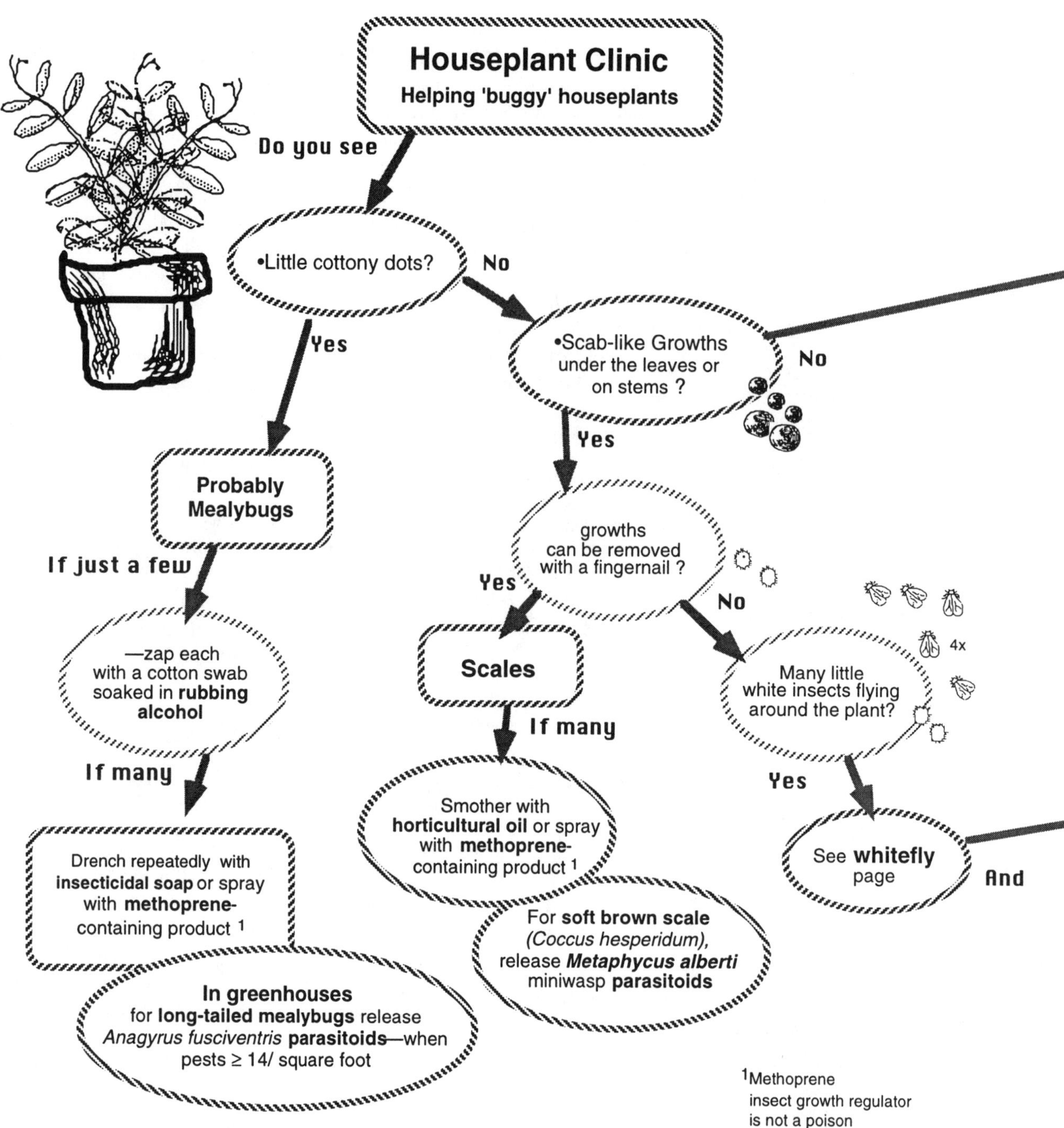
Houseplant Clinic
Helping 'buggy' houseplants
Do you see
•Little cottony dots?
No
Yes
•Scab-like Growths under the leaves or on stems ?
No
Yes
Probably Mealybugs
If just a few
—zap each with a cotton swab soaked in **rubbing alcohol**
If many
Drench repeatedly with **insecticidal soap** or spray with **methoprene-**containing product 1
In greenhouses
for **long-tailed mealybugs** release *Anagyrus fusciventris* **parasitoids**—when pests ≥ 14/ square foot
growths can be removed with a fingernail ?
Yes
No
Scales
If many
Smother with **horticultural oil** or spray with **methoprene-**containing product 1
For **soft brown scale** *(Coccus hesperidum),* release ***Metaphycus alberti*** miniwasp **parasitoids**
Many little white insects flying around the plant?
4x
Yes
See **whitefly** page
And
1Methoprene insect growth regulator is not a poison

Growing Inside

Many of the principles of IPM must be modified in the house or the greenhouse because natural enemies which readily control plant-feeding insects cannot easily get inside. At the same time problem insects or mites slip in on newly purchased plants, or even enter through an open door or window. Pests can also arrive in the planting mix. Improperly sterilized soil can carry the eggs or puparia of fungus gnats, or the spores of damping off disease *(Pythium spp)*. At the same time sterile soil may not contain any of the beneficial microorganisms with potential to counteract soil diseases.[1] Fortunately, some commercial mixes—Progrow* and Mycorimix* have biocontrol microbes added.

---

[1]A custom planting mix contains *Glomus intraradix*, a mycorrhazal fungus that colonizes plant roots & supplies them with nutrients & protects them from pathogenic fungi, e.g. *Fusarium sp.*. Order from Primier Technical Services 800-424-2554.

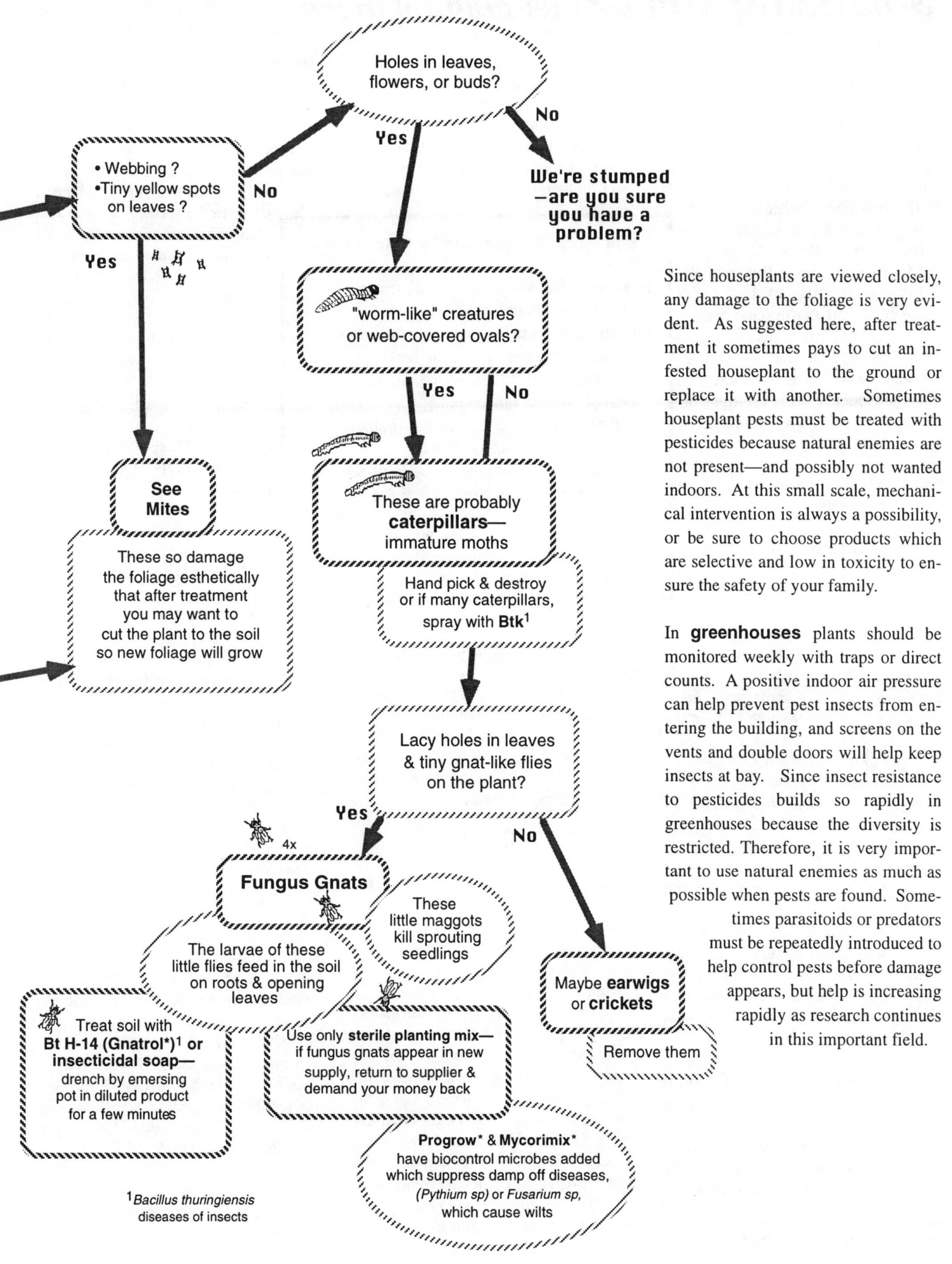

Holes in leaves, flowers, or buds?
No
Yes
We're stumped —are you sure you have a problem?
• Webbing ?
•Tiny yellow spots on leaves ?
No
Yes
"worm-like" creatures or web-covered ovals?
Yes
No
See Mites
These are probably caterpillars— immature moths
These so damage the foliage esthetically that after treatment you may want to cut the plant to the soil so new foliage will grow
Hand pick & destroy or if many caterpillars, spray with Btk1
Lacy holes in leaves & tiny gnat-like flies on the plant?
Yes
No
4x
Fungus Gnats
These little maggots kill sprouting seedlings
The larvae of these little flies feed in the soil on roots & opening leaves
Maybe earwigs or crickets
Remove them
Treat soil with Bt H-14 (Gnatrol*)1 or insecticidal soap— drench by emersing pot in diluted product for a few minutes
Use only sterile planting mix— if fungus gnats appear in new supply, return to supplier & demand your money back
Progrow* & Mycorimix* have biocontrol microbes added which suppress damp off diseases, (Pythium sp) or Fusarium sp, which cause wilts
1Bacillus thuringiensis diseases of insects

Since houseplants are viewed closely, any damage to the foliage is very evident. As suggested here, after treatment it sometimes pays to cut an infested houseplant to the ground or replace it with another. Sometimes houseplant pests must be treated with pesticides because natural enemies are not present—and possibly not wanted indoors. At this small scale, mechanical intervention is always a possibility, or be sure to choose products which are selective and low in toxicity to ensure the safety of your family.

In **greenhouses** plants should be monitored weekly with traps or direct counts. A positive indoor air pressure can help prevent pest insects from entering the building, and screens on the vents and double doors will help keep insects at bay. Since insect resistance to pesticides builds so rapidly in greenhouses because the diversity is restricted. Therefore, it is very important to use natural enemies as much as possible when pests are found. Sometimes parasitoids or predators must be repeatedly introduced to help control pests before damage appears, but help is increasing rapidly as research continues in this important field.

***Solarizing soil** & other cultural tricks*

Hundreds of disease-causing fungi inhabit soil. They range from the *damping-off* that undermines tiny seedlings to the *crown rot* that topples giant trees. You may be familiar with tomatoes which wilt in damp soil, potatoes which decline without apparent cause, trees which lose their leaves in midsummer. Each these problems can testify to the presence of a soil-borne disease.

Until recently unless a disease-resistant variety was available, the average gardener could do little culturally to avoid these plagues. Now soil solarization can help reduce many soil-borne disease pathogens and even reduce, root-feeding nematodes, and weeds.

How solarization works

Solarization is simple, safe, non-chemical, and inexpensive. Basically, a transparent polyethylene tarp placed over moist soil, allows the sun to heat the ground to temperatures that kill most soil pests, and causes favorable physical and chemical changes to the soil itself. After solarization, *plants grow better, even in plots that had no apparent pathogens. Soluble nutrients* such as nitrogen, calcium, magnesium, and potassium *may be more available to plants.* Several beneficial soil microbes—both fungi and bacteria which are disease antagonists—seem either to survive solarization, or recolonize the area soon afterward. *The net result is an increase in plant productivity and a reduction in weeds which last for several years.*

Nevertheless, soil solarization is **not a panacea.** Historically the solarized plot could not be used for a month in mid-summer. The nitrogen-fixing symbiont *Rhizobium* bacteria that enable legumes to utilize atmospheric nitrogen, are killed by the heat. (Not to worry. You can re-introduce these beneficials.) Unfortunately, the problem fungi which cause *charcoal rot of corn* and beans are resist heat. Not surprisingly, regions with high summer temperatures have greater success with solarization than cooler areas. Sunny plots become hotter than those in partial shade. Obviously plots in complete shade cannot be solarized.

Soil Fungi Suppressed by Solarization

Fusarium wilts— melon, onion, tomato, strawberry, ornamentals

Verticillium wilts—eggplant, potato, olive, pistachio, strawberry, tomato, etc.

Root rots and blights—cabbage, onion, peanut, tomato, ornamentals

Seed and seedling diseases—potato, bean, onion, peanut, ormantals

***Phytophthora* root rot**—(crown rot) pine, oak, pleach, walnut & other trees & shrubs

[1] Premier Technical Services, 800-424-2554 formulates custom potting soils containing fungal antagonists.

Solarizing

Usually, July is the best time to begin solarization, but if you live in a hot climate, any time from June to September will do. Unless you plan to treat soil which surrounds a tree or shrub, nothing should be growing in the plot. Traditionally, a *clear plastic tarp* was placed over the area, but *now it is known that a double (or triple?) tarp retains and augments the heat, allowing more rapid treatment and higher temperatures.* You might even explore the idea of spacers between the sheets. An empty closed greenhouse can also be used as a solarization chamber, or bags of dampened planting mix can be placed in the sun to be solarized.

• Prepare the soil as if you were going to plant by removing weeds, debris, and large clods • Sprinkle until moisture penetrates at least two feet. • A day or two later, after soil organisms have been activated by the water, dampen the surface again. • Anchor one or more sheets of *transparent plastic* over the soil by burying the edges in a trench. (If you live in a windy region, or if nights are cool, use 4 mil plastic). • Pull the plastic tightly to prevent the air pockets which retard soil heating. For a large area, several plastic sheets can be glued together with a long lasting heat-resistant glue. Gaps between sheets, reduce effectiveness.

Leave the film in place 4 to 6 weeks (2 to 4 weeks for a double layer) to allow high temperatures to penetrate deeply. Generally, the longer the tarp remains over damp soil, the deeper the heat will penetrate. (In a hot climate, soil two inches below the surface can reach 140° F, and a still lethal 102° at 18 inches). Use a soil thermometer to monitor the process. • After solarization, remove plastic and allow the soil to dry to a workable texture. It can then lie fallow, or be planted immediately.

Many weed seeds are killed by solarization—especially annuals. Perennial weeds are more difficult. However, in one study[1] where Johnsongrass, and Burmudagrass were rototilled and then solarized, growth was controlled. To avoid moving viable weed seeds to the surface, it is best to cultivate solarized soil shallowly. The beneficial effects last about three years. If you wish to avoid weeds for a long period in a permanent border planting, see *Designing Weeds Out of the Urban Landscape,* IPM Practitioner, 15(6), 1993.

Especially in areas with sandy soils, **root-feeding nematodes** can make gardening difficult. In agriculture,

[1] Cal. Agri. 47(1):19-22, 1993

these nematodes have often been controlled with the ozone-depleting toxin methyl bromide and other extremely toxic fumigants such as dichloropropene (Telone*). There are several cultural ways to reduce nematode damage but each of these are either less effective or more time consuming than the chemicals. Orchard soils seem to be most vulnerable since tree roots and their troublesome nematode parasites sometimes penetrate four feet beneath the surface.

Rotation for a few years to unrelated crops can starve out root nematodes, but may not be feasible. A marigold cover crop which is then incorporated into the soil will reduce certain root nematodes and soil fungi such as *Verticillium sp.* for several months. *Incorporation of compost is very important.* A high level of organic matter favors fungal, bacterial, and insect natural enemies of these nematodes. Some soils are even known to be "suppressive," perhaps because they contain high populations of effective natural enemies such as the fungus, *Hirsutella rhossiliensis.* Unfortunately research on predators of root nematodes is in its infancy.

Efforts are being made to formulate *H. rhossiliensis* for use as a soil additive to suppress nematodes.[1] Fungal spores of *Metarhizium sp.* are also helpful soil additives, but the benefits do not persist more than one year. Adequate soil moisture levels are also useful since nematode natural enemies thrive under moist conditions. The chitin-containing, soil amendment, **Clandosan***, seems to stimulate production of an enzyme, chitinase, which destroys nematode eggs, while subsequent chitin breakdown releases ammonia to kill the nematodes themselves.[1]

The Crucifer Trick

To further refine solarization, incorporate residues of cruciferous plants—cabbage, broccoli, cauliflower, mustard, etc. Sulfur-containing volatile compounds—alyl isothiocyanate and ammonia from decomposing vegetation, when added to the heat from solarization enhances fungus-killing effects—and produces antifeedant activity against mealworms—which last for 6 months. Watch out though. This also prevents tomato growth.

Obtain discarded crucifers in the market (1/3 pound per square foot of garden space), or chop up a cruciferous cover crop. Dry the vegetables in the sun on a plastic sheet for 10 days. Incorporate into the top few inches of soil. Proceed with solarization

Green manures

Green manures (cover crops) are plants which are left on the surface or incorporated into the soil. They can • Improve fertility • Help prevent erosion • Suppress weeds • Move nutrients upward in the soil • Increase nutrient availability • Add nitrogen (legumes) • Conserve moisture and fertility by capturing and holding nutrients in the upper layers of the soil.

Managing green manures

Green manures are managed in three ways—*overwinter crops, main crops,* and *underseeded* cover crops. **Overwinter crops** are planted in fall and grow all winter or until winter killed. Winter rye, oats, annual ryegrass, hairy vetch are good choices. In orchards, for example, these grow during the period when uptake of nitrogen by trees is at a minimum and leaching from rainfall may be greatest. The legume cover crops capture the greatest amount of nitrogen. They can be turned into the soil in spring, or composted separately and returned to the bed when finished. Nonlegumes take longer to decay in soil since the microorganisms of decay must scavenge nitrogen from the soil to breakdown carbon-rich plants. Legumes which contain a higher nitrogen-carbon ratio, decay rapidly, providing nitrogen to help decay carbon-rich plants, and later to the crop at a period when its most needed.

Main crop cover crops occupy the garden during the growing season in place of a normal crop. They also work well in orchards. Buckwheat, alfalfa, fava and soy beans, and clovers are good choices. The crucifer—Juniper Rape *(Brassica napus)* when incorporated into soil during a couple of seasons, can suppress Columbia root-knot nematodes of potatoes.[2] Proprietary mixes of crops which help sustain beneficial insects are also available.[3]

Undersowing or overseeding is the practice of growing a green manure crop along with the main crop—something like planting desirable weeds between the rows. Like weeds, covercrops can overwhelm young crops if they both start at the same time. In overseeding, the crop is kept weed free for 4-6 weeks before the green manure is sown. Clovers, hairy vetch, and soybeans are good choices for undersowing because they are low growing, and they fix nitrogen. To plant, drill in the seeds into damp soil between the main crop rows. In this situation, "sweet corn undersown to soybeans, almost totally inhibits potato-scab organisms in the soil."[4,5]

---

1 IPM Pract. 15(2):15-16, 1994

2 Plant Disease 77:42-46. 1993

3 Agri. Ecosys. Environ. 50:11-28, 1994

4 Mother Earth N. S/O, 1989
Phytopathol. 28:289-295, 1988

5 Phytopathol. 33:899-905, 1993.

Controlling insects with Entomopathogenic (beneficial) Nematodes

If you have ever found holes in your root vegetables, dead spots in your lawn, tiny notches around leaves of flower petals, or had your lawn trashed by grub-feeding raccoons you should investigate entomopathogenic nematodes. No doubt you are already familiar with roundworms—nematodes that chew on plant roots. Not all nematodes live this way. We are talking here about nematodes which are insect pathogens, feeding on insects which live at least part of their lives in the soil.

Insect Parasitoids

At first glance entomopathogenic nematodes (EPNemes) seem almost too good to be true. These little worms seek out and destroy insects that nibble plant roots, and leave no toxic residues. EPNemes hone in on insect excretory products, and enter insect prey through natural openings. Inside the body cavity they release their private ***Xenorhabdus sp.*** bacteria. (Between 20 and 250 of these symbiotic bacteria are carried along by each juvenile nematode). *Xenorhabdus* bacteria have been found only in EPNemes and their infected insect hosts.

The bacteria multiply rapidly in the infected insect, causing septicemia and death within two or three days. The nematodes complete two generations while feeding on the bacteria and the tissues of the dead host. Eventually, when all nutrients are depleted, infective stage juvenile EPNemes of the second generation emerge from the cadaver to search for another host. At optimum temperature and moisture—such as in a lawn in summer—these generations are completed in 6-18 days.

If no prey is available, or moisture and/or temperature is inappropriate, juvenile EPNemes either die or enter a dehydrated resting stage. If dryish soil is again watered, resting juveniles rehydrate and become infective again. Alternately, if suitable hosts are available in warm moist soil—as in sod infested with Japanese beetle larvae—EPNemes will continue to recycle, and may even multiply from year to year. In most situations, however, EPNemes should be reapplied annually at a time when target pests are active in the soil.

Ideal Insecticide?

EPNemes have many of the characteristics of an "ideal insecticide". They're safe to use. In tests where enormous numbers were injected into, or fed to test animals, they caused no harm. Tests for dermal and eye irritation were also negative. And they're selective. These nematodes effect only insects, so other soil dwelling creatures such as *earthworms are not harmed.*

Nonetheless a EPNemes product is not your normal "spray". Like all nematodes, *EPNemes require warmth and moisture.* They die quickly if you spray them on dry, sunny foliage, even though they've occasionally been effective on artichoke pests in foggy areas. They can be applied in water or even sprayed on the soil using a conventional hose-end sprayer. (Or, because they can clog small holes, we've found it best to pour them from a watering can which is agitated continuously). Usually they're watered onto sod, mixed into moist soil near plants, or distributed along the row when seeds are planted. *For best results soil must be warm (60-82° F) and moisture ample.*

You'll apply about 9000 EPNemes per foot of row, or 35,000 around each transplant, to control cutworms, beetle larvae, wire worms or others of their ilk. You may wonder whether you really need such enormous numbers? Indeed you do. These are the experimentally determined concentrations needed to give good soil insect control. After all, these tiny worms cannot crawl very far, and they have their own soil-borne enemies—bacterial and fungal pathogens—to contend with. You need to allow for some losses.

Available products

Since the EPNemes multiply naturally only in soil-dwelling insects, it has taken several years to develop *artificial food* to raise them in the large quantities needed for commercial marketing. In addition, since the juvenile worms are potentially very fragile, methods had to be developed to protect them during transit and storage. Currently most are shipped stabilized on amorphous clay or other solid substrate. These EPNeme products can be stored in the refrigerator for about 6 months, but it's best to used them as soon as possible. *Steinernema carpocapsae (Neoaplectana carpocapsae)* and *Heterorhabditis bacteriophora,* are the commonly available species. *H. bacteriophora* has shown superior host-seeking abilities, and tends to move deeper into the soil than *S. carpocapsae* strains, but it is more difficult to culture on artificial media and is shorter lived in storage, so may be more expensive and less available. *(S. carpocapsae* is active at slightly lower temperatures than *H. bacteriophora.* Other strains and species are being tested, so keep your options open. Some brand names of EPNemes are Biosafe*, Bioflea*, Bioquest*. These excellent predators may not be available in the local supermarket or nursery. You may have to call producers—BioLogic, Biosys, HydroGardens, Nematec, or Praxis—to find a local supplier, or order by mail from catalog suppliers. We've found Bioflea* in some pet stores for use on flea larvae growing in the lawn.

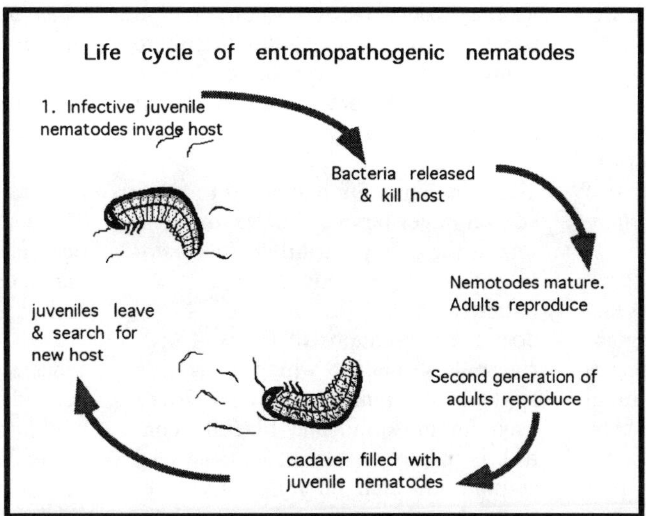
Life cycle of entomopathogenic nematodes
1. Infective juvenile nematodes invade host
Bacteria released & kill host
Nemotodes mature. Adults reproduce
Second generation of adults reproduce
cadaver filled with juvenile nematodes
juveniles leave & search for new host

How to use EPNemes

Though infective juvenile EPNemes live naturally in damp soil, numbers are seldom sufficient for natural control. However, *when you apply a product containing EPNemes to warm damp soil, pest insect control can be superior to that from toxic pesticides—and certainly they're safer to you and the environment.* To use the EPNemes, add tepid water as directed and when the product disperses in the water, use the product promptly—it contains fragile living worms after all—and cannot be stored after water is added. Be sure to agitate gently as you pour evenly from a sprinkling can containing large holes. The worms tend to settle to the bottom.

If you're **planting** seeds of vegetables such as carrots, beets, or onions, or pieces of potato, you can add nematodes to the planting water, or side-dress with EPNemes just as the seedlings emerge. Similarly, EPNemes can be applied near the roots of perennial plants at a season when soil-borne larvae are active—late spring and early fall for **black vine weevil** larvae. Use a good insect book, or consult your farm advisor to determine when underground pests are active in your garden. After treatment, maintain even soil moisture for at least a few weeks to sustain the EPNemes .

To control lawn pests—including flea larvae, white grubs,[1] sod webworms, and cinchbugs

- Remove thatch
- Apply 1 inch water 24 hours before treatment so soil insects move upward (they move downward as the soil dries).
- Make sure that soil temperature is ≥ 55° F for *Steinernema glaseri* [2] or ≥ 60° F for *Heterohabditis bacteriophora.* (I you use more than one nematode species, you should be able to control several kinds of pests). Apply 20 million nematodes per 1000 square feet.
- After treatment, water lightly every other day for 2 weeks to allow the infective juveniles to penetrate the turf and reach the pests. If you've had trouble with **slugs** in harborages, apply *Stienernema carpocapsae* to these shelters.

If you have a history of **borers** in your fruit trees, search the trunks as described on borer page for frass-filled holes.[3] Clean out the holes, and push in tiny (1/2" by 1/2") sponges which have been saturated with infective EPNemes. The nematodes will move into the hole and attack the borer. The sponge

- Maintains the high humidity needed by the worms
- Marks which holes have been treated
- Keeps the EPNeme suspension from leaking out of the hole.

An eye dropper or garden syringe can be used in early spring to squirt EPNemes into the terminal whirl of corn plants to control **armyworms**, or, into the tips of silking corn ears to zap newly-hatched **corn ear worms** *(Heliothis zea). They are not effective* on **squash vine borers**, but Bt can be injected to eliminate these vine borers. All and all these beneficial entomopathogenic nematodes represent an excellent new biological control tool for control of pest insects.

[1] White grubs are larvae of Japanese & other scarab beetles

[2] Recommended for white grub control

[3] Frass = insect feces

Using **Diseases** *for ecological control*

If you imagine an ideal pesticide, what would it be like? Obviously non-toxic to people, natural enemies, and the environment, but effective against pests. It would act rapidly, persist just long enough to do the job, and then disappear. *Is there such a product? Maybe—*

Insects—even diseases—have diseases of their own. Plant-feeding insects acquire most of their diseases from foods. Damp weather fungi may penetrate the bodies of others. Obviously we might be able to use insect diseases to augment our pest control efforts.

Bacterial diseases

Some people suggest that we collect groups of plant-feeding insects, grind them in a blender, and use the extracts as a spray. Such practices are now illegal because these extractions may contain harmful substances such as bacterial *exotoxins.*

Of the over 100 kinds of bacteria recovered from insects, only a few are successfully mass produced on artificial foods and marketed for insect control. By law, none of these strains can produce exotoxins. The most versatile bacterium is ***Bacillus thuringiensis***, or **Bt**. Each available Bt strain is selective, affecting a single insect order—caterpillars, or mosquito or beetle larvae—but is widely toxic to juveniles within that order.

Bts have no contact activity, so insects are unaffected unless they consume its spores. Thus, they are safe for natural enemies. Bt products are not toxic when eaten by mammals, birds, amphibians, or fish—though some *inert ingredients in* Bt products may be a problem. Even though Bts are harmless to "higher" animals that eat them, they might be a problem if *injected* into the body or squirted directly into the eye. Allergic individuals may react adversely to *any* foreign protein. This demonstrates that there is no free lunch. Even insect disease may represent some minimal risk if used inappropriately.

These products *are* damaging to related non-target larvae. For example, in forests the caterpillar-killer, *Bt kurstoki,* wipes out populations of butterfly larvae just as it does the populations of forest caterpillars against which it is applied. Fortunately, *Bt isreaelensis* used for mosquito and blackfly control, is unlikely to affect its beneficial syrphid and tachinid fly relatives because they do not live in water. However, *Bt san diego* and its twin, *Bt tenebrionis* applied to control Colorado Potato and Elm Leaf Beetles, could potentially affect predatory beetle larvae if they were to consume pollens on sprayed plants. The Diamondback and Greater Wax moths are susceptible to *Bt aizawai.* New Bt strains suppress plant-feeding nematode, ant, and corn rootworm larvae.

***Bacillus thuringiensis* Products**

Bt Subspecies	Target insect	Products
israelensis	mosquitoes, blackflies	Teknar, Bactimos, Vectobac, Gnatrol
kurstoki	caterpillars	Javelin, Dipel, Attack, Biobit, Cutlass, etc.
tenebrionis san diego	beetles	Trident, M-one M-Track, Novodor
aizawai	wax moth diamondback moth	Certan Florbac, Centari

How Bts work?

When an insect eats food treated with Bt, it consumes bacterial spores containing a crystalline *endotoxin.* These crystals dissolve in the *alkaline insect gut* —but not in the acids found in the stomachs of higher animals. Digestive enzymes then transform this toxin into another chemical which binds to the gut lining of the pest. *The selectivity of each Bt is dependent on this selective gut -binding ability.*

After binding, the gut is immediately paralyzed, and the larva stops feeding. Soon crop contents leak into the hemocoel[1] through holes in the gut wall. The insect soon dies from a lethal septicemia as the bacteria multiply. Eventually, each dead insect will contain infective Bt spores.

Since susceptibility to a particular Bt depends on gut binding, resistance could appear if the endotoxin no longer binds to the target gut. This occurred after **diamondback moth** caterpillars were repeatedly sprayed with Btk. Resistance has also been selected in laboratory strains of **Indian meal moth**. One strategy to help prevent resistance would be to use mixtures of several Bt strains, but this is expensive. Recently it was discovered that Bt's effectiveness depends in part on the toxic content of the plants themselves. A tannin-rich extract mixed with Bt increases its effectiveness.[2]

Another bacteria, ***Bacillus populiae,*** can provide long term control of soil-dwelling grubs of **Japanese** and other soil-dwelling scarab beetles by causing **milky spore disease**. *B. populiae* spores spread slowly from diseased larvae to healthy larva, to eventually provide permanent control in pastures and lawns. (Adults may still fly in to damage your fruits). ***Bacillus sphaericus*** synthesizes crystal proteins that are toxic to mosquito larvae after they dissolve in the gut. Unlike crystals of *B.t. israelensis, B. sphaericus'* crystals persist in water for a long time. So far they kill the pesticide-resistant larvae of *Anopheles gambiae*—the principal vector (carrier) of malaria—and *Culex quinquefasciatus*, an encephalitis vector which are little affected by Bti. These toxic proteins do *not* harm other creatures that may consume them. A Bs product is in the works.

---

[1] The open blood system which surrounds the organs of insects—heart, gut, malphigian tubules, & reproductive organs.

[2] J Econ Entomol 88:270-277, 1995.

Advantages & disadvantages

Since spores of commercial *Bacillus* strains have a long shelf life, they are readily formulated for use in sprays. Nonetheless, a proper Bt application for caterpillar control requires extra know-how. *Timing is critical.* • If possible, apply these sprays just before the eggs hatch, or when the larvae are very small • Agitate the tank to keep spore particles in suspension • Evenly coat the *lower leaf surfaces* where young insects hang out. • Do not wet the leaves enough to cause run off. • Infected larvae will stop feeding before the plant can be seriously damaged • Spray toward evening so infective particles will be consumed before they can be degraded by ultraviolet rays. (M-cap*, which contains the crystal, but not the spores, encased in killed *Pseudomonas* bacteria, may persist longer). • A feeding stimulant, such as **Entice***, should increase Bt consumption.

One or another insect-specific bacteria can control many pests of agriculture, forestry, and medicine. They should be a great success—being selective, safe, biodegradable. *If they would only automatically move to new growth and affect more kinds of insects.*

Research is moving in that direction. Products such as Foil* contain both the Bt for caterpillars and the Bt for some beetles. The genes for some Bt crystals have been inserted into some crop plants. These plants kill susceptible insects that eat them *Doesn't that sound great ?* Wait! Every plant we know that contains toxins is host to resistant insect feeders. *Experience with pesticides suggests that insect resistance to toxins is rapidly selected.* The Bt situation is serious. If, in the future most crop plants contain the same few Bt toxins, resistant pests will be rapidly selected. *We will have lost the almost perfect insecticides.*

Baculoviruses

Over 500 viruses have been isolated from insects and mites. Among these, the nuclear polyhedrosis viruses (NPV) are unique to insects. A number of viruses are used to control insects overseas, but currently in North America, only government scientists use products based on these diseases. The U.S. Forest Service applies NPVs to control gypsy moth and Douglas-fir tussock moth. The codling moth NPV is registered by the University of California at Berkeley, but the product is little used by growers because the virus kills so slowly that treated apples are blemished by "stings". Heliothis NPV—registered as Eclar*—is not available at present.

Other Microbial Pesticides

Name	Target pests	Products
Bacillus popilliae	scarab beetle larvae	Doom, Milky Spore
Agrobacterium radiobacter	crown gall disease	Galltrol-A, Gallex
Pseudomonas fluorescens	*Pythium, Rhizoctonia*	
Heliothis NPV	*Heliothis sp.*	Elcar
Tussock moth NPV	Douglas fir tussock moth larvae	
Gypsy moth NPV	Gypsy moth larvae	
Pine sawfly NPV	Pine sawfly larvae	
Hirsutella thompsonii	Citrus rust mite	
Trichoderma harzianum	Wood rot	Binab T
T. polysporium	Wood rot	

Most NPVs degrade readily in sunshine, but their major drawbacks are high cost of production and slow speed of kill. In order to overcome the slowness, efforts are being made to insert genes for toxic proteins into these viruses. Most interest is currently directed at *Autographa californica* and *Anagraplha falcifera* NPVs because these viruses kill more than 30 species of moth caterpillars.

One advantage of NPVs may be their ability to be distributed by other animals. For example, the NPV of the velvet bean caterpillar is spread by predatory insects and birds to other leaves where caterpillar feeders may consume them. Since they are very selective, they offer no risk to non-target animals

Fungal diseases

Few insect fungal diseases are available commerically, possibly because most affect several different *orders* of insects. For example, the convergent ladybird beetle is sensitive to 4 of 5 candidate disease fungi.[1] Unfortunately, most insect disease fungi are very sensitive to climactic conditions—requiring high humidity, and are rapidly degraded by UV light. In addition, these fungal spores frequently trigger allergic reactions in sensitive individuals.

In spite of this, the insect fungus *Beauveria bassiana*—may soon be available. Another fungus, *Metarhizium anisopliae,* is the active ingredient in a bait station for cockroach and fly control. *Vericillium lecanii* may be available soon to control whiteflies, aphids, and thrips. Because of their environmental sensitivity, damp soil may be the best place to use insect fungi, yet no products for fungal control of soil-borne insects are currently anticipated.

A few insect fungi are selective. The alien gypsy moth, *Lymantria dispar,* now resident of eastern North America is attacked by a fungal pathogen, *Entomophaga maimaiga.* This disease, which is native to Japan, seems to have been accidentally introduced into this hemisphere.[2] It is specific to Gypsy Moth, and is able to spread rapidly on its own.

Diseases of diseases

Fungi and bacteria are candidates to inhibit plant diseases. Of these, *Gliocladium roseum,* which inhibits several diseases including the grey mold, *Botyritis cinerea,* may be available soon. *Sporothrix flocculosa* is antagonistic to powdery mildew of roses.[3]

[1] Environ Entomol 23:1960-1962, 1994. [2] Amer Entomol 41:31-42, 1995. [3]Plant Dis. 78:420-424, 1994.

Other possible insect predators

Perhaps you've wondered why we've not classified birds or other animals as pest control agents. Here's what we know.

Do birds control insects?

We all know that songbirds eat insects at least part of the time—when they are feeding nestlings, for example. And some birds—swallows, swifts, warblers—eat only insects. Obviously birds eat other things too; including seeds, fruits, leaves, reptiles, amphibians, worms, mice, other birds, and fish.

We also know that in spite of the efforts of seed-eating birds, weeds are always with us. Likewise fish-eating birds never consume all the fish. Similarly, pest insects keep ahead of insect-eating birds—and that's not enough. *After all, we demand perfect fruits and vegetables.*

So even though birds can not do it all—are not even the most important insect control agents —it can be advantageous to provide some of the things birds need. If you want to encourage insect-eating birds, you can not keep cats, unless you keep your cats indoors. Cats are a serious threat to songbirds—killing about half of the young birds fledged each year. To protect birds, you should avoid toxic insecticides, and never use spray trees or shrubs which contain bird nests.

Encouraging birds

• Provide a birdbath • Plant native trees and shrubs that produce berries or blossoms, and encourage your neighbors to do the same • Keep old snags and large dead limbs unless they threaten structures or pathways. They provide house sites and food for woodpeckers and other hole-nesting birds. • You may want to build or purchase 4 x 4 x 10 inch bird houses with a 1 inch hole, 2 inches below the top. A side door should provide access so you can clean the box at the end of the nesting season. Place houses on tree trunks at least 10 feet high •

If you live in a rural area, you can larger houses for hawks and owls to help control the rodents on your land. In the suburbs you can • Fill squirrel-proof feeders with the raw peanuts, oil seeds, raisins, or suet that are relished by insect eating birds. • Support conservation organizations which work to protect natural habitats throughout the world. Migratory birds are everywhere threatened by habitat destruction.

Bats harvest insects & pollinate flowers

Birds are not the only insect control agents. Night flying insects are prey for bats. You may have thought of bats as pests, but think again. Whereas birds hunt caterpillars and other soft insects for their young, bats are important pest beetle and moth eaters. In one summer the 150 little brown bats in a typical nursery colony can eat ≈38,000 cucumber beetles, 16,000 June bugs, 19,000 stinkbugs, and 50,000 leafhoppers.[1]

Other bats are important pollinators of fruiting plants, and tropical fruit bats are a major factor in dispersing the seeds of fruiting trees. To encourage bats you can install a couple of large bat houses on the sunny east or south face of your house or other high structure. Bats are likely to find it in the spring when they return after migration. Bat houses should be in the sun for at least four hours a day unless you live in a very hot climate. Bats like a very warm situation to raise their young—75-95° F. Lack of safe roosting space seems to be a critical factor in a major reduction of bat numbers worldwide.

You may have heard that bats present a threat of rabies. Bats *can* acquire rabies, but rabies incidence in bats is no greater than that in other mammals, and they would not bite you unless you pick up a sick one. Never handle bats without gloves. If you find bats in your attic they should be excluded to protect the sanitation of your house. You can install a substitute bat house nearby to which they can move. Never try to move a nursery colony when babies are present. Wait until the bats leave in fall and then block the entrance so they can't enter next year. The entrance can be very small because bats can enter a tiny crack. Any such cracks should be plugged with a tough plastic caulk. *Never use pesticides in a effort to remove bats.* "Bat pesticides" are a long term hazard to you, and a threat to the survival of these valuable creatures.

Pay attention to what happens to the caves and abandoned mines in your area. Though some bats migrate south in winter, others hibernate in large underground cavities which maintain a constant cool temperature through the winter. Efforts to "cleanup" and close caves and mines can mean the death of millions of bats. If a cave has become an attractive nuisance, the best solution may be to install a special barred gate which keeps people out, but allows bats to enter. Good bat hibernation sites are far and few between.

Bat Conservation International, P.O. Box 162603, Austin, TX 78716-2603 can provide more information about the role of bats worldwide.

---

[1] Bats 11(1):1993

Indoor Pests

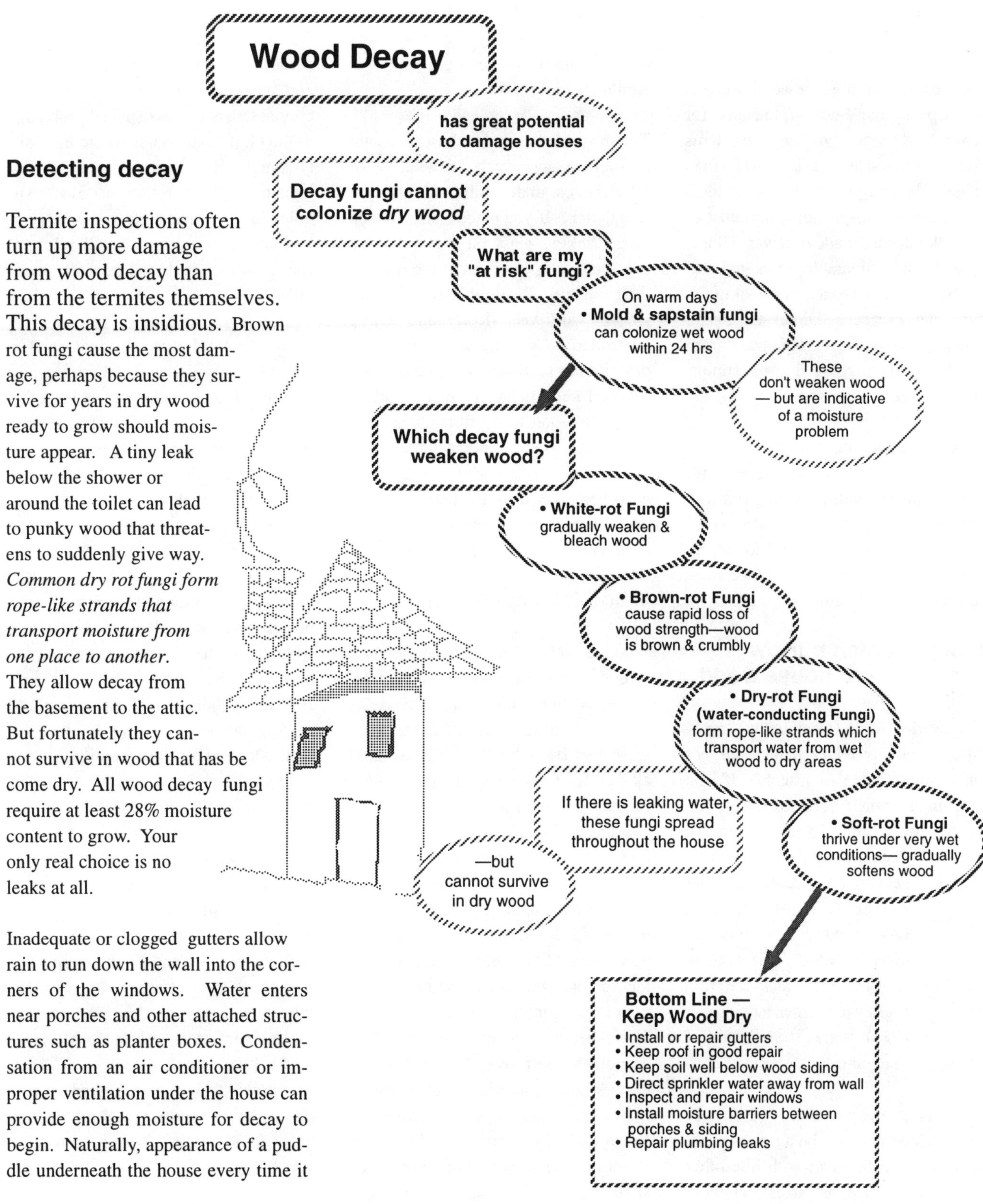

Wood Decay
has great potential to damage houses
Decay fungi cannot colonize *dry wood*
What are my "at risk" fungi?
On warm days
• Mold & sapstain fungi can colonize wet wood within 24 hrs
These don't weaken wood — but are indicative of a moisture problem
Which decay fungi weaken wood?
• White-rot Fungi gradually weaken & bleach wood
• Brown-rot Fungi cause rapid loss of wood strength—wood is brown & crumbly
• Dry-rot Fungi (water-conducting Fungi) form rope-like strands which transport water from wet wood to dry areas
If there is leaking water, these fungi spread throughout the house
—but cannot survive in dry wood
• Soft-rot Fungi thrive under very wet conditions— gradually softens wood
Bottom Line — Keep Wood Dry
• Install or repair gutters
• Keep roof in good repair
• Keep soil well below wood siding
• Direct sprinkler water away from wall
• Inspect and repair windows
• Install moisture barriers between porches & siding
• Repair plumbing leaks

Detecting decay

Termite inspections often turn up more damage from wood decay than from the termites themselves. This decay is insidious. Brown rot fungi cause the most damage, perhaps because they survive for years in dry wood ready to grow should moisture appear. A tiny leak below the shower or around the toilet can lead to punky wood that threatens to suddenly give way. *Common dry rot fungi form rope-like strands that transport moisture from one place to another.* They allow decay from the basement to the attic. But fortunately they cannot survive in wood that has be come dry. All wood decay fungi require at least 28% moisture content to grow. Your only real choice is no leaks at all.

Inadequate or clogged gutters allow rain to run down the wall into the corners of the windows. Water enters near porches and other attached structures such as planter boxes. Condensation from an air conditioner or improper ventilation under the house can provide enough moisture for decay to begin. Naturally, appearance of a puddle underneath the house every time it rains, or damp dirt piled up against the wood siding are a sure way to trouble. These can even promote decay from soft rot fungi.

The best way to prevent wood decay is to inspect your house frequently for leaks and repair of any problems found—obviously easier said than done. Twice a year would be an ideal frequency for inspections, but most of us look once a decade or never. Closely check all vulnerable joints and crevices. Install screened vents so moisture can escape. Direct the water which flows off the roof away from the house by digging ditches, sumps, or dry creeks if necessary.

Seal all wood-concrete interfaces to prevent standing water. Check for dark stains beneath plumbing fixtures, and poke the wood with a sharp pick to search for rot. If decay is found, replace the damaged area and take steps to prevent moisture in the future.

Insects which burrow into house wood

Carpenter Ants *(Camponotus spp.)*
Moist wood provides habitat for not only fungi, but also insects. If you live in a moist, forested area, you damp house may shelter a relative giant among insects, the carpenter ant. Carpenter ant workers can be 1/2 inch long, while other ants are much smaller. Termites can be this size, but they lack the thin waist, the elbowed antennae, and a bump which protrudes from the tip of the waist of all ants.

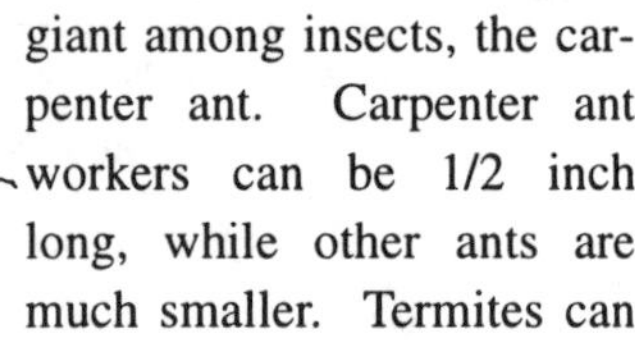

A few carpenter ants that come searching for food may not be a serous problem, and can be dealt with like other indoor ants. (See ant pages). However, winged reproductives or frequent carpenter ant trails may indicated that there is a nest in the house. Since such nests are hollowed out of the wood, they eventually may cause serious structural weakening. But this would take a very long time.

The most likely site for these nests are in moist places such as window or door frames, under stairs, or along the foundation. If you place a stethoscope or a drinking glass on the wall, you can hear carpenter ants moving in their tunnels. Remember that carpenter ants work very slowly, and can be controlled by keeping wood structures dry. Repair sections which have wood rot, and keep them dry in the future. Keep firewood away from the house. Puff boric acid or other borate into vulnerable wall voids. Keep tree branches away from the house. Methods which eliminate termites will also eliminate nesting carpenter ants.

Wood-boring beetles

Wood is always subject to the feeding of one or another wood-boring beetle. Those beetles whose larvae feed directly beneath the bark of living trees are called **bark beetles**. These usually prefer trees stressed by climactic factors. They are not a problem inside buildings, though newly felled trees may still contain these larvae.

Other beetles attack the heartwood of newly killed trees. If they survive the processing of the lumber, they may be incorporated into the home or the furniture and continue to develop there. These beetles also enter in firewood. The **old-house borer** *(Hylotrupes bajulus)* attacks sapwood or seasoned softwoods. **Powderpost beetles** *(Lyctus spp.)* feed on hardwoods in houses if they have a moisture content of about 12%. Old house borers spend 2 o 10 years in the larval stage. Powderpost beetles complete development in one to three years.

Adults of both beetles emerge in spring and summer. They soon mate and again lay eggs in wood cracks and crevices. They cause special problems in the Gulf Coast states where humidity is high. Borer presence may be recognized by the round or oval exit holes in the wood surface which give it a shot hole effect. Small piles of fine sawdust are found beneath these holes.

In the West, **false powderpost beetles** may attack hardwoods. The most notorious of these, the leadcable borer *(Scobicia declivis)*, attacks newly painted houses, corks in bottles containing alcoholic beverages or wine casks. The larval tunnels can mine a 2 foot long gallery just beneath the surface during an 8 month growing period. Repeated breeding by leadcable borers can completely riddle hardwood with larval tunnels. The adults appear to be attracted by heat, and sometimes bore into lead or asphalt roofing materials perhaps because of their odor and high temperature.

Some books suggest that false powderpost beetles can be killed in a freezer, but we did not kill them when we placed a piece of furniture at 0°F for 2 weeks. The first two borer groups can be controlled by finishing the wood with a good sealer. Even fumigation is not always effective against the false powderpost beetles. Try heating furniture infested with leadcable borers to 130°F for ≥ 45 minutes. This temperature might be achieved by enclosing the furniture in a double plastic bag and placing it in the sunshine on a hot day.

Terrifying termites

Most of us shudder if we hear our home is infested with termites. We may even have visions of the building collapsing! And no wonder. These little "dead-wood processors" are the most important indoor insects. Luckily you may be able to avoid termites if you adopt a few preventive measures.

Termites and their fungal allies are major recyclers of dead wood, returning wood nutrients to the soil. They are also relished by woodpeckers and other bark-gleaning birds. Several mammals, including bears, are looking for termites when they tear open rotten logs. Obviously when we use wood to build our homes, we can expect termites to come along to do their job. Three major termite lifestyles impact wooden houses.

Termite colony lifestyle

Termites are sometimes called "white ants". They *do resemble* ants, and, like ants they live in colonies. Unlike ants, however, they live hidden lives—within the protection of the wood which serves as both shelter and dinner. Protozoa (single-celled animals) inside their digestive system secrete enzymes which digest cellulose, enabling termites to utilize wood nutrients. Without these protozoa, termites would die.

The whitish female worker termites are the offspring of one large mother—a virtual egg-laying machine. She mates only once to get the process going. Once a year each colony produces dark-colored, winged male and female reproductives which swarm out synchronously to mate and start their own nests in suitable dead wood.

Setting up housekeeping

Damp forests (or damp houses) are suitable for **damp wood termites** *(Zootermopisis sp.)*. Since these large—inch-long—termites *require* ample moisture, dry soil and dry timbers will keep them at bay.

The 1/3 inch long **subterranean termites** *(Reticulitermes sp.)* thrive at the soil-wood interface. Since their nests are underground, they tunnel primarily into wood scraps or untreated wooden posts which directly contact the ground. Subterranean termites also move along crevices or construct clay tubes to reach above-ground wood. If you maintain wood-free dry soil beneath your house, keep garden soil at least 6 inches away from wood siding, and check the foundation annually to detect and destroy termite transport tubes, subterranean termites will be unable to colonize.

Another subterranean termite, the **Formosan termite**, *Coptotermes formosanus,* has slipped into Hawaii and warm, moist coastal areas of continental U.S. Their colonies are much larger than those of our native subterranean termites—up to 7 million foragers in a colony—so they pose an unbelievable threat. In areas where these have colonized, it is especially appropriate to add a 20 inch sand barrier between native soil and your house foundation. (Use only sand with 1.7-2.4 mm particle size). Sand barriers keep soil-dwelling termites at bay permanently as long as the sand is not disturbed. More information about the barriers can be obtained from Isothermics, Inc., P.O. Box 18703, Anaheim, CA 92817-8703, 714-778-1396.

Attic rafters and other unpainted wood surfaces can be directly colonized by swarming, 1/2 inch long, **drywood termites**, *Incistermes sp.* Since these termites require neither external moisture nor soil contact, their presence can go unsuspected for many years.

Recognizing Termites

Many homeowners fear termite invasions—but fail to take steps which can help prevent expensive repairs or fumigation. Learn to distinguish termites from ants, and learn to recognize termite frass.[1] Most worker termites are white, while all ants are colored. *A typical ant is much smaller and slimmer than the average termite.* Worker termites are seldom seen unless their tunnels are broken open, but their frass can pile up as minute little spheres below "kick holes".

At a season that is typical of each species, dark termite reproductives come boiling out of holes in soil or wood. In the arid west, subterranean termites swarm on the first sunny day after the first soaking autumn rain. Some termite species swarm at dusk so their movements are less obvious, but if you find winged termites inside your house, take notice.

Termite reproductives (above) have four gauzy wings, which are about three times as long as their bodies. These wings readily fall off almost as soon as the termite reaches the ground. Then these newly wingless termite reproductives run around in pairs looking for suitable wood in which to start a new colony.

(Swarming ant reproductives have unequal wings which do not fall off. Some male ants

[1] Frass = feces

cluster around a much larger female. The two sexes of other ants are equal in size and resemble a group of wasp parasitoids filling the air.) *Ants are usually much smaller than termites.* You can distinguish wingless termite reproductives from the large wood-boring **carpenter ants** by noticing that termites have broad waist and thread-like slightly curved antennae. Ants have a *thin waist with a bump in the center, and elbowed antennae.* Any damage from carpenter ants will be superficial and local.

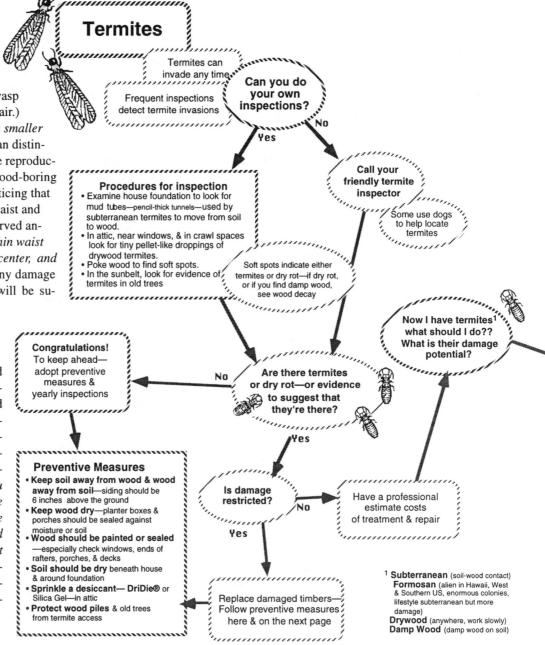

Termites

Termites can invade any time

Frequent inspections detect termite invasions

Can you do your own inspections?

Yes

Procedures for inspection
- Examine house foundation to look for mud tubes—pencil-thick tunnels—used by subterranean termites to move from soil to wood.
- In attic, near windows, & in crawl spaces look for tiny pellet-like droppings of drywood termites.
- Poke wood to find soft spots.
- In the sunbelt, look for evidence of termites in old trees

Soft spots indicate either termites or dry rot—if dry rot, or if you find damp wood, see wood decay

No

Call your friendly termite inspector

Some use dogs to help locate termites

Are there termites or dry rot—or evidence to suggest that they're there?

No

Congratulations! To keep ahead—adopt preventive measures & yearly inspections

Preventive Measures
- **Keep soil away from wood & wood away from soil**—siding should be 6 inches above the ground
- **Keep wood dry**—planter boxes & porches should be sealed against moisture or soil
- **Wood should be painted or sealed**—especially check windows, ends of rafters, porches, & decks
- **Soil should be dry** beneath house & around foundation
- **Sprinkle a desiccant— DriDie®** or Silica Gel—in attic
- **Protect wood piles** & old trees from termite access

Yes

Is damage restricted?

Yes

Replace damaged timbers—Follow preventive measures here & on the next page

No

Have a professional estimate costs of treatment & repair

Now I have termites[1] what should I do?? What is their damage potential?

[1] **Subterranean** (soil-wood contact)
Formosan (alien in Hawaii, West & Southern US, enormous colonies, lifestyle subterranean but more damage)
Drywood (anywhere, work slowly)
Damp Wood (damp wood on soil)

Prevention

In general, dampwood and subterranean termites require dead wood that is in contact with the soil, because they die if exposed to drying conditions. *Anything you can do to separate the wood in your house from dampness and soil, will help prevent their success.* Unfortunately, drywood termites are able to invade dry bare wood.

You can help foil termites, by painting exposed wood. Watch especially, that paint on ends of rafters, porches, and decks does not deteriorate. Keep soil away from the foundation, and remove scrap-wood from under the house. Don't allow sprinklers to splash the siding since *damp wood is vulnerable to both termite and fungal attack.* Remove limbs which over hang the roof so dead branches containing drywood termites or carpenter ants cannot fall onto the roof, allowing them to get into the attic through cracks between the shingles. A **desiccant** in the attic will dry out invading insects.

If, in spite of your efforts, termites do invade, there is no need to panic. *It takes many years for termites to much threaten a structure.* Take time to research the safest method to eliminate your colonies. Be aware that most termite companies do not guarantee treatments for drywood termites, and the persistent chemicals they often use on the soil threaten the environment.

Their soil pesticide barriers were designed to prevent termite access to the structure, but they allow movement of toxics into the water supply, and evaporate into household air.

Termite control strategies are in a state of flux. The fumigant, methyl bromide—an ozone depleter—is to be

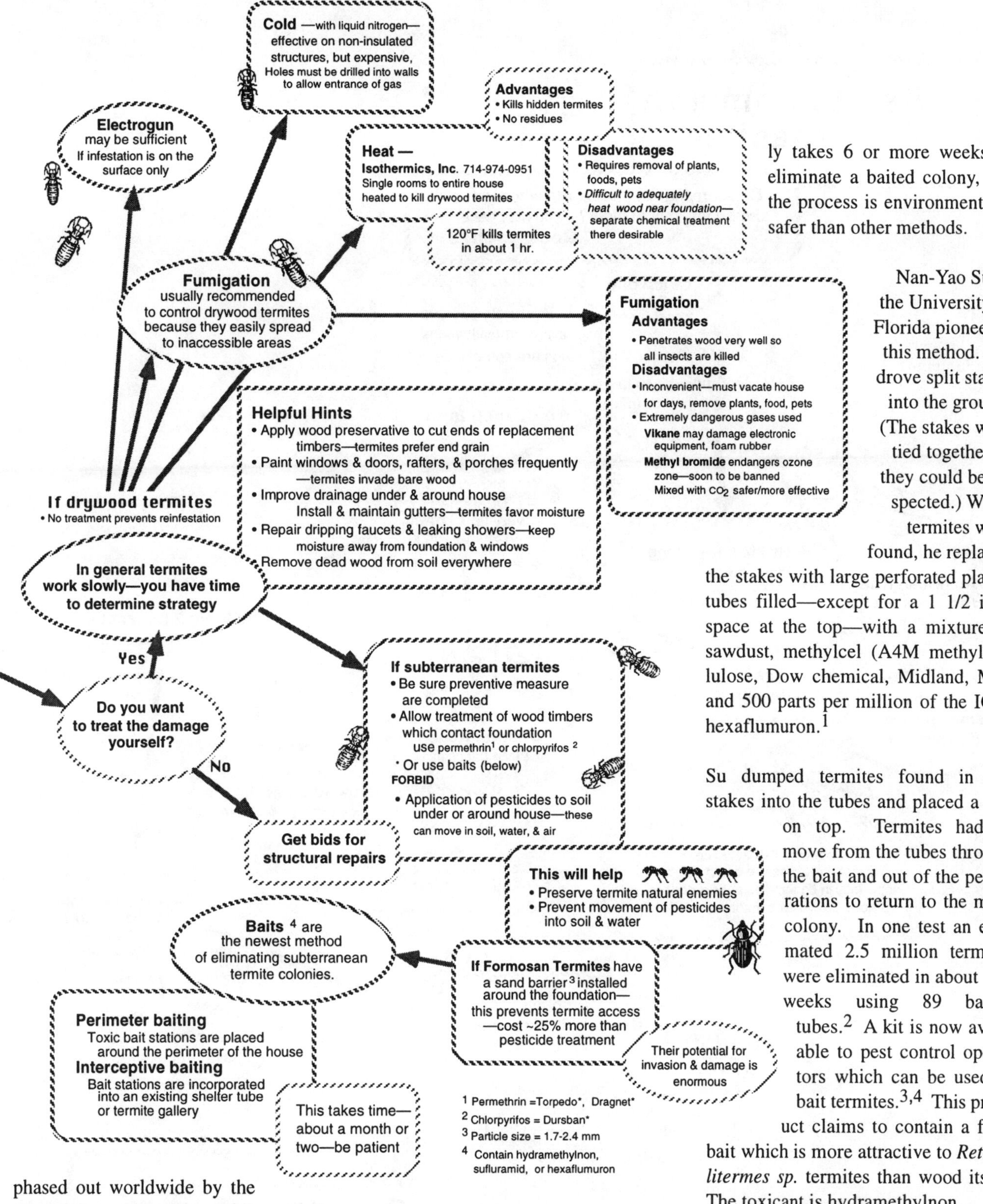

Cold —with liquid nitrogen—
effective on non-insulated
structures, but expensive,
Holes must be drilled into walls
to allow entrance of gas
Advantages
• Kills hidden termites
• No residues
Electrogun
may be sufficient
If infestation is on the
surface only
Heat —
Isothermics, Inc. 714-974-0951
Single rooms to entire house
heated to kill drywood termites
Disadvantages
• Requires removal of plants, foods, pets
• Difficult to adequately heat wood near foundation—separate chemical treatment there desirable
120°F kills termites
in about 1 hr.
Fumigation
usually recommended
to control drywood termites
because they easily spread
to inaccessible areas
Fumigation
Advantages
• Penetrates wood very well so all insects are killed
Disadvantages
• Inconvenient—must vacate house for days, remove plants, food, pets
• Extremely dangerous gases used
Vikane may damage electronic equipment, foam rubber
Methyl bromide endangers ozone zone—soon to be banned
Mixed with CO2 safer/more effective
Helpful Hints
• Apply wood preservative to cut ends of replacement timbers—termites prefer end grain
• Paint windows & doors, rafters, & porches frequently —termites invade bare wood
• Improve drainage under & around house
Install & maintain gutters—termites favor moisture
• Repair dripping faucets & leaking showers—keep moisture away from foundation & windows
• Remove dead wood from soil everywhere
If drywood termites
• No treatment prevents reinfestation
In general termites
work slowly—you have time
to determine strategy
Yes
Do you want
to treat the damage
yourself?
No
If subterranean termites
• Be sure preventive measure are completed
• Allow treatment of wood timbers which contact foundation
use permethrin1 or chlorpyrifos 2
• Or use baits (below)
FORBID
• Application of pesticides to soil under or around house—these can move in soil, water, & air
Get bids for
structural repairs
This will help
• Preserve termite natural enemies
• Prevent movement of pesticides into soil & water
Baits 4 are
the newest method
of eliminating subterranean
termite colonies.
If Formosan Termites have
a sand barrier3 installed
around the foundation—
this prevents termite access
—cost ~25% more than
pesticide treatment
Their potential for
invasion & damage is
enormous
Perimeter baiting
Toxic bait stations are placed around the perimeter of the house
Interceptive baiting
Bait stations are incorporated into an existing shelter tube or termite gallery
This takes time—
about a month or
two—be patient
1 Permethrin =Torpedo*, Dragnet*
2 Chlorpyrifos = Dursban*
3 Particle size = 1.7-2.4 mm
4 Contain hydramethylnon, sulfuramid, or hexaflumuron

phased out worldwide by the turn of the century. Meanwhile methyl bromide mixed with carbon dioxide is more effective and safer than the toxic gas alone. New research has demonstrated that subterranean termites of all kinds can be selectively controlled by baits. Several researchers reduced or eliminated Formosan termite colonies by placing wood or cardboard baits containing non-repellent, slow-acting pesticides in soil or trees infected with termites. (A slow response is necessary, because the idea is to allow termite foragers to bring the bait back to share with colony members). It usually takes 6 or more weeks to eliminate a baited colony, but the process is environmentally safer than other methods.

Nan-Yao Su of the University of Florida pioneered this method. He drove split stakes into the ground. (The stakes were tied together so they could be inspected.) When termites were found, he replaced the stakes with large perforated plastic tubes filled—except for a 1 1/2 inch space at the top—with a mixture of sawdust, methylcel (A4M methylcellulose, Dow chemical, Midland, MI), and 500 parts per million of the IGR, hexaflumuron.[1]

Su dumped termites found in the stakes into the tubes and placed a cap on top. Termites had to move from the tubes through the bait and out of the perforations to return to the main colony. In one test an estimated 2.5 million termites were eliminated in about two weeks using 89 baited tubes.[2] A kit is now available to pest control operators which can be used to bait termites.[3,4] This product claims to contain a food bait which is more attractive to *Reticulitermes sp.* termites than wood itself. The toxicant is hydramethylnon.

---

1 J Econ Entomol 87:389-397, 1994

2 J Econ Entomol 87:398-401, 1994.

3 Common Sense Pest Cont. 11(2): 5-17,1995

4 Pest Manag 10/94, 1994

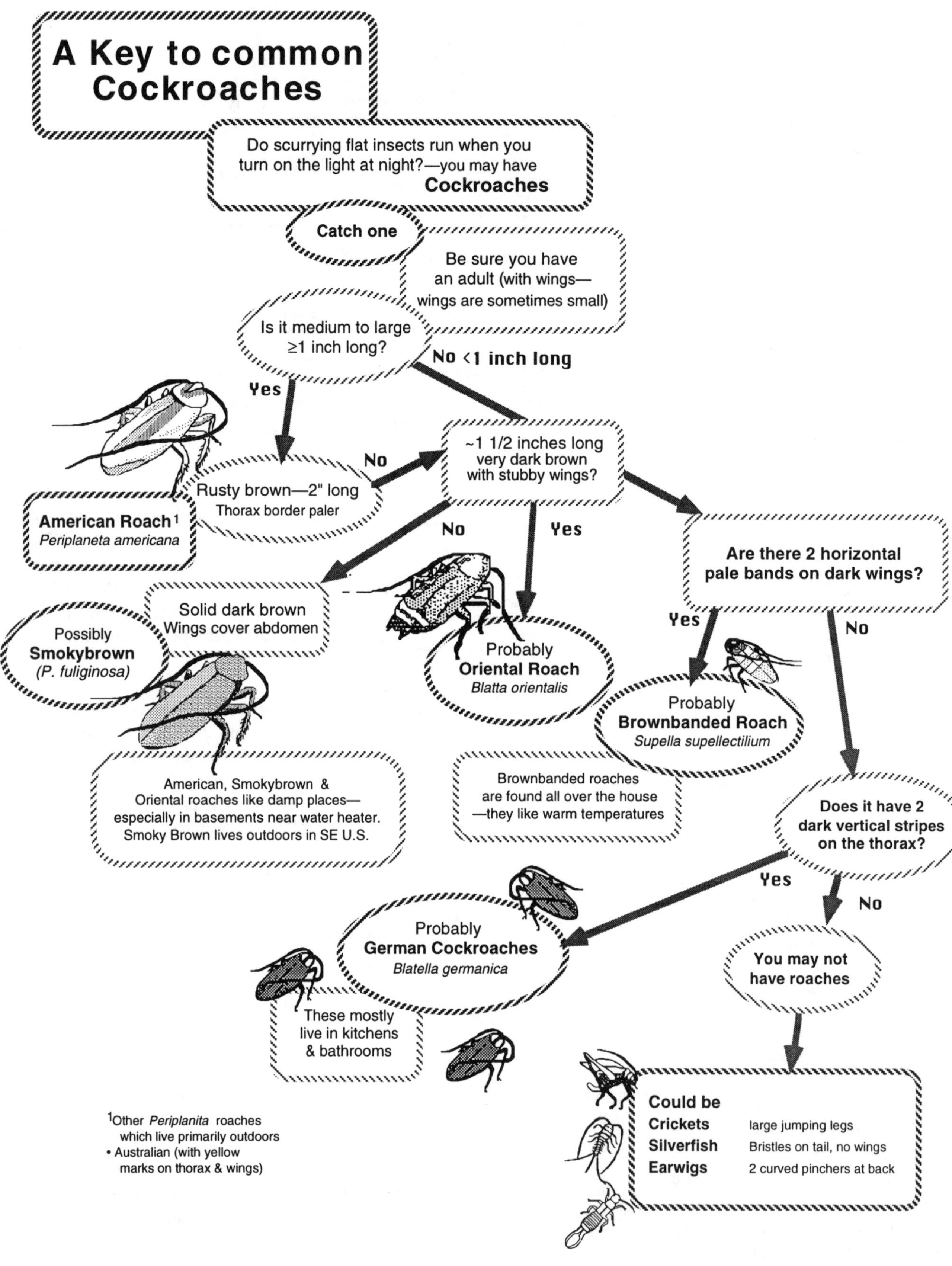
A Key to common Cockroaches
Do scurrying flat insects run when you turn on the light at night?—you may have Cockroaches
Catch one
Be sure you have an adult (with wings—wings are sometimes small)
Is it medium to large ≥1 inch long?
No <1 inch long
Yes
Rusty brown—2" long
Thorax border paler
American Roach[1]
Periplaneta americana
No
~1 1/2 inches long very dark brown with stubby wings?
No
Yes
Solid dark brown
Wings cover abdomen
Possibly Smokybrown
(P. fuliginosa)
Probably Oriental Roach
Blatta orientalis
Are there 2 horizontal pale bands on dark wings?
Yes
No
Probably Brownbanded Roach
Supella supellectilium
American, Smokybrown & Oriental roaches like damp places—especially in basements near water heater. Smoky Brown lives outdoors in SE U.S.
Brownbanded roaches are found all over the house —they like warm temperatures
Does it have 2 dark vertical stripes on the thorax?
Yes
No
Probably German Cockroaches
Blatella germanica
You may not have roaches
These mostly live in kitchens & bathrooms
Could be
Crickets large jumping legs
Silverfish Bristles on tail, no wings
Earwigs 2 curved pinchers at back
[1]Other Periplanita roaches which live primarily outdoors
• Australian (with yellow marks on thorax & wings)

What about roaches?

Cockroaches are flattened nocturnal creatures, which are reported to be almost invincible—the toughest of insects. You may have heard stories of their great antiquity, and the prediction that roaches would probably survive a nuclear holocaust. The last would be an exaggeration to say the least.

Roaches have been around a long time with little change in appearance. They eat most anything, but must have shelter from harsh weather. These two characteristics place them in direct conflict with people. They are usually considered disgusting—and no wonder. Few of us want insects tracking across our food, hiding in handy crevices, and leaving an unpleasant odor behind.

Roach Impact

Roaches neither bite nor sting, and in fact are rather delicate and easily crushed. But they do track diseases and dirt onto unprotected food. Their persistent odor stems from oily secretions which help protect them from water loss. Fortunately, there are several modern control strategies which can help you rid your house of roaches—at least in the short term. (Roaches can always return).

Life Style

Roaches are very alert. Long flexible antennae warn them of danger in front—two cerci[1] sense trouble behind. They are so flat that they can slip into the smallest crack, and long legs enable them to race across the floor at the slightest provocation. Most are active only at night—are repelled by light. Their sense of smell is so sensitive, however, that a hungry roach may come out in the daytime when you take out a sandwich or a cookie.

Young roaches, which look like adult roaches without wings, have the same lifestyle as their parents. Roaches are attracted to other roaches, so its easy to find a mixed-age group hidden together in a dark crevice, or behind a picture. It can be even more startling to turn on the light at night, and watch several dark forms scurry out of sight. Cockroaches everywhere are scavengers. Some even scavenge in caves beneath bat colonies, and others are forest dwellers.

Domestic roaches

Domestic roaches have adapted to our houses, and our food stores. They eat fallen crumbs beneath our tables and our toasters. Though roaches have functional wings, most are loath to fly. Where they hang out, varies by species. Most choose crevices or other hidden places in the kitchen, the pantry, or the bath. The large **American roach** *(Periplaneta americana),* prefers warm damp spots like the basement, while the smaller **brownbanded** *(Supella longipalpa)* gets along in most any room, and may even invade your bureau drawers. The **smokybrown** *(Periplantea fuliginosa)*—common in damp southeastern U.S.—invades homes from out-of-doors.

Although roaches sometimes occur in enormous numbers, they mature rather slowly for an insect. Development from egg to adult can take three months to a year or more—depending on species and temperature. The **German roach** *(Blatella germanica)*—now found round the world—grows more rapidly than most others.

Every few days most female roaches package about 20 eggs in a little purse-like object called an ootheca. (A few species retain the ootheca on the body until hatching, or even bear live young). The ootheca is hidden a in sheltered place—behind a picture or in a crevice. As soon as one has been shed, the female begins to develop eggs to make another.

Frequent sprays containing toxic insecticides have selected roach populations which resist most organophosphate, carbamate, and pyrethroid insecticides.[2] (Roach-repellant pyrethroids are often used to flush roaches out of hiding). As control strategies have shifted to baits, *a few roaches have even evolved resistance to the glucose sugar in a food-based bait.*[3] Fortunately, a varied control strategy which utilizes baits and non-repellant inorganic toxicants which cause water loss, enable us to eliminate roaches safely. Remember that any control effort must encompass the entire dwelling, since roaches hide anywhere from basement to attic. Obviously, cleanliness will facilitate eradication efforts.

Outdoor Roaches—If Smokybrown roaches are your problem, caulking cracks, strict storage of pet food, daily elimination of animal feces, and removal of outdoor trash will help keep their outdoor habitat less favorable, but you face an uphill battle.

Recently the **Asian roach**, was discovered in southeastern U.S. They are similar in appearance to German roaches, but have different behavior. They're common outdoors in summer, and readily fly to lights. This latter activity suggests a possible control strategy, but only experience will tell. Look for them to spread widely.

---

[1]See p. 14. [2] Pest Manag. 6/94, p. 14-16, [3] J Insect Physiol 39:925-933, 1993

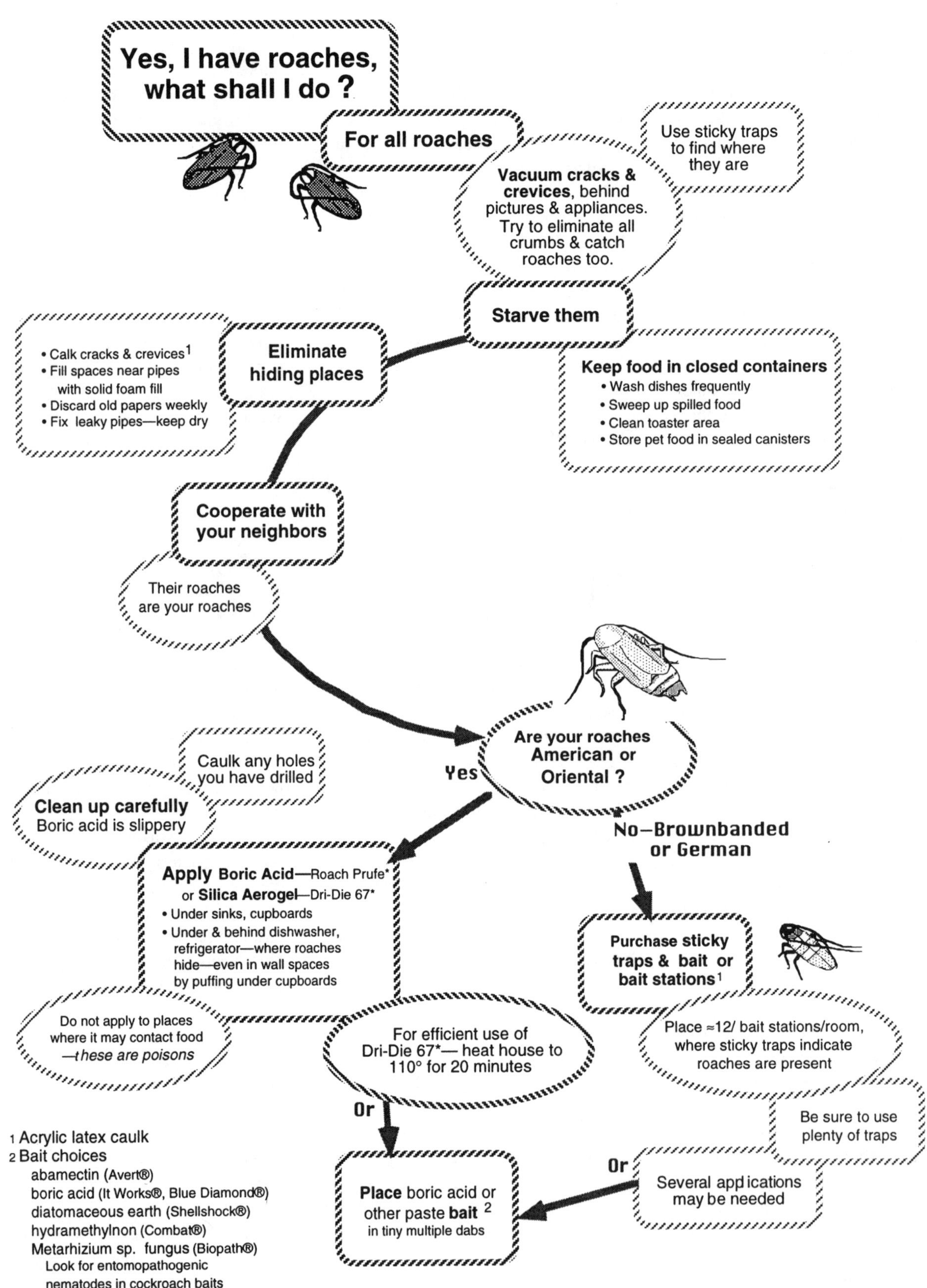
Yes, I have roaches, what shall I do ?
For all roaches
Use sticky traps to find where they are
Vacuum cracks & crevices, behind pictures & appliances. Try to eliminate all crumbs & catch roaches too.
Starve them
Keep food in closed containers
• Wash dishes frequently
• Sweep up spilled food
• Clean toaster area
• Store pet food in sealed canisters
Eliminate hiding places
• Calk cracks & crevices1
• Fill spaces near pipes with solid foam fill
• Discard old papers weekly
• Fix leaky pipes—keep dry
Cooperate with your neighbors
Their roaches are your roaches
Are your roaches American or Oriental ?
Yes
No–Brownbanded or German
Caulk any holes you have drilled
Clean up carefully
Boric acid is slippery
Apply Boric Acid—Roach Prufe* or Silica Aerogel—Dri-Die 67*
• Under sinks, cupboards
• Under & behind dishwasher, refrigerator—where roaches hide—even in wall spaces by puffing under cupboards
Do not apply to places where it may contact food —these are poisons
For efficient use of Dri-Die 67*— heat house to 110° for 20 minutes
Or
Purchase sticky traps & bait or bait stations1
Place ≈12/ bait stations/room, where sticky traps indicate roaches are present
Be sure to use plenty of traps
Or
Several applications may be needed
Place boric acid or other paste bait 2 in tiny multiple dabs
1 Acrylic latex caulk
2 Bait choices
abamectin (Avert®)
boric acid (It Works®, Blue Diamond®)
diatomaceous earth (Shellshock®)
hydramethylnon (Combat®)
Metarhizium sp. fungus (Biopath®)
Look for entomopathogenic nematodes in cockroach baits

Stored Product & other indoor critters

Even the most meticulous housekeeper is occasionally unpleasantly surprised by little 'worms' in the cereal or beetles in the pie crust mix. A whole cohort of insects and their kin is adapted to life on these and other dried foods. These *stored product insects* have remarkably catholic tastes, thriving on dried beans, cracked and whole cereals, rice, corn meal, dried fruits, nuts, flour, baking mixes, spices—even egg noodles.

With food—
Cleanliness doesn't help much

What makes the whole situation even more annoying, is the knowledge that these pests arrive in your kitchen as eggs or tiny larvae in newly purchased foods, so *there is no way to totally eliminate them permanately.* However, you can make things even worse if you let such foods sit on the pantry shelf untended—allowing these little invaders to grow up in your stores, feeding and eventually reproducing more of their kind.

Fortunately there are things you can do to keep things under control. Newly purchased grains can be heated (to about 150°F) to kill insect eggs or larvae. These sterilized products should be placed in insect-tight containers, or kept in the refrigerator or freezer to allow temperature alone to prevent insect growth and reproduction. You have to be vigilant, however, since each purchase from the grocery can reintroduce these invaders. In theory, freezing will kill these insects, but several of these stored product insects are not killed by the temperatures available in home freezers, so development continues when they are removed to room temperatures.[1] Thus heat is the best way to effectively and safely kill *Plodia* and other household insects.

In addition to the methods described here, pheromones are available which will attract the **Indianmeal moth** *(Plodia interpunctella)*. Pheromones help monitor its presence, but are seldom needed at home where prevention is always the way to go. This insect is resistant to many insecticides, and *there is no need to use pesticides to control this or other stored food insect.* Stick to cultural and barrier methods described here to keep these pests under control.

Occasionally you may be annoyed to find tiny pomice or vinegar flies, *Drosophila sp.* hanging around bananas or other ripening fruits. *There is no need to panic or use a spray* in this situation either. The scavenger fly page describes controls for these or other flies that enter the house.

Bedroom or rugs
Cleanliness helps—

The kitchen is not the only place where insects hang out indoors. Elsewhere larvae may be nibbling on natural fibers—fir, wool, and leather. In the natural world these creatures—from a variety of arthropod families—help *recycle* dead animals including their fur and feathers. Some are beetles, others the caterpillars of moths, and even arachnids—dust mites—have representatives in the cohort of household pests. Such **clothes moths,** such as *Tineola bisselliella,* and **dermestid** (carpet) **beetles** *(Dermestes sp.)* are the most familiar.

Carpet beetles are often found on window sills, where they have flown toward the light. They may have come in from the out of doors, but they may have emerged from the dusty corner of a wool rug, or that old leather dog chew forgotten under the kid's bed. You obviously do not want them to use your furniture or clothing as dinner. Careless storage practices and infrequently cleaning, allow the natural fiber pests to remain undisturbed in the dark recesses of your closet or the woolen rugs on the floor or the walls. Our chart will help you eliminate them and protect your fabrics.

In addition, if you live in a humid climate, you may have problems with still other indoor critters. **Dust mites, silverfish** *(Lepisma saccharina)* and other delicate fiber feeders multiply enormously under warm, damp conditions. In this situation, a light bulb in the closet or a dehumidifier can remove excess moisture to protect your furniture, books, and clothing from damage. Is is no secret that the droppings and body parts of dust mites are common triggers for allergies. If you have an allergy problem, know that upholstered furniture and rugs are common hangouts for dust mites. In addition to drying the atmosphere, vacuum regularly, and if allergies persist, eliminate these hideouts completely.

Common visitors

In addition to the arthropods that reside in the house, you may encounter an occasional unwanted visitor. Where *we* live the most common are ant trails or earwigs, but you may have others. The most spectacular are the craneflies—they look like giant mosquitoes—which blunder inside during the springtime. In summer, an occasional click beetle or mosquito may slip in. *In none of these situations would we resort to spray, or even*

---

1 J stored Prod Res 28:89-118, 1992

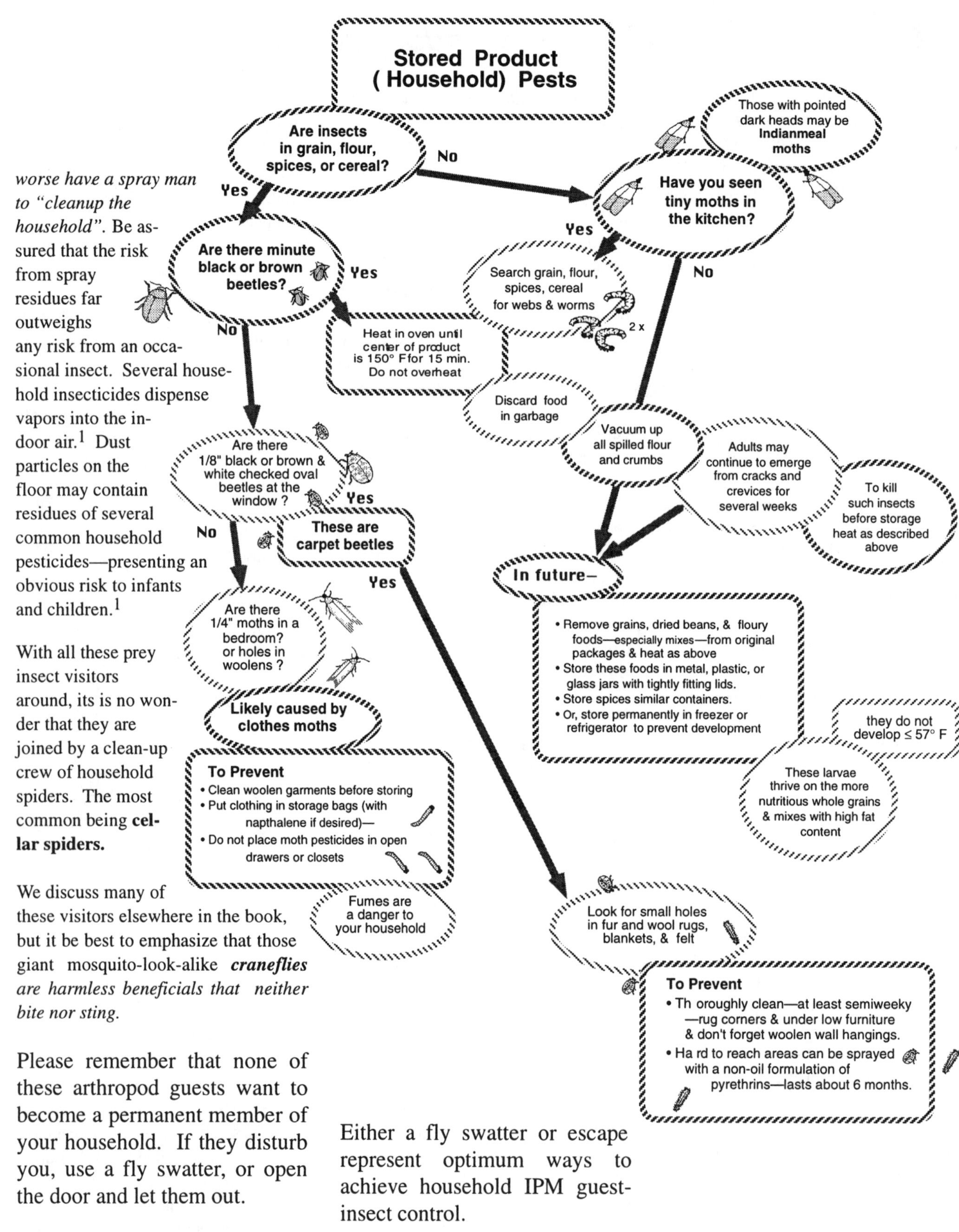
Stored Product (Household) Pests
Are insects in grain, flour, spices, or cereal?
Yes
No
Are there minute black or brown beetles?
Yes
No
Heat in oven until center of product is 150° Ffor 15 min. Do not overheat
Are there 1/8" black or brown & white checked oval beetles at the window ?
Yes
No
These are carpet beetles
Yes
Are there 1/4" moths in a bedroom? or holes in woolens ?
Likely caused by clothes moths
To Prevent
• Clean woolen garments before storing
• Put clothing in storage bags (with napthalene if desired)—
• Do not place moth pesticides in open drawers or closets
Fumes are a danger to your household
Those with pointed dark heads may be Indianmeal moths
Have you seen tiny moths in the kitchen?
Yes
No
Search grain, flour, spices, cereal for webs & worms
2 x
Discard food in garbage
Vacuum up all spilled flour and crumbs
Adults may continue to emerge from cracks and crevices for several weeks
To kill such insects before storage heat as described above
In future–
• Remove grains, dried beans, & floury foods—especially mixes—from original packages & heat as above
• Store these foods in metal, plastic, or glass jars with tightly fitting lids.
• Store spices similar containers.
• Or, store permanently in freezer or refrigerator to prevent development
they do not develop ≤ 57° F
These larvae thrive on the more nutritious whole grains & mixes with high fat content
Look for small holes in fur and wool rugs, blankets, & felt
To Prevent
• Th oroughly clean—at least semiweeky —rug corners & under low furniture & don't forget woolen wall hangings.
• Ha rd to reach areas can be sprayed with a non-oil formulation of pyrethrins—lasts about 6 months.

worse have a spray man to "cleanup the household". Be assured that the risk from spray residues far outweighs any risk from an occasional insect. Several household insecticides dispense vapors into the indoor air.[1] Dust particles on the floor may contain residues of several common household pesticides—presenting an obvious risk to infants and children.[1]

With all these prey insect visitors around, its is no wonder that they are joined by a clean-up crew of household spiders. The most common being **cellar spiders.**

We discuss many of these visitors elsewhere in the book, but it be best to emphasize that those giant mosquito-look-alike ***craneflies*** *are harmless beneficials that neither bite nor sting.*

Please remember that none of these arthropod guests want to become a permanent member of your household. If they disturb you, use a fly swatter, or open the door and let them out.

Either a fly swatter or escape represent optimum ways to achieve household IPM guest-insect control.

---

[1] EPA/6003/3-90/003, Nonoccupational Pesticide Exposure Study, 1990

Fighting fleas

Fleas are highly evolved high jumping insects which are specialized to live in the fur of mammals. You are probably already familiar with blood-sucking adult fleas—typically **cat fleas** *(Ctenocephalides filis)*—and the itching welts that appear after their bites.

Where fleas live

Adult fleas are not all there is to fleas. They are responsible for the bites which cause such serious irritation and allergies, and even "failure to thrive" in young animals. You may not be aware that they do not usually jump from one victim to another. *Their eggs, larvae, and pupae live off the animal*—in the pet's bedding, in rugs or furniture, and sometimes outdoors. The female can suck up to 30 times her weight in blood every day, and excretes 6 times her weight in nutritious digested blood feces. She drops her eggs onto the floor along with these feces.

In warm weather it takes only a few days for flea eggs to hatch into tiny wiggly legless larvae. The larvae live deep in the rugs eating the feces and other nutritious food items that may be available. In a couple of weeks they mature, molt to the pupal stage, and complete adult development in a week or two. These *mature pupae wait up to a year if necessary for a suitable host to appear.* Warmth, movement, and breath trigger rapid emergence of these waiting young adult fleas. They leap onto this new host as your familiar biting flea, and there they stay feeding, mating, and laying eggs happily for the rest of their lives.

When a pet owner moves or goes on vacation, flea eggs and larvae remain on the floor. Larval development continues. Eventually most of these immature fleas reach a mature pupal stage which contains young adult fleas. Emerging adult fleas rapidly jump onto the pet if you bring a dog or cat into a long vacant house which previously contained an animal. If no pet is available, they attack the first person who enters.

Naturally, such flea attacks on humans cause considerable distress. *The victim is likely to think that only a careless person would allow so many fleas in the house!* He or she doesn't realize that most pet owners have a similar storage bank of immature fleas in their houses. If a four-legged mammal is present, adult cat and dog fleas usually ignore people. Our cats and dogs are the major hosts of fleas in our houses and yards, but other domestic animals such as goats also host fleas, and certain people are readily bitten.

Controlling fleas

Follow our flow chart to take care of your fleas. Do not bother with dietary supplements or "organic" remedies such as aromatic leaves. *These do not affect fleas.* Neither do the ultrasound "control" devices which disturb your pet—how would you like to hear an unending ringing in your ears?—and do nothing about fleas.[1] Likewise *avoid flea collars and flea bombs which contain conventional insecticides.* These threaten your health, and that of your children and pets by filling the air with continuous pesticide vapors. Do not bother to dust boric acid into the carpet as is sometimes recommended. Boric acid affects larval fleas, *but only if ingested,* and it will not kill adult fleas since these are on your pet.

Try to complete any flea control program within a day or tow. It does little good to treat your pet, and leave the house alone, since new young adults keep emerging daily. Likewise, treating the house and the yard, does nothing about adult fleas living on your pet.

Getting started

Cleanliness is helpful in controlling immature fleas. Thoroughly vacuum rooms used by your pets, and their bedding—wash the bedding if possible. Then treat rooms frequented by the animal with a methoprene-based product. **Methoprene** is a synthetic insect juvenile hormone which stops flea development at the beginning of the pupal stage. It is not a poison. After its use, the flea cycle stops until residues disappear months later. Treated rooms remain flea-free indefinitely unless you introduce flea-infested-pets sometime after methoprene residues degrade. If fleas do reappear, repeat the cleaning and treatment again.

The fleas on your pet will eventually die of old age, or you can kill them with an insecticidal soap shampoo—perhaps a shampoo that contains citrus peal extract, **d-Limonene**. (Remember to wear gloves during the dilution process). If you still believe there are fleas emerging in the house, try one of the **light-based adult flea traps.** You may want to modify the trap as did scientists at Kansas State University.[2] They found that cats fleas were attracted to a yellow-green light. (You may want to filter or change the light in the commercial trap to achieve that color). These workers also found flea traps work better if placed on an electronic timer which turned the light off and on

[1]See, unmasking ultrasound. [2] J Med Entomol 30:901-906, 1993.

for a few seconds every few minutes.

Outdoor fleas

If there are fleas in your yard, modify your gardening practices. Water lawns no more than twice a week—sunlight and dehydration help kill larval fleas. Use **entomopathogenic nematodes**[1] formulated for flea control on lawns, or other areas your pet uses. If this area is dry, moisten the soil and keep it damp for a few days to make conditions suitable for beneficial nematode survival. If used as directed, these little worms will rapidly kill the larval and pupal fleas that are living in your yard. In addition, methoprene-containing **Petcor*** can be sprayed on the pet and its bedding. Petcor will control fleas and their eggs for several months indoors, and about a month outside.

Though cat and dog fleas are our most common fleas, they are not all there is. Almost all mammals host fleas. Several of these fleas can transmit serious diseases to humans. For more information about these diseases—see Arthropod-borne diseases.

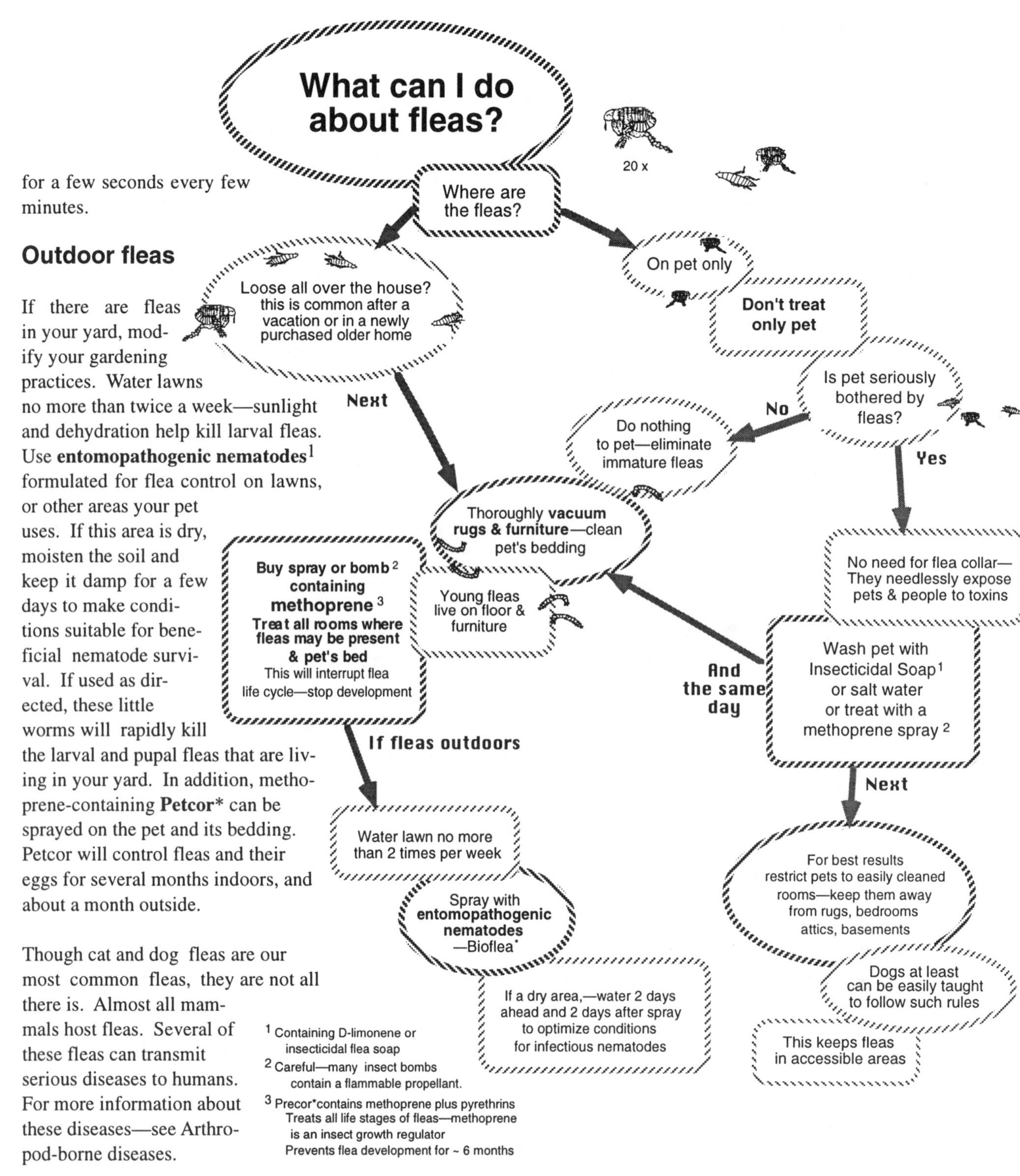

What can I do about fleas?
20 x
Where are the fleas?
Loose all over the house? this is common after a vacation or in a newly purchased older home
Next
On pet only
Don't treat only pet
Is pet seriously bothered by fleas?
No
Do nothing to pet—eliminate immature fleas
Yes
Thoroughly vacuum rugs & furniture—clean pet's bedding
No need for flea collar— They needlessly expose pets & people to toxins
Buy spray or bomb 2 containing methoprene 3 Treat all rooms where fleas may be present & pet's bed This will interrupt flea life cycle—stop development
Young fleas live on floor & furniture
And the same day
Wash pet with Insecticidal Soap 1 or salt water or treat with a methoprene spray 2
If fleas outdoors
Next
Water lawn no more than 2 times per week
Spray with entomopathogenic nematodes —Bioflea*
If a dry area,—water 2 days ahead and 2 days after spray to optimize conditions for infectious nematodes
For best results restrict pets to easily cleaned rooms—keep them away from rugs, bedrooms attics, basements
Dogs at least can be easily taught to follow such rules
This keeps fleas in accessible areas
1 Containing D-limonene or insecticidal flea soap
2 Careful—many insect bombs contain a flammable propellant.
3 Precor*contains methoprene plus pyrethrins Treats all life stages of fleas—methoprene is an insect growth regulator Prevents flea development for ~ 6 months

[1]Insect-feeding round worms, see p. 82.

Harrowing head lice

Due to their association with dirt and poverty, one of the most embarrassing thing we can encounter is a note from school which announces that *our child is infected with head lice!*

To begin, the term lice—or singular louse—can be confusing. In common use, louse (singular) can refer to several different kinds of insects, to say nothing of an unpopular person, as in, "He's a louse." In the plural form "lice" we find that **jumping lice** (psocids) and **plant lice** (aphids) are found only on plants. The **biting lice** (Mallophaga) are primarily parasitic to birds, and, **sucking lice** (Anoplura—unarmed tail), feed on the blood of mammals.

Sucking lice

Sucking lice are small wingless external parasites, usually restricted to one or a few hosts. Here we are interested in the particular sucking lice which are found on humans.

Human Lice

Head lice and **body lice**—two variations of the same species, *(Pediculus humanus)*, and the **pubic louse** *(Pthirus pubis)* are restricted to humans. The body louse clings mainly to clothing. It is a serious pest during war, or among the homeless—afflicting people who are unable to bathe and clean their clothing regularly. Body lice can transmit such serious diseases as **typhus**, **relapsing fever**, and **trench fever**. (The insecticide, DDT, was first used to control body lice). The hairy, crab-like pubic lice are most common on adults who practice promiscuous sex.

Head lice are a different story. They have become very common in children from all lifestyle backgrounds. All of their life stages live on the head. They have claws which are able to grasp hair which is round in cross section, Such hair is found on the heads of Caucasians and Asians. (People with negroid hair which is oval in cross section are not susceptible to these lice).

Head lice life cycle

Head lice glue their eggs (nits) to the hair near the scalp. During egg incubation—hatching begins after about 7 days—the hair continues to grow from the base, causing the clinging egg to move farther and farther away from the scalp. Nymphal lice reach adulthood in about 9 days. Adults live for another 10 days. Throughout their life these insects frequently bite to suck blood. These bites itch. The females usually produce several hundred eggs, most of which—all things being equal—go on to become more lice. Obviously, infested individuals should make every effort to eliminate these pesty little critters.

Unfortunately, treatment is not easy. The eggs stick tightly to the hair, and are resistant to most treatment chemicals. One **non-toxic option** is to carefully comb both eggs and lice out of the hair after shampooing with a compound which contains long chain fatty acid-based soap. This treatment, especially when combined with the heat of a blow drier, will kill and remove lice without pesticides.

Alternately, a **low-toxic insecticide** such as **pyrethrins** dispensed in a shampoo will kill the lice and most of the eggs. The treatment must be repeated after 7 days to remove all lice which have hatched from surviving eggs.

Avoid the toxic product known as Quell. This contains the organochlorine insecticide, lindane (gama HCH) as its active ingredient. Lindane is not very effective in in killing head lice lice, and it threatens the health of your child. Too many children have become ill after its use, despite the fact that many lice survived. In addition, like most other pesticides it readily penetrates the skin. It is stored in body fat for decades, and is an estrogen mimic. Estrogen mimics are linked to breast and other reproductive-system cancers and to reproductive problems.*

In addition to these head treatments, you will want to wash the bedding and avoid sharing combs and other personal articles with others. Any lice on these will not survive long away from the body, but prevention is probably appropriate.

Even after all the lice are gone your troubles may not be over. Reinfestation with head lice is very likely, since children often have very close contact with others during play. If lice come back, repeat the treatment. Fortunately, head lice are not linked with diseases or allergies.

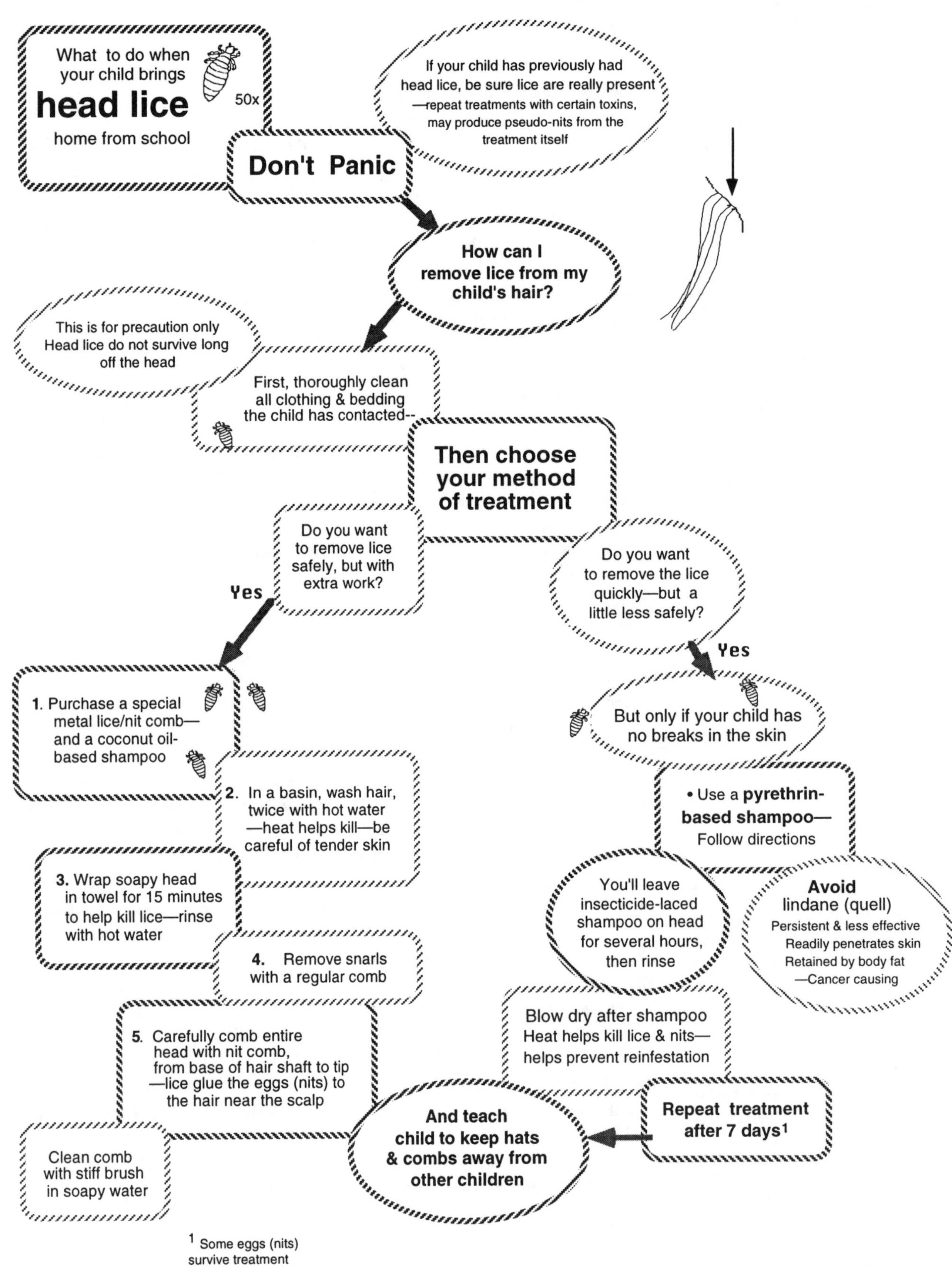
What to do when your child brings
head lice
50x
home from school
Don't Panic
If your child has previously had head lice, be sure lice are really present —repeat treatments with certain toxins, may produce pseudo-nits from the treatment itself
How can I remove lice from my child's hair?
This is for precaution only Head lice do not survive long off the head
First, thoroughly clean all clothing & bedding the child has contacted--
Then choose your method of treatment
Do you want to remove lice safely, but with extra work?
Yes
Do you want to remove the lice quickly—but a little less safely?
Yes
1. Purchase a special metal lice/nit comb—and a coconut oil-based shampoo
2. In a basin, wash hair, twice with hot water —heat helps kill—be careful of tender skin
3. Wrap soapy head in towel for 15 minutes to help kill lice—rinse with hot water
4. Remove snarls with a regular comb
5. Carefully comb entire head with nit comb, from base of hair shaft to tip —lice glue the eggs (nits) to the hair near the scalp
Clean comb with stiff brush in soapy water
But only if your child has no breaks in the skin
• Use a pyrethrin-based shampoo— Follow directions
You'll leave insecticide-laced shampoo on head for several hours, then rinse
Avoid lindane (quell)
Persistent & less effective
Readily penetrates skin
Retained by body fat
—Cancer causing
Blow dry after shampoo Heat helps kill lice & nits—helps prevent reinfestation
Repeat treatment after 7 days[1]
And teach child to keep hats & combs away from other children

[1] Some eggs (nits) survive treatment

Down the drain

We all do it. Pour it down the drain and never think about it again. those little pipes will take care of everything. We forget that they may ultimately leak into the water supply. the fact that many of us have a garbage disposal under the sink doesn't help, because we're even more likely to try to get rid of everything *down the drain.*

Why drains clog

Drains often clog because fibers like hair trap sticky substances such as grease and soap which eventually block the opening. Sometimes the blockage come from below when roots get into the sewer. In either case, the methods you choose to open a clogged drain can make a big difference in your safety and that of the environment.

Permanent help for drains

Should a sink begin to drain more and more slowly, purchase a "biological" drain cleaner.[1] The bacteria in these products consume the organic greases, soaps, and food particles which thrive in drains, providing a continuous cleanup crew. These products will not remove the hair, however. You have to do that yourself. Nonetheless, biological train cleansers should keep on working indefinitely in the absence of hair. If a slowing appears, repeat the process.

Sudden stoppages

If you have a sudden drain clog, perhaps from a misplaced toy, use a snake-like tool to remove the clog from the line, or call a plumber. *Avoid caustic chemical drain cleaners.* They are either strongly acid or strongly alkaline. They not only attack the substances which are plugging the drain, but the pipe itself. And the heat that they generate can weaken the joints. Before you know it, you can be burned by a caustic fountain bubbling out of the drain. If the clog does open, all this caustic material drains down to interfere with sewage treatment processes.

Roots in the sewer

If roots are the problem, use a mechanical rotor to remove them, or even remove the source tree if the root problem seems intolerable. (Certain trees, such as poplar, have extremely invasive roots which make them inappropriate for urban areas). Sometimes copper-based root killers are recommended to remove roots from sewer lines. At first these may seem cheaper and easier than other methods, but this is an error. These copper-based "root killers" are not very effective, *and,* they release toxic persistent copper down the drain.

Sewage treatment plants are not able to remove heavy metals from the waste stream. These continue on to pollute the river, the lake, or the bay which is the ultimate end to your sewage. Fish and shell fish are injured when they ingest metallic pollutants, and sometimes even their predators— birds and mammals are affected. The young of exposed birds hatch with physical defects—or seemingly normal birds may sometimes be unable to reproduce. Some aquatic mammals become covered with cancers, or die unexpectedly from the toxic residues in their tissues.

Certain industries release metals and other toxics during manufacturing. These threaten world ecosystems (see endocrine disruptors), and industry is increasingly being required to remove metals and toxics from the waste stream. This actually may be cheaper because valuable materials are recycled.

We hope you'll do your share toward preventing these threatening processes, by keeping toxic wastes out of drains.

---

[1] Consumer Reports (1/94) purchased these from grocery and hardware stores

Optimizing vegetable gardening

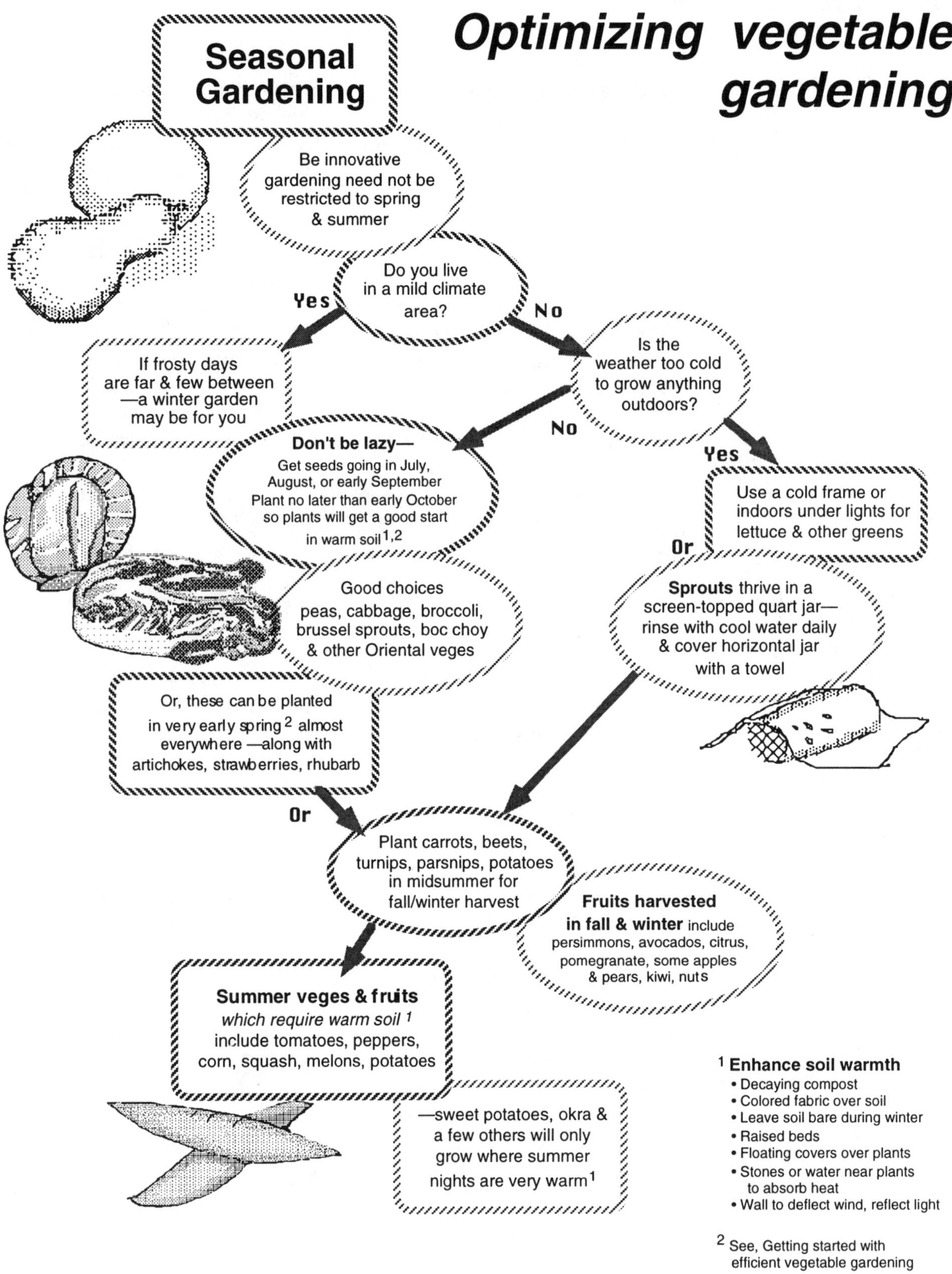
Seasonal Gardening
Be innovative gardening need not be restricted to spring & summer
Do you live in a mild climate area?
Yes
If frosty days are far & few between —a winter garden may be for you
No
Is the weather too cold to grow anything outdoors?
No
Don't be lazy— Get seeds going in July, August, or early September Plant no later than early October so plants will get a good start in warm soil 1,2
Good choices peas, cabbage, broccoli, brussel sprouts, boc choy & other Oriental veges
Or, these can be planted in very early spring 2 almost everywhere —along with artichokes, strawberries, rhubarb
Yes
Use a cold frame or indoors under lights for lettuce & other greens
Or
Sprouts thrive in a screen-topped quart jar— rinse with cool water daily & cover horizontal jar with a towel
Or
Plant carrots, beets, turnips, parsnips, potatoes in midsummer for fall/winter harvest
Fruits harvested in fall & winter include persimmons, avocados, citrus, pomegranate, some apples & pears, kiwi, nuts
Summer veges & fruits which require warm soil 1 include tomatoes, peppers, corn, squash, melons, potatoes
—sweet potatoes, okra & a few others will only grow where summer nights are very warm 1

[1] **Enhance soil warmth**
- Decaying compost
- Colored fabric over soil
- Leave soil bare during winter
- Raised beds
- Floating covers over plants
- Stones or water near plants to absorb heat
- Wall to deflect wind, reflect light

[2] See, Getting started with efficient vegetable gardening

Stretching the season & other culture tips

Vegetable and fruit gardeners often try to stretch the season. Obviously you can beat the cold by starting seeds indoors using artificial lights and a heater under the soil, or, you can save time and trouble by purchasing bedding plants. (When planting seeds, always use sterile soil as described in the houseplant page).

Warming & cooling soil

In spring, bare soil warms more rapidly than soils where plants are growing. Or you can pre-warm the soil under **transparent** or **black fabric cloth**—the latter prevents weed growth, but clear plastic heats more rapidly. After planting, you can beat the chill by enclosing tender plants in **water towers or** covering them with **floating row covers** If you retain these marvelous covers permanately over lettuce, spinach, or other greens you will harvest a quicker, tenderer, tastier, more perfect product.[1] Row covers not only ensure an earlier spring harvest, but later the shade they provide will help prolong spring temperatures in areas with hot summers.

Raised beds which drain rapidly will warm sooner than water-soaked plots. Again, a garden on a sunny hillside will be first to warm in spring. Tie plants to a trellis to raise them into the warming sun. Surround your beds with pavement or stones to absorb heat. Warm-season vegetables planted against a sunny wall thrive on the reflected heat.

Obviously, to lower heat,. do the reverse. Provide partial shade, sunken beds, cooling breezes near water, overhead sprinklers, a thick layer of compost, and plant away from walks and walls to keep foliage cooler. If you vegetables early so they will mature before hot weather begins, or include them in the fall garden.

Other row cover advantages

Row covers save water by reducing evaporation. They also protect plants from fly-in insects. This is important since aphids, thrips, and whiteflies may carry diseases. Thus, even plants which require pollination will benefit from row covers until flowers appear, since the length of time in which the plant will be exposed to diseases will be shorter.

Tips on choosing, planting & caring for vegetables

Bedding plants should always be placed into dampened holes. Some, such as tomatoes, benefit by being buried deeply so they will grow a sturdy, drought-resistant root structure. Others should be planted at the same level as they grew in the pot. After firming the soil around the seedling, water again with a weak fertilizer solution, and in the sun, provide temporary shade. Young plants should be moistened daily at first. Then water every other day for a week. Watch carefully to prevent wilting. Then except in very not climates, biweekly watering should suffice through the remainder of the season.

Be sure to **keep down weeds**, since these compete with desired plants for water, light, and nutrients. Disturb soil as little as possible while removing weeds. Black fabric cloth over the bed will prevent weed growth, prevent diseases which are splashed up from the soil itself, and save water. A heavy mulch will so the same, while cooling the soil. This may or may not be an advantage in your situation.

To keep down insects and diseases, you may want to rotate your vegetables annually (move them to a new spot). Vegetables which are related to each other are usually subject to the same pest insects, root nematodes, and diseases so they should be followed in the rotation by unrelated plants which will not provide a host for these pests.

Fortunately several modern vegetable varieties are resistant to a variety of soil diseases which are prevalent in almost all soils. Soils which contain a high level of organic materials tend to suppress some of these same pests because organic matter supports their natural enemies. Incorporate compost into your soil at least annually. In addition, every once in a while, take each bed out of the rotation and **solarize** the soil. This will reduce some of these same soil-born pests, reduce weeds, and stimulate plant growth. (Solarization is described elsewhere in this book).

Fall vegetables

Fall vegetables must be planted in summer, even though many seeds do not germinate in hot soil. To succeed, you may need to cool the planting mix and protect the young plants from the ambient heat. In addition, these seedlings may benefit from **shade cloth** overhead after they are transplanted outdoors. Since insects are very active during this period, young summer transplants will usually benefit from row covers at least until the weather cools. All this is worth it all. Those luscious fall crops will rush to perfect maturity.

---

1 Amer Veg Grow 3/94.

Tweeking Tomatoes

We're sure you're always looking for new ways to improve your tomatoes. Recently Aref Abdul-Baki and John Teasdale of USDA, Beltsville, MD, described a no-till system based on old agricultural practices which has potential to produce important yield increases.[1] (It differs from typical no-till system in which a cover crop is killed with herbicides before tomatoes or other vegetables are planted in the residues).

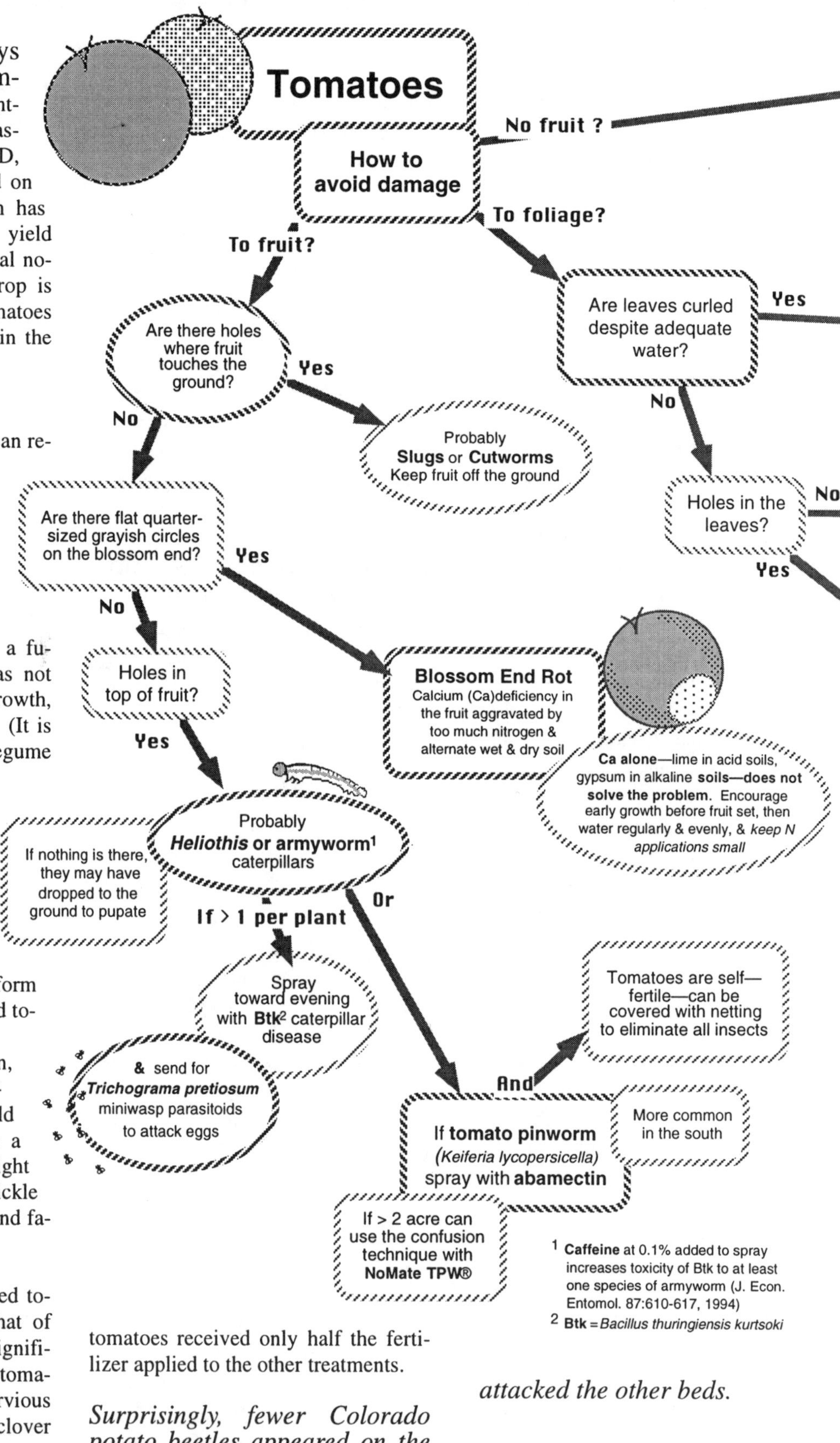

Tomatoes
How to avoid damage
No fruit ?
To foliage?
To fruit?
Are leaves curled despite adequate water?
Yes
No
Holes in the leaves?
No
Yes
Are there holes where fruit touches the ground?
Yes
Probably Slugs or Cutworms Keep fruit off the ground
No
Are there flat quarter-sized grayish circles on the blossom end?
Yes
Blossom End Rot
Calcium (Ca)deficiency in the fruit aggravated by too much nitrogen & alternate wet & dry soil
Ca alone—lime in acid soils, gypsum in alkaline soils—does not solve the problem. Encourage early growth before fruit set, then water regularly & evenly, & keep N applications small
No
Holes in top of fruit?
Yes
Probably Heliothis or armyworm[1] caterpillars
If nothing is there, they may have dropped to the ground to pupate
If > 1 per plant
Or
Spray toward evening with Btk[2] caterpillar disease
& send for Trichograma pretiosum miniwasp parasitoids to attack eggs
Tomatoes are self—fertile—can be covered with netting to eliminate all insects
And
If tomato pinworm (Keiferia lycopersicella) spray with abamectin
More common in the south
If > 2 acre can use the confusion technique with NoMate TPW®
1 Caffeine at 0.1% added to spray increases toxicity of Btk to at least one species of armyworm (J. Econ. Entomol. 87:610-617, 1994)
2 Btk = Bacillus thuringiensis kurtsoki

Legume cover crop

Many of us have found that we can reduce erosion, fix atmospheric nitrogen,[2] and improve organic content of the soil, by planting a legume cover crop in winter.

In early September these researchers planted the hardy annual legume, **hairy vetch**, into a future tomato plot. The vetch was not watered or fertilized during growth, though you may need to do so. (It is not a good idea to use *just any* legume to mulch tomatoes (or any crop) since some legumes may be susceptible to the same root-feeding nematodes as your crop. Fortunately hairy vetch is not a host).

On May 1, they cut and chopped down the vetch to a uniform mulch, and inserted five week old tomato seedlings. The dying vetch eliminated early weed completion, and cooled the soil in this hot climate. (In a cooler area this would not be an advantage. Perhaps a black fabric mulch over all might increase warmth if needed). Trickle irrigation watered the tomatoes and facilitated decay of the vetch.

The yield from the vetch-mulched tomatoes was more than twice that of un-mulched control plants, and significantly greater than yields from tomatoes planted in the other impervious black plastic or subterranean clover mulches. This, bumper crop was attained despite the fact that the vetch tomatoes received only half the fertilizer applied to the other treatments.

Surprisingly, fewer Colorado potato beetles appeared on the vetch-mulched tomatoes than attacked the other beds.

1 Hort Sci 28:106-108, 1993, Nat Gar 17(4):44-47, 1994. 2 Transfer nitrogen from the air into nitrates which fertilize the soil.

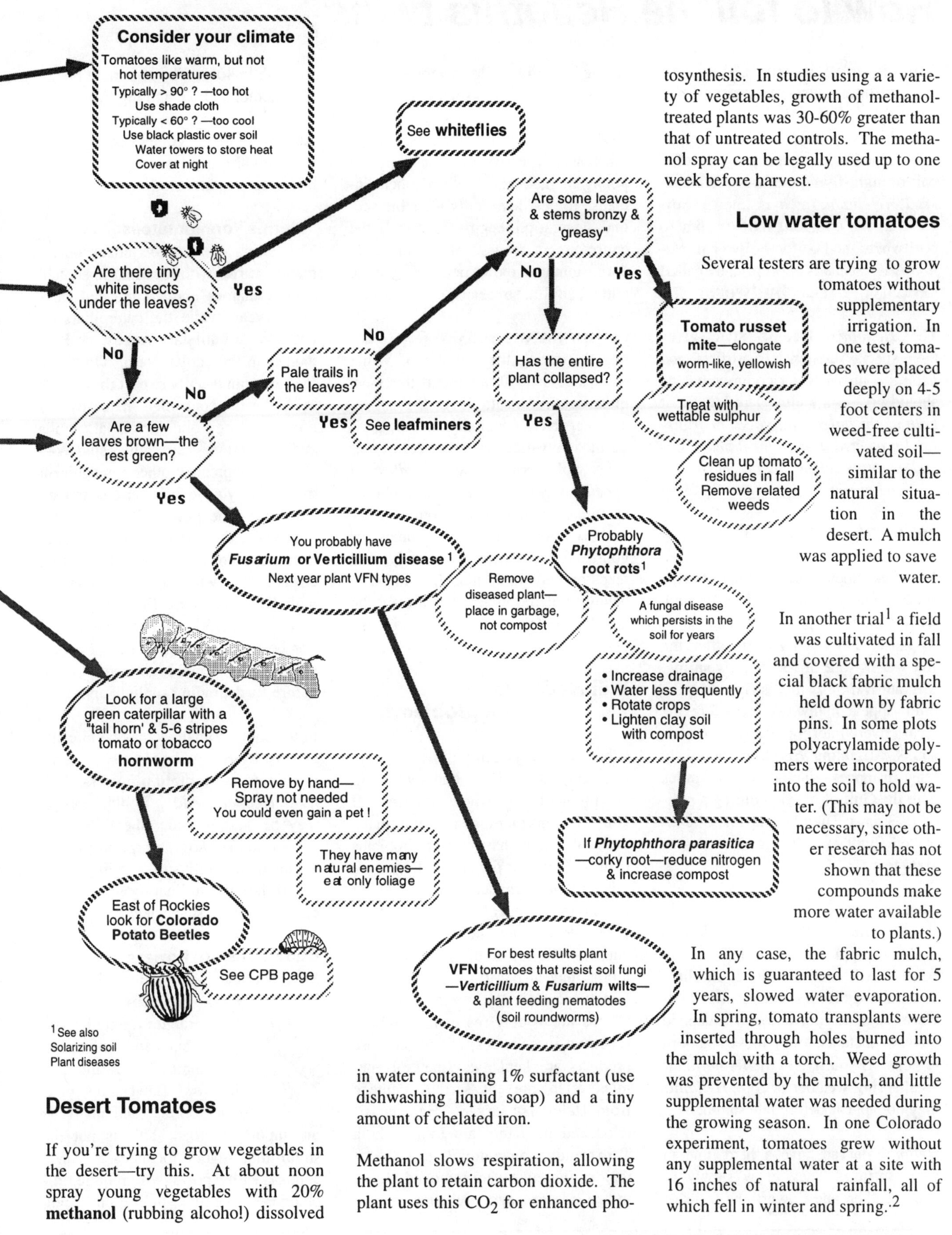
Consider your climate
Tomatoes like warm, but not hot temperatures
Typically > 90° ? —too hot
Use shade cloth
Typically < 60° ? —too cool
Use black plastic over soil
Water towers to store heat
Cover at night
Are there tiny white insects under the leaves?
Yes
See whiteflies
No
Are a few leaves brown—the rest green?
No
Pale trails in the leaves?
Yes
See leafminers
No
Are some leaves & stems bronzy & 'greasy'
Yes
Tomato russet mite—elongate worm-like, yellowish
Treat with wettable sulphur
Clean up tomato residues in fall
Remove related weeds
No
Has the entire plant collapsed?
Yes
Probably Phytophthora root rots1
Remove diseased plant—place in garbage, not compost
A fungal disease which persists in the soil for years
• Increase drainage
• Water less frequently
• Rotate crops
• Lighten clay soil with compost
If Phytophthora parasitica —corky root—reduce nitrogen & increase compost
Yes
You probably have Fusarium or Verticillium disease 1
Next year plant VFN types
For best results plant VFN tomatoes that resist soil fungi —Verticillium & Fusarium wilts— & plant feeding nematodes (soil roundworms)
Look for a large green caterpillar with a 'tail horn' & 5-6 stripes tomato or tobacco hornworm
Remove by hand—
Spray not needed
You could even gain a pet !
They have many natural enemies—eat only foliage
East of Rockies look for Colorado Potato Beetles
See CPB page
1 See also
Solarizing soil
Plant diseases

Desert Tomatoes

If you're trying to grow vegetables in the desert—try this. At about noon spray young vegetables with 20% **methanol** (rubbing alcoho!) dissolved in water containing 1% surfactant (use dishwashing liquid soap) and a tiny amount of chelated iron.

Methanol slows respiration, allowing the plant to retain carbon dioxide. The plant uses this CO_2 for enhanced photosynthesis. In studies using a a variety of vegetables, growth of methanol-treated plants was 30-60% greater than that of untreated controls. The methanol spray can be legally used up to one week before harvest.

Low water tomatoes

Several testers are trying to grow tomatoes without supplementary irrigation. In one test, tomatoes were placed deeply on 4-5 foot centers in weed-free cultivated soil—similar to the natural situation in the desert. A mulch was applied to save water.

In another trial[1] a field was cultivated in fall and covered with a special black fabric mulch held down by fabric pins. In some plots polyacrylamide polymers were incorporated into the soil to hold water. (This may not be necessary, since other research has not shown that these compounds make more water available to plants.) In any case, the fabric mulch, which is guaranteed to last for 5 years, slowed water evaporation. In spring, tomato transplants were inserted through holes burned into the mulch with a torch. Weed growth was prevented by the mulch, and little supplemental water was needed during the growing season. In one Colorado experiment, tomatoes grew without any supplemental water at a site with 16 inches of natural rainfall, all of which fell in winter and spring.[2]

---

[1] DeWitt Sunbelt, [2] Amer Veg Gro 11/93:30-32.

How to foil the Heliothis twins

Munch, munch, munch! Even experienced gardeners dread the thought of "worms" in the garden. Probably your toughest caterpillar competitors are the progeny of a pair of night-flying moths— *Helicoverpa*[1] *(Heliothis) zea* is known variously as the corn **earworm**, tomato **fruitworm**, and cotton **bollworm**. *Heliothis virescens* is appropriately called tobacco or geranium **budworm**.

The *Heliothis*' feeding style gives them special resistance to artificial and natural controls. Their common names should give you a clue. *The larvae of both moths burrow into buds or fruits--and protected from natural and artificial controls, chew on the parts you wish to harvest.*

Heliothis life cycle

Heliothis spend the winter buried about about one inch below ground. Development stops during this pupal diapause, and begins again after the soil warms to ≥ 56° F in early spring. Migrant *Heliothis* moths from Mexico often appear a few weeks before the local overwintering pupae become adults. Migrating *Heliothis* moths fly long distances—including 500 miles over the Gulf of Mexico during a period of 3 days. They are capable of controlled flight at altitudes in excess of 1000 feet.

Migrants arrive about February 1 in Brownsville and Phoenix; late March in Mississippi and central Texas; in April in Arkansas and North Carolina. The date of the first earworm or budworm eggs at your home will depend on your distance from these southern regions. If you live in the far north, or local spring weather is cool, *Heliothis* may not appear before late summer.

Heliothis larvae have a hard time in early spring. They grow slowly in cool weather, and flowers and fruits of spring-blooming wildflowers—usually in the mallow, nightshade, or clover families—are too small to provide shelter from the predators and parasitoids which arrive to consume the young marauders. Moth numbers increase to pest level only after the second generation begins to attack the enormous acreages of commercial corn, tomato, okra, peanuts, potato, cotton, alfalfa, soybeans, and tobacco.

Perhaps you've heard that few *Heliothis* fly during the full moon. While some studies tend to support this idea, most data refute it. Indeed, most researchers have concluded that the period of oviposition on sweet corn coincides with corn silking *regardless of the stages of the moon. H. zea* chooses corn over soybeans or cotton. *H. virescens* prefers tomato, petunias, or gourds; rejects corn completely, and feeds on buds more than *H. zea.* The behavior of the moths depends on the developmental condition of the plants.

Will *Heliothis* be a problem?

Whether your garden will be seriously threatened by boll and budworms will be influenced by where you live. If your's is a northern, or a cool climate, you will likely have fewer problems than will sunbelt dwellers. If you are raising tomatoes, and your neighbor has silking corn, *H. zea* will be on the corn. But when the nearby farmer cuts his alfalfa, or the corn matures, moths may arrive to oviposit on your tomato plants. Bollworms and budworms are widely resistant to broad-spectrum insecticides, but when these products are kept away, natural enemies often prevent serious damage from *Heliothis* larvae. Egg parasitoids and predators are basic. In a Texas study [2] on cotton 81 to 100% of their spring eggs were removed. Later in the season, egg predation ranged from 55 to 80%. The important predators included pirate and big-eyed bugs, Cotton Fleahoppers, Imported Fire Ant, and spiders. Green Lacewing larvae, ladybird beetles, and ground beetles were also involved.

"Worms" on tomatoes

The timing of *Heliothis* attack on tomatoes varies with location. In sunbelt areas tomatoes may be infested early in the year, while the caterpillars do not appear until late August or September in the cooler north. On tomatoes you can usually expect these pests to be well controlled naturally by mini-wasp egg and larval parasitoids and predators—especially spiders—you may appreciate other management tricks. If you've had serious tomato damage in the past, it may be worth your while to search for eggs weekly near the top of your plants. If you find eggs, spray twice at 5 day intervals with Btk containing Entice*, Gusto* or other caterpillar-feeding stimulant. For best results, spray in the evening so larvae will be able to feed all night before Bt-degrading sunlight appears.

In the south, tomatoes may be infested not just by *Heliothis*, but also with armyworms and **tomato pinworms** *Keiferia lycopersicella.* In this case it may be best to order the mini-wasp parasitoid, *Trichograma pretiosum,* to augment the ability of existing native parasitoids in eliminating most of the eggs of these pest species.

Budworms on flowers

In recent years one strain of, *Heliothis virecens* has acquired a taste for geranium, petunia, and gourd buds and other related plants. The result may be few flowers in your summer border, and no fruits on important crops. This is not the strain that favors tomatoes.[1] Since control with sprays will require impractical weekly applications, you

---

[1] Insect names are changed frequently. [2] Environ Entomol 23:1189-1202, 1994.

may want to try another tactic.

It may be possible to limit egg laying on geraniums and petunia by *illuminating your plants with a dim light between midnight and dawn, the period when most Heliothis eggs are deposited. (Remember, these nocturnal moths may avoid light).*

Earworms on corn

In most areas, only one *Heliothis* caterpillar will survive in any ear even if you do nothing. Early planting and careful monitoring are basic to unblemished ears. Early corn usually reaches the vulnerable silking stage, before earworm numbers rise. At peak silking, follow our chart for control methods.

If you live in a very warm climate like Hawaii or Florida, or want to harvest sweet corn over a long season, perfect ears may be almost impossible. In this case, you might cut off and destroy the tips of the ear and with it any developing worms—earworms are cannibalistic, and only one larvae survives to feed on the ear. (Be sure these tips are heated to kill the larvae). In a few places corn can also be infested with **armyworm** *(Spodoptera sp.)* or **European corn borer** *(Ostrinia nubilalis)* caterpillars--and they're not so obliging about killing each other. If these are common, follow our direction carefully.

Heliothis has recently extended its range to yet another plant, the Japanese Honeysuckle, *Lonicera japonica.* This vine is an aggressive invader of vacant fields and forested lands in southeastern U.S. *Heliothis* may help in its control.[2] But since land near the honeysuckle is unplowed, pupal survival may be higher than in agricultural lands, leading to further increase in the population of these pests on desired plants.

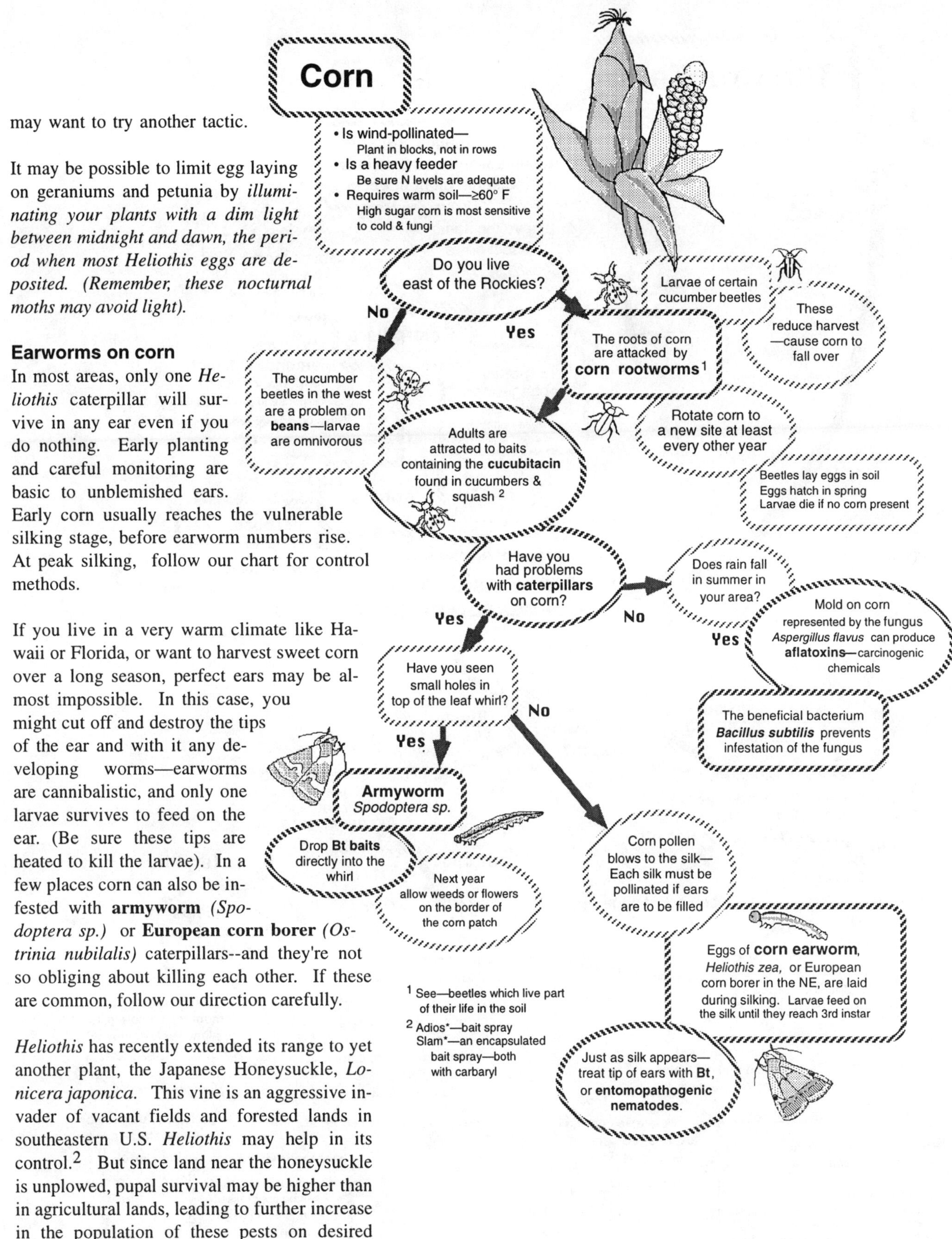
Corn
• Is wind-pollinated—
Plant in blocks, not in rows
• Is a heavy feeder
Be sure N levels are adequate
• Requires warm soil—≥60° F
High sugar corn is most sensitive to cold & fungi
Do you live east of the Rockies?
No
Yes
Larvae of certain cucumber beetles
These reduce harvest —cause corn to fall over
The roots of corn are attacked by corn rootworms[1]
The cucumber beetles in the west are a problem on beans—larvae are omnivorous
Rotate corn to a new site at least every other year
Adults are attracted to baits containing the cucubitacin found in cucumbers & squash [2]
Beetles lay eggs in soil
Eggs hatch in spring
Larvae die if no corn present
Have you had problems with caterpillars on corn?
Does rain fall in summer in your area?
No
Yes
Mold on corn represented by the fungus Aspergillus flavus can produce aflatoxins—carcinogenic chemicals
Yes
Have you seen small holes in top of the leaf whirl?
The beneficial bacterium Bacillus subtilis prevents infestation of the fungus
No
Yes
Armyworm
Spodoptera sp.
Drop Bt baits directly into the whirl
Next year allow weeds or flowers on the border of the corn patch
Corn pollen blows to the silk— Each silk must be pollinated if ears are to be filled
Eggs of corn earworm, Heliothis zea, or European corn borer in the NE, are laid during silking. Larvae feed on the silk until they reach 3rd instar
1 See—beetles which live part of their life in the soil
2 Adios*—bait spray
Slam*—an encapsulated bait spray—both with carbaryl
Just as silk appears— treat tip of ears with Bt, or entomopathogenic nematodes.

1 Evol 44:1326-1337, 1990. 2 Environ Entomol 23:906-911, 1994.

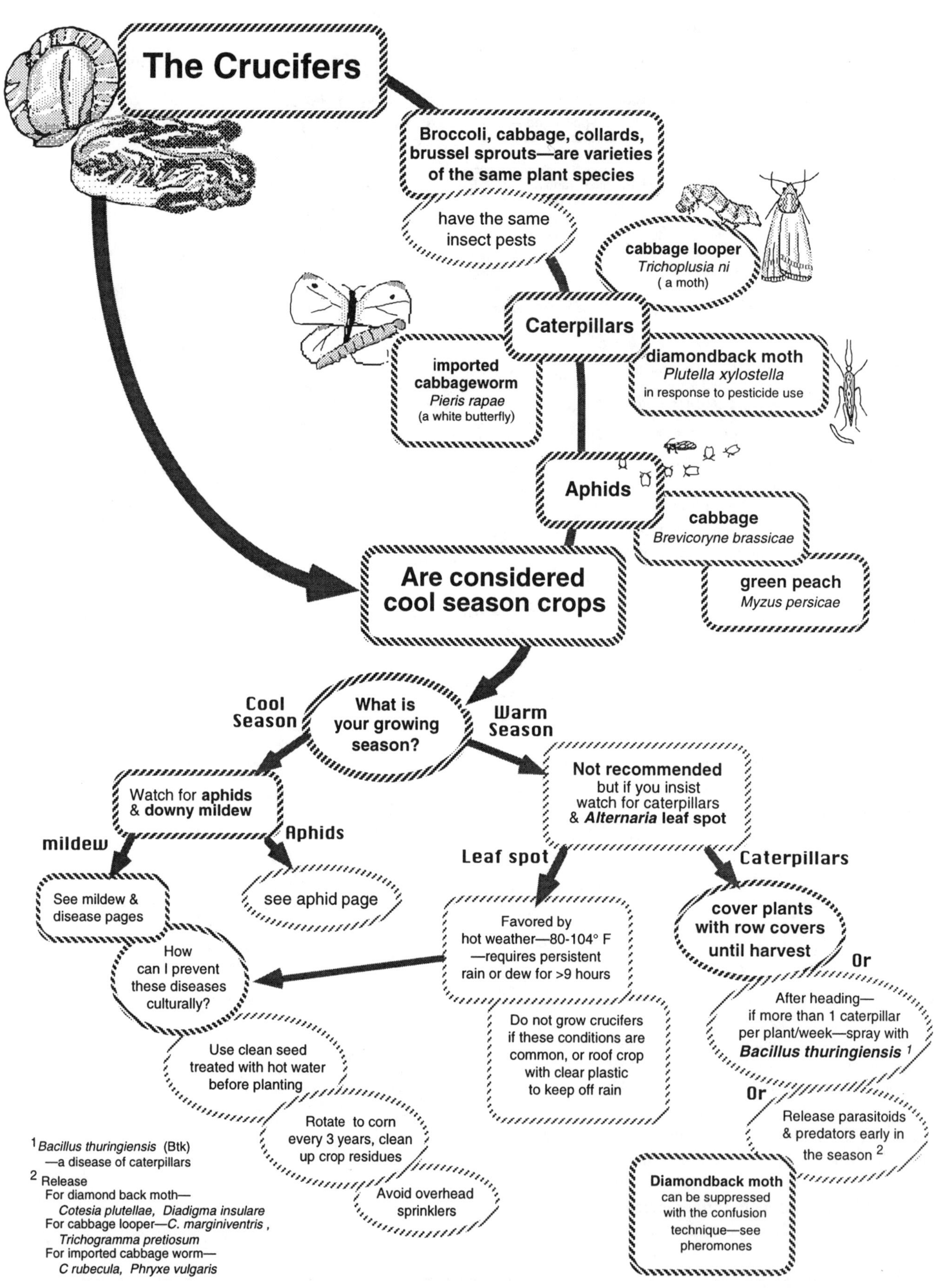
The Crucifers
Broccoli, cabbage, collards, brussel sprouts—are varieties of the same plant species
have the same insect pests
cabbage looper
Trichoplusia ni
(a moth)
Caterpillars
imported cabbageworm
Pieris rapae
(a white butterfly)
diamondback moth
Plutella xylostella
in response to pesticide use
Aphids
cabbage
Brevicoryne brassicae
green peach
Myzus persicae
Are considered cool season crops
What is your growing season?
Cool Season
Warm Season
Watch for aphids & downy mildew
mildew
Aphids
See mildew & disease pages
see aphid page
Not recommended but if you insist watch for caterpillars & Alternaria leaf spot
Leaf spot
Caterpillars
Favored by hot weather—80-104° F —requires persistent rain or dew for >9 hours
Do not grow crucifers if these conditions are common, or roof crop with clear plastic to keep off rain
cover plants with row covers until harvest
Or
After heading— if more than 1 caterpillar per plant/week—spray with Bacillus thuringiensis [1]
Or
Release parasitoids & predators early in the season [2]
Diamondback moth can be suppressed with the confusion technique—see pheromones
How can I prevent these diseases culturally?
Use clean seed treated with hot water before planting
Rotate to corn every 3 years, clean up crop residues
Avoid overhead sprinklers

[1] *Bacillus thuringiensis* (Btk)
—a disease of caterpillars

[2] Release
For diamond back moth—
Cotesia plutellae, Diadigma insulare
For cabbage looper—*C. marginiventris*,
Trichogramma pretiosum
For imported cabbage worm—
C rubecula, Phryxe vulgaris

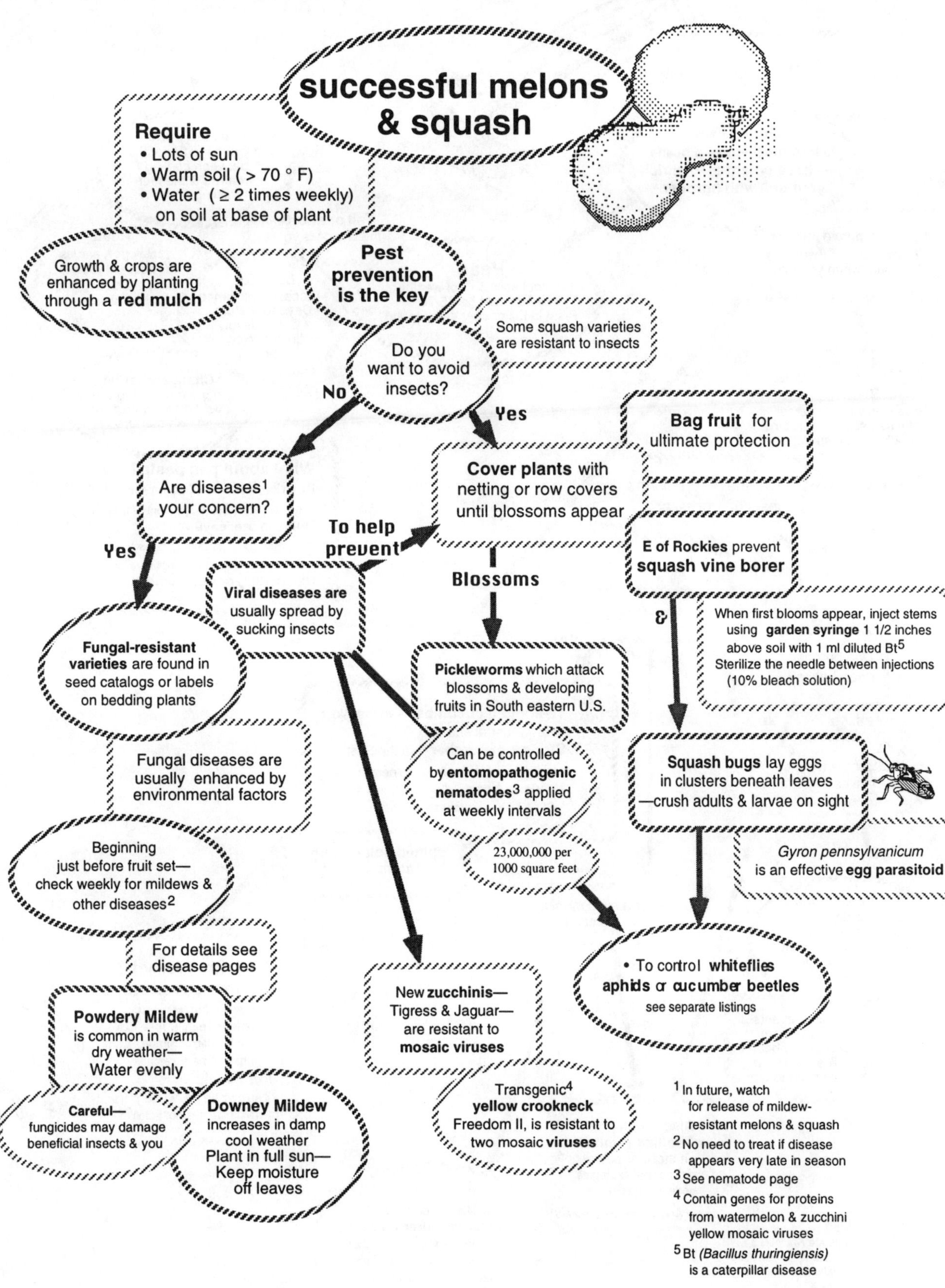
successful melons & squash
Require
• Lots of sun
• Warm soil (> 70 ° F)
• Water (≥ 2 times weekly) on soil at base of plant
Growth & crops are enhanced by planting through a red mulch
Pest prevention is the key
Some squash varieties are resistant to insects
Do you want to avoid insects?
No
Yes
Bag fruit for ultimate protection
Are diseases[1] your concern?
Cover plants with netting or row covers until blossoms appear
To help prevent
E of Rockies prevent squash vine borer
Yes
Viral diseases are usually spread by sucking insects
Blossoms
&
When first blooms appear, inject stems using garden syringe 1 1/2 inches above soil with 1 ml diluted Bt[5] Sterilize the needle between injections (10% bleach solution)
Fungal-resistant varieties are found in seed catalogs or labels on bedding plants
Pickleworms which attack blossoms & developing fruits in South eastern U.S.
Can be controlled by entomopathogenic nematodes[3] applied at weekly intervals
Squash bugs lay eggs in clusters beneath leaves —crush adults & larvae on sight
Fungal diseases are usually enhanced by environmental factors
23,000,000 per 1000 square feet
Gyron pennsylvanicum is an effective egg parasitoid
Beginning just before fruit set— check weekly for mildews & other diseases[2]
For details see disease pages
• To control whiteflies aphids or cucumber beetles
see separate listings
New zucchinis— Tigress & Jaguar— are resistant to mosaic viruses
Powdery Mildew is common in warm dry weather— Water evenly
Transgenic[4] yellow crookneck Freedom II, is resistant to two mosaic viruses
Careful— fungicides may damage beneficial insects & you
Downey Mildew increases in damp cool weather Plant in full sun— Keep moisture off leaves

1 In future, watch for release of mildew-resistant melons & squash
2 No need to treat if disease appears very late in season
3 See nematode page
4 Contain genes for proteins from watermelon & zucchini yellow mosaic viruses
5 Bt *(Bacillus thuringiensis)* is a caterpillar disease

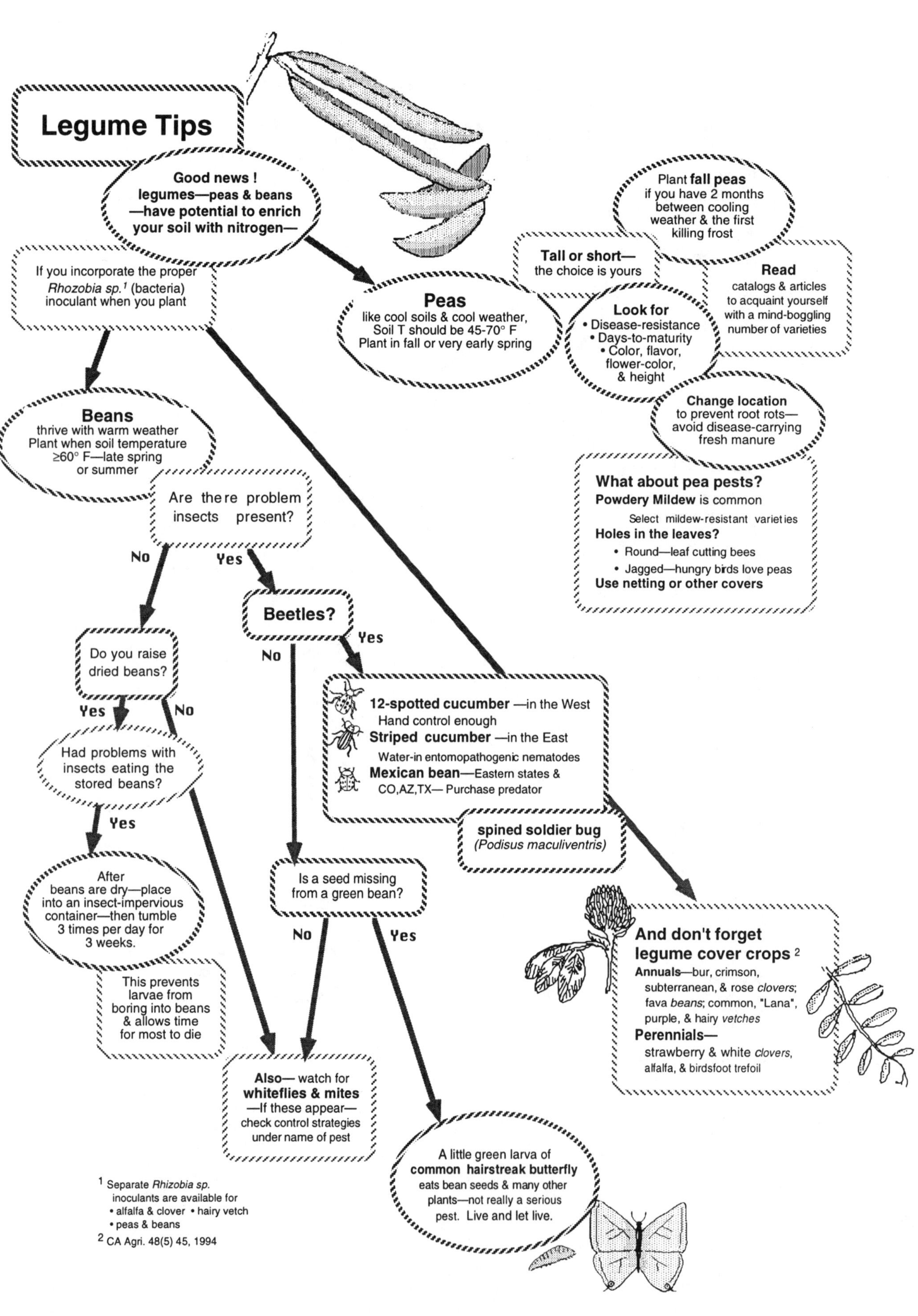
Legume Tips
Good news ! legumes—peas & beans —have potential to enrich your soil with nitrogen—
If you incorporate the proper Rhozobia sp.1 (bacteria) inoculant when you plant
Peas
like cool soils & cool weather, Soil T should be 45-70° F Plant in fall or very early spring
Plant fall peas if you have 2 months between cooling weather & the first killing frost
Tall or short— the choice is yours
Read catalogs & articles to acquaint yourself with a mind-boggling number of varieties
Look for • Disease-resistance • Days-to-maturity • Color, flavor, flower-color, & height
Change location to prevent root rots— avoid disease-carrying fresh manure
What about pea pests?
Powdery Mildew is common
Select mildew-resistant varieties
Holes in the leaves?
• Round—leaf cutting bees
• Jagged—hungry birds love peas
Use netting or other covers
Beans
thrive with warm weather Plant when soil temperature ≥60° F—late spring or summer
Are there problem insects present?
No
Yes
Beetles?
Yes
No
12-spotted cucumber —in the West
Hand control enough
Striped cucumber —in the East
Water-in entomopathogenic nematodes
Mexican bean—Eastern states & CO,AZ,TX— Purchase predator
spined soldier bug (Podisus maculiventris)
Do you raise dried beans?
Yes
No
Had problems with insects eating the stored beans?
Yes
After beans are dry—place into an insect-impervious container—then tumble 3 times per day for 3 weeks.
This prevents larvae from boring into beans & allows time for most to die
Is a seed missing from a green bean?
No
Yes
Also— watch for whiteflies & mites —If these appear— check control strategies under name of pest
A little green larva of common hairstreak butterfly eats bean seeds & many other plants—not really a serious pest. Live and let live.
And don't forget legume cover crops 2
Annuals—bur, crimson, subterranean, & rose clovers; fava beans; common, "Lana", purple, & hairy vetches
Perennials— strawberry & white clovers, alfalfa, & birdsfoot trefoil

[1] Separate *Rhizobia sp.* inoculants are available for
• alfalfa & clover • hairy vetch
• peas & beans

[2] CA Agri. 48(5) 45, 1994

Getting Going with Asparagus

Asparagus is a long-lived perennial

Prepare
Prepare
Prepare

To get rid of weeds & soil-born diseases

Fusarium wilt

Solarize[1] soil in mid-summer

Heat kills disease fungi
some weed seeds
some root nematodes

Choose stock carefully
Jersey Giant (males)
Disease resistant
Vigorous

Plant about 6 inches deep—12 inches apart
Deep trenches are out!

Keep down weeds
Mulch Mulch Mulch

Compost options
Wood chips, Straw, Composted manure

No cultivation ever!

Control Insects[2]
Asparagus beetle
Crioceris asparagus
Spotted Asparagus Beetle
Crioceris duodecimpunctata
Asparagus aphid
Brachycorynella asparagi

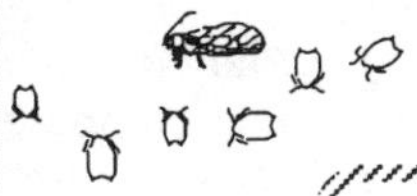

Place Row covers over young shoots
Knock adult beetles into soapy water

The first year harvest lightly—water weekly

Stop harvest when pencil-sized spears appear

Little summer water is required in moderate climate after first year

Let leaves grow throughout the remainder of the summer
In fall cut back foliage—add compost

[1] See Solarization

[2] Watch for introduction of Bt product for these beetles
See aphid page

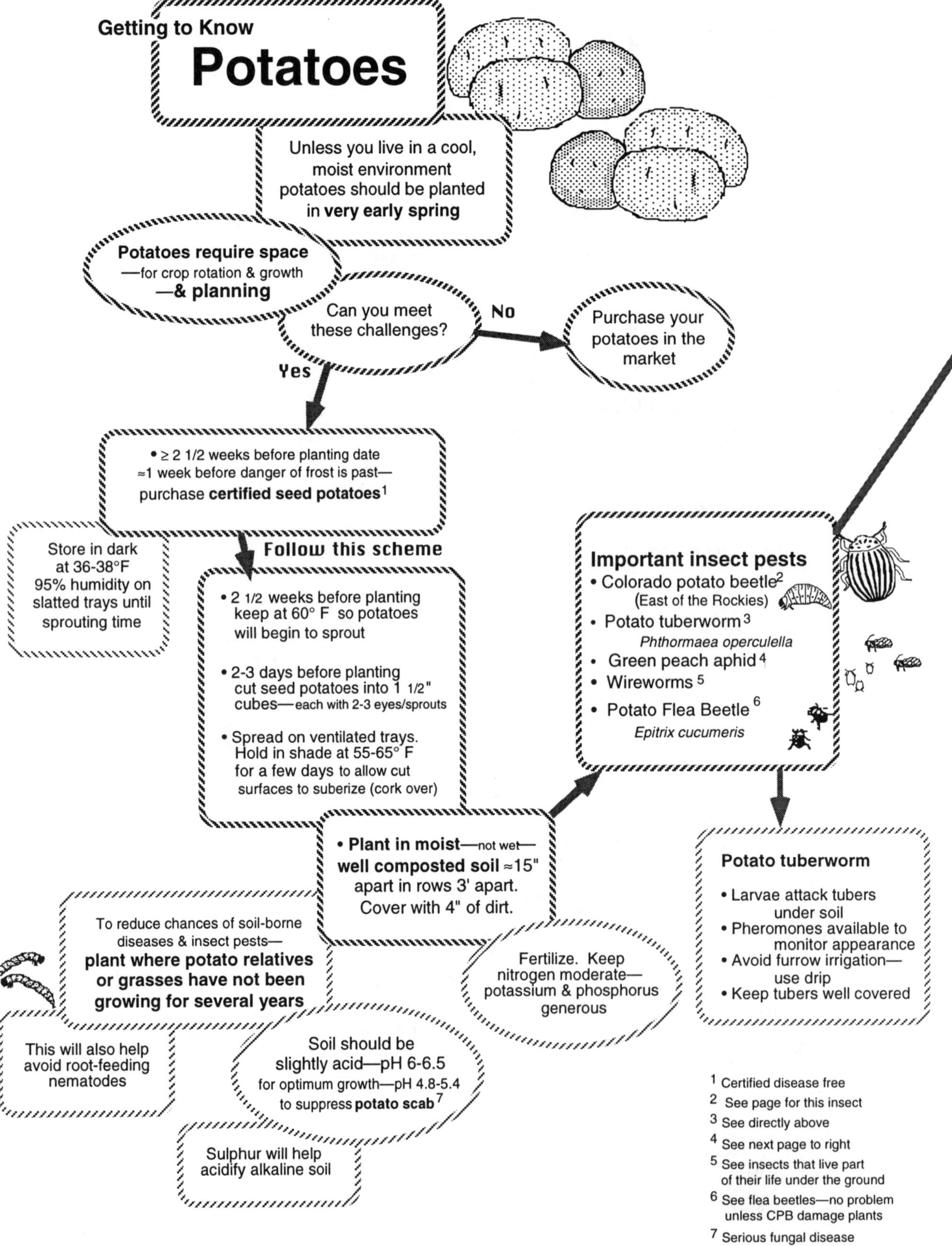

Getting to Know
Potatoes
Unless you live in a cool, moist environment potatoes should be planted in very early spring
Potatoes require space —for crop rotation & growth —& planning
Can you meet these challenges?
No
Purchase your potatoes in the market
Yes
• ≥ 2 1/2 weeks before planting date ≈1 week before danger of frost is past— purchase certified seed potatoes1
Store in dark at 36-38°F 95% humidity on slatted trays until sprouting time
Follow this scheme
• 2 1/2 weeks before planting keep at 60° F so potatoes will begin to sprout
• 2-3 days before planting cut seed potatoes into 1 1/2" cubes—each with 2-3 eyes/sprouts
• Spread on ventilated trays. Hold in shade at 55-65° F for a few days to allow cut surfaces to suberize (cork over)
• Plant in moist—not wet— well composted soil ≈15" apart in rows 3' apart. Cover with 4" of dirt.
To reduce chances of soil-borne diseases & insect pests— plant where potato relatives or grasses have not been growing for several years
This will also help avoid root-feeding nematodes
Soil should be slightly acid—pH 6-6.5 for optimum growth—pH 4.8-5.4 to suppress potato scab7
Sulphur will help acidify alkaline soil
Fertilize. Keep nitrogen moderate— potassium & phosphorus generous
Important insect pests
• Colorado potato beetle2 (East of the Rockies)
• Potato tuberworm3 Phthormaea operculella
• Green peach aphid4
• Wireworms5
• Potato Flea Beetle6 Epitrix cucumeris
Potato tuberworm
• Larvae attack tubers under soil
• Pheromones available to monitor appearance
• Avoid furrow irrigation— use drip
• Keep tubers well covered
1 Certified disease free
2 See page for this insect
3 See directly above
4 See next page to right
5 See insects that live part of their life under the ground
6 See flea beetles—no problem unless CPB damage plants
7 Serious fungal disease

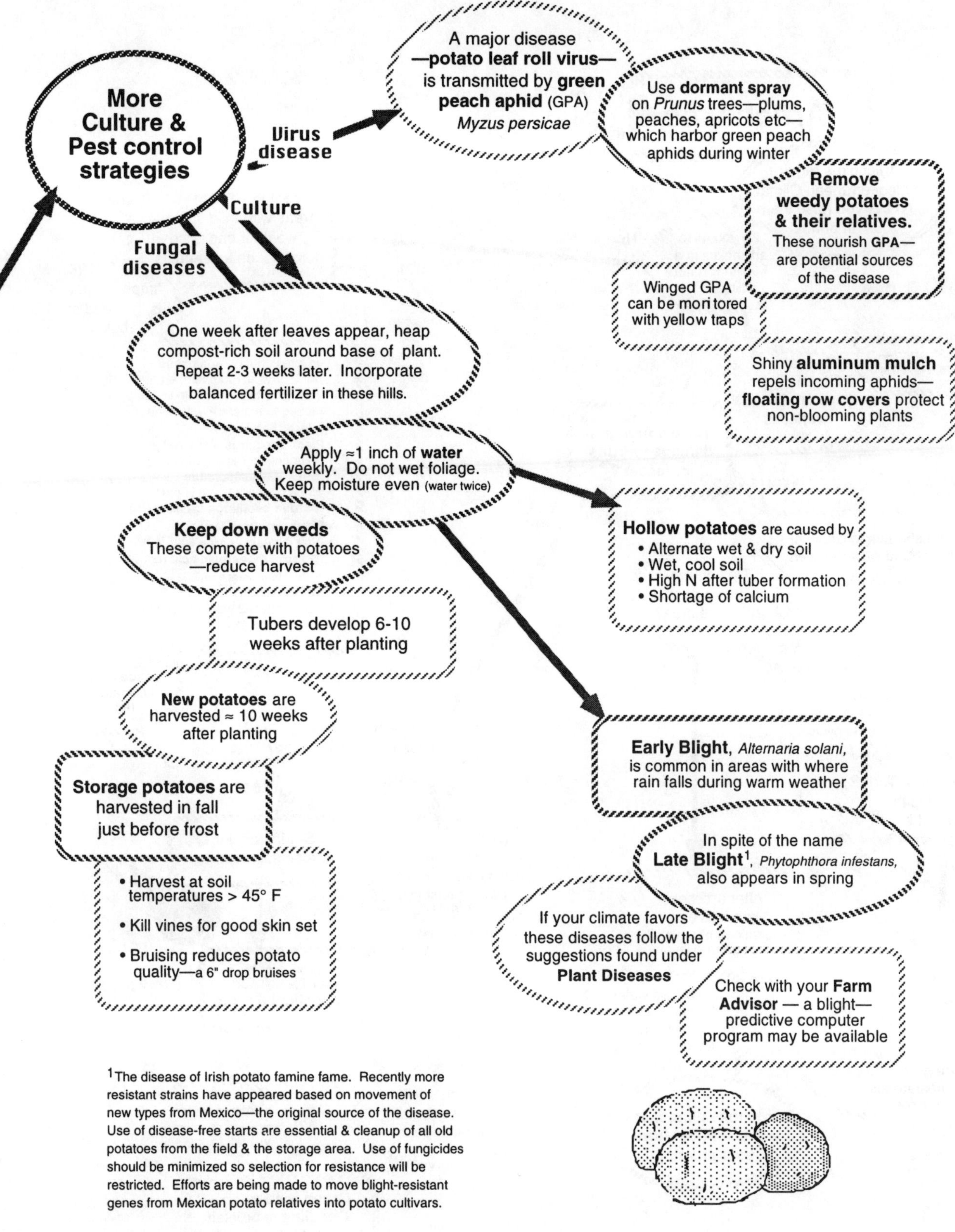
More Culture & Pest control strategies
Virus disease
Culture
Fungal diseases
A major disease —potato leaf roll virus— is transmitted by green peach aphid (GPA) Myzus persicae
Use dormant spray on Prunus trees—plums, peaches, apricots etc— which harbor green peach aphids during winter
Remove weedy potatoes & their relatives. These nourish GPA— are potential sources of the disease
Winged GPA can be monitored with yellow traps
Shiny aluminum mulch repels incoming aphids— floating row covers protect non-blooming plants
One week after leaves appear, heap compost-rich soil around base of plant. Repeat 2-3 weeks later. Incorporate balanced fertilizer in these hills.
Apply ≈1 inch of water weekly. Do not wet foliage. Keep moisture even (water twice)
Keep down weeds These compete with potatoes —reduce harvest
Tubers develop 6-10 weeks after planting
New potatoes are harvested ≈ 10 weeks after planting
Storage potatoes are harvested in fall just before frost
• Harvest at soil temperatures > 45° F
• Kill vines for good skin set
• Bruising reduces potato quality—a 6" drop bruises
Hollow potatoes are caused by
• Alternate wet & dry soil
• Wet, cool soil
• High N after tuber formation
• Shortage of calcium
Early Blight, Alternaria solani, is common in areas with where rain falls during warm weather
In spite of the name Late Blight1, Phytophthora infestans, also appears in spring
If your climate favors these diseases follow the suggestions found under Plant Diseases
Check with your Farm Advisor — a blight— predictive computer program may be available

[1] The disease of Irish potato famine fame. Recently more resistant strains have appeared based on movement of new types from Mexico—the original source of the disease. Use of disease-free starts are essential & cleanup of all old potatoes from the field & the storage area. Use of fungicides should be minimized so selection for resistance will be restricted. Efforts are being made to move blight-resistant genes from Mexican potato relatives into potato cultivars.

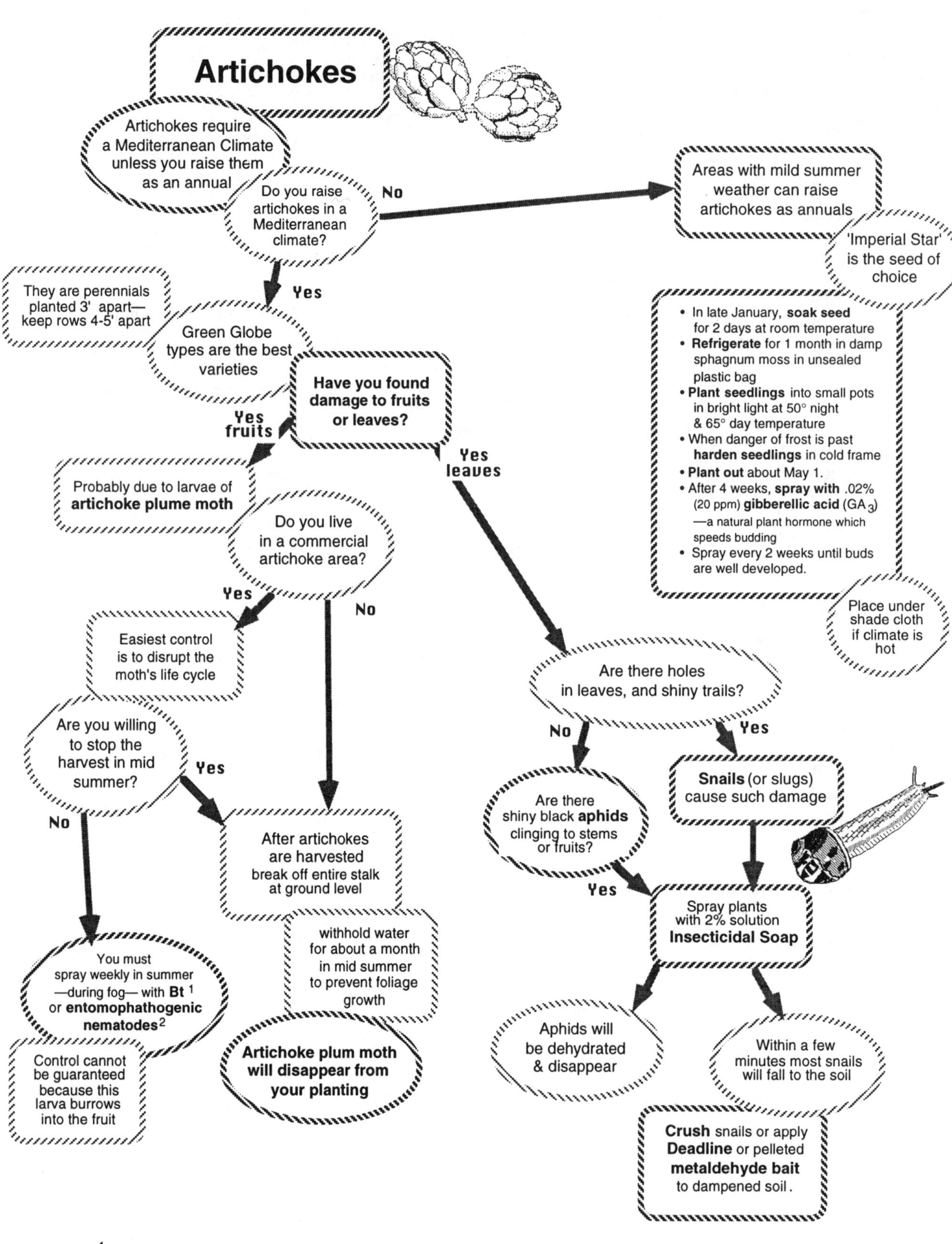
Artichokes
Artichokes require a Mediterranean Climate unless you raise them as an annual
Do you raise artichokes in a Mediterranean climate?
No
Areas with mild summer weather can raise artichokes as annuals
'Imperial Star' is the seed of choice
• In late January, soak seed for 2 days at room temperature
• Refrigerate for 1 month in damp sphagnum moss in unsealed plastic bag
• Plant seedlings into small pots in bright light at 50° night & 65° day temperature
• When danger of frost is past harden seedlings in cold frame
• Plant out about May 1.
• After 4 weeks, spray with .02% (20 ppm) gibberellic acid (GA 3) —a natural plant hormone which speeds budding
• Spray every 2 weeks until buds are well developed.
Place under shade cloth if climate is hot
Yes
They are perennials planted 3' apart— keep rows 4-5' apart
Green Globe types are the best varieties
Have you found damage to fruits or leaves?
Yes fruits
Yes leaves
Probably due to larvae of artichoke plume moth
Do you live in a commercial artichoke area?
Yes
No
Easiest control is to disrupt the moth's life cycle
Are you willing to stop the harvest in mid summer?
Yes
No
After artichokes are harvested break off entire stalk at ground level
withhold water for about a month in mid summer to prevent foliage growth
Artichoke plum moth will disappear from your planting
You must spray weekly in summer —during fog— with Bt 1 or entomophathogenic nematodes2
Control cannot be guaranteed because this larva burrows into the fruit
Are there holes in leaves, and shiny trails?
No
Yes
Are there shiny black aphids clinging to stems or fruits?
Yes
Snails (or slugs) cause such damage
Spray plants with 2% solution Insecticidal Soap
Aphids will be dehydrated & disappear
Within a few minutes most snails will fall to the soil
Crush snails or apply Deadline or pelleted metaldehyde bait to dampened soil.

1 See *Bacillus thuringiensis*

2 See entomopathogenic nematodes

Successful Root Vegetables

All root vegetables thrive best in moist loamy loose soil. Long narrow vegetables, such as carrots and rudabegas require the soil to be deep as well, unless you buy stubby cultivars. If your soil is not of this ideal type, add amendments. Clay soils can be loosened somewhat by adding sand or other mineral supplements. Both clay and sandy soils benefit from organic additives such as compost which improve the structure of clay, help hold water in the sand, and provide nutrients to either. Raw, uncomposted organic additives, such as sawdust, may also be useful, but they must be supplemented with some type of nitrogen fertilizer, or they will compete with your crops for essential nitrogen as they are broken down by microorganisms.

Name	Season/Temp.	Water	Fertilize	Pests	Other
Beets	Fall or spring	Keep moist	neutral pH, K [7], P [7]	Carrot weevil[1,2] Wireworms[5,6] Flea beetles[6] Leaf miners[1,2]	
Carrots	Warm soil	Keep moist	low N [7] high K	Carrot rust fly,[1,2,4] Carrot weevil[1,2,3] Wireworms [5,6]	
Jicama	Long warm season required	Keep moist	balanced		Perennial Vine
Onions	Spring or fall	Keep moist	Balanced	Onion fly[1,2] Wireworms[5,6]	Stop water when tops fall
Radish	Spring	Keep moist	Balanced	Root maggots[1,2]	Sun, partial shade , grows in 3 wks
Potatoes	Very early spring Certified seed potatoes	Keep moist	Acid soil, Balanced	CO potato beetle[6] wireworms[5,6] Leafhoppers/Euro corn borer [1] Leaf miners [1,2]	Dry before cool,dark storage
Yams, etc	Warm spring Certified slips,	Drought resist Water deeply	≥ pH 7, 5-10-10	Wireworms[5,6] flea beetles[6] Sweetpotato weevils[1,2,3]	Nights (≥ 55° F)
Turnips & Rudabegas	Fall, 4-6 weeks before frost	Weekly		Root maggots[1,2]	Turnips mature 2 mo Rudabegas-3 mo

[1]Row covers [2]Entomopathogenic nematodes at planting, later if needed [3]Crop rotation/ cultivation/soil solarization [4]Plant late in season [5]Potato/carrot pieces in soil as **trap crop** pull up frequently/remove wireworms [6]See this pest's page
[7]N = nitrogen, K = potassium, P = phosphorous

A luscious lawn—safely

More money, time, energy, and chemicals are put into lawns than any other part of the urban landscape. Indeed, it's even difficult to find lawn fertilizer these days because of the proliferation of "*weed and* feed", or "*weed*, feed, *and kill*" products. *On a typical golf course, pesticides are applied at nearly seven times the average used on agricultural land.* All 18 major "lawn care" pesticides lack adequate data: on toxicity, environmental fate, and persistence. Yet, *a lawn can flourish with proper cultural care, fertilizer, and water alone*—as is demonstrated by the pesticide-free lawn on the Washington, D.C. Mall. Good lawn care is really IPM in action.

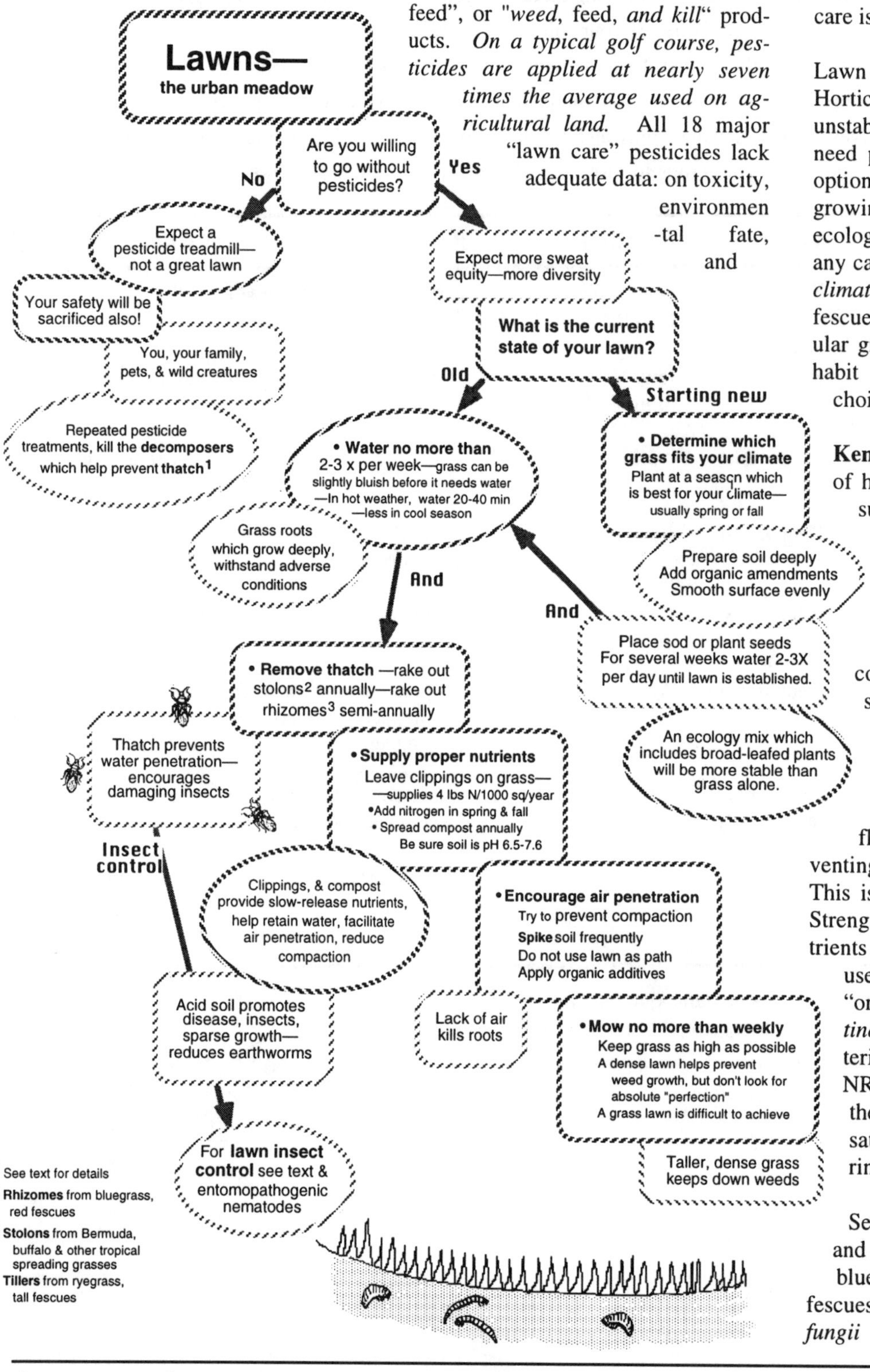

Lawn management begins at planting. Horticulturally, an all-grass lawn is an unstable monoculture. Do you really need perfect turf? Another possible option, a mixture of grasses and low-growing broad-leaved perennials—an ecology mix—is easier to handle. In any case, *your "lawn" should fit your climate.* Although Kentucky blue or fescue mixtures are still the most popular grasses, this may be a matter of habit or ignorance of other possible choices.

Kentucky bluegrass is intolerant of heat, requires frequent water, is susceptible to diseases. *Most of those lawn chemicals are applied to control diseases!* Kentucky bluegrass is subject to **necrotic ring spot** (NRS} *(Leptosphaeria korrae).* In cool weather, this disease causes spots with red and straw-colored blades. In warm weather infected turf wilts and yellows. An IPM control strategy for NRS uses Nutra Aid to flush out toxins which are preventing beneficial microbial activity. This is followed by Green Magic or Strengthen and Renew to add nutrients and beneficial microbes.[1] Or, use Lawn Restore which contains "organic" nutrients plus *Actinomycete* fungi and *Bacillus* bacteria[1] which are antagonistic to NRS. According to the EPA[2] either of these strategies provide satisfactory control of necrotic ring spot.

Several grasses are more drought and disease resistant than Kentucky blue. Some perennial ryes and tall fescues contain symbiotic *endophyte fungii* (fungi which live inside

Lawns—
the urban meadow

Are you willing to go without pesticides?

No

Expect a pesticide treadmill—not a great lawn

Your safety will be sacrificed also!

You, your family, pets, & wild creatures

Repeated pesticide treatments, kill the **decomposers** which help prevent **thatch**[1]

Yes

Expect more sweat equity—more diversity

What is the current state of your lawn?

Old

• Water no more than 2-3 x per week—grass can be slightly bluish before it needs water
—In hot weather, water 20-40 min
—less in cool season

Grass roots which grow deeply, withstand adverse conditions

And

• Remove thatch —rake out stolons[2] annually—rake out rhizomes[3] semi-annually

Thatch prevents water penetration—encourages damaging insects

Insect control

• Supply proper nutrients
Leave clippings on grass—
—supplies 4 lbs N/1000 sq/year
•Add nitrogen in spring & fall
• Spread compost annually
Be sure soil is pH 6.5-7.6

Clippings, & compost provide slow-release nutrients, help retain water, facilitate air penetration, reduce compaction

• Encourage air penetration
Try to prevent compaction
Spike soil frequently
Do not use lawn as path
Apply organic additives

Lack of air kills roots

Acid soil promotes disease, insects, sparse growth—reduces earthworms

For **lawn insect control** see text & entomopathogenic nematodes

• Mow no more than weekly
Keep grass as high as possible
A dense lawn helps prevent weed growth, but don't look for absolute "perfection"
A grass lawn is difficult to achieve

Taller, dense grass keeps down weeds

Starting new

• Determine which grass fits your climate
Plant at a season which is best for your climate—usually spring or fall

Prepare soil deeply
Add organic amendments
Smooth surface evenly

And

Place sod or plant seeds
For several weeks water 2-3X per day until lawn is established.

An ecology mix which includes broad-leafed plants will be more stable than grass alone.

1 See text for details
2 **Rhizomes** from bluegrass, red fescues
3 **Stolons** from Bermuda, buffalo & other tropical spreading grasses
Tillers from ryegrass, tall fescues

---

1 See sources. 2 EPA, 1989. Integrated pest management for turfgrass & ornamentals, p. 60

leaves) which synthesize a mixture of alkaloids which deter common lawn insects especially leafhoppers and flea beetles.[1] (Obviously, these cultivars should not be planted where livestock graze, but they do not harm beneficial insects, earthworms or people.)[2] In the high plains Blue grama or Buffalo Grass will provide an informal drought-resistant meadow that seldom needs mowing.[3] New varieties include Buffalo 609, Cherokee, Texoka, and Prairie.

It is best *replace bluegrass with more vigorous varieties* no matter where you live.[4] In the northeast, mixtures might include perennial ryegrass, mixed with red or tall fescues. In the northwest, the climax lawn should be bent grass, ('Bardot' or SR 7100'). Some good cultivars among turf-type tall fescues which are adapted in the sunbelt are 'Hubbard 87', 'Shenandoah', 'Guardian'. and 'Crossfire'. New, improved varieties are released frequently.

Improving your lawn

All lawns can be improved by proper management practices. In established turf, *focus on increasing turf density.* •**Adjust watering**. Most lawns receive too much water. Excess water drowns root tips, increases disease, and keeps lawn grubs (beetle larvae) near the surface in the root zone. In this situation you may assume that the resultant yellowing foliage is caused by water stress, *and apply even more water.* Usually two or three deep waterings per week are optimal. (see Water Wisdom). *Turf requires air* as well as water. A spiking machine which removes small soil plugs helps provide air.

(**Thatch** is a layer of dead grass stems, roots, and leaves which pile up on the soil surface of certain lawns.) Thatch prevents water penetration and enhances survival of such pest insects as **cinch bugs** (Eastern U.S. only). Grasses which spread by **rhizomes** (underground horizontal stems), and especially those which multiply via **stolons** (horizontal creeping stems) are more likely to develop a heavy thatch layer than are grasses which spread by **tillers** (side branches at the crown). In addition, repeated **insecticide treatments** aggravate thatch build-up by killing detritis[5] decomposers—soil dwelling earthworms, bacteria, mites, and protura and collembola (important detritis-feeding insects).

How Grasses Spread

Type of stem	Name	Grass
Underground horizontal	rhizomes	red fescue bluegrass
Horizontal creeping	stolons	Bermuda, buffalo
Side branches at the crown	tillers	tall fescue ryegrass

Troubleshooting lawns

Lawns require lots of ***nitrogen****.* A uniform yellowish color during the growing season in a properly-watered lawn, indicates a nitrogen shortage Most lawns benefit from supplemental N fertilizer in spring and fall, but lawns which are mulched by their own clippings require less. In fall you should apply a balanced mixture—equal amounts of nitrogen, potassium, and phosphate—to encourage root growth. Avoid 'weed and feed'', and weed, feed, and kill' products which will kill the detritis[1] feeders and insect natural enemies and threaten the natural environment.

Certain N fertilizers—especially ammonium sulfate and sulphur-coated tend to acidify the soil. Check the pH of your soil to be sure it is in the 6.5-7.6. Earthworms thrive in this neutral range. If the pH[6] is acid—<pH 6.5—add **lime**; if alkaline—>pH 7.6—add **sulphur**.

Any yellowing of new growth may indicate iron deficiency. **Soil alkalinity** is the most common cause of iron deficiency in turf. Sulfur increases soil acidity. If your soil tends to be alkaline, apply sulphur after aerating the turf to increase water infiltration. Sulfur, and other fertilizers, should be washed off the grass immediately after application to prevent damage to the grass blades.

Where soil is only slightly alkaline, regular application of acid-forming fertilizers such as ammonium sulfate will lower the pH. If more iron is needed, ferrous sulfate or ferrous ammonium sulfate have been shown to produce better *long-term* greening than iron chelate, but an iron chelate foliage spray will produce greening within 3 days. If the pH is in the proper neutral zone, and grass is still yellow, take steps to improve the root system.

There are several possible causes of weak roots. These include drought; improper drainage, compost, or light; over-irrigation, compaction, disease, and insect or root nematode damage.

How mowing affects grass

One of the best ways to guarantee pest problems is to mow improperly. Mowing stresses grass. Lawns which are mowed frequently, and cut too short are weakened. USDA[7] scientists are able to increase lawn disease incidence at will by lowering mower height. After mowing, a well-watered, well-

[1] J Econ Entomol 88:367-379, 1995. Environ. Entomol. 24:1196-1200, 1995. [2] EPA, 1989. Integrated pest management for turfgrass & ornamentals, p. 123. [3]Plants of the Southwest, Agua Ri, Rt 6, Box 11A, Santa Fe, NM 87505. [4]Chewings fescues are JamestownII, Banner & Longfellow. Red fescues are Cindy, Dawson, & Ensylva. Hard fescues are Reliant, Spartan, & Aurora, Harrowsmith Country Life10/94, [5] Detritus=small particles of plant or animal material. [6]Measure of acidity-alkalinity [7] United States Department of Agriculture

nourished, well-aerated lawn responds with a spurt of top growth in two phases. The first phase involves the elongation of existing cut leaves, the second, the initiation and development of new leaves.

Under optimal conditions, mowing increases the number of individual grass plants, making for tighter, more weed-resistant turf. On the other hand, if repeated close mowing occurs simultaneously with one or more additional stresses—too much or too little water, heat, compaction—grass plants become both smaller in size and fewer in number. As the lawn thins out, weeds and diseases can invade easily.

To minimize potential problems caused by mowing, *cut grass as high as is consistent with satisfactory growth and appearance—as infrequently as possible.* Prostrate, low-growing grasses such as bermuda grass and creeping bent grass tolerate low mowing heights—3/4 to 1 inch. The erect-growing tall fescues or Italian ryegrasses should be cut 1 1/2 to 3 inches high. For Kentucky blue/fescue mixtures the proper mowing height is about 2 inches.

In very hot weather the mowing height of cool-season grasses should be taller. Never remove more than 30 to 40% of the grass blades at any one mowing. An interval of 7 to 14 days between cuttings allows grasses time to recover from the previous mowing and enter the second growth phase where sod-thickening new tillers are produced. In most situations *leaving the clippings on the lawn provides fertilizer*—slow release nitrogen, phosphorous, potassium, minerals—and mulch. This not only helps the lawn, but reduces the amount of waste in the local land fill.

Insects on lawns

An appropriate response to weeds, disease, or insect pests on a lawn is not usually pesticide use. *Heavy duty chemicals are never appropriate in routine lawn care.* A Kentucky study found lawns treated with common lawn-care fertilizers, herbicides, and insecticides had higher leafhopper and flea beetle populations after the first year, because natural enemies had been killed. In this high-maintenance-plot, soil pH declined because ammonium nitrate fertilizer was applied to an already acid soil. Thatch was two times thicker after two years and >3x thicker after four years than in control plots. Another study showed that broad-spectrum pesticides kill beneficial spiders, ants, predatory beetles and mites while survival of Japanese beetle and armyworm larvae increased. In addition, pest beetle larvae tend to decrease in lawns which contain clover or other non-grass plants, while high maintenance turf contains higher populations of these pests. Plant compost extracts deter beetle larvae, while poultry-based compost extracts are active against lawn moths.

Major Pesticides on Lawns
Chronic = x Cancer= C

	Cancer	Repro	Environ
2,4-D	x		
Atrazine	C	x	x
Benefin	x		
Carbaryl	x	x	x
Chlorothalonil	C		x
Chlorpyrifos			x
Dacthal	x		x
Diazinon		x	x
Dicamba		x	x
Glyphosate		x	
Iprodione	x		
Isofenphos			x
MCPA	x		
MSMA	?		?
Oryzalin	C		x
Pendimethalin	C		?
Trichlorfon	C		

In spite of good cultural efforts, insects occasionally invade a lawn. Fortunately non-toxic methods of lawn insect management are easy on the natural enemy community. The robust white grubs that feed on lawn roots grow up to become May, June, or chafer—scarab beetles—which live from coast to coast, and Japanese beetles east of the Mississippi River. Scarab beetle larvae succumb to bacterial "milky spore disease", *Bacillus popilliae.* Permanent control with this product takes several years, but **entomopathogenic nematodes** applied during warm weather are a rapid method of control of white grubs. This control is equal or better than that provided by potentially dangerous lawn insecticides—chlorpyrifos, carbaryl, diazinon, isofenphos, or bifenthrin. Capture adult beetles with fruit-baited traps.

Occasionally raccoons roll up well-watered turf to get at insects feeding there. Entomopathogenic nematodes will eliminate these grubs, but a quicker emergency solution is to water the lawn, wait 24 hours for the insects come to the surface, then use a lawn aerator, or Lawn Aerator Sandals. Experiments have shown that these spikes achieve 40-50% control of white grubs, equal to that of the insecticide, diazinon,[1,2] and far more safely.

Lawn moth caterpillars are also susceptible to entomopathogenic nematodes, but ***Bacillus thuringiensis*** (Btt) will get them as well. The nematodes even attack chinch bugs which thrive east of the Mississippi on lawns with a large thatch build-up. (Remove thatch before control is attempted.) The best control of chinch bugs is cultural. Careful thatch management and consistent moisture will allow other natural controls to operate. Chinch bugs thrive in St Augustine grass, the most widely planted ornamental turfgrass in the southern coastal states. A new cultivar, "Floratam" shows considerable resistance to these insects.

[1] Environ Entomol 24: 243-245, 1995, [2] EPA, 1989. Integrated pest management for turfgrass and ornamentals, p. 60

Tips about Compost

Most of us have heard of the soil-building value of compost—the dark crumbly organic product of the decay of plant materials—but actually making compost may have seemed like too much work. Don't worry. There are many ways to make compost.

The most "scientific" of these recommends a mixture of 90 parts carbohydrates[1] to 10 parts nitrogen[2] because the microorganisms (air-loving fungi and bacteria) and other minute critters which digest organic materials work best with these proportions. You need not be intimidated by these strict rules. Nature—if given enough time —will eventually compost all dead organic matter. *Your goal will be to facilitate composting according to your own energy levels.*

A simple way to compost

In the simplest solution, just pile everything in a corner—vegetables and fruits from the kitchen, prunings, grass clippings *(though these are best left on the lawn),* weeds, dried leaves, etc. Occasionally add water because things go faster if the pile is kept moist. Be aware though that years may go by before woody chunks in such a pile decay. This method does not produce the ideal "hot compost".

To speed things up—

• **Turn the pile** as frequently as possible—up to two or three times per week—but *at least twice* before it is finished. {A turned pile decomposes in 3 weeks to 6 months). Turning adds air, and gives opportunity to replace any moisture which evaporates as the pile heats up to temperatures high enough to destroy disease organisms and facilitate decay. The more you turn and sprinkle, the faster the pile will reach a black, crumbly perfection.

• **Chip or grind leaves and twigs**—small particles decay faster.

• **Keep the pile moist and aerated**—breakdown is slowed without air and ∞50% moisture. But be careful—too much water will inhibit air penetration. If rains a lot, cover the pile.

• **Use a bin or barrel** to hold materials together. One recommended bin format consists of three 4 x 3 x 3 foot hardware cloth bins, each with a front made up of single boards which can be removed one by one to facilitate turning. Raw materials are added to the first bin and unfinished compost is progressively turned into the second and third bins. Finished compost is removed from the third bin.

• **Add compost enhancers**—microorganisms which speed decay.

Not recommended—

• Dirt. In our experience dirt makes the mixture heavy and difficult to turn, but does not noticeably facilitate the decay process.

• 100% green material (grass, weeds). Things get smelly, slimy and horrible because air is excluded and moisture is too high. Always include dry substances with green plants.

What's in a compost pile ?

• **Any kind of foliage**—acid, toxic, dried, or wet materials. Pine needles, magnolia leaves, palm fronds, ivy, and other unlikely substances decay as their chemical constituents are transformed in the compost pile into simpler molecules. *These tough leaves will decay faster if they are ground in a chipper.*

• **Kitchen scraps**—fruits and their cores and peelings; vegetable wastes of all kinds. *Avoid meats and cheeses—foods composed of proteins and animal fats.* These protein foods will attract rodents, dogs, raccoons, flies, and other unwanted visitors

•**Waste Carbon**—manure, rice hulls, sawdust, straw, chopped plain newspapers, wood chips, and twigs

Three compost phases[3]

•**Temperature gradually increases** to 104-122° F as sugars and other soluble materials decay. • **Temperature increases** further to 122-150° F as cellulose and other biodegradable substances are destroyed. Some lignins break down also. Plant pathogens, weed seeds, and many biocontrol agents are killed.

• **Temperature declines**. Beneficial microorganisms recolonize from cooler regions of the pile. Helpful bacteria include *Bacillus, Pseudomonas,* and *Enterobacter spp.* and *Flavobacterium balustinum.* Beneficial fungi are *Streptomyces, Trichoderma sp.* and *Gliocladium virens.* Some of these bacteria can be added to lignin and humus substances to enrich

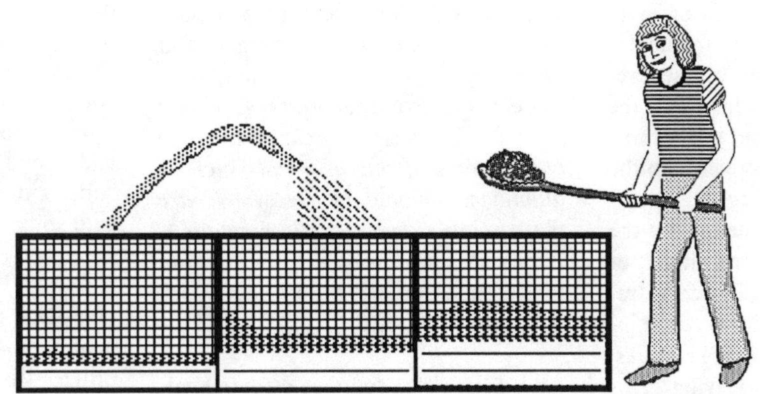

[1] Dry plant materials—sawdust, rice hulls, straw, dried leaves. [2] Fresh green vegetation or manure. [3] Plant Disease 75: 869-873, 1991.

the soil and improve its tilth.

Ideal composting goals

• **The pile must heat up** to kill weed seeds and harmful fungi. This requires moisture and air, plus sufficient vegetation to hold the heat for a few days—thus the 4 x 3 x 3 foot size, or a special large barrel which holds the moisture and heat, and has a crank which allows it to be turned easily. Turning twice (or more) stirs the mixture so that all of the contents will be heated. Plants near the edge of the pile will end in the center.

Compost often contains microorganisms which help control **crown rot** *(Phytophthora spp.)* and **damp-off disease** *(Rhizoctonia solani)* as well as *Fuarium and Phythium spp* plant diseases. Several bark-based commercial composts have been found especially beneficial in controlling these soil-borne diseases. Beneficial bacteria and fungi may not be present, however, unless the compost has been prepared with sufficient water. On the other hand, composts that contain more than a few percent sewage sludge may not suppress diseases since it does not contain the wide variety of microorganisms which are available in the bark materials. *Trichoderma* and *Gliocladium spp.* inoculants are available to help remedy this problem.

Compost bins which rest directly on bare earth will be colonized by **earthworms**. Earthworms consume organic materials. Their droppings enrich the pile as they help speed the breakdown process, and their movements help air and water penetrate.

How compost helps?

Compost which has heated thoroughly, contains few viable weed seeds. When spread as a **mulch** around plants, compost will help retain moisture and retard weed germination[1]—but be careful—mulched soils are cooler. **Root-feeding nematodes** are less damaging in soils which have a high compost concentration. This is because organic matter supports the nematodes' fungal and bacterial natural enemies.

The ideal growing medium for most plants is a loamy soil with neutral pH. (The logarithmic pH scale measures the activity of the hydrogen ions which affect many chemical and biological reactions in the soil). Organic material (compost) helps120 buffer soil, preventing it from being either highly acid or alkaline. When you combine compost with either an alkaline or an acid soil, conditions will move toward neutral. Compost also helps soil tilth. Sandy soils will hold more water. Compost lightens clay soil, allowing air and water to penetrate as it holds the minute particles apart. Compost helps prevent crusting, and increases fertility.

Never mix un-composted sawdust or other high carbon material directly into soil without including supplementary nitrogen fertilizer. Soil microorganisms require nitrogen to decompose carbon. Many plants do better if additional **nitrogen** is supplied during the growing season. Finished compost supplies some nitrogen as well as other nutrients. While it may not be provide all the nutrients required by fast growing crops, finished compost makes an excellent planting medium for raised beds. But because it may have been colonized by **sowbugs**, **earwigs**, **ants**, other critters, do not bring it inside or use it to start seeds.

Other soil tidbits

The presence of **earthworms** is increasingly recognized as indicative of soil health and an important means of ensuring soil improvement and efficient nutrient cycling. In order to reduce erosion, crops are frequently planted into the residues of the previous crop. This system increases the density of earthworms and the volume of organic matter incorporated into the soil. Earthworms working at the surface move the organic material into the soil. In one study where clover or grass were mowed and allowed to remain on the surface, earthworms increased soil nitrogen 50% in 11 weeks. This is is comparable to leaving grass clippings on a lawn.

Acid soils—If your native soil is strongly acid—below pH 5.5 or 6.0—you may need to add lime (calcium carbonate) as well as compost. Most vegetables perform best in a neutral pH range of 6.0—7.5. (Remember that each step in the scale represent 10 x more or less hydrogen ions). *A plant's poor performance in acid soil is due mainly toxic effects of metals such as aluminum or manganese which are more soluble under acidic conditions.* Increased lime raises pH as calcium ions replace some of the hydrogen ions in the soil solution.

Added lime also supplies essential calcium, and dolomite lime will supply magnesium as well. The additions should be carefully moderated, however, because manganese will be less available if soil pH becomes too high. Since clay soils have more particles, it takes a greater concentration of lime to raise the pH of a clay soil than a sandy soil. Sometimes ashes are recommended to "sweeten soils". Never add wood or coal ashes to alkaline soils, and be careful with ashes even in acid soils. Ashes are strongly alkaline.

Neutral soils—If soil pH is in the neutral range, most plants are able to utilize the essential elements phosphorus, potassium, calcium, mag-

[1] For more information on avoiding weeds contact BIRC—see sources

nesium, and nitrogen. A neutral soil provides an ideal environment for microorganisms such as **nitrifying bacteria** that convert ammonia nitrogen to the nitrate nitrogen which can be utilized by plants. A neutral soil of pH 6.6 or higher inhibits *Furarium* wilt of tomato, though potatoes are best grown at the acid pH 5-5.5 to minimize potato scab infections. In general, only plants which are native to strongly acid or alkaline soils tolerate these extreme pH conditions. Vegetation native to rainy areas thrives in acid soils, and shrubs endemic to drier areas are more tolerant of alkaline conditions.

Alkaline soils—If the native soil is strongly alkaline—above pH 8—*available* phosphorus, iron, manganese, copper and zinc will be so low as to limit growth of most plants An alkaline pH can be lowered, and these minerals made available, by adding gypsum (calcium sulphate) or sulphur. Gypsum reclaims alkaline soil by replacing sodium ions with calcium ions. (These sodium salts should then be leached[1] from the soil). Gypsum also improves soil structure so that water penetrates more easily. Approximately 50 to 90 pounds per 1000 square feet spread on the surface in spring will improve water penetration. Twice as much, spread in early winter is needed to reclaim a strongly alkaline soil. Sulphur lowers pH by providing sulphuric acid. Its application must also be followed by leaching to remove excess sodium.

Land that has grown crops for many years may be short of **calcium** because calcium is removed by many crops. Calcium will be replenished when lime or gypsum are added to neutralize the soil. High levels of **selenium** is bound in some alkaline soils. A portion of this selenium will contaminate water which contacts these soils. Some plants— especially wild mustard, are able to tolerate and accumulate this mineral in their tissues. Ongoing research will determine whether these plants can be used to remove this toxic mineral from selenium-contaminated soils.[2]

Water wisdom

We all know that plants need water, but few of us realize that *we may be giving our plants—* especially the lawn—*too much water rather than too little. When you see a yellow, scraggly, weed-studded lawn, you may think it needs more water!* You may even have installed a sprinkler system, set it to water 15 or 20 minutes in the middle of each night, and never checked it again. You could ignore the fact that the surface is furrowed where the lawn mower compacts the mud, or fail to connect this fact with an enormous water bill at the end of the month. If this is your situation, read on.

What plants require

Plants need nutrients (fertilizer), water, and *air.* Roots can only grow where air is present. Water displaces air in saturated soils causing roots to drown or grow along the surface to obtain air. These surface roots *require* daily watering because they're not in the soil where water is available. If you water daily, you'll never achieve the lush green lawn of your dreams.

If you want a beautiful lawn, robust vegetables, or outstanding trees learn about your soil. Its type determines its **water holding capacity (WHC)—** The amount of water you apply should be related to WHC. Any excess will drain away, carrying nutrients with it. Because sandy soils hold little water, they require frequent watering—or addition of compost to increase WHC. On the other hand, clay soils hold a great deal of water. Plants growing there need less frequent, slow, but deep irrigation, and also benefit from added compost to increase aeration.

Several terms describe how water and soil interact with plants. The *ideal*

moisture in any soil is called its **field capacity**. This defines the situation about 24 hours after deep irrigation, where all excess water has drained down through the root zone, and a good balance of air and water is present. As time passes without water, the soil reaches the point where any remaining water is bound so tightly to the soil particles that roots cannot extract it. This is the **permanent wilting point**. As the soil reaches the PWP, plants do not grow, and if water is not applied, will soon die.

The time it takes to go from field capacity to permanent wilting point depends on • soil type • temperature • sun or shade exposure • wind • competition, age, type, and size of plants. Sandy soils have a lower field capacity than loam or clay soils. Ob-

Root Depths of Turfgrasses

Shallow ≤ 8"	Bent
Medium 8-18"	Kentucky blue, Red fescue, Rye, St. Augustine
Deep 18-60"	Tall fescue, Bermuda, Buffalo

[1] Washed out of. [2]Cal. Agri.43(5-6):19-20, 1989

viously plants growing in sun or wind lose water faster than those in shade. The process by which plants and soil lose water is dubbed **evapotranspiration (ET)** —water *evaporates* from the soil surface, but moves directly from plants into the air via *transpiration.*

Roots of properly-watered plants extend deeply into the soil. Usually they are able to utilize most of the stored water. If a tomato's roots extend 4 feet into the soil, 40% of these roots will be in the first foot, 30% in the second, 20% in the third, and 10% in the lower foot. These deep-rooted plants are able to withstand a longer period without water than shallow-rooted plants. Water disappears from the surface first, then from gradually deeper layers.

Watering plants

The ET of plants changes seasonally. As a cool spring is followed by a hot summer and fall, into a possibly freezing winter, the ET goes from moderate to high to low. Your irrigation should reflect these seasonal water requirements. In one study[1], **turf grasses** growing in sandy loam did well when irrigation equaled 60-80% of ET. You can determine your own needs by placing jars around the lawn to measure the volume of water your most inadequate sprinkler applies during 15 minutes. If your sprinklers apply more than 1/2 inch, reduce the water we recommend proportionately. *(Deep-rooted grasses and shaded grasses require 15-20% less).*

Water lawns twice a week. Adjust the time you water seasonally. In mild climates you might water about 12 minutes in spring, 20 minutes during summer and 10 minutes later in fall. In a hot climates, sprinkle about 15 minutes in spring, 25-30 minutes in summer and 10-15 minutes in fall. Water is seldom needed in winter unless rain or snow does not fall at that time. Watch the lawn. If the grass becomes bluish, or footprints can be seen, apply water now. If this happens before the normal watering day, increase the length of watering or include and 'extra' watering for that week.

Deciduous fruit and nut trees need soil moisture at least from bloom to harvest.[2] If you live in a summer rainfall area, supplemental water may not be needed or desirable. If no summer rain falls, determine how how much water your fruit and ornamental trees and shrubs require. Extend the watering footprint a few feet beyond the drip line, and keep it away from the trunk to prevent crown rot. Water should penetrate several feet below the surface.

If winter rains were inadequate, irrigate fruit trees to field capacity before bloom, and again in late May. During summer, water fruit trees growing in sandy soils every week or so—in heavier soils, every 2 or 3 weeks. If you have fruits such as **cherries**, **apricot**, and **peaches** that split easily, avoid watering in the last few weeks before harvest. But if fruits such as **apples** or **pears** seem undersized, water just before or even during the harvest period will increase size. **Grapes** need moisture from cane growth through fruit set. **Almonds** thrive with water just before and just after harvest. In cool weather, intervals between watering can be longer.

Avoid the surface water run-off which causes soil loss. Do not flood the ground or surface roots may die from lack of air, and soil fungi will have easy access to tender rootlets under ideal infectious conditions. Don't irrigate again until surface soil is fairly dry. If you have a ground cover, you must water more frequently, but you can expect better penetration.

Shrubs and trees which are **native to your area** will not usually require or thrive on supplemental water. Indeed they can be killed by such 'kindness'. Summer water is often the cause of premature death of California's native oaks due to fungal infections which invade the roots when water is applied during warm weather.

Vegetables too must be watered carefully. Water most vegetables about twice a week—even three times for lettuce. This pattern will ensure even moisture while allowing plenty of air. Physiological diseases of vegetables —**tip burn** on lettuce, cabbage and brussels sprouts, **cavity spot** of carrots, parsnips, and potatoes; **blackheart** of celery, internal browning of Brussel sprouts; or **blossom end-rot** of tomato, pepper, and watermelon—nominally caused by lack of calcium (Ca), are triggered when excess nitrogen fertilizer is accompanied by intermittent soil drying, *even when the soil has plenty of Ca.*

These Ca-related disorders arise from poor movement of Ca into rapidly growing leaves or fruits. Most of these disorders are associated with excessive vegetative growth triggered by the nitrogen fertilizer. The growing tips and fruits of plants have high Ca requirements. During rapid growth, Ca moves preferentially into mature leaves, and young leaves and fruits may be shorted. Anything which damages the feeder roots—cultivation or flood irrigation—can also lead to Ca shortage in sensitive tissues. Hot dry winds or high temperatures can increase water loss, so adjust your watering schedule accordingly, and keep nitrogen moderate during the maturation period to avoid these Ca-related disorders.

In addition, excess water and fertilizer will leach nitrogen, as nitrate, into the water supply. In one study which used lettuce as a model vegetable, a reduced per crop rate of 1.7 pounds nitrogen, and 1 gallon water weekly per 1000 square feet, reduced nitrate leaching by seventy-five percent.[3]

---

[1]CATurfgrass Cult. 43(4):21-23, 1984. [2]Leaflet 2975, U.Cal. Div.Agri. Sci. 1977. [3]Sustain. Agri. Tech. Rev. 5(5): 9-11, 1993.

How to plant and care for trees

If you've ever seen a young tree in the center of a lawn surrounded by big stakes, you have an idea of how not to plant a tree.

Faulty planting methods

For years the instructions for tree planting suggested that you • Dig a deep hole • Combine organic amendments with the soil removed • Pack the mixture around the roots • Water • Tie the trunk to one or more strong stakes. Eventually, after many trees planted in this way stayed small and spindly for years, and were easily removed, or tipped over in wind and rain as if they had been planted recently into a pot—these planting methods became suspect.

Such inadequately planted trees were found to have roots which spiraled round and round inside the original planting hole, and they readily succumbed to crown rot disease. Now experiments have demonstrated that trees should be planted another way.

How tree roots grow

In order to plant a tree successfully, learn how trees grow. Though many trees are described as having tap roots, most tree roots grow quite differently. Trees typically have four or more main **transport roots** which grow radially outward from the trunk about a foot below the surface. These major roots branch and become smaller over a radius of three to thirteen feet, to form a network of rope-like roots less than one inch in diameter. As the tree grows larger, these transport roots send down **striker roots**, which grow vertically downward until they encounter obstacles or insufficient oxygen. Striker roots often branch to form a second, deeper layer of transport roots that grow horizontally just above the oxygen-deprived region of the soil.

Under normal conditions *transport root systems grow away from the trunk a distance two or more times the height of the tree.* A complex system of smaller roots branches outward and upward from these main transport roots. Each of these smaller roots branches many times, splitting into multiple fine **feeder roots**. These feeder roots are the primary sites of absorption of water and minerals. *Most feeder roots are located in the top twelve inches of the soil.* If compost is present on the surface, feeder roots grow upward into the litter to obtain nutrients.

Root requirements

Roots require oxygen, water, mineral nutrients, and moderate temperatures Generally *roots cannot grow into compacted soil or into soil layers that lack oxygen.* The action of frost, and the alternate swelling and shrinking as soil changes from wet to dry and back again, tends to heave and break up the soil's upper layers. The organic matter from decomposing leaf litter provides energy for millions of insects, worms, nematodes. moles and other creatures that tunnel through these surface layers. The combined effect of climate and tunneling is to loosen the surface layers of undisturbed soils until more than 50% of their volume is pore space. Air, water, minerals, and roots easily penetrate these fluffy layers.

Roots thrive in such neutral deep loam soils, but are stunted in shallow or wet soils. They grow most deeply in sandy or other soils which allow oxygen to penetrate deeply. In very dry sandy soils, roots sometimes penetrate as much as 50 feet to obtain water. Conversely, in swampy areas where oxygen supplies are limited, roots tend to be many branched and shallow. Some swamp-dwelling trees have evolved special structures which permit them to absorb oxygen under water, and specialized metabolism that tolerates the toxic substances which are produced by underwater fermentation.

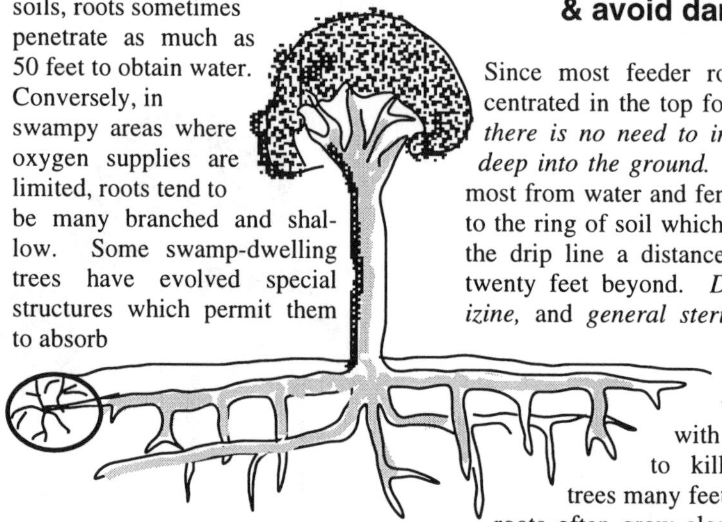

Other species, plums, cherries, apricots, apples, pears—members of the rose family—are unusually sensitive to reduced oxygen. Cherry roots, for example, contain toxic cyanide gas when oxygen is limited. The 24 hour flood which accompanied Hurricane Agnes in 1973, killed most the of cherry trees around Hain's Point in Washington, D.C.

Why roots grow that way

Trees cannot be categorized as a "shallow-rooted" or a "deep-rooted" per sé. The ultimate structure of the roots of any tree depends on local soil struture, and availability of water, oxygen, and mineral nutrients. Roots typically grow parallel to the surface, so trees on slopes may have roots that grow uphill. Roots searching for essentials may grow unbelievable distances along cracks, or they may remain near the trunk if all nutrients are easily obtained nearby. Tree roots are also effected by temperature. During freezing weather, a cover of litter or snow which prevents the ground from freezing, allows roots to continue to grow. A protective mulch layer will prevent excess summer heat from cooking surface roots.

Supply essentials & avoid damage

Since most feeder roots are concentrated in the top foot of the soil, *there is no need to inject fertilizer deep into the ground.* Trees benefit most from water and fertilizer applied to the ring of soil which reaches from the drip line a distance of a few to twenty feet beyond. *Dicamba, simizine,* and *general sterilants* are examples of herbicides which interact with surface roots to kill or damage trees many feet away. Since roots often grow along cracks and crevices of pavement, any contact herbicide applied to kill weeds or unwanted tree sprouts, can threaten distant trees via their wide-ranging roots.

Why urban trees die

Soil compaction and crown rot are major killers of trees. Roots cannot penetrate compacted soils. Any excessive pressure on the soil surface, caused by trampling of people or livestock, construction equipment, or parked cars tends to close the pore spaces which allow roots to absorb essential water and oxygen. Water applied near the base of the trunk—at the crown—drives out soil oxygen, and, during warm weather, facilitates penetration of the motile spores of crown rot disease. Crown rot disease destroys the cambium layer which conducts water and minerals to the leaves, and food to the roots. *Impervious black plastic* used to eliminate weeds, may also prevent water and oxygen from reaching roots. (Black garden fabric which allows water and oxygen to pass, is a better choice. In fact some studies show that young trees surrounded by dark garden fabric—which prevents weed growth—grow more rapidly than trees which are surrounded by mulch or cultivated bare ground).[1]

Surface cultivation damages feeder roots which surround the trunk. Extensive plantings of shrubs and especially grass compete for essential nutrients. **Trenching** or major digging which cuts several transport roots can seriously damage mature trees. *Deep digging for foundations or pools, even many feet from mature trees can kill them within a short time.* Often the owner is unaware of the ultimate cause.

The trees which are most affected by urban problems are those surrounded by **pavement**. Paving not only cuts off air, but the soil must be compacted in order to support the impervious surface. Recently[2] efforts have been made to help urban trees. The idea is to combine two very different particle sizes in the area surrounding existing and future trees. Such a mix—and the pavement itself—should begin at least 3-4 feet from the trunk to allow room for root expansion. The soil mixture should be composed of ≥1 1/2" river rock or 3/4" gravel combined with a good sandy loam soil which has adequate compost included. In this situation, the rocks support the load, and the crevices between them allow root penetration, while the soil provides water, air, and nourishment.

How to plant a tree

Obviously, trees grow from seeds, and a seed planted in place can yield an ideal, strongly-rooted tree. However, most of us are impatient—looking for a jump start. Or, we may desire a specially structured patented tree, so we purchase a little tree. If a still larger specimen is desired—we don't recommend this—be especially careful to follow these directions because the *larger specimens are not usually as successful as smaller trees.*

When to plant

Most hardy deciduous trees should be planted near the end of the dormant season as 'bare root' whips. Evergreen trees do better when transplanted from containers into warm fall or spring soil. (Spring is best in cold climate areas.) If your bare-root tree cannot be planted immediately, store it in a cool place, in dampened sawdust or other loose media. If you soak the roots, do not leave them submerged for more than an hour.

Where to plant

It's important to take into account the root growth habits of trees. *Avoid planting them into grassy or weedy soil.* These plants compete strongly with tree roots for water and nutrients. Even a legume cover crop should be kept several feet away from the base of the tree.

Before you dig make sure that the dirt is moderately damp—neither too wet or too dry. When the moisture is correct, a shovel full of dirt will crumble easily. (If you dig into wet soil, the shovel itself slicks the side of the hole, sealing the pores. This results in a pot-like hole which tends to retain the roots permanately. On the other hand, if you plant in a dry hole, the roots will lose moisture to the dirt itself, and will also tend to remain within the watered planting hole).

Dig a wide shallow hole

If you're planting into previously compacted soil, deeply cultivate the compacted area to aerate and loosen the soil. In loose fertile soils you need only dig a wide, relatively shallow hole which will encompass the root mass of the young tree without *horizontal* cramping. In addition, you may want to use a digging fork to fracture the soil surrounding the hole so that the roots can easily penetrate this area.

The idea is to encourage the roots to move out into the native soil. Obviously then, *you won't be adding amendments to the dirt which will fill the hole.* Since the roots should grow primarily into native soil beyond the hole, *it's best to choose tree varieties which thrive in your situation.* Apply any compost or fertilizer on the soil surface, primarily at and beyond the drip-line. This will encourage your tree to develop the type of roots which will withstand wind. It will grow long horizontal transport roots and deep striker roots which work together to support theweight of the tree.

Planting the tree

After digging, make a little cone of soil in the bottom of your wide, relatively shallow hole. Be sure the crown will be positioned at or slightly above the normal soil line. Trim off broken roots, and a similar amount from the top. Spread the roots of bare root trees widely over the cone. (If your tree has been in a container, loosen the roots and shake off the planting mix which would tend to keep the roots in the tiny hole. As above, carefully spread these loosened roots over the cone. If the roots are going round and round already, you have a root-bound plant which should be returned to the seller.)

After the roots are positioned, *fill the hole with the native dirt,* making sure that there are no air pockets. Tamp the soil firmly around the roots. Then soak the mound and the area beyond the hole. Cover the entire area over the roots and beyond with a deep mulch and dark fabric cloth, if desired. In some situations, normal rains will provide adequate moisture, otherwise use drip or basin irrigation to water weekly for the first summer and fall. Apply the water to a doughnut shaped area beginning a few inches from the trunk and reaching beyond the edge of the mound. The second year deeply

[1] Fruit Grower, p 24, 3/95. [2] Growing Points 1(1-2): 1&1-2, 1994.

water an even wider area monthly. Apply the moisture at and beyond the dripline. *Never allow sprinklers to hit the trunk of any tree. Saturation of the crown during warm weather promotes infestation with crown rot.*

Care after planting

In later years, drought-resistant trees will require little supplementary water, but be sure all fruit trees receive a good soaking—natural or supplementary —before bloom, and again 3-4 weeks before fruit harvest. (Watering in the last two weeks before harvest promotes splitting of some fruits—especially cherries, peaches, nectarines, and some apricot varieties).

Unless the trunk is weak, **most young trees do not require staking**. If staking is required, place two stakes perpendicular to the prevailing wind. Loop a wire covered with old hose around the tree and fasten it to each stake *just at the level which will hold the tree upright. Be sure that the tree can sway slightly in the wind.* This slight stress will strengthen and stiffen the trunk. After a year or so remove the stakes. The **trunks of young trees** are vulnerable to sunscald, insect, or even rodent attack. Cover trunks with a tree wrap or diluted (1:1) latex white indoor paint, to protect them from damage. Then sit back and reap the benefits of your green thumb ways.

Tree IPM—should include preservation of insect natural enemies and maintenance of high organic content in the soil. One way to do this is to plant cover crops under mature trees—leaving a bare area at the crown. An un-mowed vetch, clover, or annual grass cover crop, or a mixture of these planted in fall, can be allowed to flower and set seeds. When it is mowed, natural enemies will move into the tree canopy, as the drying cover prevents the growth of weeds and increases nutrients and organic matter in the soil. Both vetch and clover increase soil nitrogen, and all three increase water penetration and help prevent erosion.

How to Plant a Tree

- Cultivate the planting area widely
- Plant on a slight mound to provide drainage
- Dig a wide, relatively shallow hole
- Fill the hole with water
- Don't add amendments to the removed dirt
- Make a dirt cone in the bottom of the hole
- Spread roots over the cone (shake off planting mix, if present)
- Cover roots with soil firmly—avoid air pockets
- Water thoroughly
- Cover planting area with compost
- Water weekly this summer and fall
- Water at the drip line—keep water a few inches away from the trunk

Warding off frost

Some of us live where temperatures go into deep freeze through a long winter—others live in the mild sun belt. But no matter where you are, you're probably trying to grow plants which could succumb to an unexpected cold snap, with temperatures much lower than the average winter temperatures in your area.

In the sun, belt cold temperatures may drop into the teens or twenties—temperatures which sound like a heat wave to the residents of Zone 1. Nonetheless most of us may come to the day when we're trying to protect tender trees or shrubs from the cold. Unusual freezes are more damaging if they come in early spring when plants have begun to break dormancy. In addition, you may want to modify temperatures any time of year to favor the needs of a favored plant.

Water moderates cold

There are several time-honored techniques to reduce the effects of a cold snap. Since water has the capacity to hold an enormous amount to heat, running the sprinkler during the freeze is one way to moderate temperatures. In a long cold snap this obviously could cause a flooding problem as well as being very expensive, *and,* if you stop at the wrong time can do more harm than good. In any case, *watering before an expected freeze is helpful.* Damp soil stores a significant amount of heat which will be released during the cold. In addition, water-stressed plants are more likely to die from weather extremes.

Plant covers

During the dormant season, soil or mulch can be heaped over low growing plants to protect them from cold. Row covers will help protect low plants, and larger sizes can cover individual trees—but should be kept away from the foliage. Covers combined with wind breaks are even more helpful. Plants under the shelter of a deciduous tree will be less vulnerable to cold than those in more open sites. Plants near the top of a slope experience less cold than those at the bottom of a hill where the cold remains. Plants sited on the south side of hillsides, buildings, or walls with black porous plastic or gravel ground covers will benefit from warmer soil, and reflected sun. (Conversely, in a hot climate, sites in partial shade or at the bottom of slopes will provide protection from searing sunshine).

Chemicals— Several products help provide protection from frost. Certain polymers function as antitranspirants —preventing water loss. The recombinant bacterial spray, Frostgard*, replaces the ice-nucleating *Pseudomonas fluroescens* bacteria which trigger the freezing process. Protection provided by these products is limited to temperatures a few degrees below the average minimum.

After a freeze

Should your plants appear dead after a freeze, do not rip them out immediately. Wait until at least early summer—then search for stump sprouts. Many "dead" trees and shrubs recover after a heavy frost. When they get going again, carefully prune out any dead wood. Often they will recover completely.

Information about tree roots & how trees grow is based on Perry, T.O. 1989. Tree Roots: Facts and Fallacies. *Arnoldia* 49 (4):3-29.

Looking at apples

A dry, warm summer and cool winter is ideal for cultivation of most fruits. If your temperatures are below 50° F for the 900 hours of 'winter chill" needed by most apples, you can choose almost any apple variety. You must select 'low chill' varieties if you live in the mild-winter sunbelt or near a large body of water where summers are mild and frosts unusual.

It's difficult to raise apples in regions where warm summer rains trigger diseases. Fortunately, several new disease-resistant cultivars will allow you to raise apples in summer rainfall regions without using fungicides. Obviously, these multiple-disease-resistant types will thrive elsewhere as well. In addition, fireblight-resistant varieties such as Crispin, Empire, Golden Delicious, Red Delicious or Yates, can be planted where other diseases are rare. (If you have a fireblight-susceptible apple variety, read the section on fireblight control.)

Controlling Pests

Many pests and diseases can be suppressed when apple trees are leafless.
• Rake up and hot-compost[1] apple leaves to remove **apple scab spores**.
• Just before bloom, apply a dormant oil spray to suppress **aphids** and **mites**

Cultural tips

• *Nourish predators and parasitoids* of apple pests by including daisy and carrot family plants in your garden
• To lengthen apple storage and prevent **corky spot**, **bitter pit** and **water core**—physiological responses to lack of available calcium in heavy or sandy soils—spray 2% **calcium nitrate** or **calcium chelate**[2] one or more times before harvest, or dip newly-picked apples for 2 minutes in this solution. Acid soils and excess nitrogen and potassium promote these disorders. (With bitter pit, small brown spots appear throughout the flesh. Watercore-blemished fruits have a water-marked look). Use the left-over calcium solution as a nitrogen fertilizer. (Fuji, a delicious new apple which has surface cracking problems may respond favorably to calcium treatments. In addition, Fuji fruits should should be encouraged to grow rapidly just after petal fall so the blossom end will close as rapidly as possible).

• In warm humid climates apple fruits are sometimes attacked by fungal surface diseases—**sooty blotch** or **flyspeck**—which make them look dirty. These blotches can be removed after harvest by submerging the fruit in .05% chlorine bleach solution (2.5 tablespoons bleach to 1 gallon water) for ≈7 minutes, then rinsing and brushing the fruits to remove the loosened deposits. (Be sure to wear gloves and work outdoors as bleach is an irritant).

• Fruit overheating can be mitigated with **evaporative cooling**. When temperatures in the canopy > 90°F, spray the foliage with water for 10 minutes. Allow the tree to dry for about 45 minutes. If temperature rise again, repeat the process. *Once begun, evaporative cooling must be continued for the rest of the season or the fruit will be susceptible to sunscald.* These fruits gain size and color. *Store apples in zipper bags at ≈32°F to slow ripening.*

Arthropod pests of apple

Codling moth, a **key pest** of apples, may not find your young apple tree for several years. But when they do appear, they will eventually damage 60-90% of the fruits unless you intervene. Unfortunately, predators and parasitoids do not control CM enough to suit most of us. (See chart for apples which are reportedly resistant to "insects"—probably CM). CM control is not easy, but can be accomplished safely by following our recommendations. Efforts are being made to establish two promising **codling moth parasitoids** in California—*Liotryphon caudatus* to destroy overwintering larvae, and *Trichogramma enecator* to attack larvae inside the apples. If these become established, fewer CM will overwinter to penetrate apples the following year.

Plum curculio and several leafrollers, e.g. **redbanded leafroller** *(Rascista cercerisella)* and the **tufted apple bud moth** *(Platynota idaeustalis)*—sometimes attack apples east of the Rockies. **Apple maggot** is spreading across the country. Most apples host at least a few aphids in early spring, though these usually decline without causing serious damage. If possible avoid M.7A (Emla 7) and other rootstocks which are susceptible to **woolly apple aphid** *(Eriosoma lanigerum)*. Control choices for any of these pests are critical because *most broad-spectrum pesticides trigger serious outbreaks of* ***spider mites, aphids, leaf miners.*** *or* ***leafrollers****, while non-chemical methods are seldom sufficient for* ***codling moth*** *control.*

Choosing apple trees

Seedling apple trees usually grow too tall for easy care, and the quality of their fruit is unknown. *We recommend that you choose named varieties grafted to dwarfing rootstocks.* Dwarf apple trees bear at a younger age, are more productive, take less care and space than do standard trees. They are best ordered bare root by mail.[3] When they arrive, plant them according to our directions for planting trees. The shipper will tell you where to position the graft.

Intermediate dwarfing rootstocks—MM111, MM9, Emla 106 or Mark—are adapted to a variety of soils and produce good self-supporting trees. If you want good-sized apples without damage to your tree's structure, even dwarf apples must be pruned in the dormant season; the fruits thinned in early spring.

1 See Tips about Compost. 2 1/3 cup or 2.5 oz. per gallon water 3 See sources

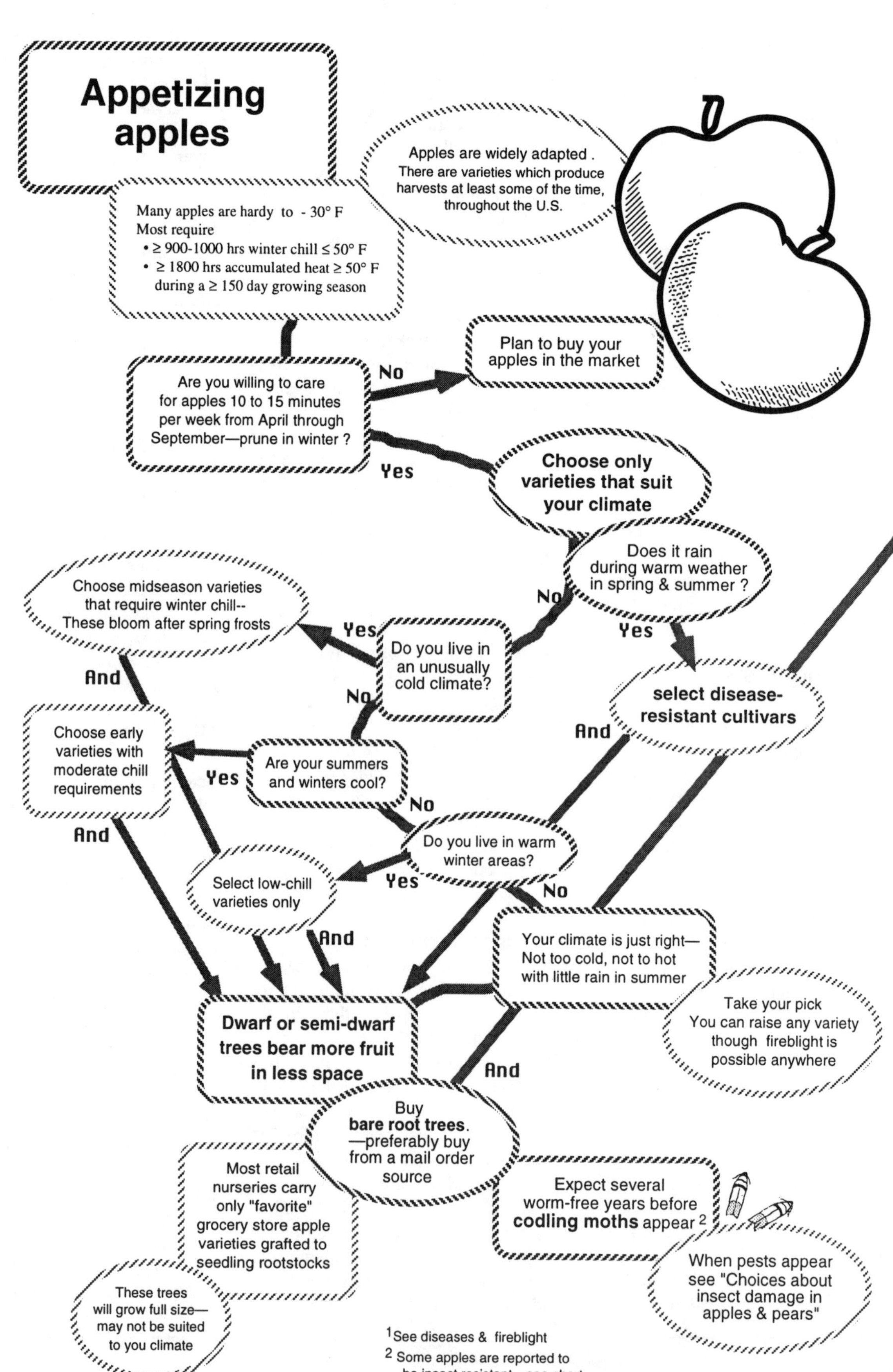

Appetizing apples
Apples are widely adapted . There are varieties which produce harvests at least some of the time, throughout the U.S.
Many apples are hardy to - 30° F
Most require
• ≥ 900-1000 hrs winter chill ≤ 50° F
• ≥ 1800 hrs accumulated heat ≥ 50° F during a ≥ 150 day growing season
Are you willing to care for apples 10 to 15 minutes per week from April through September—prune in winter ?
No
Plan to buy your apples in the market
Yes
Choose only varieties that suit your climate
Does it rain during warm weather in spring & summer ?
No
Yes
select disease-resistant cultivars
Do you live in an unusually cold climate?
Yes
Choose midseason varieties that require winter chill-- These bloom after spring frosts
And
No
Are your summers and winters cool?
Yes
Choose early varieties with moderate chill requirements
And
No
Do you live in warm winter areas?
Yes
Select low-chill varieties only
And
No
Your climate is just right— Not too cold, not to hot with little rain in summer
Take your pick You can raise any variety though fireblight is possible anywhere
And
And
Dwarf or semi-dwarf trees bear more fruit in less space
Buy bare root trees. —preferably buy from a mail order source
Most retail nurseries carry only "favorite" grocery store apple varieties grafted to seedling rootstocks
These trees will grow full size— may not be suited to you climate
Expect several worm-free years before codling moths appear 2
When pests appear see "Choices about insect damage in apples & pears"

[1] See diseases & fireblight

[2] Some apples are reported to be insect resistant—see chart

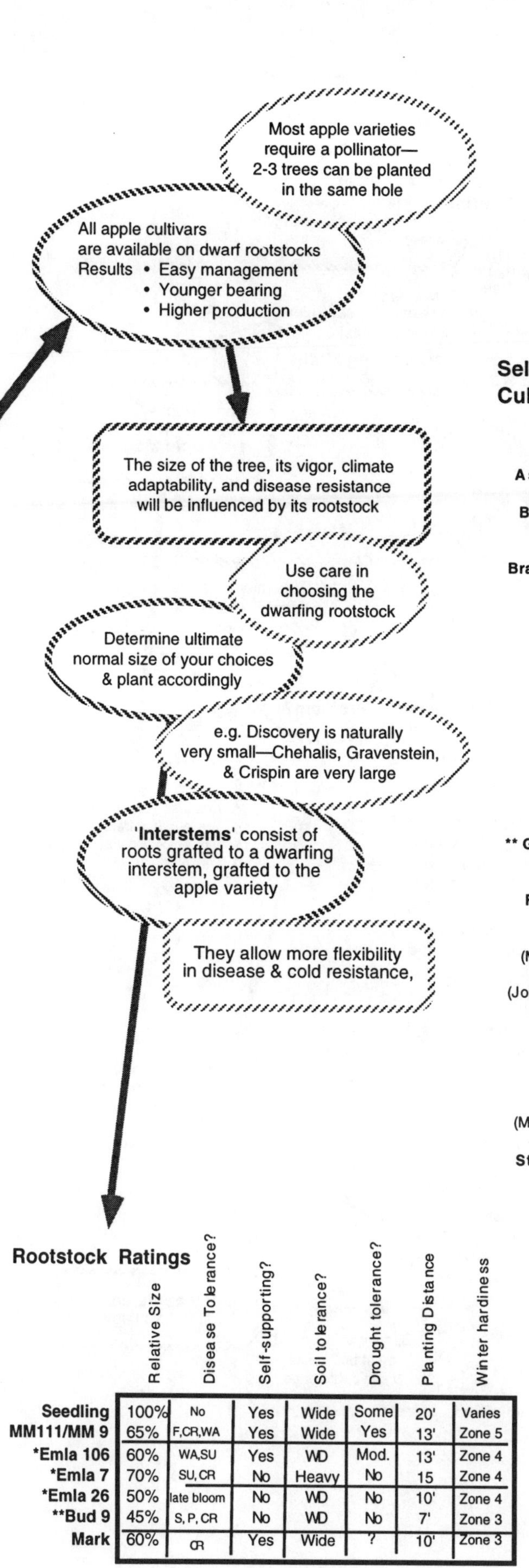
Most apple varieties require a pollinator— 2-3 trees can be planted in the same hole
All apple cultivars are available on dwarf rootstocks
Results • Easy management
• Younger bearing
• Higher production
The size of the tree, its vigor, climate adaptability, and disease resistance will be influenced by its rootstock
Use care in choosing the dwarfing rootstock
Determine ultimate normal size of your choices & plant accordingly
e.g. Discovery is naturally very small—Chehalis, Gravenstein, & Crispin are very large
'Interstems' consist of roots grafted to a dwarfing interstem, grafted to the apple variety
They allow more flexibility in disease & cold resistance,

Rootstock Ratings

	Relative Size	Disease Tolerance?	Self-supporting?	Soil tolerance?	Drought tolerance?	Planting Distance	Winter hardiness
Seedling	100%	No	Yes	Wide	Some	20'	Varies
MM111/MM 9	65%	F,CR,WA	Yes	Wide	Yes	13'	Zone 5
***Emla 106**	60%	WA,SU	Yes	WD	Mod.	13'	Zone 4
***Emla 7**	70%	SU, CR	No	Heavy	No	15	Zone 4
***Emla 26**	50%	late bloom	No	WD	No	10'	Zone 4
****Bud 9**	45%	S, P, CR	No	WD	No	7'	Zone 3
Mark	60%	CR	Yes	Wide	?	10'	Zone 3

* Emla are viral-free M rootstocks

Selected Apple Cultivars

	Resists (Scab, Powdery Mildew, Fireblight, Rust)	Chilling Required (Low, Medium, High)	Ripening (Early, Medium, Late)	Hardiness (Very, Moderate, Tender)	Flavor (Fair, Good, Excellent)	Keeping Quality (Short, Medium, Long)	Color (Red, Yellow, Green, Russet)	Use (Dessert, Cooking, All Purpose)	Growing Season (Sort, Medium, Long)	Insect Resistance (Excellent, Moderate, Some)[1]
Akana	S, M	M	M	V	E	L	R	D	M	
Anna		L	F	T	E	M	GR	D	S	
Arkansas Black	P, M,F	M	VL	M	G	L	R	D	L	
Ashmead's Kernel	M	H	L	M	E	L	YR	D	L	
Beverly Hills	coastal	L	E	M	G	M	R	A	S	
Belle de Boskoop	S	M	M	M	E	VL	GRRu	C	S	
Blairmont	S,F,P *	M	L	M	E	L	R	M	M	
Braebum	?	M	L	M	E	L	GR	D	L	
Bramley's Seedling	S,F, P,R	M	E	M	E	L	GYR	C	L	
Chehalis	S, F,P	M	M	M	G	M	Y	A	S	
Cox's Orange	?	L	L	L(hc)	E	M	YR	D	L	E
Pippin	M,F *	M	M	M	E	L	Y	A	L	
Crispin (Mutsu)	S,P,F *	M	E	M	G	M	R	D	M	
Dayton	S, M	M	E	M	E	S	R	DC	S	
Discovery	S,M	L	E	V	G	?	YR	D	S	E
Earliblaze	S,F	M	M	M	E	L	RY	D	L	
Elstar	S, F,R	M	L	M	E	L	RO	A	M	
Enterprise	S,P	M	L	M	E	L	R	D	M	
Fall Russet	S,F,P,R	M	L	M	G	L	R	A	S	
Freedom	P,F,R	L	E	M	G	L	GR	D	M	
Fuji	P,F,R	M	L	M	E	M	RY	A	M	
Gala	S,F,M	M	L	M	E	VL	Y	M	S	
Gold Rush	F	M	M	V	E	L	Y	A	S	S
**** Golden Delicious**	S,F,R	M	VL	M	G	L	YRu	A	L	M
Golden Russet		M	E	M	G	VL	G	A	L	
Granny Smith	S,M	M	L	V	E	S	GR	C	M	S
Red Gravenstein	S,R,R	M	L	M	E	M	R	A	M	F
Jonafree		M	M	M	E	L	GR	A	M	F
Jonagold	S,F,P,R	M	M	M	E	L	R	D	L	E
(McIntosh) **Liberty**	F	H	L	V	E	L	R	D	S	S
McIntosh	F	H	L	V	E	VL	R	A	M	M
(Jonathon) **Melrose**	F,R	M	E	M	E	V	G	A	M	
Newton Pippin	S,P,F	M	M	M	G	S	R	D	S	
Prima	S,R,M	?	E	?	E	S	YR	D	S	
Pristine	F	L	L	M	F	VL	R	D	L	S
Red Delicious	S,F,R	M	M	M	F	S	R	D	S	
Redfree	S,P,R	M	L	M	E	M	R	A	M	
Shay	S,P	M	M	M	E	L	R	D	M	S
(McIntosh) **Spartan**	S,F,R	H	L	V	G	S	YR	C	S	
Wealthy	F,R	M	E	V	E	L	GR	D	M	S
Stayman Winesap	S,F,P,R	M	E	M	G	M	R	A	M	
Williams Pride	S,P	M	E	VL	E	M	YR	D	L	E
Swaar	S,M	M	L	M	E	S	R	A	M	E
Wolf River	F,R	L	E	M	E	M	R	A	M	
Wynooche	S	M	E	M	E	VS	YG	C	S	

* **Resistant to other diseases** —leafspot and white rot—seediseases
Not suitable as pollinators— Seedling, Crispin, Elstar, Freedom, Red Gravenstein, Jonagold, Williams Pride
** **Self Fertile**

Abbreviations:

c=cold, CR=Crown Rot, F= Fireblight, h=hot, N= Nematodes, P= Powdery Mildew, R= Cedar Apple Rust, S= Scab, Su= Suckering from rootstock, WA=Wooly Aphid, WD+=Well Drained.

[1] Information on insect resistant apples from Mother Earth News # 145, p. 78-85,1994. Resistance in apples without ratings are unknown.

Choices about insect damage in apples & pears

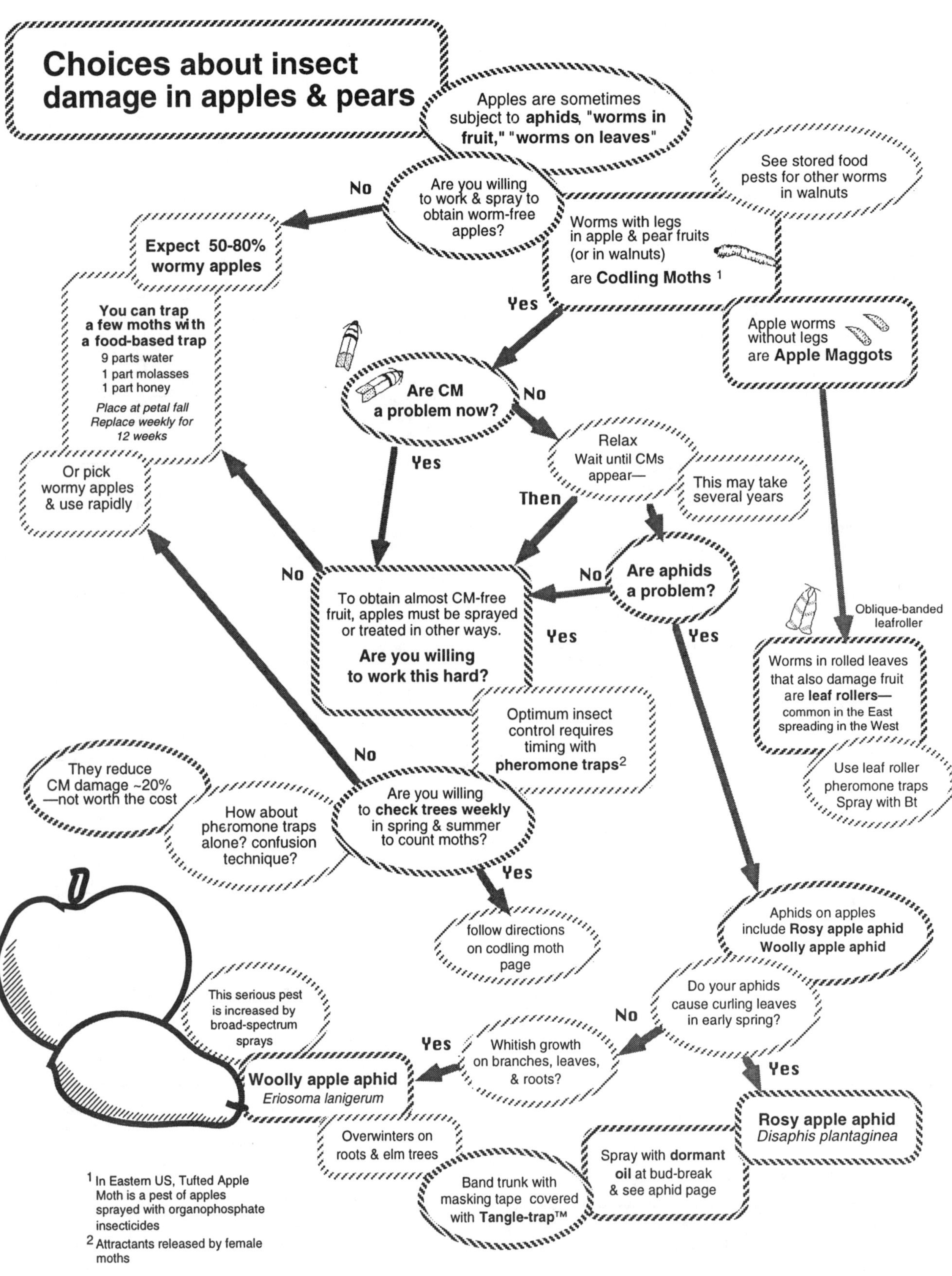

Apples are sometimes subject to aphids, "worms in fruit," "worms on leaves"
Are you willing to work & spray to obtain worm-free apples?
No
Expect 50-80% wormy apples
You can trap a few moths with a food-based trap
9 parts water
1 part molasses
1 part honey
Place at petal fall
Replace weekly for 12 weeks
Or pick wormy apples & use rapidly
See stored food pests for other worms in walnuts
Worms with legs in apple & pear fruits (or in walnuts) are Codling Moths 1
Yes
Apple worms without legs are Apple Maggots
Are CM a problem now?
No
Relax
Wait until CMs appear—
This may take several years
Then
Yes
No
To obtain almost CM-free fruit, apples must be sprayed or treated in other ways.
Are you willing to work this hard?
No
Are aphids a problem?
Yes
Yes
Oblique-banded leafroller
Worms in rolled leaves that also damage fruit are leaf rollers— common in the East spreading in the West
Use leaf roller pheromone traps
Spray with Bt
Optimum insect control requires timing with pheromone traps2
No
They reduce CM damage ~20% —not worth the cost
How about pheromone traps alone? confusion technique?
Are you willing to check trees weekly in spring & summer to count moths?
Yes
follow directions on codling moth page
Aphids on apples include Rosy apple aphid Woolly apple aphid
Do your aphids cause curling leaves in early spring?
No
Yes
This serious pest is increased by broad-spectrum sprays
Whitish growth on branches, leaves, & roots?
Yes
Woolly apple aphid
Eriosoma lanigerum
Overwinters on roots & elm trees
Band trunk with masking tape covered with Tangle-trap™
Rosy apple aphid
Disaphis plantaginea
Spray with dormant oil at bud-break & see aphid page

1 In Eastern US, Tufted Apple Moth is a pest of apples sprayed with organophosphate insecticides

2 Attractants released by female moths

Apple maggot

The apple maggot, *Rhagoletis pomonella,* is the larvae of a Tephretid (true) fruit fly which can be recognized like all of its Tephretid fellows by distinctive dark patterns on the wings. This maggots of this little Eastern North American fly has burrowed into apples for more than a century. Apples are a new host for this fly. Originally they laid their eggs into **hawthorn fruits**. In the mid nineteenth century, a few—perhaps a new species in the making—began to oviposit[1] in apples. Now the hawthorn and the apple races of the apple maggot do not interbreed.[2] The apple race began in Eastern U.S., but people have carried it accidentally to some western regions where it is spreading rapidly. Should you find maggot damage to your apples for the first time, report your find to your farm advisor and follow our control directions.

The apple race is attracted by the odor of apple and red balls the size of apples. These characteristics enable us to trap them and avoid the use of insecticides. In early June, hang three red sticky spheres about 30 inches apart in the foliage of each mature apple tree. If you do the same with Ladd* traps, you'll include an attractant apple odor which is even more effective.

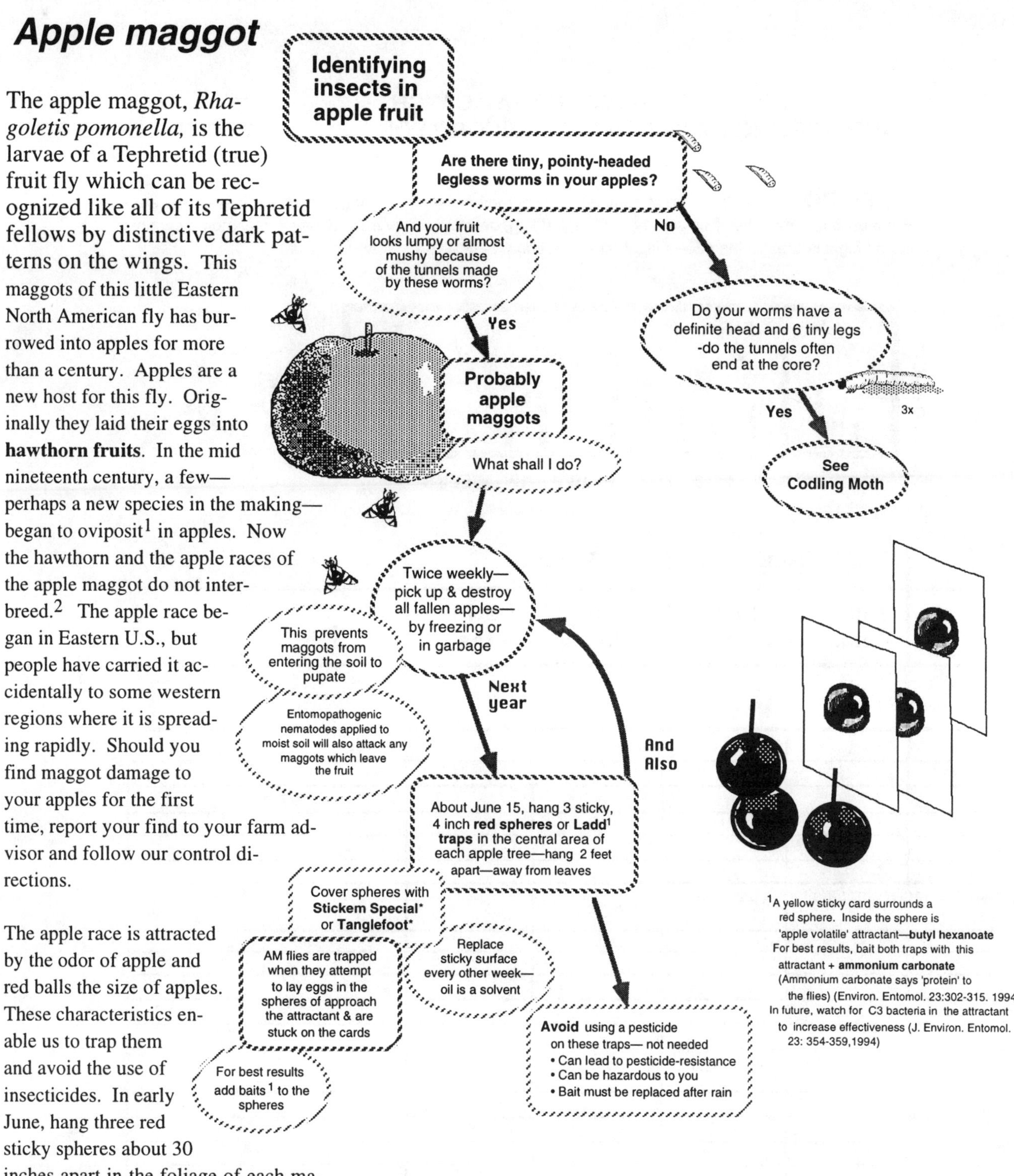

Identifying insects in apple fruit
Are there tiny, pointy-headed legless worms in your apples?
And your fruit looks lumpy or almost mushy because of the tunnels made by these worms?
No
Yes
Do your worms have a definite head and 6 tiny legs -do the tunnels often end at the core?
Probably apple maggots
What shall I do?
Yes
3x
See Codling Moth
Twice weekly—pick up & destroy all fallen apples—by freezing or in garbage
This prevents maggots from entering the soil to pupate
Entomopathogenic nematodes applied to moist soil will also attack any maggots which leave the fruit
Next year
And Also
About June 15, hang 3 sticky, 4 inch **red spheres** or **Ladd**[1] **traps** in the central area of each apple tree—hang 2 feet apart—away from leaves
Cover spheres with **Stickem Special*** or **Tanglefoot***
AM flies are trapped when they attempt to lay eggs in the spheres of approach the attractant & are stuck on the cards
Replace sticky surface every other week—oil is a solvent
For best results add baits [1] to the spheres
Avoid using a pesticide on these traps— not needed
• Can lead to pesticide-resistance
• Can be hazardous to you
• Bait must be replaced after rain

[1]A yellow sticky card surrounds a red sphere. Inside the sphere is 'apple volatile' attractant—**butyl hexanoate** For best results, bait both traps with this attractant + **ammonium carbonate** (Ammonium carbonate says 'protein' to the flies) (Environ. Entomol. 23:302-315. 1994) In future, watch for C3 bacteria in the attractant to increase effectiveness (J. Environ. Entomol. 23: 354-359,1994)

Females seeking to insert eggs in colorful "fruits" are trapped on the sticky surface. Since young flies arrive for weeks, the traps should remain until harvest. Replenish the adhesive every two weeks. Vegetable oil is a solvent for the sticky coating. If a few apples are discovered by these or other insects, the fruits usually fall before before they can mature and burrow into the soil. If you pick up fallen fruits weekly, you can interrupt this cycle. In apple maggot country, expect 75 to 100 percent maggot-ruined apples without controls. But well managed sticky spheres can be as effective as frequent insecticide sprays in preventing apple maggot damage.

[1] Lay eggs [2] Nat. Hist. 102(9):4-10, 1993

PHEROMONE TRAP CATCH
AND CODLING MOTH CONTROL RECORD FOR ________YEAR

DIRECTIONS —Place trap at petal fall. Count moths weekly. Change trap bottom every 6 weeks. Rake up & destroy fallen fruit weekly. When thinning, destroy wormy fruit. Spray if total moths caught in one flight is greater than 20--a flight takes several weeks

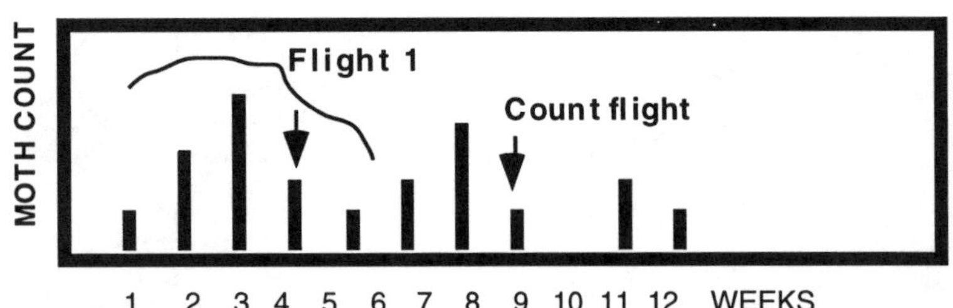

MOTH COUNT
Flight 1
Count flight
1 2 3 4 5 6 7 8 9 10 11 12 WEEKS

	TREE 1		TREE 2		NOTES
Date	Total Moths	New Moths	Total Moths	New Moths	Detail
Place trap--wait one week					
1					
2					
3					
4					
5					
6					
Count moths/ replace trap bottom & attractant					
1					
2					
3					
4					
5					
6					
Count moths/ replace trap bottom & attractant					
1					
2					
3					
4					
5					
6					

HARVEST SUMMARY:

	Tree 1	Tree 2
Number Fruits		
Wormy Fruits		

Wormy fruits/Total Fruits x 100
= % wormy fruits

Coping with codling moths

Most fruit growers eventually find 'worms' in their apples, sometimes their pears, and even their walnuts. The codling moth (CM), *Cydia pomonella,* the insect which is often responsible, is an old world native which is now found wherever apples are grown.

If your goal is perfect apples, you can't get by with control by natural enemies only—they're not perfect. Just a few years ago commercial apple growers were using a calendar-based spray schedule to control CM and the other pests which were triggered by their toxic sprays. *Some growers sprayed as many as 15 times per season* to control insects and diseases. Surprisingly, during >30 years, codling moths did not show resistance to the organophosphate insecticides (OP) used for their control. Some even suggested that the moth was not capable of showing resistance to this class of compounds. They were wrong, as we know now since CM in some regions have low levels of resistance to OP insecticides.[1] Obviously, use of any insecticide should be restricted as much as possible to minimize resistance and secondary pest upsets.[2]

Codling moth life cycle

Over most of their range, codling moths have two to three generations (flights) per year. The first flights come from the over-wintering population, and later flights from the broods of the year. After spending the winter as mature resting larvae, CM molt to pupae (pupate) in early spring. (Both larvae and pupae are protected within thin cocoon-like webbings which are hidden in cracks or bark crevices).
The adult moths begin to emerge from these pupae within a few weeks. The first few emerge about the time of apple petal fall—from March to May according to local climate. Male moths appear first, normally about three days before females. Timing of flight activity depends on temperature, with flight ceasing completely below 55° and above 85° F. During cool weather CM emergence is delayed.

Young CM adults require several days to mature. Eventually, receptive females release a sex pheromone[3] which attracts males for mating. After mating, each female lays about 100 eggs. These are placed singly on leaves and twigs. In cool weather she may oviposit for a two to three week period, but usually she lives for a shorter time. The eggs mature after a minimum of 5 days, hatching into tiny caterpillars. These fragile babies have only a few hours to find a fruit and burrow in.

Codling moth control strategies

With codling moths as with other pests, control strategies work best if they are used during a vulnerable portion of the life cycle. Insects which bore into fruits must be controlled before they enter the fruit if damage is to be avoided. Obviously, you'll need to know when the eggs are laid, and when they hatch. Beginning in the 1950's, researchers in Nova Scotia began studies which led to successful integrated control of apple pests. They were able to apply many fewer sprays than were common at the time because they timed their sprays to the CM life cycle and used relatively selective, non-persistent pesticides which affected target pests without appreciably harming natural enemies..

We've successfully tested the integrated codling moth control program presented here in home gardens in the San Francisco Bay Region. It is based on codling moth research of these and other scientists published in the scientific literature. The program assumes that the home apple grower can spend 15 minutes weekly on CM control in spring and summer, that good home control is 85-95% sound fruit, obtained after using no more than 2 low-toxic sprays in situations where there are two flights per year, and a third spray if there are three codling moth generation .

To monitor the CM life cycle we use sticky traps baited with CM pheromone. These lures attract a portion of the CM males to their deaths. We use these catches to time our spray applications to coincide with maximum period of egg hatch, ensuring that most young larvae will be killed before they can enter the fruit The sprays we recommend do not trigger pest upsets, so you will not need extra sprays to control secondary pests. Alternately, we tell you when to release *Trichograma* mini-wasp parasitoids which will attack newly-laid eggs and destroy them before they can hatch.

The apple grower who is unwilling to control CM, may spend less time on his fruit during the growing season, but at harvest must dump the crop, or spend many hours rapidly processing 50-99% wormy fruits before they spoil. The integrated CM control grower will devote a total of four hours in apple care during the season, but will be able to harvest a good crop of sound apples.

If you live in Eastern U.S. Tufted Apple Bud Moth, several leafrollers, the Plum Curculio, and the Apple Maggot may damage apples. In this situation, you may need other controls. Be very

---

[1] J. Econ. Entomol. 87:285-292,1994. [2] See page 9. [3] Volatile attractant

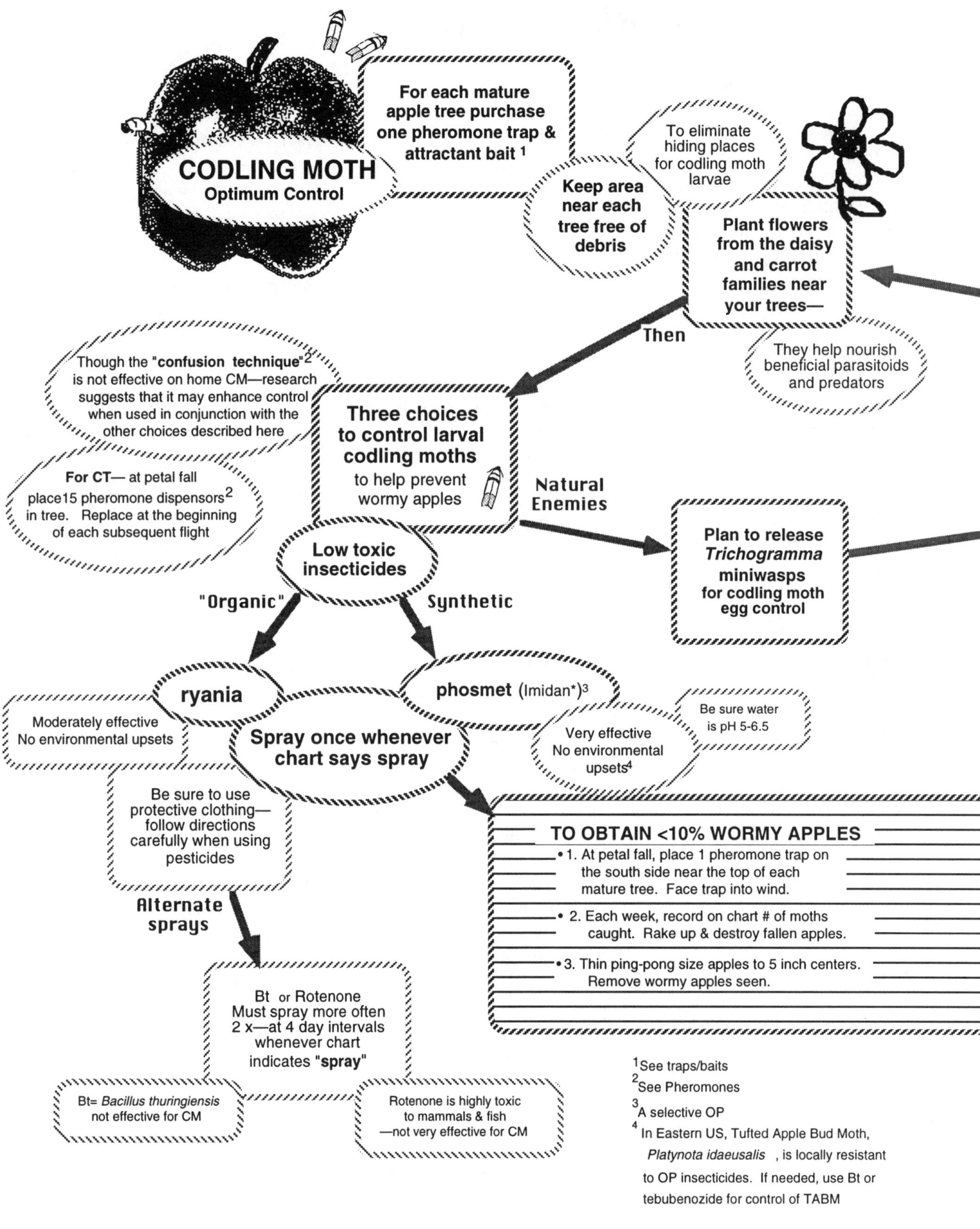

CODLING MOTH
Optimum Control
For each mature apple tree purchase one pheromone trap & attractant bait 1
Keep area near each tree free of debris
To eliminate hiding places for codling moth larvae
Plant flowers from the daisy and carrot families near your trees—
They help nourish beneficial parasitoids and predators
Then
Though the "confusion technique"2 is not effective on home CM—research suggests that it may enhance control when used in conjunction with the other choices described here
For CT— at petal fall place15 pheromone dispensors2 in tree. Replace at the beginning of each subsequent flight
Three choices to control larval codling moths
to help prevent wormy apples
Natural Enemies
Plan to release Trichogramma miniwasps for codling moth egg control
Low toxic insecticides
"Organic"
Synthetic
ryania
Moderately effective
No environmental upsets
phosmet (Imidan*)3
Be sure water is pH 5-6.5
Very effective
No environmental upsets4
Spray once whenever chart says spray
Be sure to use protective clothing— follow directions carefully when using pesticides
Alternate sprays
Bt or Rotenone
Must spray more often 2 x—at 4 day intervals whenever chart indicates "spray"
Bt= Bacillus thuringiensis not effective for CM
Rotenone is highly toxic to mammals & fish —not very effective for CM
TO OBTAIN <10% WORMY APPLES
• 1. At petal fall, place 1 pheromone trap on the south side near the top of each mature tree. Face trap into wind.
• 2. Each week, record on chart # of moths caught. Rake up & destroy fallen apples.
• 3. Thin ping-pong size apples to 5 inch centers. Remove wormy apples seen.
1See traps/baits
2See Pheromones
3A selective OP
4 In Eastern US, Tufted Apple Bud Moth, Platynota idaeusalis , is locally resistant to OP insecticides. If needed, use Bt or tebubenozide for control of TABM

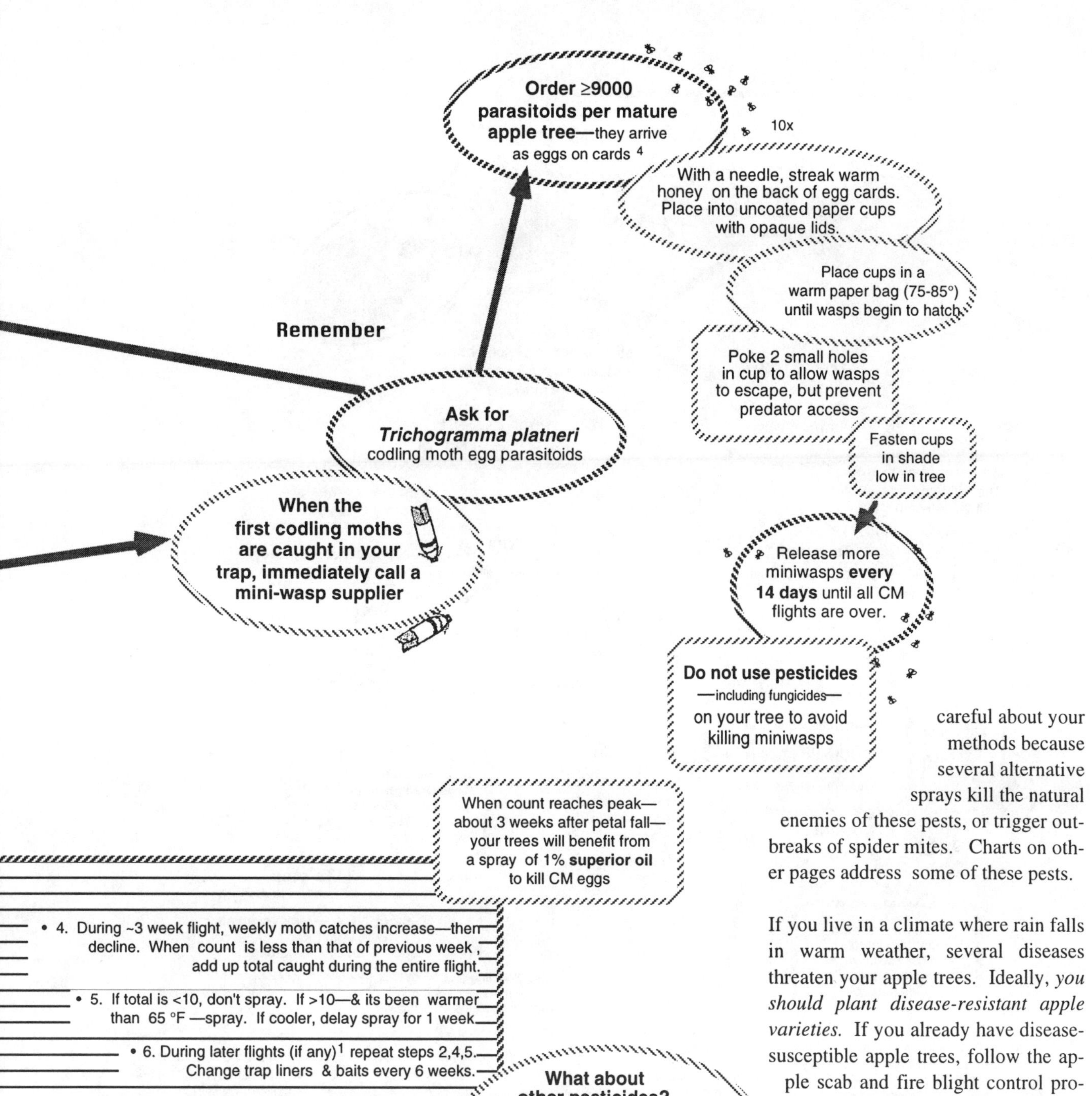
Order ≥9000 parasitoids per mature apple tree—they arrive as eggs on cards 4
10x
With a needle, streak warm honey on the back of egg cards. Place into uncoated paper cups with opaque lids.
Place cups in a warm paper bag (75-85°) until wasps begin to hatch.
Poke 2 small holes in cup to allow wasps to escape, but prevent predator access
Fasten cups in shade low in tree
Release more miniwasps every 14 days until all CM flights are over.
Do not use pesticides —including fungicides— on your tree to avoid killing miniwasps
Remember
Ask for Trichogramma platneri codling moth egg parasitoids
When the first codling moths are caught in your trap, immediately call a mini-wasp supplier
When count reaches peak—about 3 weeks after petal fall—your trees will benefit from a spray of 1% superior oil to kill CM eggs
• 4. During ~3 week flight, weekly moth catches increase—then decline. When count is less than that of previous week, add up total caught during the entire flight.
• 5. If total is <10, don't spray. If >10—& its been warmer than 65 °F —spray. If cooler, delay spray for 1 week.
• 6. During later flights (if any)1 repeat steps 2,4,5. Change trap liners & baits every 6 weeks.
What about other pesticides?
Sevin* (carbaryl)2 causes pest upsets
malathion3 degrades/causes upsets
methoxychlor & diazinon3 less selective, more toxic to you
1 In warm climates there can be 3 flights per year
2 See Class C carcinogens
3 Organophosphate insecticide
4 Directions based on Farmer to Farmer 3/95

careful about your methods because several alternative sprays kill the natural enemies of these pests, or trigger outbreaks of spider mites. Charts on other pages address some of these pests.

If you live in a climate where rain falls in warm weather, several diseases threaten your apple trees. Ideally, *you should plant disease-resistant apple varieties.* If you already have disease-susceptible apple trees, follow the apple scab and fire blight control programs detailed elsewhere in this book.

(If you raise long keeping apples, store your fruit in zipper plastic bags at 32-34° F and 99% humidity. The sugar in the apples keeps them from freezing, and the bag soon fills with carbon dioxide released by the ripening fruit, and lack of oxygen slows further maturation for weeks or months). This method works so well that we keep golden delicious apples

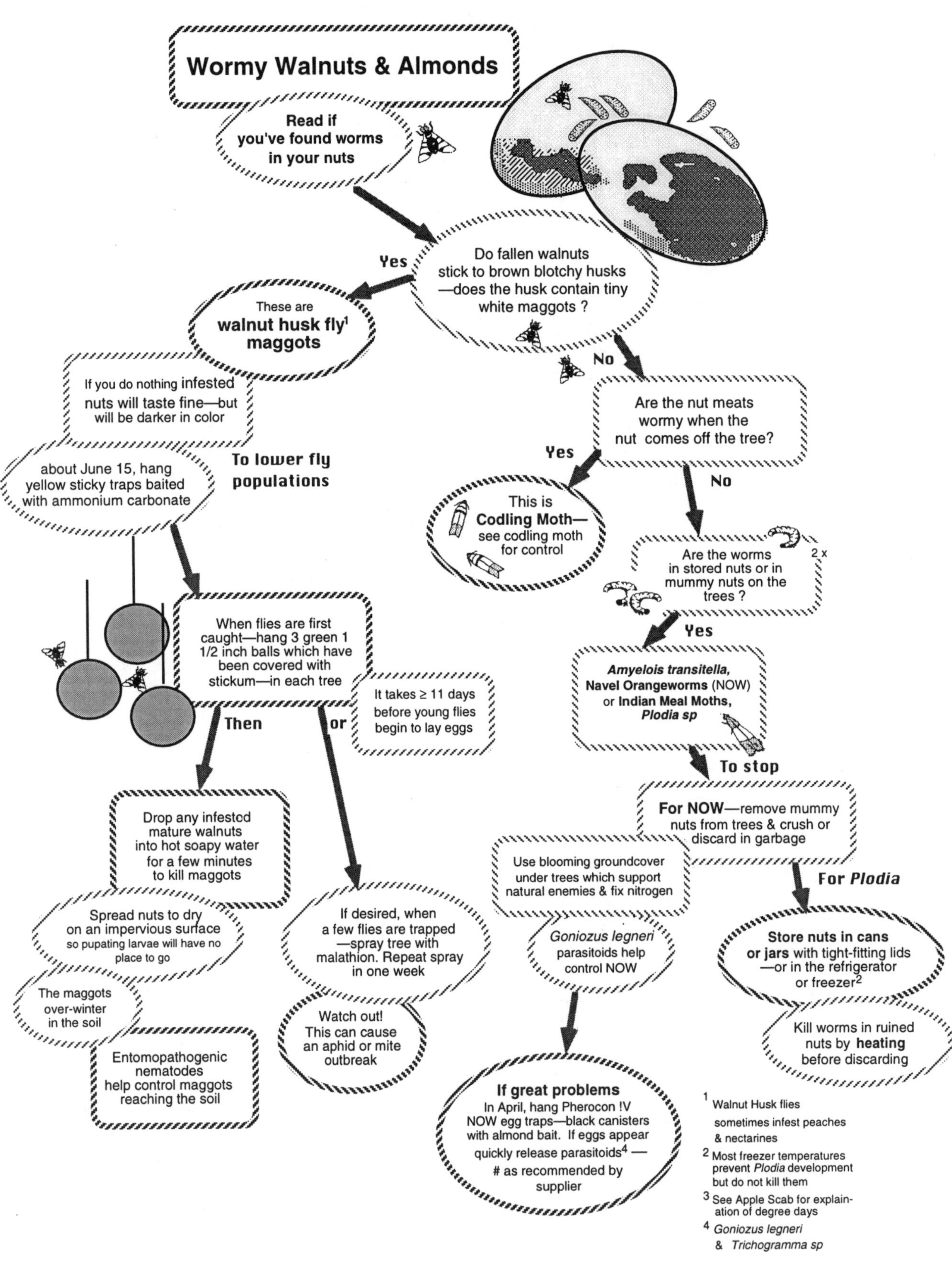
Wormy Walnuts & Almonds
Read if you've found worms in your nuts
Do fallen walnuts stick to brown blotchy husks —does the husk contain tiny white maggots ?
Yes
These are walnut husk fly[1] maggots
If you do nothing infested nuts will taste fine—but will be darker in color
To lower fly populations
about June 15, hang yellow sticky traps baited with ammonium carbonate
When flies are first caught—hang 3 green 1 1/2 inch balls which have been covered with stickum—in each tree
It takes ≥ 11 days before young flies begin to lay eggs
Then
or
Drop any infested mature walnuts into hot soapy water for a few minutes to kill maggots
Spread nuts to dry on an impervious surface so pupating larvae will have no place to go
The maggots over-winter in the soil
Entomopathogenic nematodes help control maggots reaching the soil
If desired, when a few flies are trapped —spray tree with malathion. Repeat spray in one week
Watch out! This can cause an aphid or mite outbreak
No
Are the nut meats wormy when the nut comes off the tree?
Yes
This is Codling Moth— see codling moth for control
No
Are the worms in stored nuts or in mummy nuts on the trees ?
2 x
Yes
Amyelois transitella, Navel Orangeworms (NOW) or Indian Meal Moths, Plodia sp
To stop
For NOW—remove mummy nuts from trees & crush or discard in garbage
Use blooming groundcover under trees which support natural enemies & fix nitrogen
Goniozus legneri parasitoids help control NOW
If great problems In April, hang Pherocon !V NOW egg traps—black canisters with almond bait. If eggs appear quickly release parasitoids[4] — # as recommended by supplier
For Plodia
Store nuts in cans or jars with tight-fitting lids —or in the refrigerator or freezer[2]
Kill worms in ruined nuts by heating before discarding
1 Walnut Husk flies sometimes infest peaches & nectarines
2 Most freezer temperatures prevent Plodia development but do not kill them
3 See Apple Scab for explaination of degree days
4 Goniozus legneri & Trichogramma sp

Perfect pears

In theory, a moderate climate is suitable for culture of almost any pear variety, but the popular summer variety, *Bartlett's* extremely susceptibility to fireblight disease makes success with Bartlett difficult everywhere. If raising pears is your dream consider planting one of the disease-resistant cultivars, even though we suggest ways to keep susceptible varieties going too. As with most other fruits, you will have more choices if you order bareroot trees from a mail order nursery.

Pears are divided into **European**—your traditional sweet, juicy pears—and **Asian**—less-sweet and crunchy. Most pears should be picked in a mature, green state and ripened off the tree. European pears are ready to pick when they can be removed easily when lifted. Asian pears should be harvested when fruit at the top of the tree just begins to change color ≈180 days after full bloom.[1] *Harvest as soon as fruit is mature to help prevent decay.* If picked too late, the center of the pear will soften and brown rapidly. *Bartlett, Seckel,* and the fireblight-resistant varieties, *Harrow Sweet* and *Magness* keep a about 6 weeks in the cold—32°F—at moderate humidity. The traditional "winter pears" *d-Anjou, Bosc,* and *Comice* can be stored for months. Bring mature green pears into room temperature to ripen.

Critters on pears—

At home, its possible to raise pears without insecticides. You'll probably not be bothered by the **pear psyllid**, the most troublesome pest of commercial pear growers. The sucking of these little, leaf-hopper-like insects causes fruit damage and a sticky honeydew. In absence of pesticides, natural enemies control psyllids satisfactorily. When commercial growers use insecticide sprays to control **codling moth**, the natural enemies of the psyllids are destroyed. If CM appear on your pears, see our codling moth page. If you have a psyllid problem, apply **dormant oil** just as buds swell in the spring. This will smother psyllid eggs and nymphs.

Should your pears have scarred, russetted fruits and blistered leaves, your problem is probably due to microscopic **rust mites**. To prevent damage, apply dormant oil at bud swell. Then monitor pears for russet mites in early spring by placing double-backed tape around a few small branches. Every few days check this tape under a 10x magnifying glass looking for little worm-like mites with 2 pairs of legs near the front end. If you find them, spray immediately with superior oil or abamectin. Alternately, you can measure spring heat gain as described in our chart to pinpoint the optimum timing of the spray.[2]

Sometimes pear foliage is skeletonized by sawfly larvae known as **pear slugs (pear sawfly)**. Knock these from the trees with insecticidal soap or a hard water spray. Since they pupate in the soil, **entomopathogenic nematodes** may also help control them.

Fireblight on pears

If you have fireblight-susceptible varieties such as Bartlett, every warm spring rain will threaten the crop, and even the life tree. Fireblight is a **bacterial disease** of rose family plants. Many pear varieties are more susceptible to this disease than are *Pyrocantha*, apple, quince and others.

If the clinging brown leaves or blackened twigs of fireblight appear on any rose-family-plant, prepare a 10% bleach solution. Cut off all affected branches *at least 1 foot below obvious symptoms,* dipping your shears into the bleach between each cut. Look closely for wilted blossoms, and even sunken areas in the bark. These are fireblight symptoms too.

Detecting fireblight

If you have a fireblight susceptible pear, use a max-min thermometer to predict periods of likely fireblight infection. During bloom, determine the *daily mean temperature*. Plot this temperature on a graph during the 2 month period which encompasses spring temperatures when pears bloom —March 1 to May 1 in northern California—on the 'x' axis, and temperature on the 'y' axis. Draw a line from 62° F on the first day to 58° on the last.

If it is rainy or foggy during bloom, and, mean temperatures go higher than this reference line, fire-blight bacteria will invade the blossoms. Immediately, spray with fixed copper, Streptomycin or Terramycin to kill these bacteria. Continue spraying every 7 days until bloom ends. If mean temperatures remain below this minimum the bacteria will not invade, and you will not need to spray. (In future, one spray of beneficial bacteria, *Pseudomonas fluroescens* or *Erwinia hervicola* may be available to fight the fireblight bacteria).

In summer rain-fall areas, fire blight may begin even after the blooming period. In this situation, fireblight-susceptible pears should be monitored frequently to check for disease symptoms, and sprays should be applied after each warm rain. Obviously, resistant varieties will be a safer, easier, less expensive choice.

Proper culture during the pear growing season will help you prevent fruit spoilage after harvest. Pear fruits which contain high nitrogen (N) are susceptible to decay. Avoid N application during bloom. Apply needed N about one month before harvest, but no later. To increase calcium—which helps prevent decay—follow **calcium nitrate** directions on the "Looking at Apples" page. In the near future, spoilage antagonists—selected yeast or bacteria—may be available for post harvest treatment.

---

[1] Cal. Agri. 48(4):17-19, 1994.ê [2] Environ. Entomol 22:1325-1332, 1993

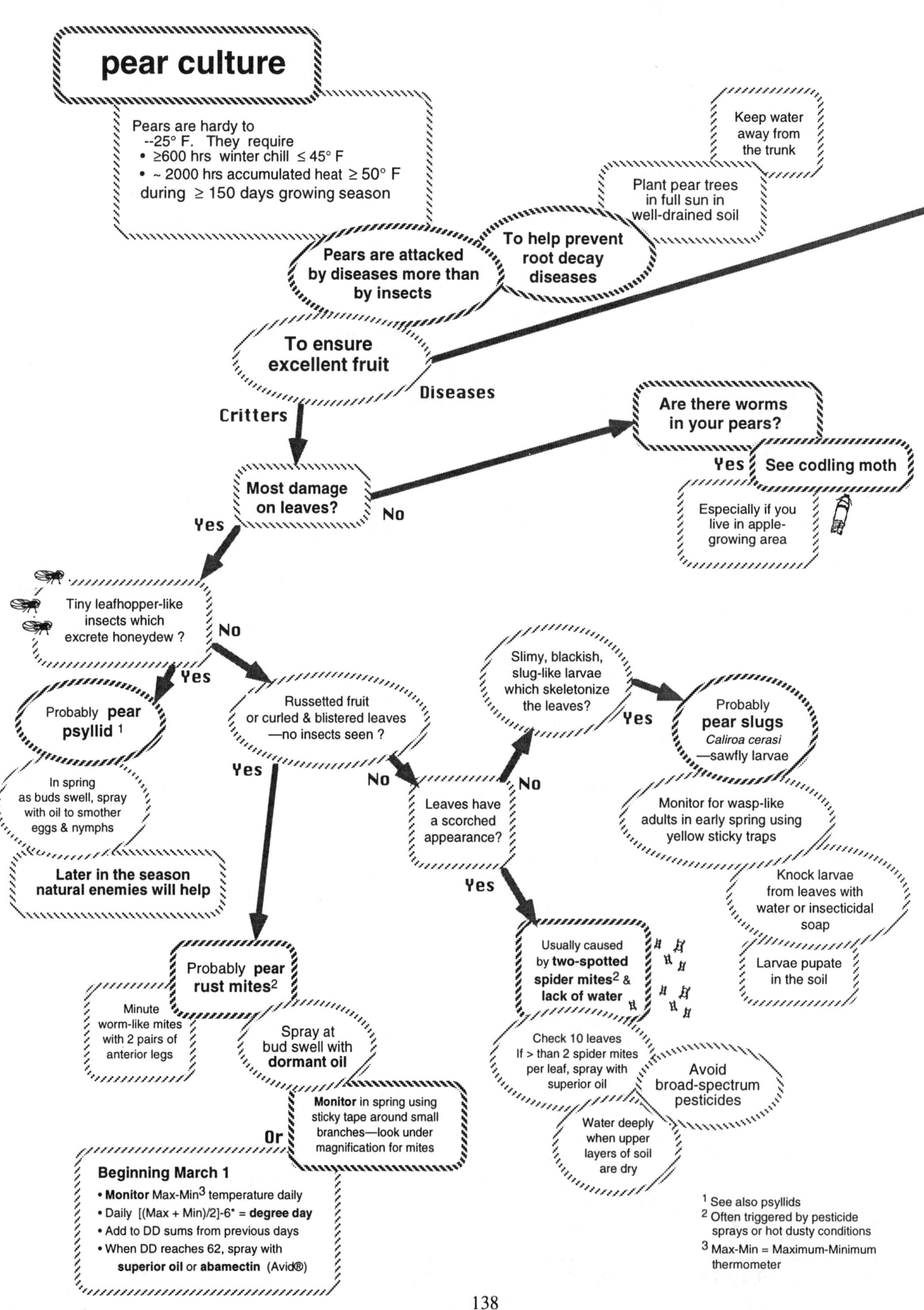
pear culture
Pears are hardy to --25° F. They require
• ≥600 hrs winter chill ≤ 45° F
• ~ 2000 hrs accumulated heat ≥ 50° F during ≥ 150 days growing season
Keep water away from the trunk
Plant pear trees in full sun in well-drained soil
To help prevent root decay diseases
Pears are attacked by diseases more than by insects
To ensure excellent fruit
Diseases
Critters
Are there worms in your pears?
Yes
See codling moth
Especially if you live in apple-growing area
Most damage on leaves?
No
Yes
Tiny leafhopper-like insects which excrete honeydew ?
No
Yes
Probably pear psyllid 1
In spring as buds swell, spray with oil to smother eggs & nymphs
Later in the season natural enemies will help
Russetted fruit or curled & blistered leaves —no insects seen ?
Yes
No
Slimy, blackish, slug-like larvae which skeletonize the leaves?
Yes
Probably pear slugs
Caliroa cerasi
—sawfly larvae
Monitor for wasp-like adults in early spring using yellow sticky traps
Knock larvae from leaves with water or insecticidal soap
Larvae pupate in the soil
Leaves have a scorched appearance?
No
Yes
Usually caused by two-spotted spider mites2 & lack of water
Check 10 leaves If > than 2 spider mites per leaf, spray with superior oil
Avoid broad-spectrum pesticides
Water deeply when upper layers of soil are dry
Probably pear rust mites2
Minute worm-like mites with 2 pairs of anterior legs
Spray at bud swell with dormant oil
Monitor in spring using sticky tape around small branches—look under magnification for mites
Or
Beginning March 1
• Monitor Max-Min3 temperature daily
• Daily [(Max + Min)/2]-6* = degree day
• Add to DD sums from previous days
• When DD reaches 62, spray with superior oil or abamectin (Avid®)
1 See also psyllids
2 Often triggered by pesticide sprays or hot dusty conditions
3 Max-Min = Maximum-Minimum thermometer

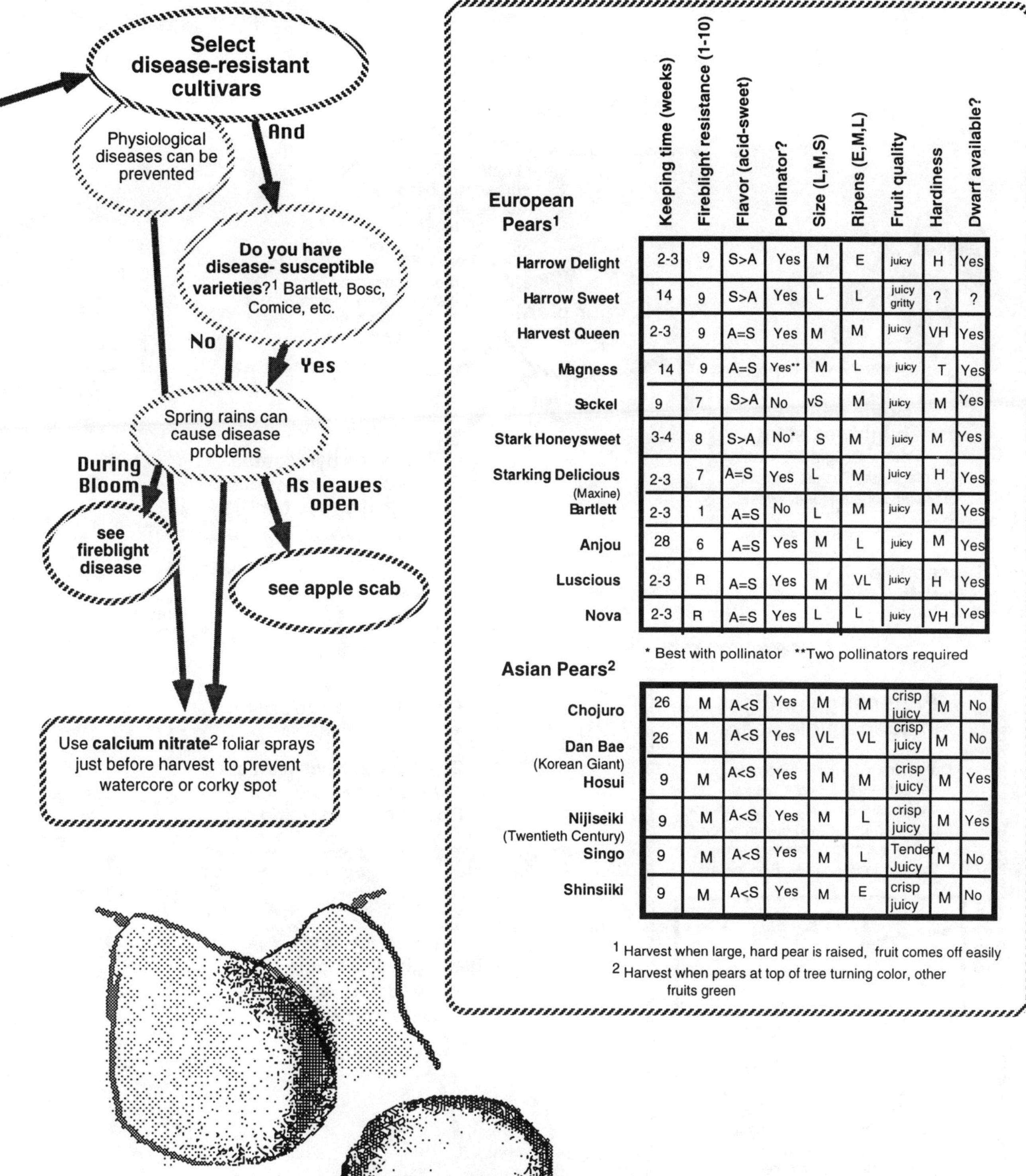
Select disease-resistant cultivars
Physiological diseases can be prevented
And
Do you have disease- susceptible varieties?[1] Bartlett, Bosc, Comice, etc.
No
Yes
Spring rains can cause disease problems
During Bloom
As leaves open
see fireblight disease
see apple scab
Use **calcium nitrate**[2] foliar sprays just before harvest to prevent watercore or corky spot

European Pears[1]	Keeping time (weeks)	Fireblight resistance (1-10)	Flavor (acid-sweet)	Pollinator?	Size (L,M,S)	Ripens (E,M,L)	Fruit quality	Hardiness	Dwarf available?
Harrow Delight	2-3	9	S>A	Yes	M	E	juicy	H	Yes
Harrow Sweet	14	9	S>A	Yes	L	L	juicy gritty	?	?
Harvest Queen	2-3	9	A=S	Yes	M	M	juicy	VH	Yes
Magness	14	9	A=S	Yes**	M	L	juicy	T	Yes
Seckel	9	7	S>A	No	vS	M	juicy	M	Yes
Stark Honeysweet	3-4	8	S>A	No*	S	M	juicy	M	Yes
Starking Delicious (Maxine)	2-3	7	A=S	Yes	L	M	juicy	H	Yes
Bartlett	2-3	1	A=S	No	L	M	juicy	M	Yes
Anjou	28	6	A=S	Yes	M	L	juicy	M	Yes
Luscious	2-3	R	A=S	Yes	M	VL	juicy	H	Yes
Nova	2-3	R	A=S	Yes	L	L	juicy	VH	Yes

* Best with pollinator **Two pollinators required

Asian Pears[2]	Keeping time (weeks)	Fireblight resistance (1-10)	Flavor (acid-sweet)	Pollinator?	Size (L,M,S)	Ripens (E,M,L)	Fruit quality	Hardiness	Dwarf available?
Chojuro	26	M	A<S	Yes	M	M	crisp juicy	M	No
Dan Bae (Korean Giant)	26	M	A<S	Yes	VL	VL	crisp juicy	M	No
Hosui	9	M	A<S	Yes	M	M	crisp juicy	M	Yes
Nijiseiki (Twentieth Century)	9	M	A<S	Yes	M	L	crisp juicy	M	Yes
Singo	9	M	A<S	Yes	M	L	Tender Juicy	M	No
Shinsiiki	9	M	A<S	Yes	M	E	crisp juicy	M	No

1 Harvest when large, hard pear is raised, fruit comes off easily

2 Harvest when pears at top of tree turning color, other fruits green

1 More listed on Fireblight page

2 1% Calcium Nitrate sprayed on foliage or used as a fruit dip

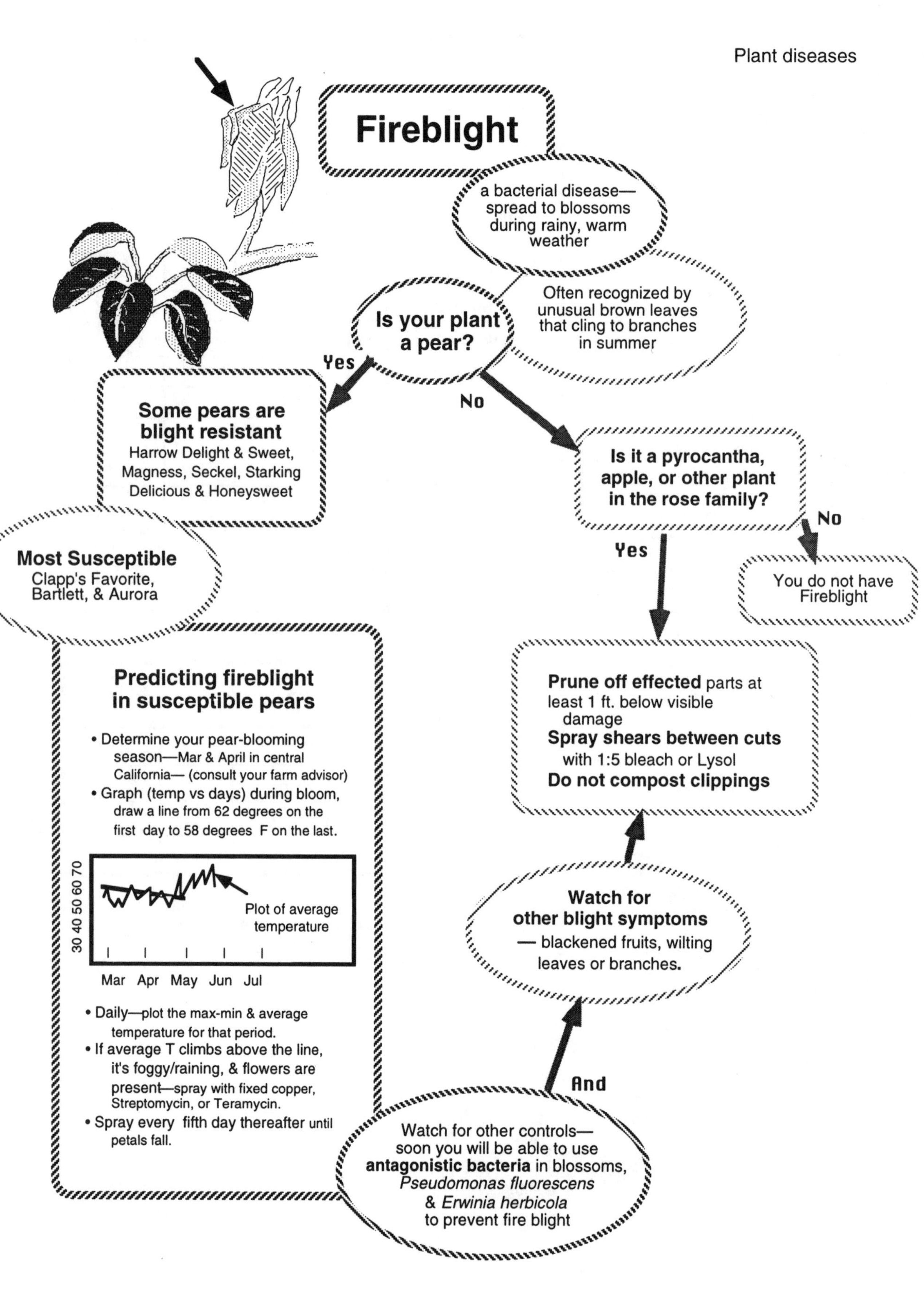

Fireblight
a bacterial disease—spread to blossoms during rainy, warm weather
Often recognized by unusual brown leaves that cling to branches in summer
Is your plant a pear?
Yes
No
Some pears are blight resistant
Harrow Delight & Sweet, Magness, Seckel, Starking Delicious & Honeysweet
Most Susceptible
Clapp's Favorite, Bartlett, & Aurora
Predicting fireblight in susceptible pears
• Determine your pear-blooming season—Mar & April in central California— (consult your farm advisor)
• Graph (temp vs days) during bloom, draw a line from 62 degrees on the first day to 58 degrees F on the last.
30 40 50 60 70
Plot of average temperature
Mar Apr May Jun Jul
• Daily—plot the max-min & average temperature for that period.
• If average T climbs above the line, it's foggy/raining, & flowers are present—spray with fixed copper, Streptomycin, or Teramycin.
• Spray every fifth day thereafter until petals fall.
Is it a pyrocantha, apple, or other plant in the rose family?
Yes
No
You do not have Fireblight
Prune off effected parts at least 1 ft. below visible damage
Spray shears between cuts with 1:5 bleach or Lysol
Do not compost clippings
Watch for other blight symptoms — blackened fruits, wilting leaves or branches.
And
Watch for other controls— soon you will be able to use antagonistic bacteria in blossoms, Pseudomonas fluorescens & Erwinia herbicola to prevent fire blight

Cherishing Cherries

Until recently, it was almost impossible for home gardeners to raise sweet cherries. Cherries were borne near the top of 30-45 foot trees, and two varieties were required for cross pollination. All that has changed. Excellent self-fertile, naturally dwarf cherries, or familiar cultivars grafted on semi-dwarfing rootstocks, are available.

Cherries require pollination. *(Compact Stella, Stella, Glacier, Lapins,* and *Starkimson Dwarf* are 'self fertile', but you still need to encourage honeybees.) If you do not have these varieties, plant a pollinator tree (or plant two or more suitable pollinators in the same hole). Fortunately, dwarf cherries can be held to 9 feet or less.

Like most fruit trees, most cherries require winter chill. In this case ≥ 800 hours less than 45° F. Coastal dwellers will have trouble getting a cherry crop, because both winter chill and summer warmth will be in short supply.

Cherry training

Pruning and training should begin the first summer after planting. Watch the growth. Cherries tend to grow strongly upward. *You should head upward growing branches to outside buds during the first and second summer.* This will force the growth outward, and keep the ultimate size moderate. Cherries bear fruits on long-lived spurs. These should be protected. You should keep crotches wide, and the canopy open. To reduce disease incidence, *confine pruning thinning to the summer season, after the fruit has been harvested.*

Threat of diseases

Rain during cherry blossoming, accompanied by average temperatures in the 50s and can trigger development of **brown rot fungi** *(Monilinia spp.)* in blossoms. Monitor temperatures during spring bloom, and spray cherry trees with sulfur or fixed copper if temperatures reach the 50s, during rain or fog. Promptly remove fallen cherries and mummies to reduce production of fungal spores. If rain falls on ripening fruits, they may crack and spoil. In an emergency, you may be able to cover a single tree with clear plastic to prevent rain damage.

Cherries and other stone fruits are also susceptible to **bacterial blight** *(Pseudomonas syringae).* To lower chances for blight, cherries should be planted in warm, sunny—but not too hot—sites in neutral, well-drained soil containing plenty of compost. (Cold stress, and sites with acid, sandy, water-logged soils containing root-feeding nematodes increase blight susceptibility). Restricting pruning to the summer season, and a copper spray (above) just before bloom, should also help prevent blight.

Cherries thrive with regular, deep irrigation, and steady balanced fertilization throughout the growing season. Water at the drip line. *Avoid sprinkler irrigation of all fruit trees.* Water on the trunk triggers *Phytophthora sp.* crown rot. (To help prevent fruit splitting, stop the water during the last few weeks before ripening.) Root-stocks are also important. The standard rootstock, Mazzard F-12-1, is resistant to both canker and *Phytophthora* root fungi, and GM 61/1 (Damil) semi-dwarfing rootstock confers some resistance to diseases, while rain during bloom, decreases resistance.

Pests

Little flies with dark patterns on the wings—**western cherry fruit flies**—*(Rhagoletis indifferens)* occasionally attack cherries in western states, while (**cherry fruit flies** *(R. cingulata)* are found in the east). Use yellow sticky cards or yellow sticky spheres to monitor and capture emerging flies—they spend the winter in the soil. Remove fallen cherries immediately—they are either diseased or contain maturing fly maggots—and next year apply entomopathogenic nematodes to the soil when soil warms in the spring, to help prevent fruit fly emergence.

Birds (and **squirrels**) love cherries— with early dark varieties being preferred. You can use bird netting to prevent their feeding. Covering your tree with netting will be relatively easy. Wrap half the net around a pole and climb a ladder to raise it over the top of the tree. If you use two or more nets bound together with twist ties, you can reach between the nets and harvest fruits throughout the season.

Cherries will not ripen further off the tree. For luscious ripe flavor, pick cherries as they ripen, and store in the refrigerator. Eat within a few days.

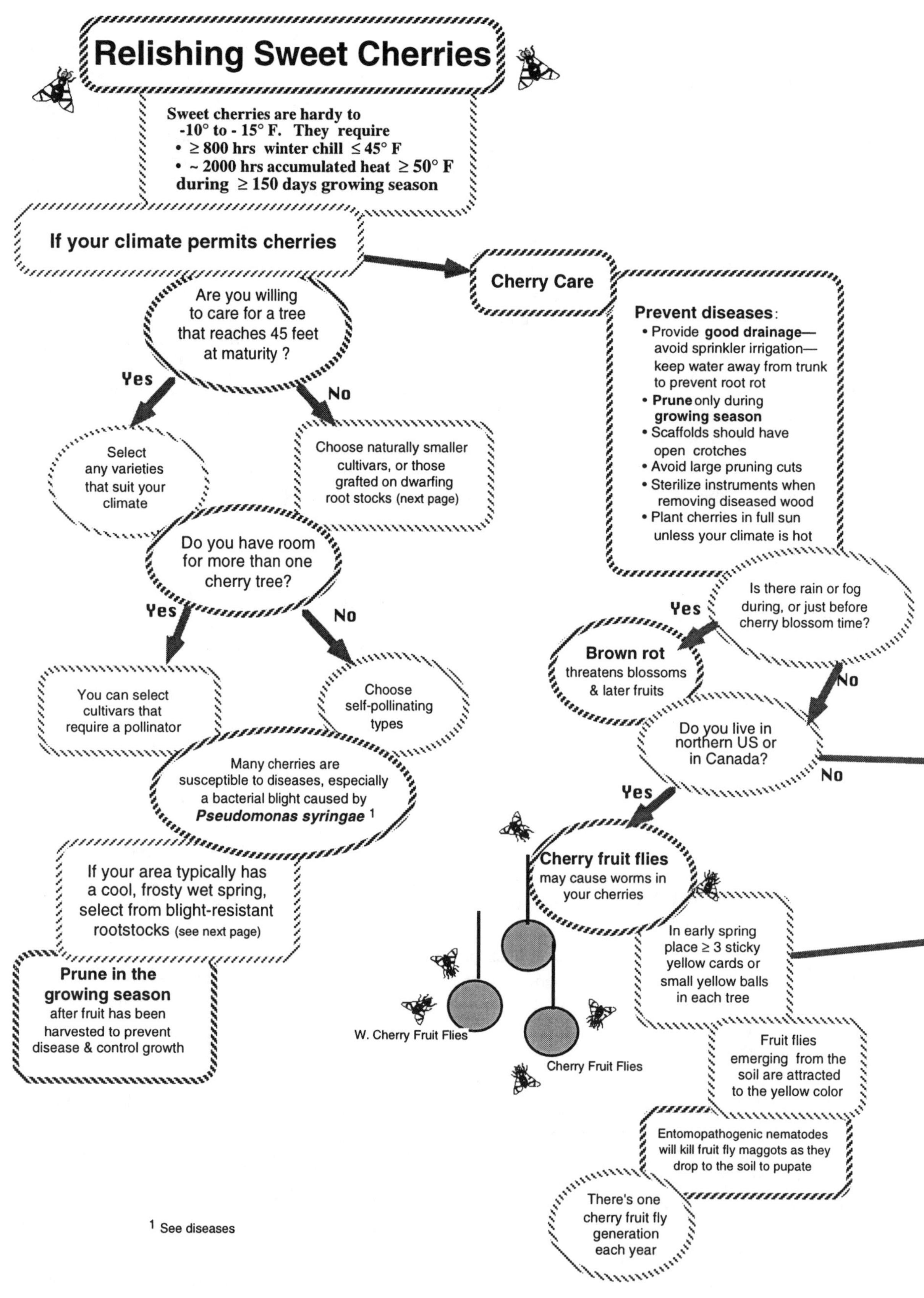
Relishing Sweet Cherries
Sweet cherries are hardy to -10° to - 15° F. They require
• ≥ 800 hrs winter chill ≤ 45° F
• ~ 2000 hrs accumulated heat ≥ 50° F during ≥ 150 days growing season
If your climate permits cherries
Are you willing to care for a tree that reaches 45 feet at maturity ?
Yes
No
Select any varieties that suit your climate
Choose naturally smaller cultivars, or those grafted on dwarfing root stocks (next page)
Do you have room for more than one cherry tree?
Yes
No
You can select cultivars that require a pollinator
Choose self-pollinating types
Many cherries are susceptible to diseases, especially a bacterial blight caused by *Pseudomonas syringae* 1
If your area typically has a cool, frosty wet spring, select from blight-resistant rootstocks (see next page)
Prune in the growing season after fruit has been harvested to prevent disease & control growth
Cherry Care
Prevent diseases:
• Provide good drainage—avoid sprinkler irrigation—keep water away from trunk to prevent root rot
• Prune only during growing season
• Scaffolds should have open crotches
• Avoid large pruning cuts
• Sterilize instruments when removing diseased wood
• Plant cherries in full sun unless your climate is hot
Is there rain or fog during, or just before cherry blossom time?
Yes
Brown rot threatens blossoms & later fruits
No
Do you live in northern US or in Canada?
No
Yes
Cherry fruit flies may cause worms in your cherries
In early spring place ≥ 3 sticky yellow cards or small yellow balls in each tree
Fruit flies emerging from the soil are attracted to the yellow color
Entomopathogenic nematodes will kill fruit fly maggots as they drop to the soil to pupate
There's one cherry fruit fly generation each year
W. Cherry Fruit Flies
Cherry Fruit Flies
1 See diseases

Sweet Cherry Cultivars

	Pollinator	Brown Rot	Cracking	Cancker	Color	Fruit size	Cold tolerance	Ripens	Flavor	Tree size
Angela	Cross	R	R		Dark Red	M	Hardy	L	VG	FS DRS
Bing	Cross		Susc.	Susc.	Dark Red	Lg	M	M	VG	FS
Black Republican	Cross		Susc.		Black	M	Hardy	L	G	FS
Black Tartarian	Cross		Susc.	Susc.	Black	M	Hardy	E	G	FS
Compact Lambert	Cross		R	Susc.	Dark Red	Lg	Hardy	L	G	M
Compact Stella	Self	MR	R		Dark Red	Lg	M	M	VG	M
Corum	Cross		R	R	Yellow-Pink	Lg	Hardy		G	FS
Early Burlat	Cross		Susc.	R	Dark Red	Lg	Hardy	VE	G	FS DRS
Glacier	Self				Dark Red	Lg	Hardy	M	G	FS
Gold	Cross		R		Yellow-Pink	Sm	Very Hardy	VL	Maras-chino	FS DRS
Hardy Giant	Cross		R		Dark Red	M	Very Hardy	M	G	FS DRS
Kristen	Cross		R		Black	Lg	Very Hardy	M		FS DRS
Lambert	Cross		Susc.	Susc.	Dark Red	Lg	Hardy	L	G	FS GD
Lapins	Self		R		Black	Lg	Hardy	L	VG	FS DRS
Rainier	Cross		R		Yellow-Pink	Lg	Very Hardy	E	VG	FS GD
Royal Ann	Cross	R	Susc.		Yellow-Pink	Lg	Hardy	E	VG	FS DRS
Sam	Cross		R	R	Black	M	Hardy	E	G	FS DRS
Starkrimson Dwarf	Self	R	R		Dark Red	M	Hardy	E	VG	M
Stella	Self		R		Dark Red	Lg	M	M	VG	FS DRS
Van	Cross		MR	Susc.	Black	M	Very Hardy	L	G	FS DRS

Good pollinators: Black Republican, Hardy Giant, Lapins, Stella, Rainier, Van

DRS=Dwarf Root Stock (20-25 feet high), E= excellent, FS= Full size (35-45 feet high), G=Good, Lg= Large, M= Moderate (size, hardiness), R= Resistant, Susc.= Susceptible

Insects are not a problem—but, **in mild climates select low-chill cherries**

To protect ripening cherries from fruit-eating birds & squirrels

Early ripening cultivars are preferably attacked by birds

House finches, Robins, Starlings, & Jays love cherries

Cover entire tree with bird netting, & tie net around trunk

Two or more nets tied together with twist ties allow picking with net in place

Harvest only ripe cherries Cherries will not ripen off the tree

Cherry Root Stocks

Mahalab	Standard —susceptible to root rots, good in sandy soils/drought
Mazzard	Standard —resistant to *Phytophthora sp.* soil borne fungi
Mazzard F-12-1	Also resistant to Canker
GM 61/1 (Damil)	Semi-dwarfing—resistant to *Phytophthora sp.* soil borne fungi
Colt	Semi-dwarfing—tolerant of wide soil variety
Gisela	True-dwarfing—trees can be held to 12' (Raintree Nursery)

Appreciating Apricots

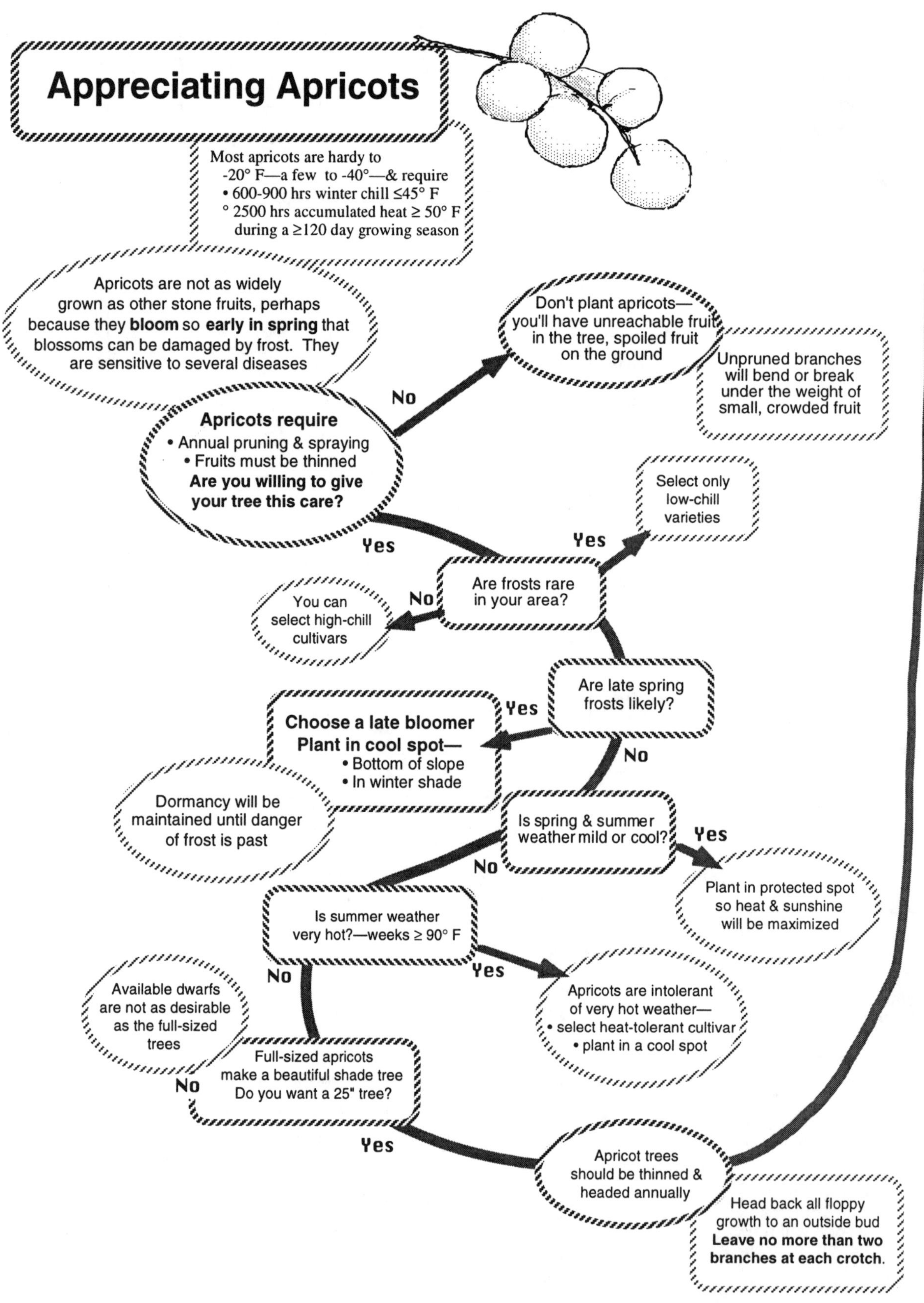
Most apricots are hardy to -20° F—a few to -40°—& require
• 600-900 hrs winter chill ≤45° F
° 2500 hrs accumulated heat ≥ 50° F during a ≥120 day growing season
Apricots are not as widely grown as other stone fruits, perhaps because they bloom so early in spring that blossoms can be damaged by frost. They are sensitive to several diseases
Apricots require
• Annual pruning & spraying
• Fruits must be thinned
Are you willing to give your tree this care?
No
Don't plant apricots—you'll have unreachable fruit in the tree, spoiled fruit on the ground
Unpruned branches will bend or break under the weight of small, crowded fruit
Yes
Are frosts rare in your area?
Yes
Select only low-chill varieties
No
You can select high-chill cultivars
Are late spring frosts likely?
Yes
Choose a late bloomer
Plant in cool spot—
• Bottom of slope
• In winter shade
Dormancy will be maintained until danger of frost is past
No
Is spring & summer weather mild or cool?
Yes
Plant in protected spot so heat & sunshine will be maximized
No
Is summer weather very hot?—weeks ≥ 90° F
Yes
Apricots are intolerant of very hot weather—
• select heat-tolerant cultivar
• plant in a cool spot
No
Full-sized apricots make a beautiful shade tree
Do you want a 25" tree?
No
Available dwarfs are not as desirable as the full-sized trees
Yes
Apricot trees should be thinned & headed annually
Head back all floppy growth to an outside bud
Leave no more than two branches at each crotch.

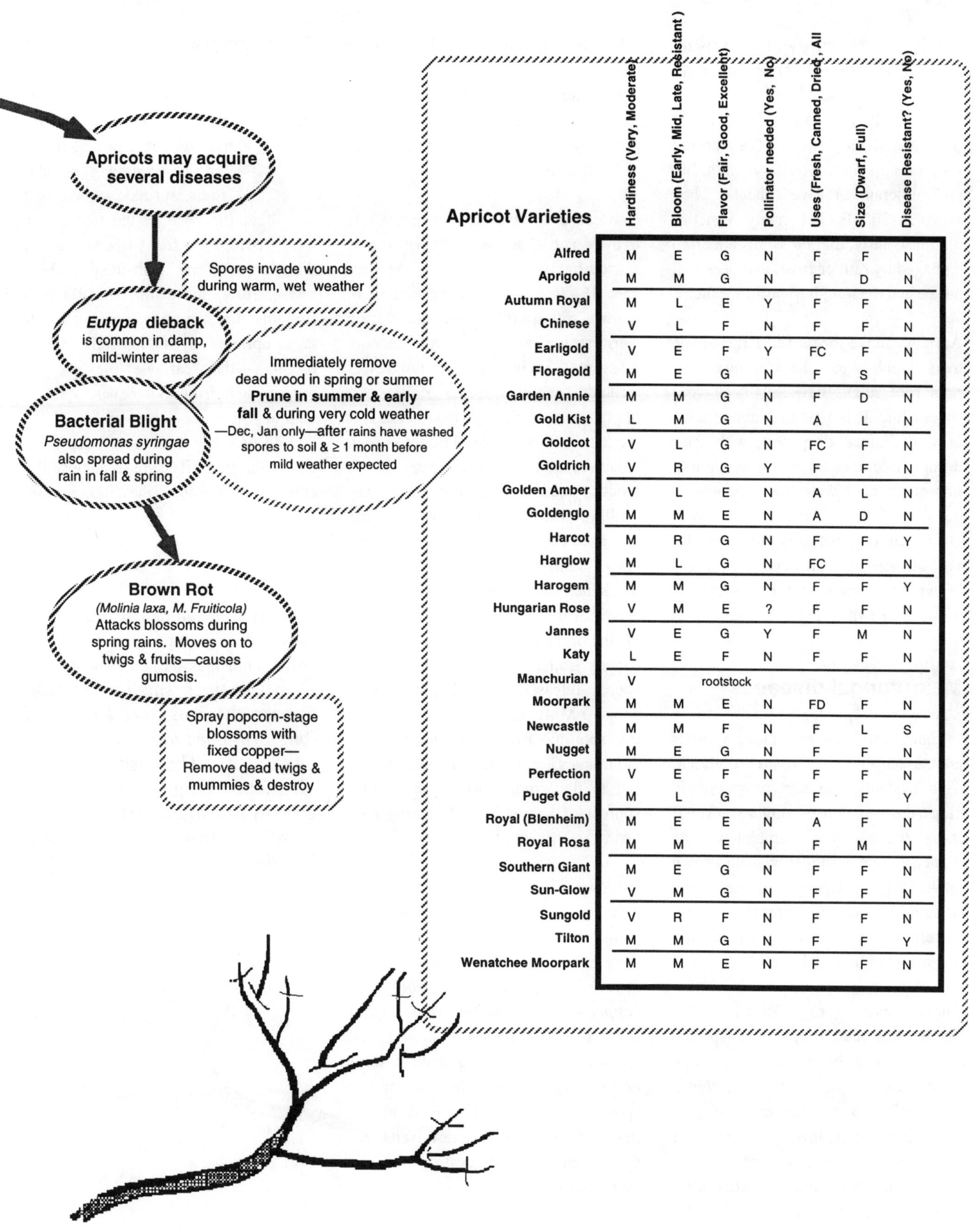

Apricots may acquire several diseases
Spores invade wounds during warm, wet weather
Eutypa dieback is common in damp, mild-winter areas
Immediately remove dead wood in spring or summer Prune in summer & early fall & during very cold weather —Dec, Jan only—after rains have washed spores to soil & ≥ 1 month before mild weather expected
Bacterial Blight Pseudomonas syringae also spread during rain in fall & spring
Brown Rot (Molinia laxa, M. Fruiticola) Attacks blossoms during spring rains. Moves on to twigs & fruits—causes gumosis.
Spray popcorn-stage blossoms with fixed copper— Remove dead twigs & mummies & destroy

Apricot Varieties

	Hardiness (Very, Moderate)	Bloom (Early, Mid, Late, Resistant)	Flavor (Fair, Good, Excellent)	Pollinator needed (Yes, No)	Uses (Fresh, Canned, Dried, All	Size (Dwarf, Full)	Disease Resistant? (Yes, No)
Alfred	M	E	G	N	F	F	N
Aprigold	M	M	G	N	F	D	N
Autumn Royal	M	L	E	Y	F	F	N
Chinese	V	L	F	N	F	F	N
Earligold	V	E	F	Y	FC	F	N
Floragold	M	E	G	N	F	S	N
Garden Annie	M	M	G	N	F	D	N
Gold Kist	L	M	G	N	A	L	N
Goldcot	V	L	G	N	FC	F	N
Goldrich	V	R	G	Y	F	F	N
Golden Amber	V	L	E	N	A	L	N
Goldenglo	M	M	E	N	A	D	N
Harcot	M	R	G	N	F	F	Y
Harglow	M	L	G	N	FC	F	N
Harogem	M	M	G	N	F	F	Y
Hungarian Rose	V	M	E	?	F	F	N
Jannes	V	E	G	Y	F	M	N
Katy	L	E	F	N	F	F	N
Manchurian	V		rootstock				
Moorpark	M	M	E	N	FD	F	N
Newcastle	M	M	F	N	F	L	S
Nugget	M	E	G	N	F	F	N
Perfection	V	E	F	N	F	F	N
Puget Gold	M	L	G	N	F	F	Y
Royal (Blenheim)	M	E	E	N	A	F	N
Royal Rosa	M	M	E	N	F	M	N
Southern Giant	M	E	G	N	F	F	N
Sun-Glow	V	M	G	N	F	F	N
Sungold	V	R	F	N	F	F	N
Tilton	M	M	G	N	F	F	Y
Wenatchee Moorpark	M	M	E	N	F	F	N

Appreciating apricots

Its hard to enjoy the unsurpassed flavor of ripe apricots unless we raise them ourselves because they're one of our most delicate stone fruits. They do not keep or ship well, require warmth, but are intolerant of excess heat. They survive -20° F, but many varieties bloom so early, that blossoms are often damaged by rain or frost, and bees will not be active enough to pollinate them.

Apricots make beautiful large shade trees, which is good because dwarf apricot root stocks have not been very successful. It is best to plant apricots in well drained deep soil, with their drought tolerance taken into account—infrequent, deep watering is the way to go. *Never plant apricots in a lawn.* Over-watering, not only ruins the flavor of apricot fruit, but encourages brown rot disease, while moisture at the root crown will encourage crown rot.

Major fungal diseases

In damp, mild-winter regions apricots are susceptible to ***Eutypa* dieback**. This systemic disease progressively clogs the sap transporting tissues. If these tissues clog completely, the branch may die suddenly, with brown leaves clinging tightly. In late spring or summer such dead branches should be removed immediately. The disease is not spread by pruning tools.

Eutypa spores are released during warm rains, and may be transported many miles in the wind. *Trees which have been pruned or injured within 3 weeks of spore release, are very susceptible to Eutypa invasion.* To reduce infection, prune apricots only in summer or in cold winter weather after drenching fall rains have washed infectious spores out of the air. This schedule will allow time for pruning wounds to heal before spores are released during warm rains in fall and spring. Remove all dead apricot trees promptly. They are a primary source of *Eutypa* spores.

One cause of apricot twig dieback is **brown rot disease**. Brown rot is caused by *Monilinia laxa* in the west and *M. fruticola* in eastern U.S. Brown rot spores germinate during warm spring rains and invade opening blossoms. The disease progresses through several stages. • Blossom blight is evident 3-6 days after infection. • Shoot or twig blight is seen 3-4 weeks later, after dead tissue blocks nutrient transport. • Non-girdling lesions become wet-looking darkened cankers which sometimes exude a lump of gum (gumosis). A blackened twig often extends from the center of this lump. • The final phase of the infection is brown rot of ripening fruits. Fruits are infected by spores released from blighted blossoms. • More spores are released from the spoiling fruits, and brown fruit "mummies" cling to the branches or fall to the ground, to become major sources of spores in early spring next year.

If brown rot is a problem in your situation, sprays are the only control. Only Tilton and Harcot varieties are resistant. *To prevent brown rot, spray popcorn stage blossoms with fixed copper*—apricots suffer from sulphur sickness. If it rains within 24 hours, spray again. Later, if a few blossoms or twigs are blighted in spite of this spray, remove and destroy dead tissues promptly. If a few fruits spoil, remove and destroy the mummies to

Other pests—

In western U.S. apricots are seldom attacked by caterpillars, but **earwigs** nibble holes in ripening fruits. To lower earwig populations, sprinkle earwig bait at the base of the tree a few weeks before the fruits ripen. East of the Rockies, the fruit-feeding **Japanese**, **June**, and **plum curculio beetles** that threaten stone fruits, also attack apricots. If squirrels are a problem—they eat one bite out of each fruit, but never stop at just a few—use sturdy netting or other barriers to keep them out of the tree. Be sure to enclose the entire tree because they'll come up from below too.

Pruning—

Apricots bear fruit on last year's wood and on fruiting spurs. Each branch can grow as much as six feet annually. To keep the trees small enough to harvest the fruit, *head back all long branches to an outside bud annually* . These should be 6-12 inches long. Also thin all growth *to wide crotches with no more than two branches at each junction.*

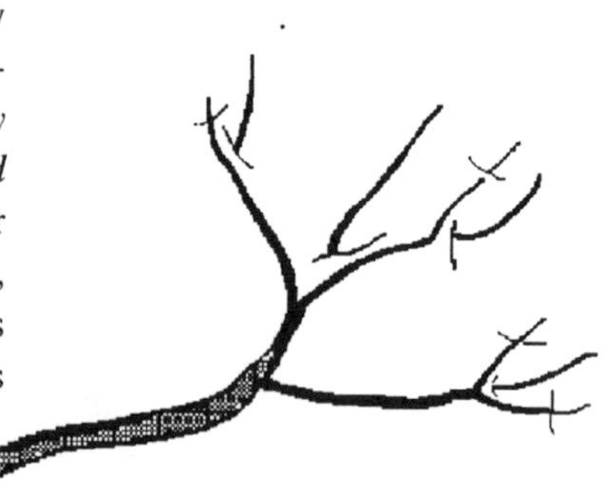

Perfect peaches

Peaches and nectarines make perfect home garden trees. They will succeed if you have a mild to warm climate, but will not do well in cool areas.

Varieties

All things being equal, you'll want to select freestone peaches or nectarines with excellent flavor. *Choose varieties that fit your climate.* Mail order suppliers are your best bet. Plant bare root trees in winter. Keep the crown slightly above the soil line as described in "How to plant trees".

Pruning and thinning

P&Ns should be pruned late in the dormant season. The fruit is borne only on last years growth. This fruiting wood should be thinned—remove every other young twig—and possibly headed to keep tree size moderate, and heavy fruits from breaking the branches. After fruit set, thin young fruits to ≥3 inch centers.

Diseases

Most P&Ns are subject to **peach leaf curl**, a fungal disease which infests opening leaves during rainy weather. These thickened and curled leaves are eventually replaced—rake up and hot-compost or destroy fallen leaves—but annual replacement of leaves is so debilitating that untreated trees die within a few years. (Unfortunately, the few available PLC-resistant peaches, have sub-standard flavor). As leaf buds begin to swell in very early spring, spray with **lime sulphur**—best—or **Bordeau solution** (copper sulfate & limestone) as directed. (Neither spray is especially toxic, but both are irritating to the skin). These compounds kill germinating spores before symptoms can appear. Sprays applied later in the season are not effective against this disease.

Stone fruits are also susceptible to **brown rot** *(Molinia spp.).* Brown rot disease spreads during damp weather, so resistant cultivars are especially desirable if you live in a foggy or rainy area. Both brown rot resistant cultivars—Harko or Merricrest nectarines—require high winter chill. Two **copper** or **sulphur** sprays, the first at the popcorn blossom stage, and the second one week later are the remedies of choice. If fruit spoilage occurs, quickly remove and destroy mummies—a source of more disease. Avoid sprinkler irrigation which tends to increase humidity and trigger **crown rot** in all fruit trees, not just peaches.

Especially in the south, **bacterial canker** (peach tree short life) caused by *Pseudomonas syringe pv syringae* is a very serious cause of early mortality of peaches. Two rootstocks—Nemaguard and Lovell—which are resistant to the **ring nematode** help prevent the root injury which allows these diseases to invade. For best results peaches should only be planted in soil where plants which are not susceptible to ring nematode have grown for several years. If you have sandy or nematode-infested ground be sure to maintain high organic matter in the soil and investigate other means of reducing nematodes. Keep compost levels high and follow other recommendations in the fungus chart. Read "Growing Grapes" for a description of hairy vetch mulches

Insect Pests

The fuzzy skin of peaches offers some protection, but nectarine fruits are easily damaged by insects. Peach damage will be sporadic in the west—from the **Oriental fruit moth** or the **peach twig borer**—but east of the Rockies several beetles—**Japanese, June,** and **plum curculio**—can also seriously damage soft fruits.

Peach twig borers *(Anarsia lineatella)* are attracted to stressed trees. Water young trees at least weekly at the drip line—later extend to biweekly, then monthly—and apply balanced nutrients regularly to reduce stress. *(Avoid too much nitrogen, since this increase both insect and disease attack.)*[1] If wilted new leaves and fruit damage from tiny (≤1/2 inch) naked brown and white banded caterpillars appear, spray each winter with dormant oil to kill both overwintering eggs and larvae of PTB, and the green peach aphids which overwinter on peach. (The aphids are major vegetable disease vectors). Spray with Btt *(Bacillus thuringiensis)* caterpillar disease at popcorn blossom and petal fall stages to control any PTB larvae that hatch. This spray can be combined with brown rot spray

The **Oriental fruit moth** *(Grapholita molesta)* a creamy caterpillar with a brown head, can cause similar but more serious damage. Monitor OFM appearance with a pheromone trap. When moths appear, immediately send for and release its parasitoid natural enemy, *Macrocentrus ancylifvorus.* Continue monitoring, and release more parasitoids at the next OFM generation. Alternately, try the pheromone-based confusion technique.[2] Multiple sources of OFM pheromone potentially prevent male moths from locating the female for mating. This product (Isomate-M) is recommended for orchards of ≥ 5 acres because adequate control has not been achieved in smaller blocks.

P&Ns are readily attacked by **peachtree borer** *(Synanthedon exitiosa).* This wasp-like *clear-winged moth* lays eggs *on the trunk near the soil line.* The offspring are caterpillars which burrow into the wood destroying the

[1]Calif. Agri. 49(4):13-18, 1995. [2]See, Insect pheromone trap strategies, p158

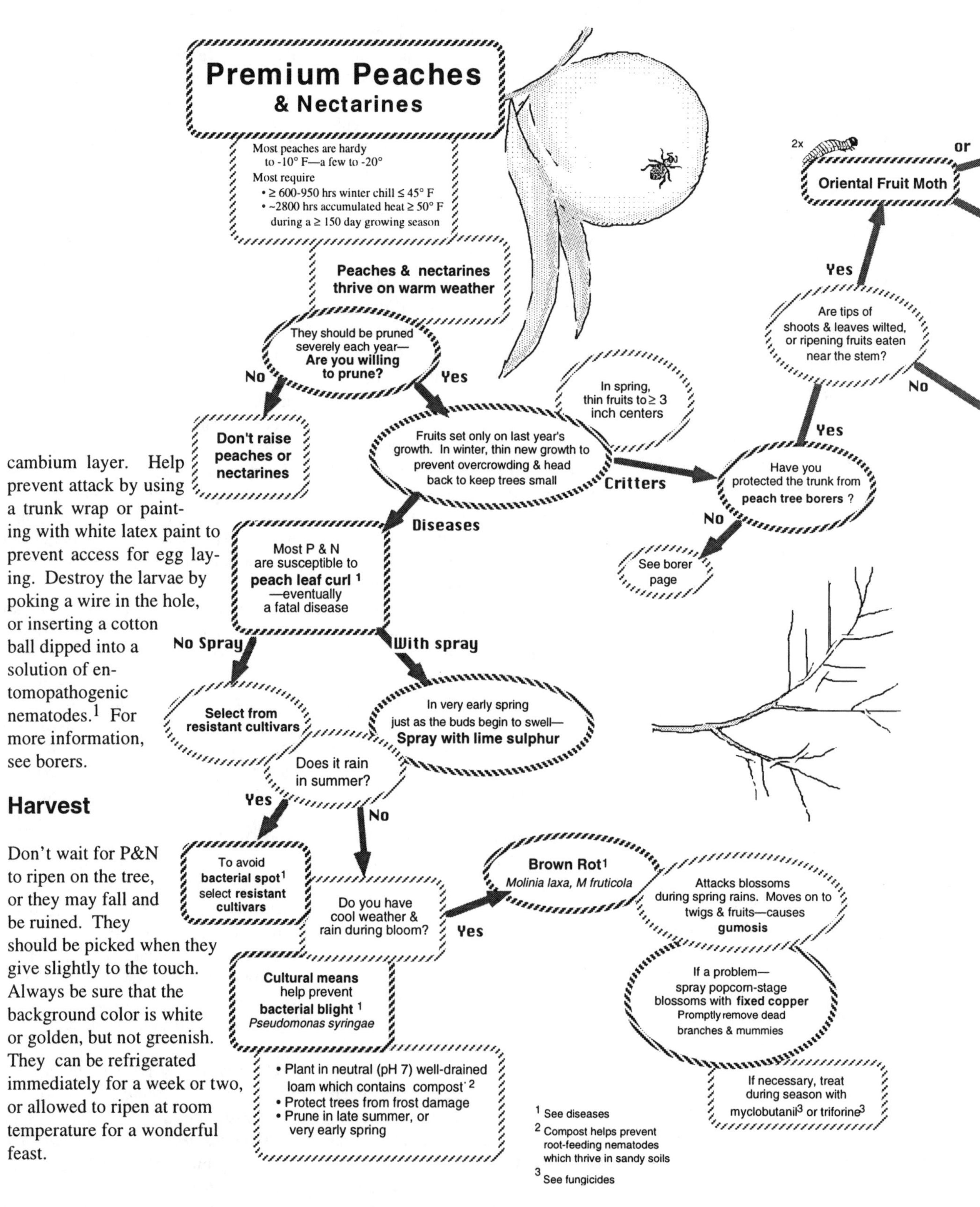

Premium Peaches
& Nectarines
Most peaches are hardy to -10° F—a few to -20°
Most require
• ≥ 600-950 hrs winter chill ≤ 45° F
• ~2800 hrs accumulated heat ≥ 50° F during a ≥ 150 day growing season
Peaches & nectarines thrive on warm weather
They should be pruned severely each year— Are you willing to prune?
No
Yes
Don't raise peaches or nectarines
Fruits set only on last year's growth. In winter, thin new growth to prevent overcrowding & head back to keep trees small
In spring, thin fruits to ≥ 3 inch centers
Critters
Have you protected the trunk from peach tree borers ?
No
See borer page
Yes
Are tips of shoots & leaves wilted, or ripening fruits eaten near the stem?
Yes
No
2x
Oriental Fruit Moth
or
Diseases
Most P & N are susceptible to peach leaf curl 1 —eventually a fatal disease
No Spray
With spray
Select from resistant cultivars
In very early spring just as the buds begin to swell— Spray with lime sulphur
Does it rain in summer?
Yes
No
To avoid bacterial spot1 select resistant cultivars
Do you have cool weather & rain during bloom?
Yes
Brown Rot1
Molinia laxa, M fruticola
Attacks blossoms during spring rains. Moves on to twigs & fruits—causes gumosis
If a problem— spray popcorn-stage blossoms with fixed copper
Promptly remove dead branches & mummies
If necessary, treat during season with myclobutanil3 or triforine3
Cultural means help prevent bacterial blight 1
Pseudomonas syringae
• Plant in neutral (pH 7) well-drained loam which contains compost 2
• Protect trees from frost damage
• Prune in late summer, or very early spring
1 See diseases
2 Compost helps prevent root-feeding nematodes which thrive in sandy soils
3 See fungicides

cambium layer. Help prevent attack by using a trunk wrap or painting with white latex paint to prevent access for egg laying. Destroy the larvae by poking a wire in the hole, or inserting a cotton ball dipped into a solution of entomopathogenic nematodes.[1] For more information, see borers.

Harvest

Don't wait for P&N to ripen on the tree, or they may fall and be ruined. They should be picked when they give slightly to the touch. Always be sure that the background color is white or golden, but not greenish. They can be refrigerated immediately for a week or two, or allowed to ripen at room temperature for a wonderful feast.

1 Roundworms that attack insects

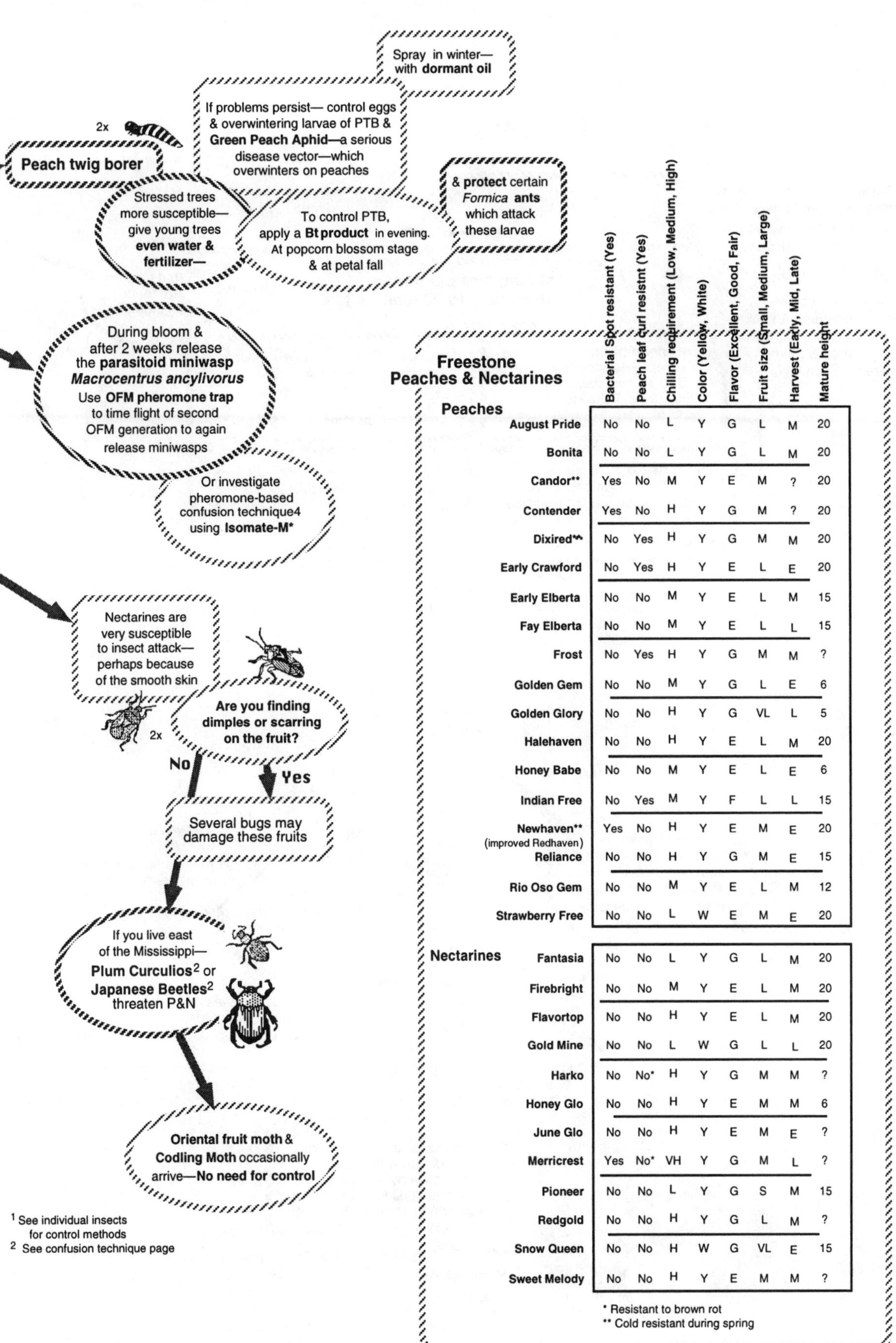
Spray in winter— with **dormant oil**
If problems persist— control eggs & overwintering larvae of PTB & **Green Peach Aphid**—a serious disease vector—which overwinters on peaches
2x
Peach twig borer
& **protect** certain *Formica* **ants** which attack these larvae
Stressed trees more susceptible— give young trees **even water & fertilizer**—
To control PTB, apply a **Bt product** in evening. At popcorn blossom stage & at petal fall
During bloom & after 2 weeks release the **parasitoid miniwasp** ***Macrocentrus ancylivorus*** Use **OFM pheromone trap** to time flight of second OFM generation to again release miniwasps
Or investigate pheromone-based confusion technique4 using **Isomate-M***
Nectarines are very susceptible to insect attack— perhaps because of the smooth skin
2x
Are you finding dimples or scarring on the fruit?
No
Yes
Several bugs may damage these fruits
If you live east of the Mississippi— **Plum Curculios**2 or **Japanese Beetles**2 threaten P&N
Oriental fruit moth & **Codling Moth** occasionally arrive—**No need for control**

[1] See individual insects for control methods
[2] See confusion technique page

Freestone Peaches & Nectarines

		Bacterial Spot resistant (Yes)	Peach leaf curl resistnt (Yes)	Chilling requirement (Low, Medium, High)	Color (Yellow, White)	Flavor (Excellent, Good, Fair)	Fruit size (Small, Medium, Large)	Harvest (Early, Mid, Late)	Mature height
Peaches	**August Pride**	No	No	L	Y	G	L	M	20
	Bonita	No	No	L	Y	G	L	M	20
	Candor**	Yes	No	M	Y	E	M	?	20
	Contender	Yes	No	H	Y	G	M	?	20
	Dixired**	No	Yes	H	Y	G	M	M	20
	Early Crawford	No	Yes	H	Y	E	L	E	20
	Early Elberta	No	No	M	Y	E	L	M	15
	Fay Elberta	No	No	M	Y	E	L	L	15
	Frost	No	Yes	H	Y	G	M	M	?
	Golden Gem	No	No	M	Y	G	L	E	6
	Golden Glory	No	No	H	Y	G	VL	L	5
	Halehaven	No	No	H	Y	E	L	M	20
	Honey Babe	No	No	M	Y	E	L	E	6
	Indian Free	No	Yes	M	Y	F	L	L	15
	Newhaven** (improved Redhaven)	Yes	No	H	Y	E	M	E	20
	Reliance	No	No	H	Y	G	M	E	15
	Rio Oso Gem	No	No	M	Y	E	L	M	12
	Strawberry Free	No	No	L	W	E	M	E	20
Nectarines	**Fantasia**	No	No	L	Y	G	L	M	20
	Firebright	No	No	M	Y	E	L	M	20
	Flavortop	No	No	H	Y	E	L	M	20
	Gold Mine	No	No	L	W	G	L	L	20
	Harko	No	No*	H	Y	G	M	M	?
	Honey Glo	No	No	H	Y	E	M	M	6
	June Glo	No	No	H	Y	E	M	E	?
	Merricrest	Yes	No*	VH	Y	G	M	L	?
	Pioneer	No	No	L	Y	G	S	M	15
	Redgold	No	No	H	Y	G	L	M	?
	Snow Queen	No	No	H	W	G	VL	E	15
	Sweet Melody	No	No	H	Y	E	M	M	?

* Resistant to brown rot
** Cold resistant during spring

Plentiful Plums

Edible Plums include **European**, **Japanese**, & **Damson** species, & several **Native** plums similar to Japanese types, but with smaller fruits

Several **hybrids** between Japanese & native plums, or between apricots or cherries & plums are also available

Most standard plum trees can be held to 20 feet.

What insects are found on plums?

European plums usually have a sweet, dryish, freestone flesh. They are very hardy, but late blooming, & therefore better adapted to areas with late frosts.

Japanese plums require a warmer growing climate, bloom earlier, are less tolerant of winter cold. Flesh is very juicy, often tart, clingstone .

Hardy to -20°F, requiring 700-1000 hrs winter chill & 2500 hrs accumulated heat ≥50°F during ≥120 day growing season

Hardy to -15°F—requiring
- 500-800 hrs winter chill ≥45°F
- 2800 hrs accumulated heat ≥50°F during ≥120 day growing season

Watch your tree—pruning needs depend on its normal growth habits

If you can't prune —forget fruit trees. Branches break., fruit grows high in tree, beyond reach.

European

Annual growth is moderate. Thin annually, but *be sure to protect the fruiting spurs* which may eventually become a large "bush".

Most European plums are self fertile

Japanese

If growth spreads, cut to inside buds. If growth is strongly upward, cut to outside buds.

Annual growth can be rapid. **Thin& head annually** to keep tree size moderate. *Be sure to save fruiting spurs.*

Most varieties require a pollinator

2-4 trees can be planted in the same hole

Thin young fruits to 3-4 inches—prop up branches which are heavy with fruit.

Diseases are not a major problem with plums. If **brown rot** appears—remove spoiled mummies. Next spring spray with copper at popcorn blossom stage.

Keep water moderate

Stanley & Green Gage are somewhat susceptible to brown rot

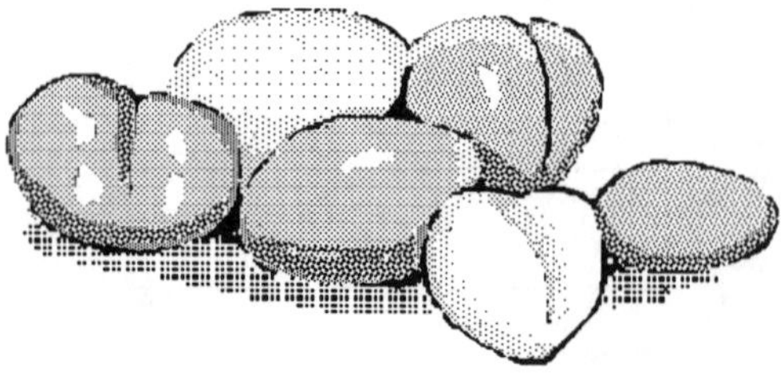

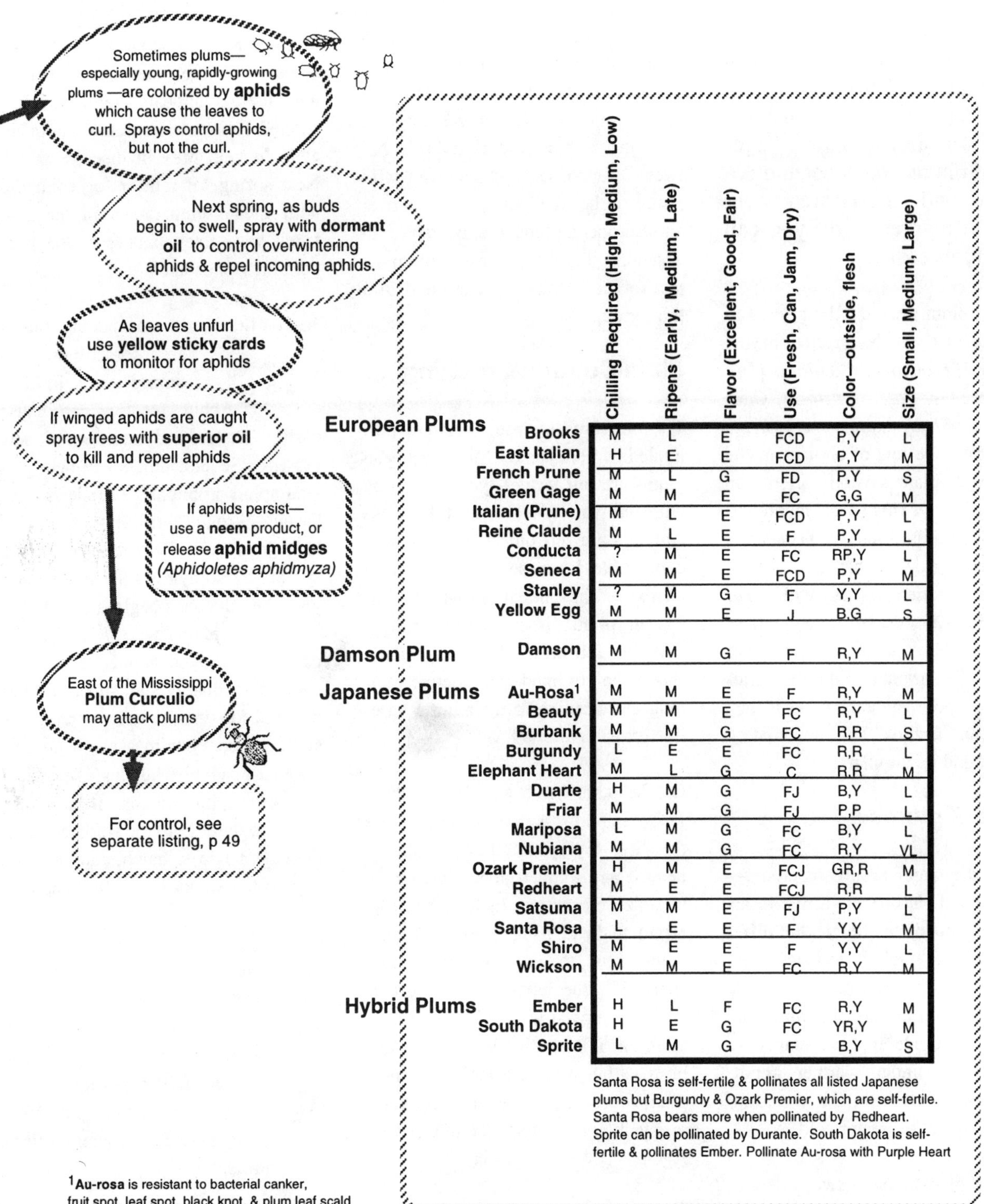

Sometimes plums—
especially young, rapidly-growing
plums —are colonized by **aphids**
which cause the leaves to
curl. Sprays control aphids,
but not the curl.
Next spring, as buds
begin to swell, spray with **dormant oil** to control overwintering
aphids & repel incoming aphids.
As leaves unfurl
use **yellow sticky cards**
to monitor for aphids
If winged aphids are caught
spray trees with **superior oil**
to kill and repell aphids
If aphids persist—
use a **neem** product, or
release **aphid midges**
(Aphidoletes aphidmyza)
East of the Mississippi
Plum Curculio
may attack plums
For control, see
separate listing, p 49

		Chilling Required (High, Medium, Low)	Ripens (Early, Medium, Late)	Flavor (Excellent, Good, Fair)	Use (Fresh, Can, Jam, Dry)	Color—outside, flesh	Size (Small, Medium, Large)
European Plums	**Brooks**	M	L	E	FCD	P,Y	L
	East Italian	H	E	E	FCD	P,Y	M
	French Prune	M	L	G	FD	P,Y	S
	Green Gage	M	M	E	FC	G,G	M
	Italian (Prune)	M	L	E	FCD	P,Y	L
	Reine Claude	M	L	E	F	P,Y	L
	Conducta	?	M	E	FC	RP,Y	L
	Seneca	M	M	E	FCD	P,Y	M
	Stanley	?	M	G	F	Y,Y	L
	Yellow Egg	M	M	E	J	B,G	S
Damson Plum	**Damson**	M	M	G	F	R,Y	M
Japanese Plums	**Au-Rosa**[1]	M	M	E	F	R,Y	M
	Beauty	M	M	E	FC	R,Y	L
	Burbank	M	M	G	FC	R,R	S
	Burgundy	L	E	E	FC	R,R	L
	Elephant Heart	M	L	G	C	R,R	M
	Duarte	H	M	G	FJ	B,Y	L
	Friar	M	M	G	FJ	P,P	L
	Mariposa	L	M	G	FC	B,Y	L
	Nubiana	M	M	G	FC	R,Y	VL
	Ozark Premier	H	M	E	FCJ	GR,R	M
	Redheart	M	E	E	FCJ	R,R	L
	Satsuma	M	M	E	FJ	P,Y	L
	Santa Rosa	L	E	E	F	Y,Y	M
	Shiro	M	E	E	F	Y,Y	L
	Wickson	M	M	E	FC	R,Y	M
Hybrid Plums	**Ember**	H	L	F	FC	R,Y	M
	South Dakota	H	E	G	FC	YR,Y	M
	Sprite	L	M	G	F	B,Y	S

Santa Rosa is self-fertile & pollinates all listed Japanese plums but Burgundy & Ozark Premier, which are self-fertile. Santa Rosa bears more when pollinated by Redheart. Sprite can be pollinated by Durante. South Dakota is self-fertile & pollinates Ember. Pollinate Au-rosa with Purple Heart

[1] **Au-rosa** is resistant to bacterial canker, fruit spot, leaf spot, black knot, & plum leaf scald

& Perfect plums

Many of us have never tasted ripe plums. You may even think that the hard, unripe supermarket varieties are just the way plums are. Not so! Tree-ripened plums are sweet and delicious, and most are never found in markets. Yet you can raise plums easily.

Standard plum trees can be pruned to moderate size, or be grafted to the semi-dwarf rootstock, 'Citation'. *(Unlike most other plum rootstocks, Citation does not produce suckers at the base).* To have lots of choices in the same space, plant several varieties in the same hole. (This works much better than a multi-grafted tree because of the diverse growth characteristics of the several varieties). As with other fruit trees, your best bet is to purchase bare-root plums from a mail order supplier. Be sure to purchase varieties which will pollinate each other if they are not self fertile. This information can be found in our chart.

Types of plums

Both of the major groups of plums—Japanese and European—thrive in areas with a moderate climate, but differ in physiological characteristics. As befits their origin, European plums are very hardy to cold, late blooming, and require only moderate heat. Japanese plums thrive under warmer conditions, bloom earlier in the year, and are less tolerant of winter cold.

European plums have a sweet, dryish, freestone flesh. They are delicious either fresh or canned, and several dry well to become "**prunes**". The juicy Japanese plums are primarily eaten fresh, though some tart cultivars can be used for jam or sauce. The two plum groups are *not compatible* with each other, but several hybrids between Japanese and native wild plums, or between apricots or cherries and European plums are available. In addition, the tart Damson plum—a jam or jelly fruit— is classified in a third group.

Plum Culture & pruning

The blossoms of tree fruits are pollinated by honeybees. Most European plums are self fertile—you can get by with one variety—but most Japanese cultivars are self unfertile, so another compatible Japanese variety must be nearby. The annual growth of European plums is moderate; fruit is born on a fruiting "bush". Pruning should be confined to moderate thinning and heading to maintain a vase-like growth pattern.

On the other hand, annual growth of Japanese plums is more vigorous. For the first few years they should be headed and thinned annually to keep tree size moderate. In fact, don't be afraid to head back during summer, being sure to protect the fruiting spurs. If your Japanese plum grows strongly upward, head to outside buds, if it spreads, head to inside buds. After they're established, most plum trees are somewhat drought-resistant, and do not tolerate wet feet. Avoid sprinkler irrigation.

Diseases and insect pests

Plums exhibit to some of the same diseases as other stone fruits, but are somewhat more resistant. If **brown rot disease** appears, remove fallen spoiled fruits and mummies immediately to help prevent disease spread. Next spring, if rain or fog coincides with mean temperature in the 50s, spray with fixed copper at the pop-corn blossom stage.

Just as the leaves are opening, plums are sometimes colonized by **aphids**. Aphid feeding can cause curling leaves and stunting of new growth. Several things can help prevent aphid problems. • Moderate water and nitrogen fertilizer to minimize lush growth. • Help repel incoming aphids, by spraying with dormant oil just when the buds begin to swell.
• Monitor plums with yellow sticky cards. If winged aphids are caught, spray immediately with superior oil as directed for summer use. If problems continue, spray with a neem product or release ladybird beetles, green lacewings, or aphid midges. If lacewings are to be used, hold the shipment until the eggs begin to hatch, and band the tree with a sticky barrier to keep ants away.

In the west, plums are free of most other insect pests. East of the Mississippi river, plums are relished by a variety of fruit-eating insects, including **plum curculio**, **Japanese**, **May**, and **June beetles.** See separate listings for controls.

Growing grapes for your table

You many want to try one or more of the tasty table grapes that grow well at home. Grapes are divided into **American** and **European** types. The early-maturing native American grape *(Vitis lambrusca)* is cold tolerant, and insect and disease resistant. Its soft pulp slips easily out of the skin, and the berries are often processed into juice. Most European *(Vitis vinifera)* grape varieties prefer a humid, mild climate, and though several cultivars have low heat requirements, most cannot withstand severe cold. The firmer flesh of European grapes is attached to the skin. They are served as table grapes, and their juice is often processed into wine.

Pruning and watering

Grapes must be pruned annually. European wine grapes are usually *spur pruned*—cut back each year to a few spurs, each with two or three buds. American grapes, and grapes raised at home are *cane pruned*—several canes with 6 to 12 buds are retained to produce next year's fruit. Established grapevines are somewhat drought resistant, but productive vines should receive infrequent, deep irrigation.

Required Nutrients

Grapes do not require a large amount of **nitrogen** (N). One application per year is usually sufficient. Apply a N fertilizer, a 3 inch layer of finished compost, or plant a nitrogen-fixing legume cover crop, to facilitate water penetration, and even out N availability. Most soils have sufficient **phosphorus** and **potassium** (K) for grape culture, but *K is sometimes unavailable in clay soils.* K deficiency can slow vine growth, trigger gradual yellowing and premature leaf fall, and reduce yields. Wet soil in spring, or other conditions that reduce root efficiency, may cause K deficiency symptoms. In late winter apply 3-4 lbs of K to deficient vines. Add K-sulphate to the bottom of two 8 inch deep furrows—18 inches from the crown. Leave the trenches open so water will move the nutrient downward to the root zone.

Zinc (Zn) **deficiency** is common in alkaline clay soils, and, perhaps unexpectedly, *soils which are high in N or organic content.* Zn deficiency is characterized by bronzy mottled leaves accompanied by sparse, bunches—berries vary in size from normal to undeveloped. (Sometimes the grapes abort completely in early spring.) In this situation, spray foliage with Zn chelate 2-3 weeks before bloom (April-May). If symptoms are severe, dig two 8 inch deep furrows in winter, 2 feet from the crown, and add 2-3 lbs of Zn-sulfate. Leave trenches open as above.

Help from a cover crop— You may want to try another system to help balance nutrients, increase the quality of the soil, even reduce the need for insect control by planting a *hairy vetch cover crop* near your grape vines. Fred and Paul Smeds[1] first planted vetch in their vineyard in fall 1988. They let it grow tall—well into May—until it flowered and set seed. They then chopped it down to make a thick mulch. Every year since, the vetch has sprouted on its own from the seed bank in the soil. They now mow the vetch in early spring to protect the grapes from frost damage (cover crops cool the area), but then allow it to regrow and set seed.

Their soil texture has improved greatly. Parasitoids and predators—spiders, ladybeetles, and lacewings—have even helped reduce the need for supplemental insect control. *Such a cover crop system may be possible for other fruit crops.*

Diseases

In areas with a dry, warm climate grapes are subject to **powdery mildew** (PM)—white powdery patches of fungus appear *on both surfaces* of young leaves—later PM attacks fruits. *(Powdery mildew is inhibited by damp weather and rain.)* PM on grapes is traditionally prevented—but not cured—by sulphur. Check unfolding leaves weekly looking for tiny fungus patches. If found, treat immediately, and next year treat before disease appears. Apply a wettable sulphur, or soap + sulphur spray. Or try coating the leaves with an anti-transpirant. These have recently been shown to prevent powdery mildew. As long as grapes are growing rapidly, apply these treatments every 7-10 days.

Grapes are sometimes destroyed before harvest by **bunch rot** *(Botrytis cinerea),* or other fungal or bacterial infection. This can be prevented culturally. Remove and destroy all mummified grapes clusters after harvest. In the future, remove a few of the leaves which are adjacent to each grape bunch early in the season to allow light and air circulation. Bunches will remain disease free. Results are superior to those obtained by fungicide sprays.

Insects

Grape leafhoppers *(Erythroneura elegantula)* are usually controlled naturally on unsprayed grapes. In the West blackberries or prunes growing within 1/4 mile of the grapes sustain

[1] Farmer to Farmer A/M, 1994.

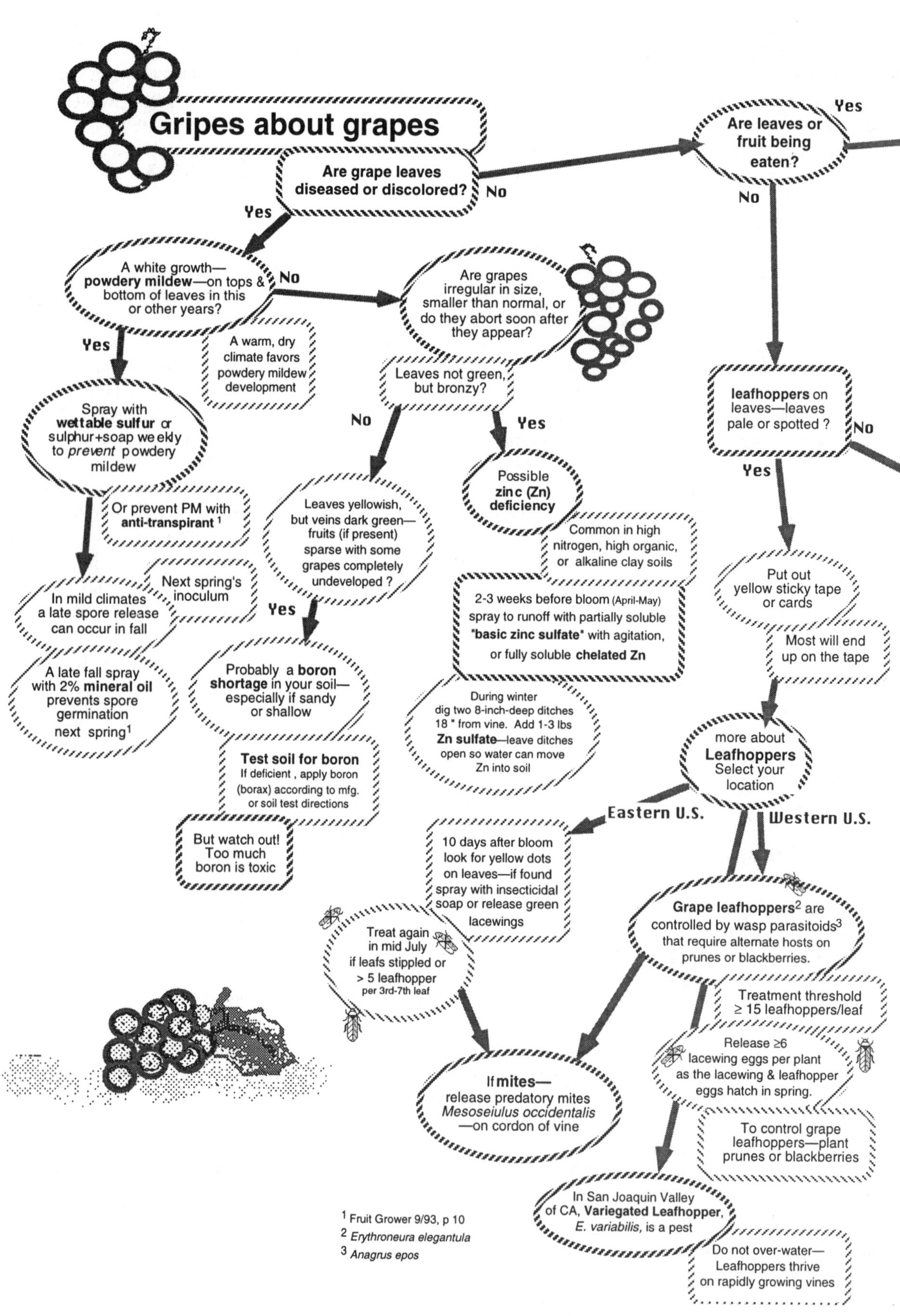
Gripes about grapes
Are grape leaves diseased or discolored?
No
Are leaves or fruit being eaten?
Yes
No
Yes
A white growth—powdery mildew—on tops & bottom of leaves in this or other years?
No
Yes
A warm, dry climate favors powdery mildew development
Spray with wettable sulfur or sulphur+soap weekly to prevent powdery mildew
Or prevent PM with anti-transpirant 1
In mild climates a late spore release can occur in fall
Next spring's inoculum
A late fall spray with 2% mineral oil prevents spore germination next spring1
Are grapes irregular in size, smaller than normal, or do they abort soon after they appear?
Leaves not green, but bronzy?
No
Yes
Leaves yellowish, but veins dark green—fruits (if present) sparse with some grapes completely undeveloped ?
Yes
Probably a boron shortage in your soil—especially if sandy or shallow
Test soil for boron
If deficient , apply boron (borax) according to mfg. or soil test directions
But watch out! Too much boron is toxic
Possible zinc (Zn) deficiency
Common in high nitrogen, high organic, or alkaline clay soils
2-3 weeks before bloom (April-May) spray to runoff with partially soluble "basic zinc sulfate" with agitation, or fully soluble chelated Zn
During winter dig two 8-inch-deep ditches 18 " from vine. Add 1-3 lbs Zn sulfate—leave ditches open so water can move Zn into soil
leafhoppers on leaves—leaves pale or spotted ?
No
Yes
Put out yellow sticky tape or cards
Most will end up on the tape
more about Leafhoppers Select your location
Eastern U.S.
Western U.S.
10 days after bloom look for yellow dots on leaves—if found spray with insecticidal soap or release green lacewings
Treat again in mid July if leafs stippled or > 5 leafhopper per 3rd-7th leaf
Grape leafhoppers2 are controlled by wasp parasitoids3 that require alternate hosts on prunes or blackberries.
Treatment threshold ≥ 15 leafhoppers/leaf
Release ≥6 lacewing eggs per plant as the lacewing & leafhopper eggs hatch in spring.
To control grape leafhoppers—plant prunes or blackberries
If mites—release predatory mites Mesoseiulus occidentalis —on cordon of vine
In San Joaquin Valley of CA, Variegated Leafhopper, E. variabilis, is a pest
Do not over-water—Leafhoppers thrive on rapidly growing vines
1 Fruit Grower 9/93, p 10
2 Erythroneura elegantula
3 Anagrus epos

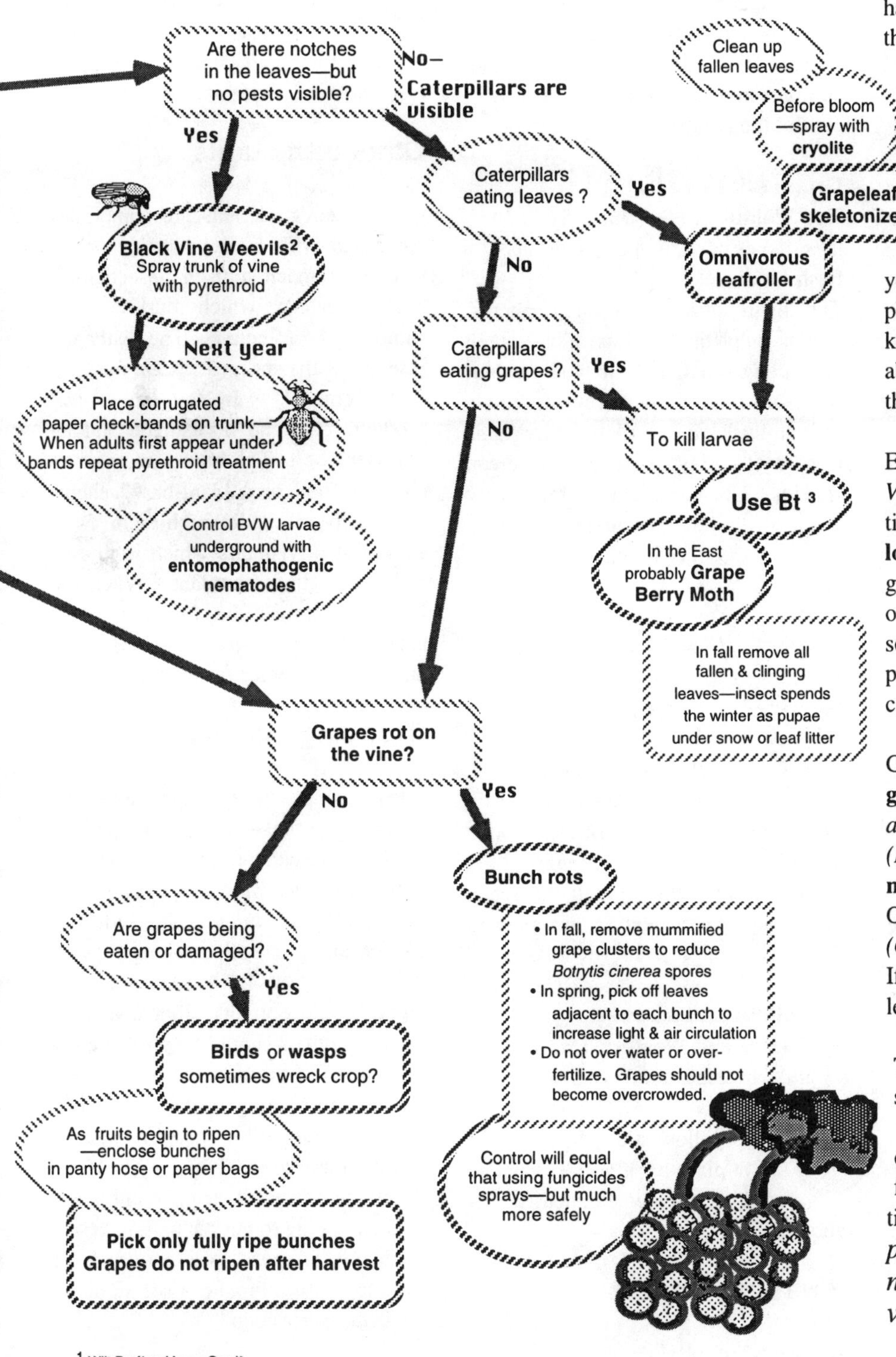

Are there notches in the leaves—but no pests visible?
No—Caterpillars are visible
Yes
Black Vine Weevils[2] Spray trunk of vine with pyrethroid
Next year
Place corrugated paper check-bands on trunk—When adults first appear under bands repeat pyrethroid treatment
Control BVW larvae underground with entomophathogenic nematodes
Caterpillars eating leaves ?
Yes
No
Clean up fallen leaves
Before bloom —spray with cryolite
Grapeleaf skeletonizer
Omnivorous leafroller
Caterpillars eating grapes?
Yes
No
To kill larvae
Use Bt [3]
In the East probably Grape Berry Moth
In fall remove all fallen & clinging leaves—insect spends the winter as pupae under snow or leaf litter
Grapes rot on the vine?
No
Yes
Bunch rots
• In fall, remove mummified grape clusters to reduce Botrytis cinerea spores
• In spring, pick off leaves adjacent to each bunch to increase light & air circulation
• Do not over water or over-fertilize. Grapes should not become overcrowded.
Control will equal that using fungicides sprays—but much more safely
Are grapes being eaten or damaged?
Yes
Birds or wasps sometimes wreck crop?
As fruits begin to ripen —enclose bunches in panty hose or paper bags
Pick only fully ripe bunches Grapes do not ripen after harvest

[1] Wilt Pruf* or Vapor Gard*

[2] See also Black Vine Weevil

[3] Bt = *Bacillus thuringiensis kurtsoki* a bacterial disease of caterpillars

miniwasp parasitoids of the grape leafhopper in the winter season. If you have a leafhopper problem—more than 15 leafhoppers per leaf in the west or 5 leafhoppers on one fourth of the sampled leaves in the east—you can release green lacewings to help control the nymphs. For best results try to synchronize your insects. (You should see lacewing eggs hatching when you place them on the grapes, and place a sticky band around the trunk to keep ants away.) Lacewing larvae eat about 250 leafhopper nymphs during their maturation process.[1]

European grapes which are grafted to *Vitis vinifera* rootstocks are susceptible to several strains of **grape phylloxera**—aphid-like insects which form galls on the roots. *Phylloxera* thrive on grapes planted in loamy or heavy soils in areas where summer temperatures remain below 90° F. They cause vines to decline and die.

Grapes in a few areas are attacked by **grapeleaf skeletenizer** *(Harrisina americana),* **omnivorous leaf roller** *(Platynota stulfana),* or **grape berry moth caterpillars** *(Endopiza viteana).* Occasionally **black vine weevils** *(Otiorynchus sp)* are found on grapes. If you see notches around grape leaves, read the vine weevil page.

To prevent **birds** or **wasps** from stealing your grapes, enclose the bunches in panty hose or paper bags before the fruits ripen, or place netting over the vines. *Do not pick too soon. Grapes do not continue to ripen after harvest.*

[1] Cal. Agri. 47:19-23, 1993

Making & using traps

Many soft-bodied plant-feeding insects are attracted to a specific color. *Aphids, whiteflies, fungus gnats, certain fruit flies, leafhoppers,* and many others approach **mustard yellow**. *Thrips* fly to **pale blue**—though one study[1] had good results with a **violet** trap in front of a **yellow** background—and *flea beetles* jump onto **white**. You can use this attraction to advantage by constructing sticky traps which can be used to monitor pest insect presence or reduce their populations.

Making flat sticky traps

The traps can be made from a variety of materials.

- Cut colored file folders into quarters, collect appropriately-colored plastic lids, or recycle the trays that hold supermarket meats. Coat the traps with cooking oil, Tanglefoot* or Stick-em Special*. If desired, place your traps into sticky plastic bags so they can be used over and over.
- Place weighed traps on the ground, or hang them at the same level as the infested foliage.
- Shake the plants frequently to dis turb the pests, causing them to fly to the traps.
- Replace your traps when they be come contaminated, or *use vegetable oil* to clean off the sticky coating.
- Remove traps when pest popula tions decline so beneficial insects do not become trapped unnecessarily.

Sticky ball Traps

Red sticky balls

The **apple maggot fruit fly** lays it eggs under the skin of developing apples. The adult female fly is attracted to red spheres. If you hang several sticky apple-sized spheres—these are available commercially—in your apple trees from June through August, most of these flies will be trapped. Phosmet codling moth sprays will also help control these flies

Green sticky balls

The **Walnut Husk** (fruit) **fly** lays its eggs into the green flesh of developing walnuts. This fly is attracted to green spheres. If you hang three or four sticky green ping pong-sized balls in your walnut tree from June through August, female walnut husk flies will be trapped as they try to lay eggs in the green spheres. Change sticky surface every two weeks. Clean with oil.

Insecticide sprays will also kill these fruit flies, but they will kill the parasitoids which control the walnut aphid. Walnut husk fly damage is cosmetic. The feeding of their maggot larvae does not damage the nut meat itself, though the green husks become blackened and stick to the nut.

Yellow ball traps—

Cherry and **Western Cherry fruit flies** are attracted to yellow spheres or yellow cards. Ping pong ball-sized yellow sticky balls should be in place at petal fall. Change sticky surface frequently (as above).

Pheromone traps

A variety of pheromones—insect attractants—are available which can be used to lure insects into sticky traps. The most common trap design is known as the wing trap, but several other designs are possible. These traps are used primarily to monitor the life cycle of pest insects such as codling moths. This enables us to properly time insecticide sprays.

Other attractants

Food-based attractants are sometimes combined with insect diseases or selective stomach poison insecticides, such as ryania, which must be consumed to be effective. The faster the insect eats the sprayed foliage the faster the control. In addition several products combine a pesticide and an attractant bait. The attractant may be either a food or a plant-based chemical, such as the **cucurbitacin** from squash family plants which is known to be a feeding stimulant. When the insect consumes the bait control is achieved. See Pheromones and other attractant strategies for more details.

Trapping mammals

Most small pest mammals—rats, squirrels, mice—can be trapped in snap or live catch traps. In all cases it is best to *place the trap along a runway used by the animal.* This will usually be along a wall or along a fence rail where you have seen them or found their droppings. Rats and other wary mammals should be pre-baited—given food in an un-set trap until they get used to coming to the bait. Most pest mammals are attracted to nuts or similar high grade baits. The food should be tied to the trigger so the animal has to tug to get the bait. If a live-catch trap is used, open both ends of the trap so the animal can see an opening at the other end.

If a poison bait or snap trap is used, be sure that the bait or the trap is invisible from above so that birds will not be attracted and killed.

---

1 J. Econ. entomol. 88:288-293, 1995.

Unmasking ultrasound & other fake control agents

You've seen them in the back of magazines and the slick paper section of the Sunday paper—in the back of garden catalogs or direct mail advertisers.

Ultrasonic Pest Repeller

Yard Guard
Untrasonic Sound Machine

Bird Guard
chases away unwanted pests

Electric Mole Repeller

Ultrasonic Pet Control

Pest-A-Cator
makes your home a roach and rodent repeller

Mosquito Hawk
repels mosquitoes electronically

Mole Chaser
Let breezes blow moles away

Mosquito repellent plant

These ads sound too good to be true. Most of them assume that ultrasound will be harmless to you, but will drive away unwanted animals.

They're just the newest alliteration in the magic pest control market. A few years ago the magic devices were dubbed **electromagnetic repellers**. They were reported to generate electromagnetic patterns that somehow disturbed pests, *but had no affect on desired creatures.* High level people in the U.S. Senate, the National Press Club and the Los Angeles Arboretum were fooled,[1] but in 1979 the EPA took them off the market because they were ineffective.

Ultrasonic devices

The advertisements claim that these ≥20,000 hertz ultrasonic devices (≥20 KHz) will "drive away rodents and insects without bothering people or pets."[2] Tests have demonstrated that the German and American cockroach, and the Oriental rat and cat fleas—four target insects for these devices—do not respond to ultrasound. On the other hand, dogs and cats can hear them, and though inaudible to people, they disturb some of us, and have not been shown to be harmless. Even more puzzling are ultrasound dog collars which are supposed to repel fleas and ticks and be "100% safe" for dogs.

The $140 Yard Guard broadcasts 3 different ultrasound frequencies which are supposed to keep unwanted animals away—*including the neighbor's pets.* The $14 Ultrasonic is not to be confused with "cheap imitations". It claims to broadcast at 32-62 KHz, frequencies above the hearing range of domestic animals, but abhorrent to rats, mice, *and fleas.* Finally there are ultrasound pet trainers which are purported to "stop dogs from jumping, barking, biting..."

Other sound control devices

The Bird Guard device contains alarm calls of some pest birds. These calls work initially, but birds soon ignore them. Meanwhile, you're hearing the constant sound of squawking birds. We do not know the effectiveness of the auditory mole repellers, but given the track record of the other devices, we have our doubts.

Several devices claim to drive away mosquitoes using sounds made by hunting bats. Since there are hundreds of bat species and thousands of mosquito species, it would be impossible for one device to broadcast the unique sounds recognized by each. Vibra Sound's "vibrations and ultrasounds" claim to drive away gophers, moles, ground, squirrels, shrews, and voles but be "harmless to children and pets."

Light traps

Some flying insects are attracted to ultraviolet light. UV lights are incorporated in an electric grill trap to literally fry incoming insects to death. Unfortunately, there is a down side to all this. These devices are non-selective. Though you may want them to capture mosquitoes and flies, they are more likely to capture rare beetles or endangered silk moths, such as the Luna, the IO, and the Cecropia. Even more surprising, *several pest mosquito species are repelled by light.* These UV traps aren't very effective against insects which approach them. UV caught only a small fraction of the flies at a poultry ranch, while fly fragments splattered a large area near the trap in a kitchen[3] —hardly our idea of a healthy home environment. Maybe we should follow the old adage—

"If it sounds too good to be true, it is."

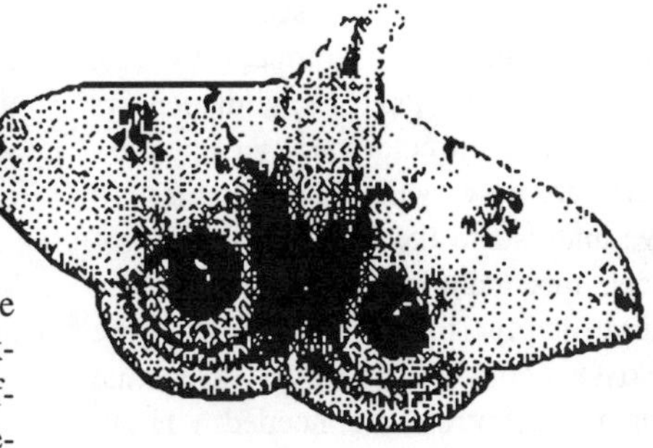

[1] Science 204:484-486, 1979, [2] J Econ. Entomol. 79:1027-1031, 1986. J Econ. Entomol. 82:516-518, 1989, J Econ. Entomol. 82:687-691, 1989, [3] j. Appl. Ent. 102:446-455, 1986, J Econ. Entomol. 82:149-151, 1989.

Insect pheromone *& other attractant* *strategies*

Ever since it was discovered that male insects are attracted to specific female *sex pheromones*—think attractant perfume—we've been trying to control pest insects by manipulating their pheromones. The chemical structure of many insect sex pheromones has been determined, and they are synthesized for use in dispensers which slowly release these volatile compounds in concentrations which are similar to those released by female insects.

In addition, *artificial lures* which were empirically discovered to attract certain insects are sometimes used in traps. Other attractant baits contain constituents which are *essential elements of larval food plants.* All these lures are more selective than are chemical sprays, but could effect applicators should they possess dangerous characteristics. For example, methyl eugenol (ME) is an extremely potent attractant for male oriental fruit flies. However, ME causes hepatic (liver) tumors in mice and has triggered abnormalities in certain bacterial tests.[1] Nonetheless ME is used as a food flavoring agent, and is rated safe for human consumption.

Pheromones used to monitor or confuse insects

Often the easiest way to determine whether a pest is in the vicinity is to place a pheromone dispenser in a sticky trap and count insects—usually males—which are trapped by the sticky surface. Pheromone dispensers designed to attract a variety of pest insects are now available (see table). If we understand the life cycle of the insect, this technique allows us to use controls precisely when it will do the most good—and even to determine whether controls are needed. However, *much as we would like to use this system to control insects, it doesn't work that way.* Only a small sample of the insect population finds its way into the widely-spaced sticky traps, and plenty of mated females are always around to lay eggs.

Alternately, we might be able to confuse the males by saturating the air with so much sex pheromone that they could not locate the females. Of course such an idea assumes that vision or sound plays little part in insect courtship. This is seldom the case at least with insects which are active in the daytime. Other problems with this idea include concentration, costs, and toxicity of the materials. Trials have demonstrated that very high pheromone concentrations are not attractive to male insects, even if the cost and safety of such a high concentrations were proved viable.

It turns out that the best way to dispense pheromone for such a **confusion technique (CT)** is one which closely mimics nature. In nature, each female insect releases her pheromone when she is receptive, and the male follows the pheromone plume upwind toward her. The dispensers used for the CT are small point sources, twist ties, flakes, or small tubes which are similar in size to a large insect. They constantly release a natural chemical signal throughout the season, and the males attempt to follow the pheromone plumes upwind to find a female. The idea is that males confused by the large number of false signals will be unable to locate any real females which are present. Obviously, the fewer females the better this works. And hopefully, the pests will not fly very far.

When small dispensers are present on about every tree or vine in orchards, vineyards, or fields (rate ~400 dispensers per acre) which are least 5 acres in size, the CT has been shown to be an adequate substitute for sprays against several pests. In orchards, dispensers are placed in the upper third of the canopy. Sedentary insects are more easily controlled by this technique than mobile species. All sex pheromones tested so far are non-toxic. Several companies market products for the confusion process. **Checkmate*** by Consep is designed to disrupt mating of Oriental Fruit Moth, Tomato Pinworm and Codling Moth. **Isomate*** twist-ties by Pacific BioControl Ltd. are designed to confuse Codling Moth, Lesser Peach Tree Borer, Oriental Fruit Moth, Omnivorous Leafroller, Tomato Pinworm, and others. Micro-Flo markets similar Isomate* attractants for Codling Moth and Oriental Fruit Moth. Trécé will soon supply mating disruptants for Tomato Pinworm and Oriental Fruit Moth. Expect other products in the future.

Perhaps because pests invade from untreated areas, the CT has not worked well for properties less than 5 acres and backyards. However, when combined with other techniques CT has been very effective in some experiments. It may be worth the effort to try a combination strategy. To use the confusion technique distribute the dispensers near the end of bloom. They're estimated to be effective for about 30-45 days. *Traditional pheromone traps must be used in conjunction with the confusion dispensers to determine whether the males can find a pheromone source.* (They work best if the pheromone concentration is higher than in traditional traps.)[2] *If many males are caught in the traps, the system is not working, and you must treat.* This can occur due to several reasons. Pest populations must be low or males will find females by chance alone. If pest populations are high in surrounding untreated areas,

[1] J. Econ. Entomol. 87;957-964,1994. [2] Environ. Entomol 24: 1201-1206, 1995.

Representative Pheromone Lures

Alfalfa looper	*Autographa californica*
Apple maggot	*Rhagoletis pomonella*
Artichoke Plum Moth	*Platyptila cardividactyla*
Beet armyworm	*Spodoptera exigua*
Black carpet beetle	*Attagenus megfatoma*
Cabbage looper	*Trichoplusia ni*
Codling moth	*Cydia pomonella*
Corn earworm	*Helicoverpa (Heliothis) zea*
Diamondback moth	*Plutella xylostella*
Dermestid beetle	*Trogoderma inclusum*
European corn borer Iowa	*Ostrinia nubilalis*
European corn borer NY	*Ostrinia nubilalis*
Fall armyworm	*Spodoptera frugiperda*
Flour beetles	*Triblium sp.*
Grape berry moth	*Endopiza viteana*
Greater peachtree borer	*Synanthedon exitiosa*
Gypsy moth	*Lymantria dispar*
Indianmeal moth	*Plodia inyterpunctella*
Lesser peachtree borer	*Synanthedon pictipes*
Obliquebanded leafroller	*Choristoneura rosaceana*
Oriental fruit moth	*Grapholitha molesta*
Peach twig borer	*Phthorimaea operculella*
Redbanded leafroller	*Argyrotaenia velutinana*
Tobacco budworm	*Heliothis virescens*

mated females may migrate into the treated area. If the temperature is too low, insufficient pheromone may be released. If the temperature it too high, too much may evaporate, the pheromone may not last as long as expected. If insect pressure continues for a long period, periodically replace the CR attractants until no more insects are trapped.

On the average the cost of mating disruption seems initially to be more expensive than sprays, but if several sprays can be eliminated, or other pests are then controlled by natural enemies, the monetary and environmental costs may be favorable. Conversely some other pests which were controlled by the sprays may increase. To be sure that this does not occur, you should monitor your crop for other pests throughout the season.

Phagostimulants—food-based attractants

Animals are obviously attracted to food as well as sex. With this in mind, some companies use specific odors from insect foods—or even the food itself—to attract insects to killing bait stations. MicroFlo uses the squash compound, cucurbitacin, in Adios*—to attract and kill adult cucumber and corn earworm beetles—and Slam® to get the beetle's corn rootworm larvae. This company has recently introduced a reduced-pesticide snail and slug product called Slug-Master*.

The well-known Japanese beetle, cockroach, and wasp traps use a similar idea. Marketed directly for the home garden are the Surefire* line from Consep, and Trappit* traps from AgriSense. Trécé markets a high quality reusable Japanese beetle trap system.

Other food attractants are designed to be added to *Bacillus thuringiensis* sprays. A recent study[1] compared the attractiveness of 5 phagostimulants to 6 important pest caterpillars. Additives which contain both protein and carbohydrates increased feeding of larval corn earworm, gypsy moth, beet and fall armyworms, and European corn borer. Larval diamondback moths ignored all of the attractants. The attractant, Mo-Bait*, which contains mainly sugars was not useful in increasing Btk consumption by these insects.

Still another idea is to use food sprays or attractants to encourage beneficial insects to move to the crop. For example, **Wheast*** and **Pred-Feed IPM*** will feed such ben-

Food Attractants

Caterpillar	*Coax* *Entice* *Gustol*	Used with Bt products to attract pest to feed on the bacteria
Cucumber beetle		
	eugenol	Feeding stimulant
	Adios	Cucurbitacin feeding stimulant/sevin pesticide
Corn Rootworm Bait	*Nemesis, CRW*	
Predatory insect food	*Wheast,, Pred-Feed IPM*	
Soldier Bug	***Resque! Soldier Bug Attracter***	

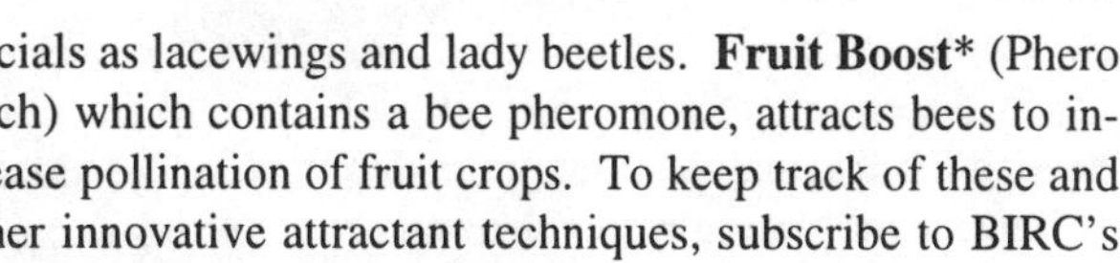
eficials as lacewings and lady beetles. **Fruit Boost*** (Phero Tech) which contains a bee pheromone, attracts bees to increase pollination of fruit crops. To keep track of these and other innovative attractant techniques, subscribe to BIRC's IPM Practitioner, 510-524-2567.

---

[1] J. Econ. Entomo. 87: 44-52, 1994

Pros & Cons of Biotech

Throughout this book we've repeatedly recommended that you search for plant strains that resist diseases or insects. Until recently such strains were only achieved after painstaking testing of seedling plants. These seedlings were obtained by crossing likely parent stock—often using wild strains for one parent and a commercial cultivar for the other. (This is but one reason why protection of wild areas is so important). Using traditional methods the incorporating multiple disease resistance into a tasty fruit may require decades.

How biotechnology works

Now biologists have begun to directly manipulate genes. Desirable genes from *related plants* can be inserted into plant cells—and the plant cells regenerated into little plants in a tissue culture flask. After these small plants are tested to determine which are expressing the target genes, the best are allowed to mature to determine their vigor and the quality of their products. Obviously such a **transgenic** system offers the possibility of speeding the search for improved plants.

In addition, genes from *unrelated plants,* or genes from *other life forms* such as bacteria or mammals can be sometimes inserted into plant cells—and function in the plant. It is these latter changes which are most controversial. None-the-less widespread fears about the safely of intergenic and intragenic transfers may be painting all such research with a broad antibiotechnology brush.

Safeguards

Current regulatory approach seeks to determine whether genetically engineered organisms will • Survive or multiply in the environment • Spread beyond the original area of application • Transfer its genetic material to other organisms • Prove harmful.

The first biotech product cleared by the EPA for use on plants is based on changes to *Pseudomonas syringae and P. fluroescens* bacteria which normally live on the surface of leaves. Though harmless to plants or animals, these bacteria increase frost damage when they secrete a protein that acts as a nucleating center for ice crystal formation. Genetic engineering has been used to *remove* the *Pseudomonas* gene that encodes this ice-nucleating protein. When this new strain replaces the wild type strain on leaves ice formation is minimized. This is unlikely to be harmful since *ice-minus strains are known to occur naturally* without apparent adverse effects.

Indeed, when studies showed that "ice minus" bacteria colonized sprayed leaves, but did not spread out of the spray zone, and treated plants were significantly protected from freezing, the product, Frostgard*, was released for sale. It would seem that biotechnology efforts such as these *that remove a gene or transfers genetic traits from one related strain to another*—projects which could be achieved by conventional crossing methods— should not present significant hazard.

If so, the FlavrSavr* tomato which contains an antisense gene in place of the gene coding for tomato's rot-inducing enzyme, would seem to be safe and beneficial. FlavrSavr* tomatoes resist spoilage during shipping even after they are allowed to ripen five more days on the vine—thereby increasing flavor and nutrients. A potato without the normal potato bruising enzyme, is also in the works. (Opponents maintain that such cultivars may allow more food production overseas, with a resulting decrease in U.S. jobs).

Biotechnology using Bt Genes

We recognize the importance of selective, safe control of certain pest insects which can be achieved by *Bacillus thuriegiensis* (Bt) bacteria.[1] In efforts to improve Bt's effectiveness and ease of use, these bacteria are the focus of transgenic research. Initial breakthroughs are already available.

Mycogen has inserted certain Bt endotoxin[2] genes into the common *Pseudomonas* bacteria which are found on plant surfaces. After the genetically engineered (changed) *Pseudomonas* synthesize the appropriate Bt endotoxin, they are killed and marketed as M-Peril* for caterpillar control and M-One* & for beetles. Bt endotoxins are easily inactivated by sunlight, by other chemicals, and by microbes. Mycogen claims that the packaging of Bt endotoxins inside the dead *Pseudomonas* cell wall protects it from rapid environmental degradation. This may not improve product performance, however, since tests indicate that *rapid kill would be the most desirable characteristic of a Bt insecticide.*

Ecogen has gone even further with Bt biotechnology. Its recombinant Bt spray, Cutlass* is available to control caterpillar damage on vegetables. Several companies are trying still other techniques to modify Bt.

Transgenic plants secrete bacterial products

Genes coding for *Bt* endotoxins are being inserted into plants as well. If successful, the plants will secrete Bt endotoxin, and be protected from caterpillar feeding, or beetle feeding or both. Monsanto has also inserted into plants genes coding for protease inhibitors which will potentially help the

[1] See, Using diseases for ecological control, p 84. [2] Toxic chemical synthetized inside a cell.

plant resist insect feeding. As of this writing none of these transgenic plants are cleared for sale.

At first glance such transgenic Bt plants may seem like a great idea. The endotoxins effect target insect pests without harming mammals or beneficial insects such as miniwasp parasitoids or lacewing larvae. Most plant feeding insects are most susceptible when they are very young, so sprays must be applied frequently to catch these early stages as they appear. Sprays will no longer required for Bt-susceptible insects on these biotech plants, and the endotoxins will be present to kill hatchings before than can do damage.

Unfortunately, *repeated exposure to any active compound always selects resistant strains in each exposed species. If, in the future Bt endotoxin genes are found in most crop plants, the effectiveness of these important compounds will be quickly lost to resistance, as has occurred with most conventional insecticides.*

This loss of Bt effectiveness could potentially be delayed by transplanting several strains of the endotoxin genes into plants, and including a mix of these strains in the seeds to be planted in a single field. This of course would greatly increase the cost of seeds, and might not greatly delay the appearance of resistant strains. *Often mutation of a single gene confers tolerance to an entire class of pesticides not just to a single active ingredient.* Insects resistant to DDT, for example, are often cross-resistant to all chlorinated hydrocarbon pesticides, and sometimes to pyrethroids as well.[1]

Lest you assume that Bt toxins are immune to these rules, *frequent sprays have already selected Bt resistant strains of the diamondback moth.* Bt resistance in several other species has easily been selected in laboratory studies. In addition, natural crossing of endotoxin-secreting plants with their weed relatives could spread the genes even farther, perhaps protecting these weeds from their insect enemies.

Other transgenic plants

Other research seeks to develop disease resistance in crop plants—an approach which has long occupied scientists using traditional methods. Many plant diseases, especially viral diseases, are not affected by chemicals, so plant strains which resist viruses are highly desirable. It is very difficult and time consuming to achieve complete disease resistance by traditional means, since most ornamental and orchard crops are subject to several bacterial, fungal, and viral diseases as well as being susceptible to soil-dwelling nematodes. The goal, obviously, is multiple disease resistance in an "ideal" plant. Already this has been substantially achieved using conventional means in several tomato and apple cultivars. Biotechnology methods should facilitate such research.

Biotech changes insect nuclear polyhedrosis viruses[3]

Practical application of nuclear polyhedrosis viruses for insect control presents several problems.

- Their very selectiveness may be a disadvantage when several pests are present, because several diseases may be required for control.
- They are difficult to culture, and therefore expensive.
- They are very slow—taking up to 5 days to kill target insects.

There have been several attempts to solve these problems by inserting genes into viruses which would enable them to synthesize toxins.

Under laboratory conditions, some of these recombinant viral pesticides kill the insects and stop their plant feeding faster than the wild-type viruses. Unfortunately these altered viruses survive in the soil more than three years, an unacceptable persistence since we don't want these changes to escape into the environment.[2] Indeed NPH viruses are known to persist in the soil, and some spread widely in the host populations. Obviously, any increase in disease frequency, will cause increased selection for resistance against them.

Controversial research

Many companies may soon market herbicide-resistant crop plants. Opponents fear that such an approach will trigger increased herbicide use. On the other hand, ability to use a more effective or safer herbicide, could reduce the need to apply a more toxic material. Another concern is that insect pollinators could transfer herbicide-resistant genes in the pollen to weeds which are closely related to a transgenic crop.

In addition, the new technologies may accelerate the world's dependence on a few crops or strains of crops as farmers take advantage of these new improvements, many of which have a limited genetic base. The use of hybrid seeds has already reduced the genetic variability of crop plants and garden vegetables. If a disease strain becomes resistant to these carefully selected plants, crops over entire regions may be affected because virtually every one has planted crops containing the same resistant genes.

---

[1] See also, How pesticides affect pest control, 8. [2] J. Environ. Entomol. 22::211-219, 1994. 3 See also, p. 84.

This is one of the main advantages of open pollinated plant. At least a few will be pre-selected to resist almost any disease.

A recent report by the National Academy of Sciences concluded that genetically altered crop plants may not directly cause serious environmental problems, but transgenic microorganisms may escape into the environment with potentially adverse side effects. Pests get around. In spite of rigorous government plant and animal quarantine programs, new pests become established in the U.S. each year. Their control is often very expensive.

Currently, study of the problems which have arisen after intentional introduction of plants and animals, may be our best model of future negative impacts from biotechnology. According to David Pimentel and his colleagues[1], 11 of the 19 most serious weeds of the world are also grown as crops. Nine of the 20 introduced domestic mammals in the U.S. are serious environmental pests in natural areas, as are 5 introduced fish. Ten other alien mammal species, including the mongoose—originally introduced to control rats in Hawaii —and 4 bird species have become serious pests.

On the other hand, the **classical biological control system** which carefully evaluates insect predators and parasitoids before they can be introduced for control of pest insects or weeds, has had few problems. These introduced insect natural enemies have performed as expected, and caused minimal environmental harm. *It may be essential to similarly evaluate each transgenic organism individually before it is released.* In these decisions, potential for short term benefits should be balanced against possible long-term costs. In addition, the fate of released organism should be periodically monitored, and procedures developed to counteract any undesirable transfer into the environment.

Some of the most desired plant biotech goals will be very difficult to achieve. The roots of legumes form symbiotic relationships with **nitrogen-fixing bacteria**. Researchers are trying to transfer these nitrogen-fixing genes into unrelated plants, or enable them to bond with the bacteria in other ways. Other projects seek to make crops more drought resistant or tolerant of saline soils. Others seek to make more productive crop plants, by introducing genes which code for the more efficient photosynthesis system found in certain wild plants. This would enable farmers to double or triple their yields. Again, whether this would be beneficial should be carefully studied.

Problem projects farther afield

In recent years human genes have been inserted into weakened bacteria which then synthesize human hormones. We now have transgenic human growth hormone and insulin in quantity—hormones which were previously harvested in limited quantities from farm animals. A first glance these projects seem to be safe and beneficial. However, the availability of a large amounts of transgenic hormones is proving to be controversial. Perhaps we need to evaluate such projects more carefully.

Several companies have been given permission to use transgenic bacteria to synthesize **bovine growth hormone**, a natural hormone synthesized by cows. When extra BGH is injected into dairy cows, their milk production is increased by 20-30%, even though they do not increase their food consumption at a comparable rate. Since BGH is a natural hormone, the milk from rbST-treated cows does not differ from "normal" milk, but there has been a demand for labeling. (Marketers can label milk from uninjected cows as not from rbST-treated cows).

Opponents question the value of these achievements. The U.S. already has excess milk. On average a 1% increase in total crop yields results in a 4.5% decrease in the market price received by farmers.

This is not the whole story. On the average, cows receiving extra BGH acquire bacterial infections at twice the rate of untreated cows. The U.S. General Accounting Office and the Public Health Service have suggested that greater human health risks could occur if antibiotics used to treat this **mastitis** were to contaminate the food supply.[2] Antibiotics given to infected cows can be excreted in the milk. It is well known that routine exposure to antibiotics selects for antibiotic-resistant bacterial strains.

Well documented human disease outbreaks[3] have demonstrated that antibiotic-resistant bacterial strains from cattle can readily spread to humans via contaminated milk and meat. BGH proponents state that every truck-load of milk is tested for residues of certain antibiotics. Random testing is done for several other antibiotics. The farmers are severely penalized if antibiotics are found. For further reading see.[4]

---

[1] BioSci. 39:606-614, 1989, [2]Osburn, et al, 1993. Safety of bovine somatotropin in diary cows. UC Davis, CA,
[3] JAMA 258: 3269-3274, 1987, N Engl J Med 316:565-570, 1987.[4] Cal. Agric. 48(2)7-8, 1994

Living with feathered & furry neighbors

We're not usually programed to think of animals covered with fur or feathers as "pests", but when they contact us in our homes, we sometimes find that *their* lifestyle makes *ours* more difficult.

Rodents

Mammals are classified by the shape and arrangement of their teeth. Rodents have two upper incisors (front center teeth), and no canine teeth. Since their major foods are obtained by gnawing, this distinctive tooth arrangement is obviously appropriate. Though many rodents have little impact on human interests, some rats, mice, pocket gophers, and squirrels cause problems. Fortunately in natural settings rodents are suppressed by predators—hawks, owls, coyotes, foxes, bobcats, snakes, etc. If you live in the country, you can augment rodent controls by building **housing for raptors**—see next page. Place 3" of sawdust in the bottom of a nesting box. For American Kestrels (Sparrow Hawks), mount the boxes 20-30 feet high in the open. For screech Owls, the box should be at least 10 feet high, near the edge of a wooded area. To keep out squirrels, place a predator guard on the pole beneath the box.

Pocket Gophers

Almost anyone who attempts to grow plants in western, central, or southeastern United States may eventually find the characteristic mounds of pocket gophers *(Thomomys sp.)*—look for the earthen plug within. Even though you may believe in live-and-let-live, gophers cannot be ignored. A hungry gopher can kill a grown tree, to say nothing of what happens when they sally down a row of vegetables. We're not usually tolerant of their 'natural rototiller' function when they remove our favorite plants.

Most gophers are between seven and eight inches long, though the giant pocket gopher reaches 12 inches. Gophers are vegetarians, with a penchant for roots. To reach their favorite goodies, they spend their life in tunnels located six to eighteen inches beneath the surface. Several structural adaptations enable them to thrive in their underground plant-eating lifestyle.

Their incisors are enlarged for biting tough roots and hard dirt—so much so that they can't close their mouths completely. A fur-lined mouth pocket enables them to transport tender roots down to the nest located in a lower burrow. Their large forepaws sport formidable digging claws. The eyes and ears are small—perhaps to keep out dirt. The posterior end is relatively narrow, and the tail short, enabling a gopher to turn readily underground, or run either backwards or forwards with ease.

Except during the breeding season, pocket gophers are solitary. The burrow system of an established female may encompass 2000 square feet—large enough to supply food for both the owner and her litter. She may give birth to five or six offspring three times per year. Obviously, in the absence of hawk, owl, snake, coyote, or fox enemies, you can have a problem if a female pocket gopher sets up housekeeping on your property.

Rats

Most rats are innocuous rodents which fit well into the environment. Only two are major pests world wide. The heavier of these, the **Norway,** or **brown rat** *(Rattus norvegicus)* is familiar to most of us in its white or piebald laboratory rat alliteration. Wild Norway rats have a brownish back, with a grayish belly and feet. They are robust, with large ears and a scaly tail which is shorter than the body. Though they can climb, they tend to live in basements or sewers, or burrow in the ground near garbage sources. Big cities are a major habitat of Norway rats because they are a major source of uncovered garbage. Should you live in such a place, be sure your garbage is contained at all times. In buildings, sealed trash compacters are the most effective Norway rat control instruments.

The other major pest rat, **roof or black rat** *(Rattus tattus)* climbs readily, builds its nests above the ground in dense trees, shrubs, or attics in the suburbs—hence "roof rat". Except in forested areas, native rats are much less likely to frequent buildings than these two.

Though these problem rats can reach an impressive 16 inches, 12 inches is typical. The roof rat is slender, its tail longer than its body, and its ears are larger than those of the Norway rat. Its color can be either grayish-brown or black. In the U.S. roof rats live along both coasts and across the humid south.

Since they're active at night, you may not know when rats are around unless you see their droppings or find a midden (hiding place where they feed). Both these rats eat a great variety of your favorite foods. Stored grain and other starchy foods are consumed or despoiled by raison-sized oval droppings. While the Norway rat readily seeks out garbage, roof rats are more likely to exploit snails, fallen fruits, pet foods, and wild seeds. Both capture young birds and their eggs and other helpless creatures, and both are a potential source of disease—their fleas spread bubonic plague and typhus fe-

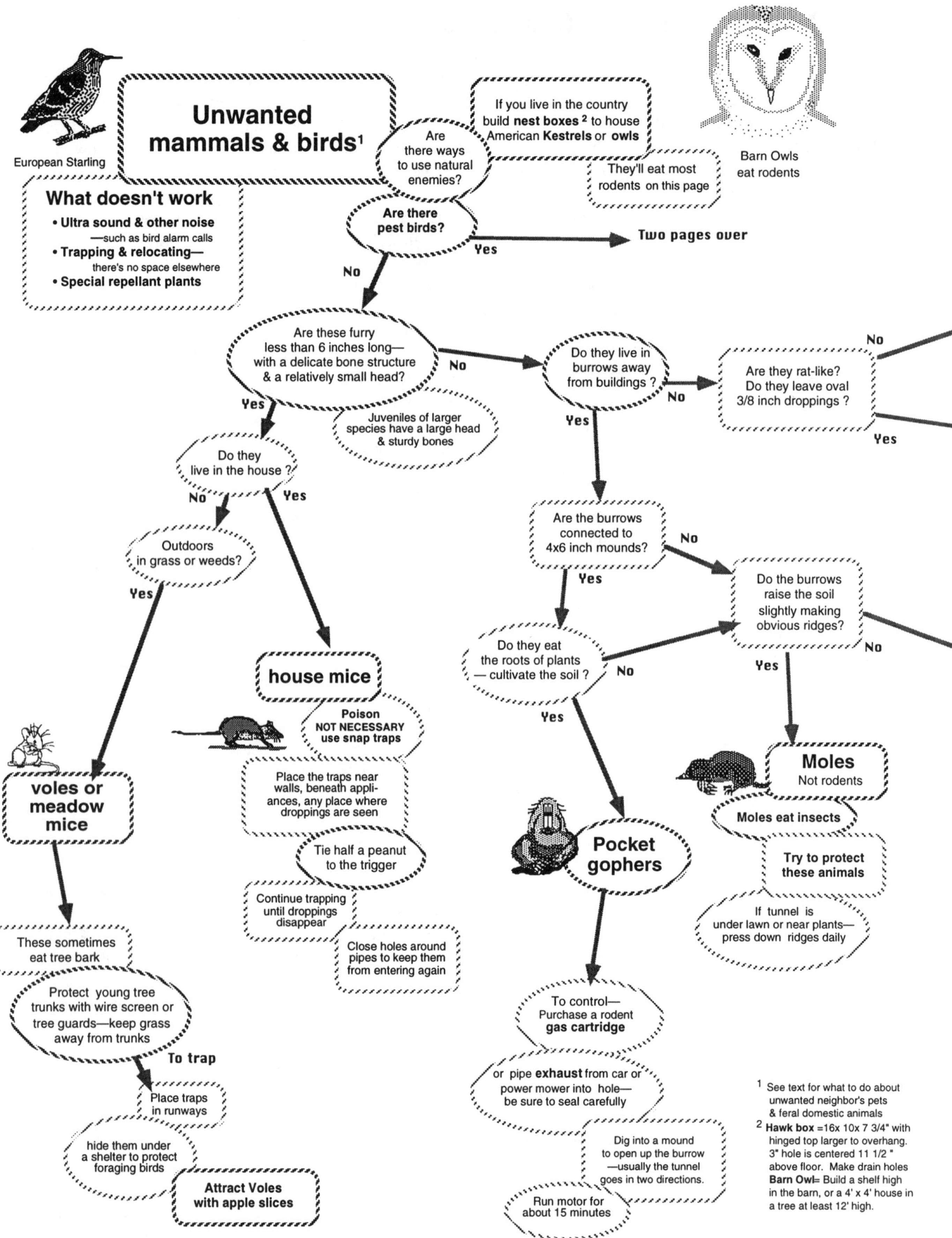

European Starling
Unwanted mammals & birds[1]
What doesn't work
• Ultra sound & other noise —such as bird alarm calls
• Trapping & relocating— there's no space elsewhere
• Special repellant plants
Are there ways to use natural enemies?
If you live in the country build nest boxes [2] to house American Kestrels or owls
They'll eat most rodents on this page
Barn Owls eat rodents
Are there pest birds?
Yes
Two pages over
No
Are these furry less than 6 inches long— with a delicate bone structure & a relatively small head?
Juveniles of larger species have a large head & sturdy bones
No
Do they live in burrows away from buildings ?
No
Are they rat-like? Do they leave oval 3/8 inch droppings ?
No
Yes
Yes
Do they live in the house ?
No
Yes
Outdoors in grass or weeds?
Yes
voles or meadow mice
These sometimes eat tree bark
Protect young tree trunks with wire screen or tree guards—keep grass away from trunks
To trap
Place traps in runways
hide them under a shelter to protect foraging birds
Attract Voles with apple slices
house mice
Poison NOT NECESSARY use snap traps
Place the traps near walls, beneath appli- ances, any place where droppings are seen
Tie half a peanut to the trigger
Continue trapping until droppings disappear
Close holes around pipes to keep them from entering again
Yes
Are the burrows connected to 4x6 inch mounds?
No
Yes
Do the burrows raise the soil slightly making obvious ridges?
Do they eat the roots of plants — cultivate the soil ?
No
No
Yes
Yes
Pocket gophers
To control— Purchase a rodent gas cartridge
or pipe exhaust from car or power mower into hole— be sure to seal carefully
Dig into a mound to open up the burrow —usually the tunnel goes in two directions.
Run motor for about 15 minutes
Moles
Not rodents
Moles eat insects
Try to protect these animals
If tunnel is under lawn or near plants— press down ridges daily

1 See text for what to do about unwanted neighbor's pets & feral domestic animals

2 **Hawk box** =16x 10x 7 3/4" with hinged top larger to overhang. 3" hole is centered 11 1/2 " above floor. Make drain holes **Barn Owl**= Build a shelf high in the barn, or a 4' x 4' house in a tree at least 12' high.

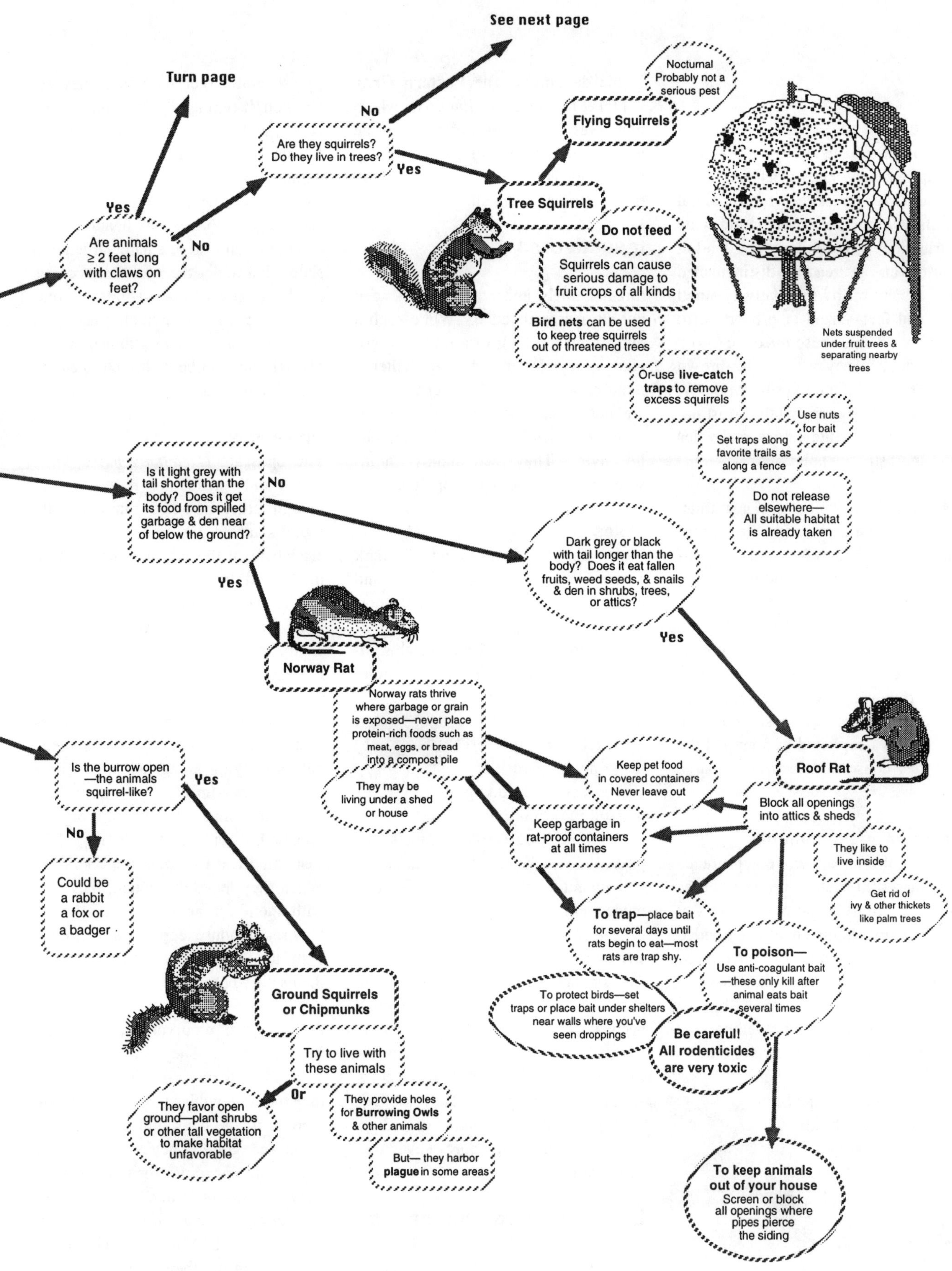
See next page
Turn page
No
Are they squirrels?
Do they live in trees?
Yes
Nocturnal
Probably not a
serious pest
Flying Squirrels
Yes
Are animals
≥ 2 feet long
with claws on
feet?
No
Tree Squirrels
Do not feed
Squirrels can cause
serious damage to
fruit crops of all kinds
Bird nets can be used
to keep tree squirrels
out of threatened trees
Nets suspended
under fruit trees &
separating nearby
trees
Or-use live-catch
traps to remove
excess squirrels
Use nuts
for bait
Set traps along
favorite trails as
along a fence
Do not release
elsewhere—
All suitable habitat
is already taken
Is it light grey with
tail shorter than the
body? Does it get
its food from spilled
garbage & den near
of below the ground?
No
Dark grey or black
with tail longer than the
body? Does it eat fallen
fruits, weed seeds, & snails
& den in shrubs, trees,
or attics?
Yes
Yes
Norway Rat
Norway rats thrive
where garbage or grain
is exposed—never place
protein-rich foods such as
meat, eggs, or bread
into a compost pile
They may be
living under a shed
or house
Keep pet food
in covered containers
Never leave out
Roof Rat
Block all openings
into attics & sheds
Keep garbage in
rat-proof containers
at all times
They like to
live inside
Get rid of
ivy & other thickets
like palm trees
Is the burrow open
—the animals
squirrel-like?
Yes
No
Could be
a rabbit
a fox or
a badger
To trap—place bait
for several days until
rats begin to eat—most
rats are trap shy.
To poison—
Use anti-coagulant bait
—these only kill after
animal eats bait
several times
To protect birds—set
traps or place bait under shelters
near walls where you've
seen droppings
Be careful!
All rodenticides
are very toxic
Ground Squirrels
or Chipmunks
Try to live with
these animals
Or
They favor open
ground—plant shrubs
or other tall vegetation
to make habitat
unfavorable
They provide holes
for Burrowing Owls
& other animals
But— they harbor
plague in some areas
To keep animals
out of your house
Screen or block
all openings where
pipes pierce
the siding

ver.

House mouse

The only mouse likely to enter houses is appropriately known as the house mouse *(Mus musculus)*,. an animal which now has an almost world wide distribution. A similarly-sized adult mouse can be readily distinguished from a baby rat by its relatively small head and feet—sized in proportion to the body. Adult house mice are 6 to 8 inches long. They are grayish-brown on the back with a lighter brown belly, and a long slender scaly tail. (Most native mice have white bellies, and voles have short stubbly tails).

Like rats, house mice are nocturnal. They leave distinctive little black droppings wherever they go, and their unpleasant smell alone would make them unwelcome guests. They will eat almost anything, and foul what they do not eat. While they readily support themselves out of doors in good weather, they are likely to enter houses in the fall and set up housekeeping in the back of a cupboard or drawer. Like pest rats, house mice can be a source of disease.

Squirrels and chipmunks

Because of their attractive appearance and interesting behavior, most of us welcome squirrels and chipmunks—at least initially. Squirrels can be divided into ground squirrels—which burrow in the ground—and tree squirrels—which construct nests in trees. Chipmunks are small, ground-dwelling, short-tailed rodents with stripes on face and body. Some ground squirrels have a stripped body, but their heads always lack stripes. All squirrels and chipmunks —except flying squirrels—are diurnal (active in the daytime). The **Eastern Gray squirrel** *(Sciurus carolinensis)*, which now lives in cities everywhere, can be terrible pests in a fruit garden. They take one bite out of each ripening fruit—spoiling them all.

Insectivores

Small tunnels under the garden need not always be dreaded. While such a burrow may belong to a mouse, a gopher or a vole, it can also shelter a mole or a shrew. Moles and shrews are not rodents—their true name insectivores describes their voracious life style. They feed mainly on insects, earthworms, snails, or slugs.

Moles

Moles are 3 to 4 inches long with dark brown silky fur, no visible ears and minute eyes. Their noses and short tails are pointed, and their enormous digging forepaws stick out at rights angles to the body. They will be more common if soil-borne insects are present. Their feeding may help rid your garden of pest insects and adding air to the soil. You may be willing to press down these little feeding tunnels that pass under a vulnerable area, while still tolerating the little creatures that made them.

Shrews

The smaller shrews are similar in appearance, but their forepaws are small because they do not dig nor live in holes, though they may use the tunnels of other burrowers to search for prey. They are seldom present in non-forested areas, and you may never encounter them.

Large suburban mammals

If you live in the suburbs or the country, several larger mammals may set up housekeeping. Opossums, raccoons, and skunks thrive in our urban forests. Remember that these are wild animals—not furry cartoon characters. Do not feed them unless you wish to encourage problems. A handout here and there can lead to a bare garden or a skunk den under the porch. Raccoons can be a danger to pet rabbits or guinea pigs—even cats or small dogs. And watch out, a 'possum's amazing row of teeth may not be restricted to eating your fallen fruits.

Opossums

The opossum *(Delelphis marsipialis)* is the only marsupial in the U. S., though other pouched mammals are found south of our borders, as well as elsewhere in the world. They've been introduced to our Pacific Coast and they're even more common in their native range—southeastern U.S. and south.

Opossums are renowned for their fecundity. You may have seen pictures of a mother possum with six or seven babies hanging along her tail. These start out as—up to 13—little naked, bee-sized imps developing in her pouch. Each clings tightly to a life-sustaining teat for about three months. When they leave the pouch, they stay with mom for another month before they set up housekeeping on their own, with the females becoming mothers themselves before they're a year old.

Possums are omnivorous, eating almost anything. They're as happy with your corn, berries, or baby chicks as they are with wilder fare—mice, earthworms, toads, eggs and birds, snails, fruits and grain. They're solitary and nocturnal, spending their days in a cozy, grass-lined den in a hollow tree,rock pile, or a burrow dug by another mammal. When disturbed at the nest or during their hunting forays,

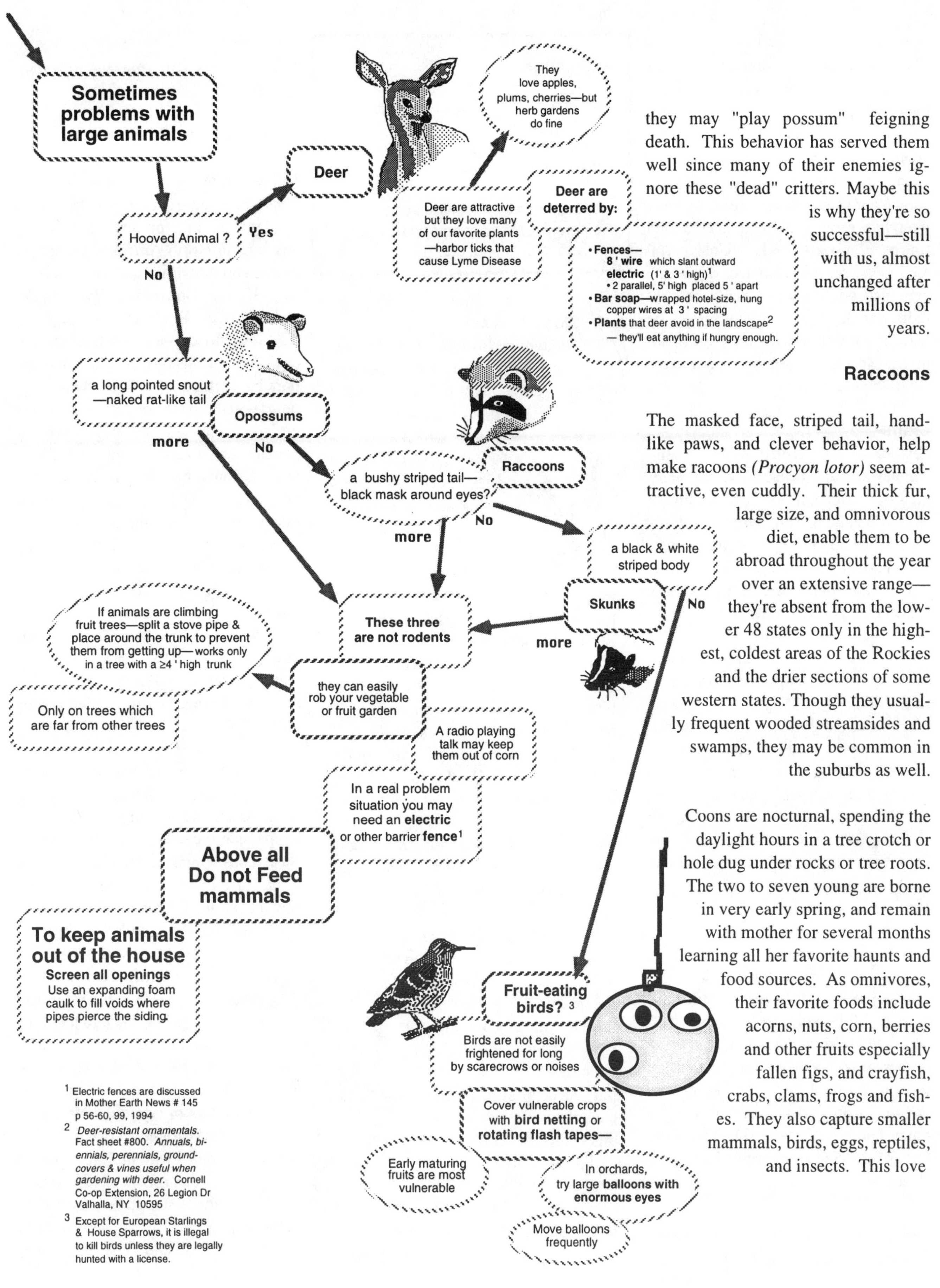
Sometimes problems with large animals
Hooved Animal ?
Yes
No
Deer
They love apples, plums, cherries—but herb gardens do fine
Deer are attractive but they love many of our favorite plants —harbor ticks that cause Lyme Disease
Deer are deterred by:
• Fences— 8 ' wire which slant outward electric (1' & 3 ' high)[1] • 2 parallel, 5' high placed 5 ' apart
• Bar soap—wrapped hotel-size, hung copper wires at 3 ' spacing
• Plants that deer avoid in the landscape[2] — they'll eat anything if hungry enough.
a long pointed snout —naked rat-like tail
Opossums
more
No
a bushy striped tail— black mask around eyes?
Raccoons
more
No
a black & white striped body
Skunks
No
more
These three are not rodents
If animals are climbing fruit trees—split a stove pipe & place around the trunk to prevent them from getting up—works only in a tree with a ≥4 ' high trunk
Only on trees which are far from other trees
they can easily rob your vegetable or fruit garden
A radio playing talk may keep them out of corn
In a real problem situation you may need an electric or other barrier fence[1]
Above all Do not Feed mammals
To keep animals out of the house
Screen all openings
Use an expanding foam caulk to fill voids where pipes pierce the siding.
Fruit-eating birds? [3]
Birds are not easily frightened for long by scarecrows or noises
Cover vulnerable crops with bird netting or rotating flash tapes—
Early maturing fruits are most vulnerable
In orchards, try large balloons with enormous eyes
Move balloons frequently

they may "play possum" feigning death. This behavior has served them well since many of their enemies ignore these "dead" critters. Maybe this is why they're so successful—still with us, almost unchanged after millions of years.

Raccoons

The masked face, striped tail, hand-like paws, and clever behavior, help make racoons *(Procyon lotor)* seem attractive, even cuddly. Their thick fur, large size, and omnivorous diet, enable them to be abroad throughout the year over an extensive range—they're absent from the lower 48 states only in the highest, coldest areas of the Rockies and the drier sections of some western states. Though they usually frequent wooded streamsides and swamps, they may be common in the suburbs as well.

Coons are nocturnal, spending the daylight hours in a tree crotch or hole dug under rocks or tree roots. The two to seven young are borne in very early spring, and remain with mother for several months learning all her favorite haunts and food sources. As omnivores, their favorite foods include acorns, nuts, corn, berries and other fruits especially fallen figs, and crayfish, crabs, clams, frogs and fishes. They also capture smaller mammals, birds, eggs, reptiles, and insects. This love

1 Electric fences are discussed in Mother Earth News # 145 p 56-60, 99, 1994

2 *Deer-resistant ornamentals.* Fact sheet #800. *Annuals, biennials, perennials, groundcovers & vines useful when gardening with deer.* Cornell Co-op Extension, 26 Legion Dr Valhalla, NY 10595

3 Except for European Starlings & House Sparrows, it is illegal to kill birds unless they are legally hunted with a license.

This love of insects sometimes causes trouble in the fall when they roll back lawn grass to capture the large grubs which are maturing there. Proper lawn cultural practices will reduce the chance that such infestations will occur. Coons are solitary and nocturnal, though several m167ay gather a rich source of prized foods. Unless you feed them, raccoon damage to yur gardens and poultry will usually be sporadic and local, though they may be blamed for damage done by other animals, especially squirrels. Corn is the most vulnerable crop.

Skunks

Few of us are thrilled when we encounter a skunk because we are wary of their 'weapon'. The common striped skunk, *(Mephitis mephitis)* joins its smelly mink, otter, and weasel relatives in the family Mustelidae. Skunks are found over U.S., southern Canada, and northern Mexico.

Skunks are strictly nocturnal, hunting for literally anything to eat from berries to carrion. They like to den in burrows in the ground, or *under buildings*—yours! Nothing can be worse than the odor and noise which can occur should a female skunk sets up housekeeping in your basement or crawl space. She and her young are very difficult to remove, so be warned. Keep openings tightly screened to prevent access to these areas.

Should you or one of your pets have an unpleasant encounter with a skunk, the sulfurous odor can be removed with the following concoction which was developed by a biochemist.[1] Wear rubber gloves and be *careful to keep the mixture away from eyes and mouth.* Apply to the animal using a pump spray bottle and rub it into the fur. After 15 minutes, rinse it off with clear water.

Anti skunk

1 quart 3% hydrogen peroxide (from drug store)
1/4 cup baking soda
1 teaspoon liquid soap

In 2 quart bowl mix baking soda into the peroxide. Add soap and pour in spray bottle. Do not store.

Dogs and cats

Though we love our own pets, we may view the pets of others as pests. Most cities have leash and noise abatement laws which help control dogs, but cats can present serious problems as well.

Many problems occur when pets are allowed to roam. Dogs are pack animals. A dog pack, which may form spontaneously, can endanger children, deer, and other mammals and birds. Cats are the major threat to birds. A hunting cat can easily kill most of the juvenile songbirds in a neighborhood. In the U.S., cats are believed to kill half of the songbirds fledged each year.

Not only bird lovers should be concerned about cats. Visiting cats often use your yard as a litter box. This is not just a nuisance. *Their hidden feces can spread serious disease to young children or pregnant women who dig in the sand or dirt (or clean the litter box.).* If you have trouble with cats digging, try covering bare soil with lawn clippings or pine needles. If this is not enough, chicken wire or other screen over bare soil will prevent digging of both dogs and cats. We recommend that neither of these household pets be allowed to roam free. And that's not all. *Be careful. Cat scratches can transmit infections and diseases.*

Problems with Birds

Unless a hunting season has been designated for a particular bird species, it is illegal to kill, or hold in captivity any bird in North America, except for **European Starlings** *(Sturnus vulgarus),* **House Sparrows** *(Passer domesticus),* or **Rock Doves** (pigeons) *(Columba livia)*—all of which are aliens. Though pigeons are attractive and popular with some people, their droppings—and those of other flocking birds—can cause enormous property damage and even present health hazard. Usually barriers are installed to keep pest birds away from buildings. Special control permits are sometimes issued to cities to eliminate roosting flocks of blackbirds and cowbirds. Another option in larger cities is to build shelves on skyscrapers to encourage Peregrine Falcon nesting, or the hawk population is increased by releasing immature Peregrines on skyscrapers. Peregrines are skilled pigeon hawks.

If birds are a serious problem to your crops—usually to cherries, berries, or corn—place bird netting over the crop. Crops can be covered, or bicolored flash tapes which frighten birds as they rotate in the wind, can be installed a few feet above the plant. Scare balloons also are successful if used properly. But you must *move them frequently to increase the scare element.* Birds soon habituate to anything which remains static. In all these efforts, remember that most birds are protected by law. *Even adoption of orphaned birds is illegal without a permit.* Individuals who molest protected birds in the United States or Canada should be reported to the Department of Fish and Game or the U.S. Fish and Wildlife Service.

---

[1] Mother Earth News 6/7, 1995, p 10.

Plant disease control strategies

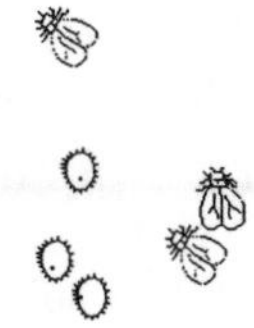

Dissecting plant diseases

A plant acquires disease • during a favorable climactic event • in the presence of a fungal pathogen • on a susceptible host. This phenomenon is sometimes described as **the plant disease triangle.** *A change or elimination of any one of the elements of the triangle will prevent disease.*

Culture influences fungal & bacterial development

The timing and severity of pruning, the frequency of, and type of irrigation and fertilization, the amount of sunshine, air movement, soil composition, and drainage are all important elements of an anti-disease strategy.

Provide optimum soil nutrients

- *Adjust soil pH*—acid-alkaline balance—to optimize crop growth conditions (e.g. potatoes growing in soils with pH 5.2 will resist *potato scab* disease; *club root disease* of cabbage is inhibited by soil pH ≥ 7.0.)

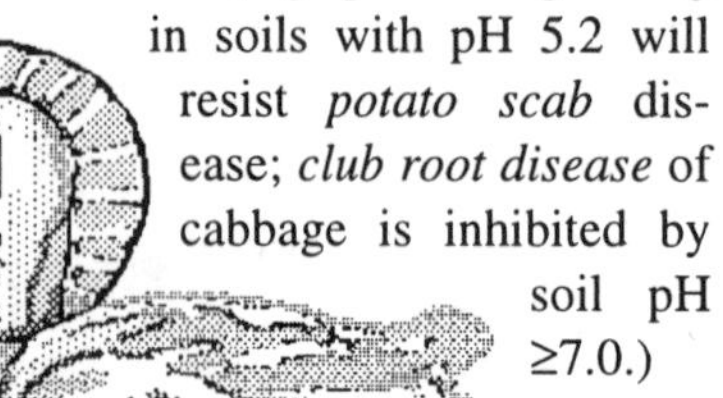

- A deficiency or surplus of any of the **micronutrients** manganese, boron, copper, and molybdenum—favors disease development. Each disease must be considered individually.

- *Provide a balanced amount of the* **macronutrients**— nitrogen, phosphorus, potassium, calcium, magnesium, iron, silicon, and sulfur. Sulfur deficiency in onions and magnesium deficiency in citrus may result in undesirable physiological disorders.

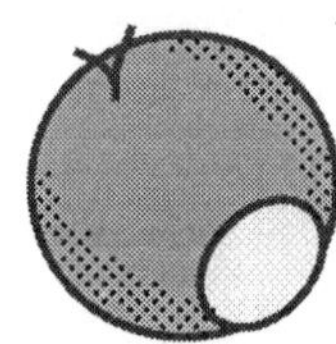

Blossom end rot of tomato and other vegetables is prevented when calcium and soil moisture are in adequate supply.

Many plants respond with lush growth after high levels of inorganic **nitrogen** are supplied. Excess nitrogen increases susceptibility to powdery mildews, leaf rusts, verticillium wilt, and fire blight. On the other hand, too little nitrogen can also predispose a plant to disease. Soil which is high in organic materials—such as that supplied by compost—will tend to buffer nutrient imbalance.

Despite the fact that **silicon** is the second most abundant element on earth, it may be unavailable to plants. Cucumbers, corn, sorghum, barley, pine, and citrus and others respond to silicon enhancement. Silicon is believed to help the plant overcome environmental stresses such as drought, salinity, and toxic minerals including aluminum and manganese. *Powdery mildews* of wheat, barley, muskmelon, squash, and cucumbers decrease when plants receive silicon supplements—100 ppm potassium or sodium silicate in water. Sprays using 1000 ppm silicon are also effective.

Manage water

- *Prevent waterlogged soils* by planting root-crowns on a small mound and avoiding overwatering.

- *Eliminate sprinkler irrigation* to to reduce splashing of spores and the resulting rapid propagation of foliage diseases.

- *Use antitranspirants* to save water; protect plants against invasion of a variety of virulent fungi.

- *In situations where rain falls almost daily,* protect sensitive crops under a permanent clear plastic roof, but keep sides open so air and pollinators can enter.

Reduce disease inoculum

- *Rotate crops* to reduce soil-borne fungal spores. Spores tend to die out during the period when resistant crops are grown. Proper rotation requires knowledge of potential diseases since *related plants are often susceptible to the same diseases*—you shouldn't rotate from tomatoes to eggplant or tomatillo since all three belong to the same plant family.

- Plant *certified disease-free plants and seeds* or cultivars which are resistant to troublesome diseases.

- *Porous fabric* over soil prevents splashing of soil particles containing spores onto plants.

- *Organic manures and compost* contain antagonists of soil-borne disease spores—amoeba and fungal parasites, predators, and competitors

- *Sanitation*—prompt destruction —sometimes burial—of diseased foliage and fruits reduces future sources of disease.

- *Solarization*—uses the sun to heat moist soil for four to six weeks under clear plastic, thus kills the spores of disease fungi, bacteria, and weed seeds. See also solarization.

- *Suppressive soils*—prevent certain root diseases. Studies suggest this is based on antagonistic or antibiotic bacteria or fungi. These factors can be transported to other soils, and they are destroyed by 130° F heat or fumigation by such pesticides as methyl bromide. Such serious diseases as *Fusarium, Phytophthora, Rhizoctonia solani* have been repressed by these soils. In a few situations the suppression developed after several years of monoculture.

- *Harmless antagonists*— bacteria and fungi—are available commercially to colonize roots or wounds before disease organisms can attack. Some of these antagonists synthesize natural antibiotic or antifungal agents.

- *Cross protection*— nonpathogenic strains of disease organisms can sometimes be applied to susceptible plants. The plants respond by producing resistance factors which inhibit the pathogen. (This strategy may harm other cultivars which are not resistant to these new strains. However, adaptation of multilines—each resistant to a different component of the pathogen population—reduces this danger).

- *Mycorrhizae*— symbiotic associations between fungi and roots—can increase or decrease the resistance of plants to certain diseases. Mycorrhizae are known for their beneficial effects on uptake of certain nutrients such as phosphorus.

- *Observe plant quarantines* to help prevent introduction of exotic diseases. Serious plant diseases have been introduced into the U.S. including *Dutch elm disease, chestnut blight, white pine blister rust, potato wart disease,* and *grape downy mildew.* A few large scale eradication programs—such as that which eliminated citrus bacterial canker in Florida—succeed (all infested orchards were destroyed), but most fail.

Analyzing resistance

Resistant strains of important crops are now widely available, but *total resistance-based disease control may not be attainable.* Efforts to breed disease immunity have resulted in enormous savings in costs and reductions in fungicide use. Unfortunately, most plants are susceptible to several diseases, so the effort must include breeding for multiple disease resistance. For example, you can obtain tomatoes and apples with multiple disease resistance, but tomatoes as least can acquire blights during excessively rainy weather.

- *Disease tolerance* is the ability of a plant to survive and produce satisfactory yields while infected with a disease.

- *Apparent resistance* is a plant's ability to avoid disease. This can break down when some growth condition changes, demonstrating that the plant is still susceptible.

- *Static resistance* is a characteristic of the plant to resist a disease—in the absence or the presence of the pathogen. Examples are increased thickening of the cuticle, natural chemicals in the host which inhibit disease development, or ability of the plant to heal over mechanical injury, thus preventing invasion of disease.

- *Dynamic resistance* is initiated by the host only when a pathogen is present, as when a plant walls off an invader.

- *Immunity* implies complete resistance to an infectious pathogen. eased foliage and fruits reduces future sources of disease inoculum.

- *Static resistance* is a characteristic of the plant to resist a disease—in the absence or the presence of the pathogen. Examples are increased thickening of the cuticle, natural chemicals in the host which inhibit disease development, or ability of the plant to heal over mechanical injury, thus preventing invasion of disease.

- Resistance due to direct host protection against disease can be temporarily conferred by fungicides or protective surfactants. In addition, insecticides may prevent disease by protecting the plant from insect vectors of diseases. Similarly, herbicides (or mechanical weeding methods) may prevent disease by destroying weedy disease hosts. This is difficult if the disease is serious and the hosts common. Citrus bacterial canker in Florida succeeded because all infested orchards were destroyed, but most such campaigns fail.

Unfortunately, even inherited resistance will be of no use if new diseases or new strains of a particular disease appear.

Apple Scab IPM

It would be great to plant apples and get luscious tree-ripened fruit with little effort. Unfortunately that doesn't happen. Obviously apples are attacked by several insect pests. And, traditional "grocery store" varieties readily succumb to **apple scab**—a serious fungus disease which causes scaly blemishes and misshapen apples. You may have a scab-susceptible apple tree growing in your garden. If so, frequent warm rains, will trigger scab-by apples, unless you control the scab fungus. We recommend that you plant the newer scab-resistant varieties, but you can help prevent scab on susceptible trees by following our directions.

You can of course apply scab fungicides at 10 to 14 day intervals from early spring until August. But this takes a lot of time and effort, and has several other hazards. *Many fungicides may trigger cancer or birth defects, or both.* Fungicide-resistant scab is widespread.

In addition, many fungicides kill the mite predators that biologically control pest mites. The result: outbreaks of pest mites and serious damage to the tree unless miticides are applied—a continuation of the pesticide treadmill.

Our Scab IPM method may seem a little complicated at first because it's based on research into scab life cycle, but it will help you eliminate many sprays and reduce the chances of developing scab resistance to sprays.

Scab Biology

On warm spring days during rain, *scab* ascospores (they take the place of seeds) are spread by the wind to developing leaves and fruits. If conditions remain warm and wet the ascospores begin to grow and eventually the fungus penetrates apple leaves and fruits. *Once established, a scab infection is difficult or impossible to stop. Most control programs are designed to prevent the initial infection.*

Start your prevention program by raking up and composting or destroying fallen apple leaves during fall. Apple scab fungi overwinter in leaf litter. Next you'll utilize a few quick measures—*date of silver tip, average-temperature-during-rain*, and *degree days* to predict ascospore release.

Scab predicting method

- In early spring, watch for **silver tip**—apple tree buds swell revealing grey tips, but no green leaflets are visible.
- Then, each morning determine the previous day's average temperature using a max-min thermometer.
- Next calculate **degree days**—*a measure of yesterday's net heat gain.* (Since scab can't grow during freezing weather, subtract 32°F from the average temperature to get degree days—the hours when the scab was growing).

Example:
(Max T + Min T ÷ 2) - 32° = Degree Days
(75° + 55°÷ 2) - 32° = 33 degree days

> For math buffs only :
> The date of the first ascospore discharge is determined by the equation, Y (days) = 0.09 X (days) + 0.2 ± 1.0 days, which shows the mathematical relationship between time-since-silvertip and temperature

Directions for Apple Scab IPM

Every day after silver tip

- Record the *cumulative* total number of days since silver tip
- Total-degree-days-since-silvertip.
- Locate days-since-silvertip in Chart 1, column 1.
- If today's total-degree-days-since-silvertip ≥ the ascospore degree day threshold in Chart 1, column 2, the first ascospores will be discharged during the next rain.

Or, anticipate discharge by estimating whether your total degree-days will soon degree-day threshold, spray just before rain is anticipated to prevent infection. *Record data on a copy of page 174*

When to spray for apple scab

Do not spray until the first spring ascospore discharge is about to occur. Then, you'll spray whenever a "**scab infection period**" occurs. (It has to be wet and warm for quite a while for scab to get going).

> **Almond & Pear Scab**
>
> If there are many yellow spots & holes on leaves, & almond drops many leaves in early summer or pear fruits have brown blotches, you have scab. To reduce the number of spores in perennial lesions on the twigs, spray in January with a 16% solution of lime sulfur.

A *"scab infection period"* is based on the interaction of the wet period—the length of time the foliage remains wet—and the average temperature during the rainy day.

- *After each rain*, locate the average-temperature-during-rain (Chart 2, column 1).
- If the length of rain was < than the number of hours required for a primary infection at your rain's average temperature (Chart 2, column 2; Primary), *do not spray.*
- Conversely, if the wet period was ≥ than this primary period, *spray.*

- **During intermittent rain**, add wet periods together unless they are separated by more than 10 hours of dry sunny weather.
- **If scab is already present**, the length of the wet-period needed for an infection to occur is found in Chart 2, column 3: Secondary.
- **If you did not spray before a rain**—
  - Treat within 48 hours after an infection-initiating-rain if average temperature was 43°—
  - Within 24 hours for 53°—
  - Within 18 hours for 64°F.

According to some researchers, it is better to apply a fungicide during a break in the rain, or even during a light rain, than not to spray at all. Since fungicide-resistant scab is present in many regions, consult your farm advisor to obtain the name of a low-toxic efficacious scab fungicide for your area.

Be sure to use protective clothing, and follow dilution and spray directions carefully.

- As you continue to sum degree days, you'll be able to determine the week when 100% of the ascospores have been discharged using the formula

$$Y = 0.06 X 9.6 \pm 5.8 \text{ days}$$

(X = total-degree-days-since-silvertip
Y = total days-since-silvertip)

- After 100% discharge, no more fungicide sprays will be needed this year.

But be sure to clean up leaves in fall.

WHEN TO SPRAY FOR SCAB in _________ (year)

Directions: Record data daily from February to June each year

Today's Date	Max T	Min T	Degree Days	Days-since -Silvertip	Total-°-days since-ST

If Total-degree-days-since-silvertip equals Days-since-silvertip in Chart 1 **spray—**

Spores will be released at the next rain

If rain falls before you spray-- you can determine whether an "infection period " has occurred by comparing your data with Chart 2

(T= temperature ° F, Max= maximum, Min=minimum, ° =degree, ST =silvertip)

Chart 1. $Y = (0.09 \cdot \mathbf{X}) + 0.2 \pm 1$

Days-since silvertip (**Y**)	Total-degree-days-since-silvertip (**X**)
2	46
4	86
6	125
8	163
10	203
12	240
14	280
16	338

Chart 2 Temp. effects on Scab During Rain

At Av. T. of	Hrs wetting needed to Infect: Primary	Secondary
79	13	9
61-75	9	6
57	10	7
54	12	8
52	13	9
50	14	9
48	15	10
46	17	11
44	22	15
43	25	17
41	34	23
34-39°	48 +	32 +

Chart 1. Adapted from Highlights Agri. Resear. Ontario. Vol. 6(3):7-9. 1983
Chart 2. Adapted from Publ. #360, Ministry Agri. & Food, Ontario, 1985. pg.16

Selected fruit tree disease profiles

Brown Rot

Brown rot is a common spoilage fungus which affects **stone fruits** and **almonds** causing a spreading brown spot on ripening fruits. It is caused by several *Monilinia sp.* fungi. Brown rot is more common in rainy, than in dry areas, and more common in apricots and peaches than other fruits.

Though brown rot appears superficially to affect only the fruits themselves, it begins each year in the blossoms. The brown rot spores invade blossoms during rain. In early spring, spores are released from mummies (last year's spoiled fruits), and later from this year's spoiling fruits. The disease spreads from the blooms to the twigs—which may die—and finally to the young fruits.

Reducing incidence of brown rot

- Avoid sprinkler irrigation of fruit trees.
- Fertilize only after harvest and with balanced fertilizer (medium to low nitrogen), and water deeply.
- Clean up fruit mummies quickly so spore release will be minimized.
- In fall, rake up leaves and put them into a hot compost pile.
- **If brown rot is seen every year**, spray with a fixed copper fungicide at the red bud or popcorn blossom stages.

If rain falls during bloom, repeat the spray. Sometimes brown rot is a problem even on green fruits. In such a situation remove spoiled fruits and spray with copper or a systemic fungicide. *Such applications should be avoided if possible to minimize fungicide residues on fruits or copper buildup in the soil.*

Brown rot sometimes attacks fruits after harvest. Commercial growers treat these fruits with fungicides. Ongoing experiments[1] indicate that peaches and apricots can be dipped into hot water—apricots into 125°F water for 2 minutes; peaches for 2 1/2 minutes—to kill the spores. Store fruit in the cold to further retard brown rot.

Eutypa Dieback

Eutypa dieback *(Eutypa armeniacae)* causes a pitchy crusty bark in **apricots** and **grapes**, ***Ceanothus*** and **choke cherries**. Eutypa blocks the plant's water conducting vessels—the zylem. This causes twigs or entire branches to die at the height of the growing season. The leaves are left clinging like flags, and the infected limbs become brittle and easily broken. *Such limbs should be removed immediately.*

Eutypa dieback *is not* spread by pruning tools. Once a limb dies, it takes two to three years before a fruiting body grows from the dead tissues, and begins to produce spores which spread the disease. A blackened crust appears as the fungus matures, and a cut into the blackened wood reveals perithecial cavities holding spores. Fruiting bodies discharge spores during during warm rain—especially in fall and early spring. Spores can be the carried by the wind from an infectious source up to 40 miles away. These spores readily invade wounded tissues.

Pruning wounds lose their susceptibility to *Eutypa* infection about 2 to 4 weeks after pruning. Careful timing of pruning can minimize it spread. Summer and early fall pruning is safe if you live where summer rains do not fall. Infection potential is greatest during fall and spring rains, because spores are released during warm rains. *In areas with dry summers, pruning should occur in early fall or midwinter, several weeks before spores will be released to allow the tree to heal.*

Infected grapevines should be cut back to completely healthy wood in late spring. The systemic fungicide, benomyl (Benlate*)—1/5 lb per gallon water—is registered as a wound paint to protect against *Eutypa* dieback. Apply the fungicide directly to large cuts with a paint brush. As with all pesticides wear protective clothing—especially rubber gloves in this case so you do not contact the product. Benomyl has been linked with a serious birth defect in humans and may be a carcinogen. Only very selective applications such as this one would seem appropriate for this compound. This application method will not result in benomyl in the fruit.

[1] Sustain. Agric. 6(2):8-9, 1994

Selected disease profiles

Powdery Mildews

Anyone who has ever grown peas or roses—almost any tree or shrub—has seen the chalky spores of powdery mildew. Only conifers are completely resistant. Though symptoms usually appear to be identical in all plants, powdery mildew is caused by hundreds of different fungi. The powdery mildew on your vegetables is not the same as that on your fruit trees or vines, and some plants have more than one kind of mildew attacking their tissues. On the other hand the powdery mildew on one plant may spread to another. Fortunately, researchers have introduced several **mildew-resistant plant varieties** and they are the anti-mildew remedy-of-choice.

Though several diseases disperse during rain, *germination of powdery mildew has been reported to be inhibited by rain.* However, recent research[1] shows that grape powdery mildew releases its ascospores after warm spring rains. In any case, *moderate temperatures—70-85°—during periods of high humidity are most favorable to powdery mildew growth.* New leafy growth is most susceptible, but twigs and fruits are also attacked. The disease attacks *both the lower and upper surface* of affected leaves. These diseased leaves remain stunted and twisted instead of growing and expanding normally.

Powdery mildews grow in living tissue. On roses, grapes, apples, peaches, and plums, they survive from one season to the next in infected buds. Some overwinter in fruiting bodies lodged in bark crevices. In strawberries the disease overwinters on the lower leaves. Powdery mildews of annual vegetables overwinter on weeds.

Fortunately powdery mildews can often be suppressed by simple means. Select resistant varieties. In the dormant season **remove** shoots on which the disease was seen. Discard susceptible roses, they're not worth the trouble. Soft growth is most susceptible. Avoid conditions, such as excess water and fertilizer, that prolong succulent growth, and be sure sunlight is optimal. Provide good air circulation. The diseases are favored by dry weather with warm days and cool nights.

Protective fungicides

Use preventive fungicide treatments on susceptible trees and vines. Timing is critical. *Many fungicides must be applied before the disease attacks.* • Powdery mildew on **roses, cucurbits, herbs** and **flowers** can be prevented by **wettable sulphur** sprays. Do not use sulphur on hot days (≥90° F, and be aware that sulphur and oil combinations must not be used on green foliage. • **Sodium bicarbonate** (baking powder)—1 tablespoon per gallon of water—combined with **superior oil**—2.5 tablespoons per gallon—prevents powdery mildew if it is applied every 14 days • Similarly, 3 drops of liquid dishwashing detergent and 3 tablespoons **vegetable oil**—sunflower, olive, olive, canola, soy, corn, safflower—in each gallon of water prevent several powdery mildews.

• **Antitranspirant** coatings which prevent water loss, are protective against several fungae. Roses are protected for 30 days against powdery mildew—3.5 tablespoons per gallon—and blackspot—10 tablespoons per gallon. • For **peaches**, spray with **lime sulphur** just as the buds swell in the spring. (This also prevents peach leaf curl). Spray susceptible apples with **wettable sulphur** or lime sulphur at green tip, and then sulphur or **sulphur-soap** fungicide at two week intervals until small fruit is seen. Apple scab sprays will also control powdery mildew. (Better yet, plant disease-resistant apple cultivars). Never use sulphur on apricots. • A **Neem oil** product, Neem Guard* repels whiteflies and prevents powdery mildew.

• **Grapes** are very susceptible to powdery mildew. After a dormant lime sulphur spray, use wettable sulfur or sulphur-soap fungicide between budbreak and 2 inch growth. Or, a new fungal pathogen, **AQ**[10] *(Ampelomyeds quisqualis)—* a *parasite* of powdery mildew—can help prevent the disease on grapes. • After an initial sulphur spray at first bloom to reduce mildew lesions, AQ[10] *is applied under humid conditions.* The AQ[10] spores penetrate powdery mildew during the 2-4 hours after spraying. Apply AQ[10] again after 7 to 10 days. It is likely that this product will be registered for other crops in the near future.

Downy mildew

Downy mildews are diseases of herbaceous plants, such as vegetables, melons, and flowers. They are common in areas with cool, moist climates, and *appear only after rain* (or sprinkler irrigation). Plants with downy mildew have yellow blotches on top of the leaves, and a white powdery growth on the lower surface. **To prevent downy mildew** • Select resistant varieties • Space plants widely to facilitate air movement • Install drip irrigation • In areas where the disease is common, avoid planting in early spring or late fall when weather favors the mildew • Destroy diseased plant residues to prevent reinfection.

[1] Phytopathology, 80:393-401, 1990 & 80:1198-1203, 1990.

PLANT DISEASES

In general plants respond to optimal conditions by resistance to diseases. On the other hand, stresses promote diseases.

Plant stresses can include:

- Water stresses (flood or drought)
- Temperature (chilling—including watering of seedlings with cold water—or overheating)
- Soil compaction (oxygen stress)
- Nutrient imbalance
  Trace element deficiencies & excesses—high salinity, fertilizer burn, improper pH
- Heavy pest infestations
- Pesticides applied too often or at improper rate
- Air pollution (smog)
- Improper pruning—including too many large cuts, or failure to thin fruits or foliage
- Transplant stress

Fungus on trees and shrubs—some vegetables

Name	Hosts	Symptoms	Controls	Other
Anthracnoses *Apiognomonia veneta* *A. errabunda* *Gnomonia leptostyla* *Glomerella cingfulata* *Colletotrichum gloeosporioides* *A. quercina* & others	 Sycamore, elm Ash Walnuts *Prunus sp.*, citrus, palms, Rosacae, nuts, succulents, & others Oak	**Leaf browning, twig small branch dieback** Severely infected leaves may fall Several spp. of fungus produce similar symptoms	Plant resistant cultivars Fungicide sprays not practical for mature trees Avoid sprinkler irrigation Rake up fallen leaves & hot compost, or bury Sterilize pruning tools with 20% bleach solution	Splashing rain under cool to warm, but not cold conditions spreads fungus to newly expanding leaves Unsightly, but seldom fatal Frequent spring rains increase infections Prune dead branches & discard
***Botrytis* rot** *Botrytis cinerea*	**Bunch rot** (grapes) **Grey mold** (vegetables, small fruits)	Vegetables & fruits covered with **grayish mold**, later turning brown	Early in season, remove leaves which shade grape bunches Spray with antitranspirants, Biofilm* or Vapor Gard* Remove all residues to hot compost, or discard	**Encouraged by cool dampness**. Stake plants or cover soil with porous plastic to prevent rain splashed spore contact Pick ripe fruits regularly
Brown rots *Monilinia fructicola* *Monilinia lasa*	Peaches, cherries nectarines, plums apricots, prunes, almonds,	**Brown spoilage of fruits** and blossom blight Post harvest decay Twig death **During rain, spores spread from mummies or soil to fruit**	Spray with copper or lime sulphur just before bloom. No sulphur on apricots Remove & destroy fruit mummies, dead leaves Ripe fruits susceptible to spoilage during rain or fog	Do not use sulphur within 30 days of oil spray Avoid sprinkler irrigation & too much nitrogen Watch for registration of *B. subtilus* for post harvest control of brown rot
Phytophthora citrophthora	Citrus	**Brown spoilage of fruits**	Spores spread from mummies or soil to fruit during rain. Remove & destroy mummies	Prune foliage away from soil Use copper shield around trunk to prevent snail damage
Downy mildews *Bremia lactucae*	**Vegetables**, grape, rose, many others	Wooly tree-like tufts *on lower surface* of,	Plant resistant roses, vegetables (Cindy, Citation, Excalibur & Nancy	Spores disperse during rain Rake up infected leaves—

Name	Hosts	Symptoms	Controls	Other
Downy mildews (continued) *Peronospora spp.*	broccoli	leaf, blemishes on top	are resistant broccoli varieties)	do not compost
Leaf spots *Entomosporium mespili* *Entomosporium maculatulm*	Pome & Rosacae, e.g. pear, quince, loquat, Pyrocantha, cotonester, toyon, hawthorn etc	**Dark-centered bulls-eye spots** on leaves, fruit, or twigs	**Spread during warm rain, sprinklers** Prune out spotted twigs in winter Succulent growth susceptible Rake up, or bury fallen leaves	Look for resistant cultivars Avoid wetting foliage. Use sulphur + soap product after rain
Diplocarpon rosae	Black spot of rose	**Round dark spots on leaves** which turn yellow & fall. Plant is weakened	**Wet leaves, high humidity, heat favor infection**. Spores are on fallen leaves & infested twigs. Remove these sources of inoculum. Do not use sprinkler irrigation. Increase air flow—avoid crowding	If symptoms appear, baking soda + oil applied semi- weekly (2 tsp soda, 2 tablespoons oil per gallon)[1] Plant resistant cultivars, or mix resistant & susceptible
Coccomyces leaf spot *Blumeriella jaapii*	Cherries & plums	**Large round brown spots** (later holes) appear on mature leaves. Infested leaves fall	Spread during mild weather rain Control as above	Separate strains on cherry & plum
Guignardia blotch *Guignardia bidwellii*	Horse chestnut, Buckeye	East of Great Plains	Control as above	
Peach Leaf Curl *Taphrina deformans*	Peaches, nectarines Redhaven peach resistant	**Distorted leaves on new growth**	Spray with lime sulphur just as buds begin to swell in spring Cannot treat in growing season	Spores from infested leaves all over plant Weakens/ &kills tree
Powdery mildews *Podosphaera spp &* *Sphaerotheca spp* Many spp	Apples, pears, stone fruits, grapes, roses **vegetables**, flowers	**White powdery patches *on both surfaces* of leaves** Spores grow in "chains" Favored by dry, ~warm weather. *Rain inhibits*	Spray with soap+ sulphur [1] Apply as directed on label every 14 days as needed, or use antitranspirants Wilt Pruf* or Vapor Gard* Plant resistant cultivars if possible	During growing season, avoid pruning &N fertilizer Remove infested twigs in dormant season. Treat grapes beginning on 2 inch growth Treat every 7 to 10 days
Scabs *Venturia inaequalis* *Venturia pirina*	Some apples & pears and others On pears	**Brownish lesions** on leaves & fruits Growth ceases, leaves fruits fall prematurely	Fungus in fallen leaves. Rake up & hot compost. Prune off/ destroy diseased twigs. Plant scab-resistant fruit trees	Warm temperature + rain trigger infection. Spray with antranspirant—Vapor Gard* early in season, or soap+sulphur [1] weekly until petal fall
Spilocaea pyracanthae	Pyrocantha, loquat, toyon	Similar to apple scab Dispersed to new growth in spring	Select resistant cultivars *P. coccinca* 'Gov't Red', 'Prostrata', *P. koidzumii* Bella', 'Duval', 'Santa Cruz prostrata', *P. rotersiana,* 'Flava'	Susceptible cultivars can can lose fruits and leaves
Shot hole *Stigmina carpophila* (Coryneum blight)	Apricots, almonds nectarines, peaches	**Small round spots with brown centers** contain dark specks (spores) Later spots fall from leaves leaving "shot hole"	24 hrs of continuous wetness required for infection. Only on upper surfaces of fruits, leaves & twigs. After severe infestation, spray with Bordeaux or fixed copper	Avoid sprinkler irrigation Remove & destroy infected tissues. Apply sprays before first fall rains & again at pink bud (also controls peach leaf curl)
Verticillium wilt	>200 spp	Soilborne fungi invade	Use only resistant species &	Sunshine, regular watering,

[1] Look for registration of baking soda for fungal control

Name	Hosts	Symptoms	Controls	Other
Verticillium wilt (continues) *Verticillium dahliae* *V. albo-atrium*	Herbaceous plants Woody landscape plants	the xylem causing **brown discoloration** of **trunk, branch dieback** on one side of plant, leading eventually to death Leaves first yellow along vein	cultivars in contaminated soil Remove infected plants, & solarize[2] soil to kill fungal spores with wet heat. Some weeds are susceptible & increase spore load in the soil Resistant plants available for some Consult lists of resistant spp. Crop rotation of little value	high potassium & low nitrogen help. Plants less susceptible during hot weather. Nematodes & trauma increase susceptibility *Bacillus subtilus* inoculation can prevent infestation with *V. dahliae*
Fungal Cankers				
Black Knot *Apiosporina morbosa*	Many fruit trees, especially plum	**Rough, black swellings on twigs, causing dieback** Santa Rosa, Formosa, Shiro, President plums resistent	**Ascospores are ejected into air in spring during rain**. Common in wet climate areas. Optimum temperature 70-75° F	**Remove lesions in winter** Put prunings into garbage because fungus keeps growing on prunings
Cypress canker *Seridium cardinale*	Monterey cypress Italian cypress	Lesions on bark & cambium, bleeding kills trees	**Fungus attacks trees in wet weather** in warm weather develops rapidly Plant these species only along the coast	Remove diseased branches 6" below visible infection in hot, dry summer Spray wounds with fungicide
Cytospora Canker *Cytospora cincta* *Cytospora leucostoma*	Stone fruits cherry Plum, peach	Lesions/ gummosis on bark, twigs blossoms, fruit Wounds susceptible for 30-60 days White latex paint on trunk protects	**Fungus spread by wind, during & after rain.** *C. cincta* thrives 64-75° F *C. leucostoma* thrives 81-91° F Fungicides do not control	Infests stressed or injured trees. Difficult to separate from bacterial canker Young trees may die
Dutch elm disease *Ceratocystis ulmi*	European & American elm species Asian elms are resistant	Spores spread to elms by the feeding of bark beetles or by root grafting Toxin from fungus interferes with water transport & kills susceptible tree	Obvious **1st symptoms** are wilting & **browning of foliage at top of tree** Disease has spread to most states Elm bark beetles develop in the phloem of weakened, diseased, dying *or newly cut elms.* In spring, young beetles emerge & fly to feed & lay eggs on new elms, spreading the disease	Only rapid identification & removal of diseased elms (including chipping of the wood) has been proved to be cost effective in slowing spread of the disease Valuable trees can be injected with fungicides annually Look for development disease-resistant strains of American elm
Eutypa Dieback *Eutypa armeniacae*	Apricots, Grapes *Ceanothus* *Manzanita* *Prunus spp*	Apricot, sudden collapse of branches in mid-to late summer, w/brown leaves rough, black cankers around wounds developing in 1 yr **Spread by spores released fall, spring** **Remove diseased wood in summer**	**Not spread by pruning tools** Grapes, In spring growth weak & stunted. Leaves small, chlorotic Flowers drop. Branches die in midwinter. Usually only on 5-6 year old vines. Cankers surround pruning wounds. Prune grapes in very late winter (early March)	Prune young apricots in July or August, mature apricots same or late Nov through Dec., but only after ≥ 1/2 inch *of rain has fallen, & weather is cool* Can paint large wounds with Benlate (1/5 lb/ gallon) Remove diseased wood in summer as soon as seen
Pine pitch canker *Fusarium lateritium*	Pine, SE US, California	Needles on affected branch die, canker on branch, resin flow	**Spores disperse to wounds during rain.** Remove affected branches Avoid too much nitrogen	Avoid pruning during wet warm weather. Can kill tree. Insects may vector

2 See solarize

Name	Hosts	Symptoms	Controls	Other
Wood Rots Most are fungal many species	Fruit & Nut trees Most have "shelf" fruiting bodies on trunk, or mushrooms near trunk	Attack living wood through wounds or roots Prune during fungus' dormant season	Insure proper drainage, avoid water stress (too little, too much), Copper plus linseed oil or *Tricoderma sp* (**Binab T***) anti fungal products on large pruning cuts	Minimize tree wounds by pruning regularly— avoid large cuts. Prevent water from hitting trunks Search out resistant root stocks
Armillaria root rots *Armillaria mellea* *A. tabescens* *A. ostoyae*	>100 woody plants 'Oakroot fungus' Shoestring fungus In conifers at least 11 spp virulence varies	**Invades root bark, cambium & root collar** Whitish growth under bark. Honey-colored mushrooms at root crown (appear in fall) Hyphae resemble shoestrings attached to roots, under bark Rapid death	Also invades dead & dying roots Common in forest soils, landscapes, orchards. Cannot move through soil, but **root to root contact essential** Less virulent spp. can kill after stress such as defoliation changes If death occurs, remove other susceptible plants nearby to prevent further spread through the soil by root contact	Plant resistant species[3] These these resist invasion unless unusual stress Remove dead plant along with as many roots as possible Grind up all wood Solarize[2] infested soil Entire garden contaminated- with dying roots containing fungus
Crown (collar) Rot *Phytophthora cactorum* *P. cimmamomi*	>80 genera of fruit & ornamental trees & shrubs including apricot, almond, peach, apple, cherry, citrus, avocado & many others	Infests plants growing in poorly drained sites **Root rot, leading to branch dieback**, death Use resistant plants	**Infestation favored by flooding** Resting spores in soil become **flagellated zoospores** which **invade roots**. If plant dies, remove roots, solarize soil to reduce inoculum	Avoid sprinkler irrigation of trees, regular flooding of trunk. Promote drainage

Fungus on vegetables

Name	Hosts	Symptoms	Controls	Other
Late Blight *Phytophthora infestans*	Brassicas, peppers, asparagus, potato, tomato	Spread by transport of infested soil. Leaves appear water stressed, & die during first warm weather of spring No fungus is visible Rot infects fruits laying on the soil. **Keep fruits off ground**	Use raised beds & mounds **Rotate** to resistant plants. Different species attack strawberries, beans, & cole crops. In vegetables, practice strict sanitation after growing season **Cover soil with weed barrier mat** to prevent soil from splashing on plants	Use drip irrigation away from root crown Avoid sprinkler irrigation In rainy climate, cover veges with clear plastic dome with open sides to keep foliage dry
Clubroot *Plasmodiophora brassicae*	Cabbage family	Gnarled, galled roots, wilted yellowish foliage	Apply surfactant fungicide (soap) to soil at transplant time to burst spores before they infect	Spores persist >7 years in soil. Favored by acid soil A soil pH > 7.2 resists
Anthracnoses *Colletotrichum sp*	Beans, peas, squash, cucumbers, tomatoes, eggplant	**Sunken spots on fruit** and/or leaves	**Cool, wet weather favors** Increase dryness. Plant in sun Spray with copper after rain	Rotate crops. Remove crop residues. Plant resistant varieties. Solarize[2] soil
Leaf spots & early blight *Alternaria solani* *Septoia lycopersici*	Beans, peas, tomatoes, potato, broccoli, & other, vegetables	Various **brownish patches or spots** on **leaves** or dieback of lower leaves	**Overwinters in plant tissues, weeds** Hot compost all vegetables at end of season. Remove weed sources Cover soil with weed barrier mat	Plant in sun. Don't crowd Spray with fixed copper every 14 days & after rain Never touch wet leaves

[2] See solarize [3] See sources

Name	Hosts	Symptoms	Controls	Other
White mold *Sclerotinia spp*	Lettuce, carrots, cabbage, squash, cole crops, tomatoes	White mold & black sclerotia *on stems* Leaves wilt	Rotate crops. Increase drainage Restrict nitrogen fertilizer	Quickly remove & hot compost infested plants
Wilt diseases *Fusarium oxysporum*	Cabbage family watermelon	**Yellow wilted foliage** Soil-borne disease that attacks roots Persists in soil for years	Plant resistant cultivars Incorporate cabbage residues Solarize[2] for 4 weeks (2 weeks with double tarp)	High soil temperatures increase. Spores in soil are killed by heat & fumes
Fusarium sp	Asparagus, celery, cucumber, melons peas, radish, spinach, sweet potato, tomato	**Leaves yellow, then die** beginning at lower part of plant Symptoms often on one side	All but spinach have resistant cultivars available. Practice sanitation. Solarize[4] contaminated soil. Hot compost diseased plants Some inoculum in all soils	Low light & root knot nematodes overcome resistance. Buy nematode resistant cultivars Plant in sunshine
Crown rot of tomato *Fusarium oxysporum*	tomatoes	**Plants rot at soil line** in soil containing	Plant tomato seeds in soil impregnated with *Trochoderma harzianum* (competes with *F. oxysporum*)	Available as Binab*T Registered to control pruning wound fungus
Fusarium roseum	Squashes, melons, carrots	**Ripe fruits spoil** after wetting, or after harvest	Soil borne fungus. Cover soil with black woven fabric to prevent splashing	See above
Fusarium moniliforme	Corn	Ears spoil	Use resistant cultivars	Spread by thrips
Rhizoctonia solani *Alternaria alternata*	Tomato, cucumber, etc Tomato Blackmold	**Fruits spoil** on vine after late season rains Leaf symptoms like *A solani* (above)	**Begins in fruit with soil contact** &spreads from fruit to fruit Sprays with *Trochoderma sp.*— shows promise in preventing these fungi by out-competing disease organisms (Binab*T— for treatment of pruning cuts, F-Stop*—controls damping off)	Keep tomatoes off the soil Cover dirt with porous black plastic to prevent rain from splashing fungus onto plants *Trochoderma sp.* also control *Scleotium rolfsii.* Can be incorporated in soil
Blossom end rot Physiological disease	Fruits of tomato, pepper, squash or watermelon	Brownish leathery patch at blossom end	Calcium deficiency from **excess nitrogen &irregular moisture**	Water evenly. Fertilize with balanced fertilizer Add compost to soil
Tuber necrosis	Physiological disease of potato	Tubers shrivel	**Calcium deficiency** in tubers during drought	Spray foliage with antitranspirant **Folicote***
Sunscald Exposure to direct sun	Tomato fruits	Whitish or yellowish hardened patch on top of fruit	Too much exposure of fruit to sun Use disease-resistant cultivars which have lush foliage	Restrict pruning of foliage Use shade cloth
Rust	Some beans, peas, asparagus, plums	Brownish pustules	Spray with wettable sulphur Cut & irrigate asparagus	As often every as 7 to 10 days
Root Rots *Fusarium solani*	Pea & beans (dry rot) sweet potato (surface)	**Roots rot**, plants stunted Darker colored blotches	Fungus persists ≥5 years in soil Late season wet period facilitates	Rotate to non-susceptible plants

[4] See solarize

Name	Hosts	Symptoms	Controls	Other
Root Rots continued *F. moniliforme* *Sclerotium rolfsii*	Asparagus (crown) carrots, beets, potatoes, tomatoes beans & many ornamentals	**Feeder roots rot** Soft root rot, mustard seed-like sclerotia on the soil surface	Check for sclerotia on soil surface Plant OK if ≤ 1 sclerotia/ cup of soil Use disease-free & resistant stock	Bury plant residues & sclerotia ≥ 4 inches to prevent germination Add calcium to soil just before planting. Fertilize twice with high N
Pythium ultimum *Rhizoctonia solani*	Peas, beans, beets, carrots, & others	**Roots destroyed**	Add large amounts of compost to soil (~30%)	Compost contains *Pythium*-antagonistic fungal species Improves soil physical properties, aeration, water holding capacity
Bacterial diseases	Diseased tissues exhibit no spores or powdery growths. They often look watery			
Bacterial Leaf & Shoot Diseases				
Bacterial Blights *Xanthomonas campestris*	English walnuts catkins, shoots die	**Distorted leaves** Cultivars (Payne, Ashley, Serr, Eureka)	Infestation > in early blooming Control difficult. Apply copper sprays at bloom	Spread by rain, sprinklers
X. vesicatoria	Bacterial spot of tomato	**Rusty spots on leaves** &fruit, defoliation	**Diseased plants are source** Purchase only clean plants Remove & destroy diseased plants	Increased by rain or sprinkler irrigation Infected seed may be source
X. campestris *(Bacillus campestris)* *Erwinia carotovora*	Black rot of crucifers Soft rot of crucifers	Darkening, then yellowing &drying of veins, followed by ' rapid decay from a secondary bacterium. Infected leaves contaminate soil as long as plant residues are present	In cool weather; symptoms less obvious, disease may invade seed Row covers keep off **insects** that **spread infestation** Rotate crops. Plant brassicas no more than every 3rd year Remove diseased plants immediately	Buy disease-free seed —avoid bedding plants. Soak fresh seed in 122° F water for 30 minutes Look for resistant strains—Shogun Green Valient broccoli—
Erwinia tracheiphila	Wilt of curcubits	**Plants rapidly wilt** & die. Spores overwinter in cucumber beetles	Spread by feeding of cucumber beetles Warm, wet conditions promote Immediately compost dying plants	Grow these plants under row covers until blossoms
Fire Blight *Erwinia amylovora*	Rose family plants especially pear, pyrocantha, quince especially if bloom occurs during warm rain	Systemic disease Invades flowers, shoots, branches foot below obvious lesions Provide good air circulation Plant resistant cultivars	**Wilted brown leaves hang down** Fruits blacken & die Prune diseased branches at least one fungicide after warm rain Avoid sprinkler irrigation	Overwinters in canker on branch. Prune out. Spray with bactericide or copper Monitor critical temperature to determine whether bacteria will reproduce
Olive knot *Pseudomonas savastanoi*	Olive	**Gall on branches**	Prune out gall 6" below stain (harbors bacteria) Sterilize tools	Infection through leaf scar during rain
Bacterial canker **(Gummosis, Blast)**	Stone fruits, citrus, conifers, oaks, etc. cankers on limbs	**Bud, blossom, twig, branch dieback** (blast) Amber gum (gummosis) Bacteria always present on leaves Cut 6" below stain	Worst infections in tree's first year Young trees may die. Most severe if freeze during blossoming. White latex paint on trunk helps prevent infection & death of young trees.	On apple/pear resembles fire blight. Delay pruning young Don't plant trees in unmodified sandy soil which favor root nematodes. These

Name	Hosts	Symptoms	Controls	Other
Bacterial diseases (continued), Leaf & shoot diseases (continued)				
Bacterial canker (continued *Pseudomonas syringe pv syringae*		Dark wet-looking cankers on limbs. Bacteria present on leaves	Cut 6" below stain. Some root stocks & cultivars resistant	increase susceptibility
Bacterial Root Rots				
Corky Root *Rhizomonas uberifaciens*	Lettuce	**No tap root**, few other roots that break easily	Increased by soil compaction, water saturated soils, high nitrogen fertilizer	To reduce: Use rye cover crop, add compost, avoid high nitrogen fertilizers, do not over water
Crown gall *Agrobacterium tumefaciens*	>600 hosts Pome & stone fruits, nuts, grapes, black & raspberries	**Galls, especially at root crowns** caused by soil-inhabiting bacterium Bacteria enter root wounds (from insects or nematodes) during wet weather. Roots respond with gall growths. Death may be due to secondary pathogens	Decaying galls release bacteria back to soil Look for resistant strains Dip roots of young hosts into solution of related bacterium, *Agrobacterium radiobacter*, (NORBAC 84C) before planting	Solarize[2] infested soil Trim large galls & treat with Gallex* in dormant season Do not treat more than one circumference at one time Repeat after 12 months
Potato scab *Streptmyceds scabies*	Potatoes	Damaged fruit	Apply soil sulphur & compost to lower pH	Soil pH should be ≤5.2
Micoplasmas				
Buckskin Disease	Sweet Cherry	**Small colorless fruit** or **rapid branch dieback** depending on rootstock (Mahaleb resistant, but susceptible to root rot & *Prunus* stem pitting)	Monitor **leafhopper hosts** with yellow sticky traps. Delayed dormant oil/insecticidal soap & superior oil/soap spray last during cherry bloom, last week of May	Spread by Flor's & mountain leafhoppers Spray other hosts—privet pyrocantha, viburnum Choose well drained site Prune in summer
Viruses				
Tobacco mosaic Tobacco ringspots	Beans, tomatoes many ornamentals contain, but disease not demonstrated	**Necrotic foliage** with twisting, yellowing Tomato fruits show greenish patches	Insects not implicated in Smokers, cultivators can easily from diseased to susceptible plants	Remove diseased plants during dry weather & discard Clean hands, clothing before contact with susceptible crops
Mosaics	Lettuce watermelon- 1 & 2 Corn Zucchini yellow (pumpkin, squash, cucumbers, melons)	**Stunting & yellowing** especially of outer leaves in patches "Ferny" leaves, lumpy squash/melons	**Spread by infected seed & aphids** from infested weeds—remove broadleaf weeds. Monitor vectors & anitation—as spotted wilt below **Spread by aphids, whiteflies.** Cover young plants with row covers until bloom. No resistant plants available	Purchase certified virus-free seed. Remove over-ripe lettuce immediately to lower aphid habitat. At bloom, weekly sprays with JMS* Stylet Oil or Saf-T-Side,[5] reduce aphid-borne viral transmission

5 ClawEL Division of Brandt Chemical Co.

Name	Hosts	Symptoms	Controls	Other
Insect transmitted viruses & micoplasmas— Sweet potato whiteflies, leafhoppers, thrips				
Lettuce infectious yellows	Curcubits, lettuce	As above until blossoms open	Cover with spun-bonded polyester Spray weekly with superior oil	Mow weeds
Squash leaf curl	Curcubits			
Tomato spotted wilt	Tomato, pepper, peanuts, lettuce, ornamentals eg. petunias	**Leaves wilt & die** Fruit with rings Thrips larvae acquire virus. Thrips adults transmit diseases	Reduces yields of tomato & pepper **Overwinter on** volunteer peanut or clovers &other **wild plants** Winter weed control reduces viral inocula. Use pale blue sticky cards to monitor adult thrips	Silver paint over black plastic to repel incoming thrips Superior oil weekly can control & repel thrips Other wilt controls, same as mosaic virus
Walnut blackline	Grafted walnuts	**Death of tissue at graft line**—death of tree	Purchase only virus-free trees Spread by pollen Very slow development	ELISA test in nurseries Payne & Eureka varieties most susceptible
Soil borne Nematodes				
Pine wilt *Bursaphelenchus xylophilus*	Pine, especially scotch, red, black	Feeding clogs water system Introduced from Japan Blue stain in wood **Sudden collapse & death**	**Spread by wood-boring beetles & grafting**. White pines may resist Remove and destroy infested trees Do not store wood	Infests 15-25 yr old trees in warm weather. Avoid water stress which attracts beetles

MacNab, A.A, Sherf, A.F., and Springer, J. K., 1983, *Identifying Diseases of Vegetables.* Penn. State Univ. College of Agriculture, Univ. Park, PA
Flint, M.L. 1992. *Pests of the Garden and Small Farm.* Univ. Calif, Division of Agri. & Nat. Resources, Publ. 3332, 6701 San Pablo Ave. , Oakland, CA 94608-1239.
Sinclair, W. A., Lyon, H. H. & Johnson, W. T. 1987. *Diseases of Trees and Shrubs.* Comstock Publ. Assoc, Cornell Univ. Press.

Arthropod transmitted zoonoses
—how diseases are acquired from animals via arthropods

Diseases of whatever kind—bacterial, viral, protozoan (trypanosomes), rickettsiae, or filarial roundworm—which can be transmitted from vertebrate animals to people are sometimes dubbed *zoonoses.* Though some zoonoses are acquired directly from animals or via the environment—from food for example—many are transported to humans by blood-feeding arthropods.[1] Mosquitoes, biting flies, ticks, fleas, body lice, and some bugs are examples of blood-feeding arthropods which are known vectors of zoonoses. Chiggers (larval itch mites) and bed bugs are possible disease vectors. An *arbovirus* (from ar=arthropod bo= borne virus) is an arthropod-transmitted viral disease.

Humans are only incidental hosts in terms of the normal life cycles of zoonoses. Normal or *reservoir hosts* typically maintain these infections at a low-level without serious immune responses. On the other hand, in *incidental hosts* —such as humans or other non-reservoir hosts —infections often take a bizarre form, with symptoms and mortality greater than in normal hosts. Since local populations of incidental hosts may be entirely exterminated by the disease, they cannot be important in long-term maintenance of zoonoses. A possible case in point is represented by the lethal Embola virus which recently appeared in Africa. This disease was apparently acquired from an unknown animal reservoir. In the most extreme form such as this, the "*dead end host*", a disease does not complete its life cycle and is not passed on.

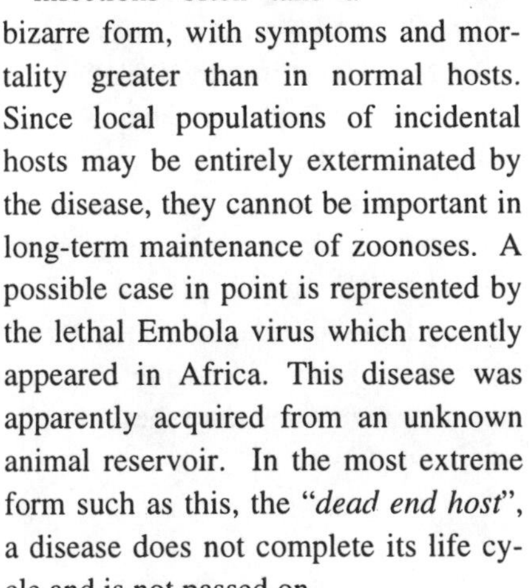

Occasionally, frequent and early reproduction of an *amplifying hosts* serves to "concentrate and amplify" zoonose disease organisms during environmentally favorable epidemic years. These diseased amplifying hosts are then present in enormous numbers, almost assuring easy transmission. However, *whether the disease is passed on to humans depends on the location, ecology, and population characteristics of these normal host species.* When humans move into, or disturb natural habitats, they may acquire unusual diseases from the animals living there.

Potentially, it would seem that almost any blood-borne disease could be transmitted by a blood-feeding arthropod to humans. They could be spread mechanically or biologically, or a fresh wound might be contaminated by disease-carrying feces voided by an infected vector.

Mechanical disease transmission

In mechanical transmission, infected blood which clings to an insect's mouthparts is carried from the normal host to a person while the blood is still fresh and a sufficient number of disease organisms are alive. Mosquitoes seldom have fresh blood on their mouthparts, and their blood meals are stored in the midgut before they feed again. Thus *mosquitoes are not known to transmit diseases mechanically.*

On the other hand, some biting flies are pool feeders. A tiny puddle of blood forms as they bite. The flies lap mouthparts, head, and front legs into the blood. If they are disturbed, they may quickly fly to another host carrying sufficient diseased blood to contaminate their next blood puddle. The horsefly-transmitted viral disease of horses, **equine infectious anemia**, is spread from horse to horse by mechanical transmission.

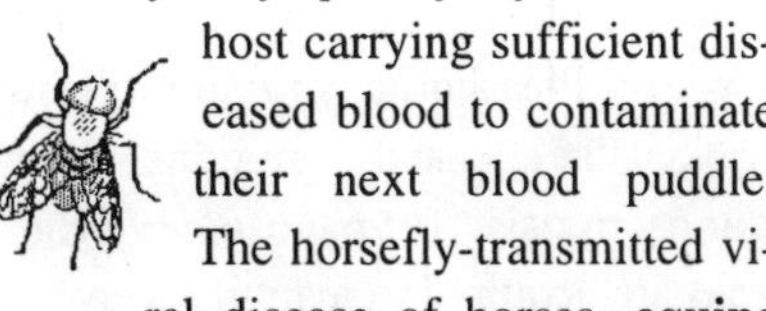

Mechanical disease inoculation

Some diseases transmitted (vectored) by fleas, survive for a time in the insect digestive tract and are injected mechanically during the bite. **Myxomatosis**, a viral disease of rabbits, and **tularemia**, a bacterial disease of rabbits and squirrels are occasionally and imperfectly transmitted to humans by flea bites from these rabbit or squirrel reservoir hosts. In the case of tularemia, transmission may be enhanced by subsequent scratching of the bite. The causal microbes of neither of these diseases is able to reproduce or multiply in fleas, so transmission is strictly mechanical.

Transmission via wound contamination

Some zoonoses are transmitted only by wound contamination. The assassin (reduviid) bug vectors of **Chagas' Disease** defecate while biting. Trypanosomes (protozoa) in the feces enter the wound when the victim scratches the itching welt which appears after the bite.

Similarly, **epidemic typhus, relap-**

[1]Animals without backbones, with jointed legs, body segments, & a chitin exoskeleton that supports the body.

sing fever, and **trench fever** are acquired from insect feces after the victim scratches the itching wound which follows the bite of a body louse. Flea-borne **murine typhus** (rickettsiae), and **murine trypanosomiasis** (trypanosome protozoa) are acquired in a similar way. In both of these, the disease organisms cycle and multiply in the digestive tract of fleas, but are not specifically injected during the bite.

Biological disease transmission

In diseases with biological transmission, disease pathogens reproduce or complete a portion of their life cycle within the arthropod vector. The several protozoans that cause **malaria**, for instance, go through a complex cycle inside the body of mosquitoes, eventually moving to the salivary glands where they are directly transmitted during the bite. They then complete their life cycle in the blood of their avian, mammalian or reptilian hosts.

Four species of protozoa cause malaria in humans. Other species of malaria protozoa attack other animals. Unlike many of the other diseases profiled here, malaria is not a zoonose since it is not acquired by humans from these other vertebrates. Important other mosquito-borne diseases with biological transmission include **filariasis** (round worms), and such arboviruses as **dengue**, several **encephalitises**, and **yellow fever**.

The mere presence of a virus and a mosquito does not guarantee disease spread. The "gut barrier" in mosquitoes prevents viral replication unless a high concentration of virus is ingested. Even if replication occurs, there are other barriers to transmission in mosquitoes so that one species may be a more effective vector than another. In one study, when a similar high concentration of encephalitis virus was present in the salivary glands of two mosquito species, disease transmission differed. A bite by only 9% of the first caused the disease, while 59% of the second did so.

The following steps are required for transmission of a mosquito-borne arbovirus infection. • A sufficient concentration of viruses must be present in the blood meal • The virus must be capable of replicating in gut cells *of this species of mosquito* • A large quantity of virus must be able to penetrate the membrane that surrounds the mosquito's gut, allowing the virus to enter the insect's hemolymph (open blood pool) • From the hemolymph, the viruses must be competent to penetrate the salivary glands • Many viral particles must be injected during a bite.

Serious flea-borne bacterial diseases with biological transmission include **salmonellosis** and **plague**. The tick-borne rickettsiae diseases **Rocky Mountain spotted fever** and **Lyme disease** are also transmitted by arthropods via biological transmission.

Arthropod Vector Control

Most of the arthropod carriers of these diseases cannot be controlled by you as an individual. If you are in an area of risk, your best chance to prevent disease transmission is to use screens, protective clothing, and insect repellents. The most effective insect repellents

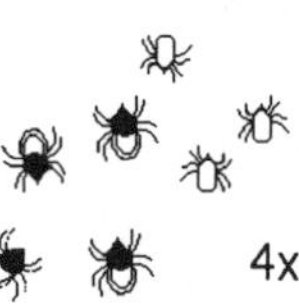
4x

contain DEET as the active ingredient. Though this material has low dermal toxicity, some of these products contain 50%-100% of this active ingredient. These concentrated products may cause serious neurological symptoms in some individuals Choose products which contain a lower concentration and apply the repellents primarily to clothing no more than twice a day. Children are more sensitive than adults to this material.

Can AIDS be transmitted by arthropods?

As can be surmised by the above summary, zoonoses can be spread in a variety of ways, but transmission is neither obvious nor automatic. If a black-legged tick bites an animal carrying the plasmodium protozoa, *Plasmodium falciparum*, that causes malaria, it would be unable to pass on the malaria because the protozoa cannot develop in ticks. Similarly, the Chagas disease organism, *Trypanosoma cruzi*, cannot be spread by the bite of a mosquito or a flea.

There is no biological transmission cycle for AIDS in blood-feeding arthropods. Repeated studies have shown that the AIDS virus does not live to be passed on by mosquito bites. It would seem that the only vector which might spread AIDS would be biting flies which lap up pooled blood. Fortunately such repeated bite patterns are rare in humans since these flies favor other hosts.

Mosquitoes carry Encephalitis

The word encephalitis is a general term meaning inflammation of the brain. Encephalides are very serious diseases, which cause death or irreparable damage to the brain. They can be caused by several viruses, even the familiar *Herpes simplex* Type 1. We focus here on encephalitis-causing *Flavivirus sp.* arboviruses[1] which can be biologically transmitted[1] by *Culex* and some *Aedes sp.* mosquitoes. In the U.S., these viruses cause **Saint Louis**; **Western**, **Eastern**, and **Venezuelan equine**; **California** and **La Cross encephalitis**. Encephalitis is especially serious in children and the elderly. The latter five viruses cause encephalomyelitdes—an inflammation of both brain and spinal cord. (In Asia, a mosquito-borne virus triggers **Japanese encephalitis.**)

Encephalitis life cycle

The common reservoir hosts[1] of encephalitis viruses are small mammals or birds, though reptiles and amphibians are sometimes involved. Usually encephalitis cycles between mosquitoes and these small animal populations. In the case of equine encephalitis, humans and horses are dead-end-hosts[1] so they are not important in maintaining the disease cycle.

These viruses are transmitted in other ways too. Some—e.g. La Cross, St Louis, and western equine—can be directly passed from an infected female mosquito to her eggs, and eventually her larvae. This allows the virus to be preserved during the unfavorable periods when mosquito eggs enter diapause. Since a major St Louis encephalitis vector, *Culex pipiens*, hibernates in protected sites through the winter, *an infected female may transmit the disease during her first spring blood meal.*

Host mosquitoes obtain the virus as they ingest the blood of an infected small animal host. The virus multiplies in the cells of the mosquito's midgut, then new virus particles move into the hemolymph[2] where they multiply in several tissues. Eventually the virus invades the salivary glands and again multiplies. Barriers at each replication step[1]—including the fact that the female must live at least 14 days for the virus to mature and move to the salivary glands—can prevent viral transmission.

Epidemic encephalitis

One or more encephalides are present at low levels in reservoir hosts[1] throughout North America, and others occur elsewhere in the world. Usually the chances of human exposure are very low. Only once or twice a decade when rainfall patterns—heavy rain every two weeks—enable host mosquito populations to reproduce rapidly at the same time that a large population of susceptible young reservoir hosts are present, do the encephalides proliferate and eventually spread to humans and/or horses.

Mosquito control agencies track increases of these viruses in reservoir host populations, so *watch for warnings of encephalitis danger in the press.* If warnings appear, take special precautions to avoid exposure. In addition, wear a mosquito repellant whenever you enter mosquito-prone areas. Apply the repellant primarily to clothing no more than twice a day, and make sure the product contains ≤30% DEET.

In Florida *Culex nigripalpus* is the major Saint Louis encephalitis host mosquito.[3] This species is very sensitive to humidity. In most years they are restricted to wooded areas. Since birds roost in the moist forests they favor, birds are the common reservoir host. After a series of heavy soaking rains, the mosquitoes are able to move at night into drier areas occupied by humans. They are not particular, feeding on reptiles, amphibians, mammals, as well as birds. In years when the infected mosquito population is large they become an important encephalitis threat.

Two other mosquitos offer special danger because they breed in close association with people, the tree hole mosquito, *Aedes triseriatus,* and the Asian tiger mosquito, *A. albopictus*—which is expanding is range in southeastern U.S. Both species breed is small containers such as tree holes, old car tires, vases, and discarded cans. Both carry La Cross encephalitis and transmit it to their offspring via their eggs. In Asia, the tiger mosquito is an important vector of **dengue**. Obviously, discarded car tires offer a serious arbovirus threat—just try to empty the water from an old tire. The Asian Tiger Mosquito is believed to have come here originally via car tires.

In your own community, help prevent pollution of the environment with toxic broad-spectrum pesticides by encouraging local mosquito control authorities to use the safe ecological mosquito control methods described on the mosquito pages in this book.

---

1 See Arthropod Transmitted Zoonoses 2 insect blood 3 Amer. Enomol. 162-167, Fall, 1994.

Malaria? Am I at risk?

The world's most important infectious disease— transmitted to some 300 million people a year, and causing 2-4 million deaths —is spread by night-biting mosquitoes of the genus *Anopheles*. Its name is **malaria**.

Approximately 100 *Plasmodium* protozoa[1] cause malaria in one animal or another. But only four—*P. vivax, P. ovale, P. marariae,* and *P. falciparum*—cause human disease. The other plasmodia affect monkeys, livestock, birds, or reptiles. Many of us think of malaria as a tropical disease because it is now most common in tropical areas, but in the past there were malaria epidemics as far north as the Arctic Circle. Malaria has been controlled by mosquito suppression in the temperate zones—primarily via water management. *P. vivax* the malaria of the temperate zones is transmitted by either *Anopheles quadrimaculatus* or *A. freeborni*..

The most efficient malaria carrier, *A. gambiae* is not present in any region where malaria is rare. *Historically whenever A. gambiae invaded a new region, major malaria epidemics erupted.* Serious epidemics were eliminated—as in South America—wherever *An. gambiae* was eradicated. Unfortunately, eradication of *A. gambiae* in Africa seems not to be an option, because Africa is its ancestral home. None-the-less there are many other *Anopheles* species which can spread the disease. The tiny Central American country of Belize, for example, has four such species. Each species exploits a different habitat. At least one can be found almost everywhere from the mountains to the sea.

Disease life cycle

A portion of the life cycle of malaria protozoa must develop in a vertebrate host, and another part in a mosquito. The cycle in the human begins when a mosquito injects disease-carrying saliva during its blood meal. Each plasmodium quickly moves to the liver where it invades a liver cell. During the next few days each of these protozoa divide into about 20,000 clones. Eventually these emerge from the liver, and move into red blood cells (RBC).

In the blood some of the parasites follow a sexual cycle which leads back to the mosquito—others divide asexually to maintain the disease in the body. Both of these developmental patterns are completed synchronously, depending on the malaria species—in either 24, 48, or 72 hours . (In humans, *P. marariae* cycles in 72 hours, *P. vivax, P. ovale,* and *P. falciparum,* mature in 48 hours). In the period just before the parasites complete RBC development, the victims have chills, but when the protozoa break out of the RBC, a high fever sends the patient to bed. During the alternate day(s) the patient feels weak but is usually able to function.

The fever begins about dusk during the time when the mosquitoes are actively biting—almost assuring that sexual stages will be ingested. Once in the mosquito, the sexual forms (gametes) mature in about 20 minutes. Soon the sperm-like *male gametes* penetrate the *female gametes,* yielding fertilized *zygotes.* About 24 hours later the zygotes enter the mosquito's stomach wall and divide into tiny *infectious cells.* Eventually these burst out of the stomach, swim to the salivary glands. When the mosquito bites, the plasmodia can move in the saliva into the blood of another victim .

In addition to its characteristic chills and fever, malaria causes an enlarged and tender spleen. The patient may be mentally confused and excessively thirsty. Anemia develops in some cases due to a rapid destruction of RBC.

Inherited malaria resistance

The indigenous people of countries where malaria has existed for millennia have a high frequency of inherited resistance to malaria. The oxygen-carrying proteins (hemoglobins[2]) in RBC which are essential to plasmodium survival have mutated in many of these populations. Blood contains more than one type of hemoglobin, and the ratio and composition of these hemoglobins change during human life. Certain malaria-resistant people have abnormal hemoglobins, or unusual hemoglobin ratios.

The abnormal hemoglobin of **sickle-cell anemia** is the best-known mutation. In malarial regions south of the Sahara, where the lethal *P. falciparum* malaria reigns, children under five years who lack the sickle-cell gene are twice as likely to have a heavy infection of plasmodia—and are far more likely to die from malaria. In some parts of Africa 40 percent of the

---

[1] Single-celled animals. [2] Essential red iron-containing proteins in blood which bind to oxygen & carry it throughout the body.

people carry a sickle-cell gene which causes the malaria-resistant sickle cell trait. This gene is also common in Mediterranean Europe, Arabia, and India. Malaria infection triggers sickling (change in shape) of abnormal RBC cells which contain the protozoa, and the infected sickled cells are destroyed by the body's own defense system effectively suppressing the infection.

Other unusual hemoglobins— hemoglobin C found in West Africa, and E in Southeast Asia—also interfere with malaria development. Elsewhere, the so-called **thalasemias**, ensure that hemoglobin is synthesized at abnormally low rates. Blood with a lower concentration of hemoglobin is unfavorable to the disease. All these changes are somewhat debilitating to the individual, but help him or her resist potentially lethal malaria.

Other inherited malaria resistance mechanisms.

Certain stages of the malaria protozoa must bind to protein receptors on the surface of RBC before they penetrate the membrane. In theory each malaria species could potentially bind to a different receptor—but *P. ovale* and *P. vivax* bind to the same receptor. More than 90% of the West African black population and 65% of the American black population lack this receptor, and are thus immune to these malarias. Such people do, however, have receptors for *P. flacipraum* the most deadly form of the disease. In addition, many people in malaria areas are deficient in an enzyme which functions in nutrient metabolism (breakdown) in RBC. This too seems to help them resist malaria.

Chemical treatments

Beginning in the nineteenth century a series of chemicals enabled us to prevent malaria and treat those who contracted the disease. Unfortunately, drug-resistant populations of the malaria protozoa have been selected and spread around the world. Many of the original medications such as **quinine** and **chloroquine** are no longer effective against these resistant strains. Recently **artemisinin**, a Chinese herbal remedy for fever has been found effective in preventing most malaria relapses. It is reported to have "no side effects." When artemisinin is combined with **tetracycline** relapses are prevented about 90% of the time.

Chances for a vaccine

According to the World Health Organization, 275-490 million people are afflicted with malaria, 90 percent of them in Africa. Of these, up to 3 million die each year. Individuals who survive repeated bouts eventually develop immunity to the infectious stage of malaria, but efforts to develop a vaccine against this stage has not succeeded so far. It may be difficult for the body to resist these protozoans because of their complexity.

Each of the four types of malaria, presents a separate immunization problem. A vaccine must be prepared against each stage of the life cycle, and some of these stages evolve rapidly. There is an ongoing effort to isolate the antigens (surface proteins) of the sexual stages with the idea that if the blood were to contain antibodies against the antigens of these sexual forms, the blood itself could prevent completion of the disease cycle. Another method of attack seeks to use molecular biology techniques to transmit malaria antibodies or the malaria-resistant gene found in mosquitoes of the genus *Culex* into the *Anopheles* mosquitoes which transmit malaria.

Currently, the most promising prospect is a vaccine which was developed against the malaria sporozoites which cause the fever and chills. Initial tests suggest that the vaccine produces an antibody response on almost 40% of volunteers.[1]

In spite of great efforts to suppress it, malaria is still with us. Travelers and residents of sub-Saharan Africa, rural Southeast Asia, or certain Pacific Islands are at greatest risk of acquiring malaria. Individuals without natural immunity to malaria can best avoid disease by preventing mosquito bites. When traveling or living in malaria areas be careful. *Use repellents—but note cautions about DEET,[2] wear protective clothing[3] stay indoors after dark, sleep only in screened buildings under mosquito netting.* If a fever should appear, think malaria and seek medical help immediately.

---

[1] Sci. 259:16-17, 1993. Sci. 261: 546-548, 1993. [2]Encephalitis page [3]Permanone tick repellent applied to clothing & mosquito netting repels and kills mosquites & many other insects. Clothing must be dried for several hours after application

Lyme & other tick-borne diseases

Lyme disease is contracted from the bite of an *Ixodes* tick infected with the bacterial spirochete, *Borrelia burgdorferi.* In the East, the vector is the **deer tick**, *I. dammini* . In the West *I. pacificus,* **western black-legged tick**, transmits the disease to humans. Lyme disease has been found in most states of the U.S., and in temperate areas around the world. The most common place to contract Lyme disease is in woods and fields where deer live.

Ticks are flattened, roundish, eight-legged spider relatives. An unfed *Ixodes* nymph is *very* tiny—about the size of a grain of salt. After feeding, they distend with blood until they reach the size of the head of a pin. Such tiny ticks are easily overlooked, especially if they feed in an out-of-the-way location. Fortunately, not all carry Lyme disease bacteria—just those which ingested disease-infected blood as larvae. In the Northeast and Midwest about 50% of *Ixodes* ticks are infected, in the West, less than 5%.

Ixodes tick lifestyle

In the East in fall *Ixodes* females feed on a deer during mating. The male soon dies, but the female drops to the ground and spends the winter in a protected spot. Her eggs are laid the following spring. The minute larval hatchlings feed on mice and birds, some of which—especially **white-footed mice** *(Peromyscus leocopus)*—may be infected with *Borrelia* bacteria. After feeding, these larvae enter a resting stage until the following spring when they molt to the *nymphal stage* most likely to bite you. These nymphs cling to grass and other low growing vegetation awaiting prey.

In the West, things are more complicated, but the disease is much less common—found in **dusky-footed woodrats** *(Neotoma fuscipes)* and **kangaroo rats**. Another tick, *I. neotomae,* which only feeds on rodents spreads the bacteria from rat to rat. Only occasionally do larval western black-legged ticks bite a diseased wood rat, thereby becoming competent to spread Lyme disease to humans.

Lyme Disease symptoms

Most people who are bitten by a *Borrelia*-infected tick notice a large spreading flat reddish inflammation around the bite. This often painful "bulls-eye rash" contains a hard center surrounded by a reddish circular swath as much as one foot in diameter. The rash is often accompanied by chills, fever, head and muscle aches, a stiff neck, and fatigue. *However some victims have no such symptoms, almost assuring that their bite will not be discovered.* Some victims progress to even more rashes and continued neck stiffness, or even meningitis[1], facial palsy or heart problems. Without treatment, about half progress to inflamed joints and an eventually permanent arthritis.

An imperfect test currently the only way to to determine whether these symptoms are caused by Lyme disease. If diagnosis is positive, antibiotics are used to kill the spirochetes. If treatment is successful the disease does not progress further, but existing tissue and arthritic damage is permanent. Unfortunately, Lyme disease found late in the course of the illness, may be resistant to antibiotic therapy. Nonetheless, those with unexplained rheumatic symptoms should be tested for Lyme disease.

How to prevent tick bites

When hiking, wear light-colored long pants. *Spray pants, socks, shoes, and jacket with an insect repellent containing ≤30% DEET.* (Hold your breath as you spray—you're not trying to coat your lungs.) If you spent a lot of time in natural areas, you might find it easier to to treat outdoor clothing with a permanent repellent containing permethrin[2] which will kill and repel ticks through about 50 washes. *This treated clothing does not eliminate the need to spray exposed skin..* When you return home, check your body all over for ticks so they will not have time to "settle".

4x

The familiar larger **American dog tick**—below—does not carry Lyme disease, but can spread **Rocky Mountain Spotted fever**. In the southeastern states, the white spotted **lone star tick**, can carry *Ehrlichia chaffeensis* bacteria which causes **monocytic Ehrlichiosis**. Recently it was discovered that the deer tick can carry the bacteria which causes **hman graulocyctic Ehrlichiosis—HGE**. HGE has been reported from the northeastern states, and is very serious. If you become ill after a walk in the wood, go immediately to the doctor. You may have missed a tick.

If you find a biting tick, grasp it with forceps and pull steadily until it comes out. Save the tick in a closed vial for identification. Note the size, coloration, and description of the ticks illustrated here. If your tick is a vector species, it can be analyzed for disease-causing bacteria. *The Ixodes ticks must bite more than 24 hours for the disease to be transmitted.* If the tick is not swollen it may not have settled long enough to have caused trouble. If you believe that you have been bitten by an *Ixodes* tick see your physician immediately, and describe your experience. You may receive antibiotics prophylactically.

If you live in deer or pack rat country, you can reduce tick populations by dragging a white flannel blanket over your yard or nearby trails weekly, to trap ticks. Keep your dogs and cats at home. They can bring home the ticks that spread Lyme disease. Permethrin-treated cotton balls[3] are available. These can be placed out for mice and pack rats. When the rodents gather this cotton for nesting material, their ticks will be killed.

---

[1]Inflammation of spinal membranes [2]Permanone tick repellent—dry treated clothing for 24 hours before use [3] See sources

Chagas' Disease

If you've ever planned to sleep without window screens or mosquito netting in rural areas of southern U.S., and especially Mexico, Central, or South America you should be aware of a group of assassin bugs known as "kissing bugs". Most assassin bugs, the Reduviidae, are valuable insect predators, but "kissing or **conenose bugs**" (bugs of the genera *Triatoma* and *Panstrongylus)* feed on the blood of warm-blooded vertebrates. And, if that were not bad enough, some are infected with a serious chronic triatomine disease, Chagas' disease, which can be transmitted to humans.

Where conenose bugs live

The principle habitat of kissing bugs is in the nests of small mammals such as wood rats, but certain species are common in the thatched roofs and wall crevices of rural houses. Conenose bugs rest during the day, and are abroad at night year round, looking for a blood meal from sleeping rodents, people, dogs, cats, chickens, turkeys, possums, armadillos, or other handy animals. Adult kissing bugs fly readily and are attracted to lights.

Chagas' disease is rare in the U.S., but common in rural areas to the south, especially in Brazil where 50% of the cases occur. In one study, 71.8% of *Triatoma barberi* collected in a Mexican village were infected with *Trypanosoma cruzi,* the trypanosome protozoa which causes Chagas' disease. In southern Brazil, *T. cruzi* infections of the local vector, *Panstrongylus megistus,* varied from 0-95%, but 44% of the people were infected with Chagas' disease.

Adult Kissing bugs bugs are large (about an inch long) and easy to see, but their nymphs which can also spread the disease, range in size from tiny to large as they pass through eight instars during the several years it takes them to mature.

Why is Chagas disease more prevalent to the south? It is likely that the major reason lies in the behavior of the insect vectors themselves. The disease protozoa, *Trypanosoma cruzi* is, not spread directly by the bite, but is deposited in feces when an infected bug defecates. Since a painful, itching welt soon appears in the bite area, the victim usually scratches. If feces are nearby, they can be scratched into the wound to spread the infection. All of the *primary vectors* of Chagas' disease defecate immediately after the blood meal, so their feces are deposited near the bite. The kissing bugs which are *imperfect vectors* do not routinely act this way. The four U.S. conenose bugs are in this imperfect vector group.

Disease characteristics

T. cruzi protozoans enter the wound and move into nearby cells where they change form. Replication occurs only within cells. Eventually, after several cell divisions, active trypanosomes break out of the cells into the blood where they circulate throughout the body. These blood-borne trypanosomes can be ingested by a biting conenose bug, or eventually move into muscle, heart, or nerve cells where the cycle recurs.

In endemic regions, the acute Chagas' disease illness is seen primarily in children—adults acquired the protozoa years ago. Acute symptoms are identical to those of many other infections, including fever, malaise, loss of appetite, swollen lymph nodes, and sometimes swollen liver. If untreated, these symptoms last for weeks or months, and 5%-10% of the children die. Fatalities are due to acute meningoencephalitis or cardiac failure.

As antibodies and other natural immune responses suppress the parasites, they decrease in number and the disease enters a chronic phase in which the trypanosomes are replicating in muscle, heart, and nerve cells. This causes a progressive loss of cells in these tissues. This continuing loss is eventually manifested as cardiac or gastrointestinal dysfunction. About 20%-40% of patients with the chronic disease exhibit progressive heart failure. The gastrointestinal problems result from the destruction of the autonomic nervous system which governs digestion. Because of its serious acute effects, serious chronic nature, and difficulty of treatment, it's obviously better to prevent Chagas' disease infection if possible.

Prevention

Even though Chagas disease is not common in the U.S., the bites can still cause problems here. The saliva can cause allergies, leading in rare cases to anaphylactic shock. In areas where kissing bugs are common houses should be screened, walls and ceilings carefully plastered, and piles of paper removed to eliminate crevices where the bugs hide in the daytime.[1] Rodents and other vectors should be eliminated in and near human dwellings. Rooms should be monitored for the presence of conenose bugs. Remember that they are attracted to lights. Outdoor lights should be located away from doors that are regularly opened at night so the bugs will not slip in. If bugs have been seen previously, use a flashlight to look for them in darkened rooms before retiring,[1] and sleep under a mosquito netting. *If you are bitten while sleeping*, (a painful itching weal appears) *do not scratch.* Wash the surrounding area and cover the wound with a bandage.

[1]Common Sense Pest Cont. 9(4):19, 1993.

Rodent-borne zoonoses—are sometimes vectored by fleas & other insects

Domestic rodents not only compete with us for food. Several harbor serious diseases which threaten our lives.

Bacterial Diseases

Most of us have heard of the Black Death, the **plague** epidemic which killed one fourth of the people of Europe and the Middle East during the fourteenth century. Though bubonic plague had been forgotten at the time, this was not the first time that plague had ravaged Europe. About 800 years earlier, there was an epidemic of similar proportions, followed in the eighth and tenth centuries by smaller outbreaks. Surprisingly, after several epidemics in the centuries following the Black Death, the disease declined precipitously. Today it appears only sporadically.

Of those who contracted the Black Death, 70%-80% died. Prognosis did not improve during later epidemics. In the 1899 Hong Kong epidemic, 95% died. Currently, plague bacteria in humans can be treated with antibiotics *if it is diagnosed within two days after symptoms appear.* After that a toxin takes effect, and killing the microbes do little good. Unfortunately, not all doctors recognize the symptoms of this now rare disease.

Symptoms of plague

The name **bubonic plague** derives from one of the early signs of the disease. Large and painful swellings (buboes) appear in the lymph nodes of the armpits, neck, or groin. Three days later untreated victims are overwhelmed by high fever accompanied by delirium. Soon black spots appear under the skin. If the patient still survives, the buboes swell larger and more painful, until they sometimes burst.

In an more serious form, **septicemic plague,** the bloodstream becomes directly infected, leading to septic shock, massive hemorrhaging and rapid death. In **pneumonic plague**, the victim collapses, spitting blood, and dies within a few days. This latter form is the only plague which is transmitted directly from person to person.

During early centuries, no one recognized that bubonic plague was spread from rats to people by fleas. The **plague bacteria** *(Yersinia pestis)* is found at low frequency in many wild rodent populations throughout the world. The infection is also transmitted from one rodent to another by fleas. The flea most often responsible is the **oriental rat flea** *(Xenopsylla cheopis).* When a flea bites an infected rodent, it ingests the plague bacteria in its blood meal. As these bacteria replicate within the flea's digestive tract, they form a solid mass that obstructs its gut. The ravenously hungry flea bites repeatedly attempting to get food. Each time it bites, plague bacteria are injected into the victim along with the saliva. If the host animal dies, the infected flea moves on, but eventually dies of starvation.

Patterns of plague epidemics

The essential requirement of a plague epidemic—a large outbreak in humans—is a rodent epizoic. In addition, humans must live in close contact with dying rodents in order for their fleas to move to people. The rodent which fit this requirement in the middle ages was the black or roof rat, which readily takes up housekeeping in human houses.

After the middle ages plague epidemics declined even though the cause and transmission of plague was unknown until 1894. According to Colin McEvedy, plague may have declined because a new species of less virulent plague Bacillus evolved. *It is well known that over time milder forms of diseases tend to displace more virulent ones.* This suggests a reasong that plague no longer spreads beyond local outbreaks. A close relative of the plague Bacillus, *Yersinia pseudotuberculosis*, induces a high degree of immunity to plague in rats, without causing illness. It is possible that *Y. pseudotuberculosis* has infested rat populations around the world lowering the lethality of plague to rats.

This does not help an individual who is bitten by a *Yersinia pestis*-infected flea which acquired the bacterium from a dying ground squirrel. Plague still cycles and kills animals. The individual human who acquires the disease is just as susceptible as the victims from the middle ages. Unless the doctor recognizes the symptoms quickly, a terrible illness or death awaits.

Warning— do not handle or approach sick or dying rodents. Their fleas may carry a lethal disease

Rickettsial diseases

Rickettsiae are minute organisms which, like viruses live only within cells. They are larger than viruses, however, and have many of the characteristics of bacteria. Thus, they are thought to be intermediate between bacteria and viruses. Several disease-causing rickettsiae are transmitted by arthropods.

Typhuses are sometimes fatal rickettsial diseases characterized by headache, high fever, and a pinkish body rash. Typhus appears in two forms—epidemic typhus1, spread from hu-man to human by the body louse, and murine typhus transmitted by fleas from rodents to humans. In both cases a stable microbe is excreted in the flea feces which infects people when they scratch an itching bite. Antibiotics are effective.

Typhuses are sometimes fatal richittsial diseases characterized by headache, high fever, and a pinkish body rash. Typhus appears in two forms—**epidemic typhus**[1], spread from human to human by the body louse, and murine typhus transmitted by fleas from rodents to humans. In both, a stable microbe is excreted in the flea feces which infects pleople when byen scratch an itching bite. antibiotics are effective.

Murine and epidemic **typhus** are caused by *Rickettsia typhi, (R. mooseri).* The murine richettia live in the epithelial cells which line intestinal tract. The disease does not harm the flea host, but is excreted over an extended period during feeding. Usually the rat flea, *X. cheopis,* or the cat flea, *Ctenocephalides felis* are the hosts. The disease enters the wound from the feces when the victim scratches the bite.

The disease in humans is characterized by fever, and usually headache and a feeling of illness. About half of the victims experience nausea and lack of appetite, and a few are bothered by light. In about 60% of the patients a rash on the trunk and limbs appears about 5 days after the fever begins. The infection usually occurs in the spring. In most cases the patient is so ill that hospitalization is indicated, though only 1% die since if appropriate antibiotics are administered.

Murine typhus is most common in sunbelt states in the United States—areas where rodents and fleas thrive. In the early 1940's the disease declined as DDT was used for flea control. (The adverse long-term effects of this pesticide were not recognized at the time.) Obviously, rat proofing of buildings, along with less toxic flea controls—described elsewhere in this book—are more appropriate preventive methods. A similar **epidemic typhus**, caused by *R. prowazekii* is can be acquired by contact with fleas of the southern flying squirrel. This illness is most common in winter.

The confusingly named **Rocky Mountain spotted fever** *(R. rickettsii)* found throughout North America, is transmitted from its primary hosts to humans by the common American dog tick. A bite by this large tick should be taken seriously. Should a sudden chills, fever, headache, prostration, muscle pains appear—followed within a few days by a high fever—inform your physician about the bite so he or she can prescribe antibiotics. If you wait for Rocky Mountain spotted fever to take its course, you could die. Fatality approaches 4%. On the fourth day of fever a rash appears on ankles, wrists, and on the palms or soles of the feet, later moving to the trunk.

Hantaviral diseases

A previously undetected hantaviral disease) was first discovered in May 1993 in southwestern U.S.[2] This usually fatal disease—so far seen primarily in young previously healthy adults—begins a with fever and flu-like symptoms which progress rapidly to serious illness as capillaries begin to leak fluids into the lungs preventing the patient from breathing. This disease was dubbed **hantavirus pulmonary syndrome (HPS)** after analyses using molecular biology techniques demonstrated that this new hantavirus is identical to hantavirus isolated previously from deer mice.[3] Like other hantaviral diseases, the infection does not spread from person to person, but from rodent carriers, their feces, or dried urine to people. Since it seems to be well established in deer mice, HPS has the potential to be very serious, and no one knows why it has not been recognized before. It has also been isolated from piñon mice,[4] western chipmunks,[5] and cotton rats.[6] It does not kill its rodent hosts. The disease can be prevented if we keep these hosts out of houses and outbuildings, and avoid contact with their excretions. HPS is not believed to be spread by rodent or insect bites. Any rodent-contaminated areas should be sprayed with with a 10% solution of bleach before cleanup. Use the fluids liberally. Do not vacuum up these materials. Wear rubber gloves, goggles, and a respirator. Any extensive cleanup should be done by trained professionals.

Other known hantaviruses have similar attributes, though they differ in their distribution, rodent host, and pathogenicity for humans. The Hantaan hantavirus associated in northeast Asia with the field mouse, *(Apodemus agrarius),* causes severe **hemorrhagic fever with renal syndrome (HFRS)**. HFRS is characterized by kidney failure and prominent hemorrhage. Seoul virus, harbored by the Norway rat[7] and Puumala virus of western Europe, harbored by the bank vole,[8] cause moderate or milder forms of HFRS. Prospect Hill, the last known hantavirus is not associated with human disease.

---

[1] *Rickettsia prowazekii* [2] Sci. 262:832-836, 850-851, 914-917, 1994. [3] *Peromyscus maniculatus* [4] *Peromyscus truel* [5] *Tamias spp.* [6] *Sigmondon hispidus* [7] *Rattus norvegicus* [8] *Clethrionomys glareolus*

Other Zoonoses & annoying biting pests

In addition to the diseases highlighted so far, there are several other arthropod-borne diseases which threaten residents and visitors in tropical lands, and other annoying pests which might be found near your own backyard.

Viral diseases

Mosquitoes are involved in the transmission of viral diseases in which humans are dead-end hosts. **Dengue**, of Africa, and the more serious **dengue hemorrhagic fever** (**DHF**), of southeast Asia and tropical America, are vectored by *Aedes sp.* mosquitoes—primarily by *Aedes aegypti.* (The recent immigrant Asian tiger mosquito,[1] is a known vector also). These diseases are characterized by high fever, bone and joint pain, headache, nausea, vomiting, fatigue and depression. Internal bleeding from DHF causes some fatalities. Any breakdown in mosquito control makes them a threat, and there is no vaccine.

Yellow fever is an arbovirus[2] transmitted by *Aedes aegypti* mosquitoes which can kill up to 50% of its victims. *Fortunately an effective vaccine is available.* Yellow fever is a threat in its place of origin—equatorial west Africa—in Central and South America, and the Caribbean. Symptoms include sudden fever, headache, backache, nausea, vomiting; later bleeding from nose and mouth, vomiting of blood, jaundice, lesions on several internal organs, and kidney failure. Those who survive are immune to subsequent infection.

Filarial nematode diseases

Several filarial nematode diseases (**filariases**) transmitted by mosquitoes—including the common house mosquito *(Culex quinque faciciatus)*—are endemic in equatorial Africa and southeast Asia, in northeast coastal South America and southern Panama. Since the nematode worms *(Wuchareria sp.* or *Brugia sp.)* only build up to large populations after repeated mosquito bites, they are not a threat for most tourists, but residents of these areas are at risk. Though many people harbor these parasites in their blood and lymph nodes without apparent symptoms, some experience recurrent fevers, swelling of limbs, swollen lymph nodes, and occasionally grossly swollen limbs and genitalia (**elephantiasis**).

Another important filarial disease, **onchocerciasis** or river blindness, is spread by the bites of Simuliid black flies. The larvae of these vectors live in rushing streams in West Africa, East Africa, Yeman, and in the Americas from Mexico to Brazil. The adults, which bite in the daytime, viciously attack humans. The bite causes extreme pain and itching, and *the disease organisms enter the scratches.* In the body several worms cluster in conspicuous subcutaneous nodular tumors. When the larval worms migrate to the eye, complete blindness can result.

Flies vector protozonan diseases

African sleeping sickness *(Trapanosoma gambiense* and *T. rhodesiense)* is a triatomine disease transmitted by tsetse flies from cattle to people. These flies are so aggressive, and the disease so serious—untreated people eventually become comatose and die—that whole areas of Africa where the fly is endemic are uninhabitable to people and their cattle. Many native animals are reservoirs for the disease. The human immune system fails to develop resistance to the trypanosomes.

Leishmaniasis, another third-world protozoan disease, is transmitted by bites of **sandflies**. A vaccine is available, and insect repellents help prevent bites from these minute flies.

Mite-caused problems

A pleasant walk in the park on a spring morning can lead to a row of itching red spots around your waist, your wrist, or the top of your socks which can last for days. What's even more surprising is that it's difficult to find any cause for all this trouble.

If you live in southern U.S. you're at risk for this itching for an extended period, farther north it can last only a few weeks—at about the same time every year. What's going on?

If you think about what you were doing before these spots appeared, you will realize that you were walking in a wild area through grass or brush. Nothing happened at first, but a few days later itching red spots appeared. This itching and the spots remained for several days.

It's very likely that your spots were caused by the bites of a larval mite known as **harvest mite** or **chigger**. These are so small—.005 inch —that they are barely visible. They wait on vegetation for a victim—you. Once aboard, they crawl around on the skin until they reach a barrier like the top of the socks or the belt line. Next they insert the mouth into the outer layer of skin, excrete a skin-dissolving saliva, and begin to feed. This might be fine since the feeding is rather superficial, but the saliva causes irritation. Long after the chigger has dropped off you begin to notice itching spots which last for several days. Though the itch is annoying, these little arachnids do not cause disease in this country. (In Asia and Australia certain harvest mites serve as vector of **scrub typhus**). Sur-

[1]*A. albopictus.* [2] See Arthropod Transmitted Zoonoses

prisingly, in their other instars—nymphs and adults—these harvest mites are insect predators. You may have even seen the little red adults crawling through the dirt along with their free-living relatives. Fortunately, you can avoid these spring surprises if you spray your clothing when you go into natural areas with an insect repellant containing DEET—choosing a product that contains ≤30% of this active ingredient. Do not apply more than twice a day, and remember that children are more sensitive to DEET than adults.

Several other mite families sometimes interact with people. One group feeds on several kinds of dried foods. Occasionally these get on people causing a dermatitis called **grocer's** or **miller's itch**. Even more troubling, are parasitic mites which burrow into the skin of people and other animals. These **scabies mites** cause severe irritation, which leads to scratching and often infection. A physician can prescribe ointments to eliminate the parasites, but clothing and bedding should be carefully washed.

Mites with similar habits attack dogs and other mammals causing **mange**.

Heartworm Disease of Dogs

Dogs are part of the family. If given good food, love, and exercise we hope to enjoy them for a very long time. Unfortunately, things are not as easy as we might wish because of the threat of heartworm disease. *Because of heartworm, the traditional doghouse in the backyard may not be such a great idea.*

Heartworm is a **filarial nematode disease** of dogs and other carnivorous animals—including cats—which is spread by mosquitoes. (Humans sometimes serve as dead-end hosts) Though heartworm probably originated in South-east Asia, and is still more common in regions with tropical climates, it now has a worldwide distribution. The infective agent, *Dirofilaria immitis*, like other parasitic nematodes has a complex life cycle which includes both mammals and mosquitoes.

Filaria life cycle

In the dog, the cycle begins when any of 60 mosquito species injects *D. immitis* infective larvae (IL) along with its saliva into a mammalian host. The IL grow for several months in the tissues near the injection site. Then the young worms migrate in the blood into the heart and the pulmonary arteries. There, they mature after an additional 2-3 months. The adults are 1/2 to 1 inches long. They spend the remainder of a 5 year life span inside the heart area. Obviously their presence can block blood flow to the lungs, liver, and kidneys, leading to malfunction of these organs. They also interfere with normal valve action in the heart.

Every day mature female *D. immitis* produce many young (microfilariae). These live in the blood vessels. Since microfilariae are as wide as the small vessels, they block the blood flow, especially to the lungs and the liver. The destruction of lung tissue leads to coughing. Cirrhosis of the liver causes jaundice, anemia and general weakness. The microfilariae have a nocturnal activity pattern with coincides with the feeding cycle of the mosquito. In temperate regions they show a seasonal cycle too, increasing five to ten fold in the blood during the summer months. When a mosquito bites a diseased animal at this time, about 24 microfilariae are ingested with the blood meal.

In the mosquito, about half of these microfilariae escape from the gut into the hemolymph (blood) to complete development to infective larvae in the malpighian tubules which function as an insect kidney. The speed of IL maturation depends on temperature, taking 8 to 10 days in warm regions, and about two weeks in areas with moderate climates. The IL then move to the mosquito's mouth, where they are transmitted in the saliva when it bites. The cycle is complete.

Treatment

Heartworm is a serious disease which is difficult to treat. Although the usual strategy is to kill adult worms first, and then the microfilariae, may veterinarians are now reversing this order. Much of the organ damage is caused by the microfilariae. If these are destroyed first, the diseased organs start to repair and the animal's health improves. The dog is then better able to tolerate the arsenic drug which is needed to kill the adult worms. In any case, death of the microfilariae can be very stressful to the host, since their death fills the blood with toxic wastes. *Obviously, prevention of heartworm disease is the prudent way to go.*

Dogs (and cats) that live in heartworm areas can only be kept healthy in two ways. We recommend the first—keep pets inside a screened house when mosquitoes are about so they cannot be bitten. The alternative is to daily feed a preventive medicine which kill the disease organisms, but exposes the dog to continuous pesticide.

Rabies

Rabies, a neurological disease which is always fatal to humans, is another problem organism that was accidentally introduced into America from the old world. Though the first report of a rabid dog occurred in Virginia in 1753, Democitus and Aristotle were familiar with the disease in Europe more than 2000 years ago. Mongeese in Asia and civet and polecats in Africa have been identified as rabies reservoir hosts.[1]

From such early beginnings, rabies gradually spread in the Americas from rabid dogs and cats into the wild populations of racoons, skunks, foxes, cats, and bats. Rabies spread into wild populations continues to this day. The reverse—spread to humans from wild animals has mainly be stopped in the U.S. because of rabies vaccination of dogs, though rabid cats are a very real threat because fewer pet owners vaccinate their cats. In their wanderings, cats are exposed to potentially rabid animals. (All mammals and even birds are susceptible to rabies, though carnivorous animals present the greatest danger of infection).

Even more importantly, capture of wild animals for the pet trade and their transport and release by hunt clubs, exposes buyers to rabies, and inadvertently transports diseased animals all over the country. Wild rabid raccoons are a greater threat to dogs, and therefore to people, than the other potential hosts because they thrive in the suburbs where some people even feed these apparently attractive animals. In one widely reported case, at least 25 people had to be treated for rabies after a baby raccoon was "rescued" in South Carolina.[2]

Though rabies in America came from accidental introductions of rabid animals, laboratory studies indicate that rabies is not identical in its several hosts, and some native animals seem to have become reservoir hosts. Skunks and long tailed weasels may be such natural carriers who do not always die from rabies. On the other hand, dogs, cats, and humans are incidental hosts[1] who always die from the disease. The rabies strain in bats seems to differ from that in other mammals.

Disease progression

Rabies is spread by the virus-laden saliva of an infected animal—usually a skunk, fox, coyote, raccoon, dog, cat, or bat. *If you are bitten by any animal, the most important initial response is to quickly run water over the wound to flush out as much bacteria or virus as possible.* Be sure to report the attack, and make sure that the animal is captured. (A positive test for rabies can only be determined by laboratory analysis of the suspect animal's brain. These animals are held in quarantine for two weeks to determine whether rabies symptoms become evident.) If rabies is detected, or the suspect animal cannot be studied, rabies immunization injections should begin immediately.

The virus binds to the nerves and slowly travels up the nervous pathway to the brain. The length of time this takes depends on the distance between the bite and the brain, and the number and severity of bites but incubation can take weeks or months. The virus can first be detected in the brain area which controls the area bitten.

Once the virus reaches the brain, it causes encephalitis and begins to travel down nerves to the salivary glands. The first symptoms of rabies are mild—a headache, sore throat, fatigue, fever. The first signs of aggressiveness develop at about the same time that the virus reaches the salivary glands. The victim now rapidly declines with seizures, hallucinations, and muscle spasms. Drinking brings on painful throat contractions, so rabies victims avoid water—the hydrophobia which has become another name for the disease. Coma and death follow.

Preventing rabies

An adult animal immunized properly with one or more doses of rabies vaccine, has little chance of developing rabies or transmitting the virus. Semi-annual vaccination of all pets, and people who are occupationally exposed to potentially rabid animals is recommended. The vaccine induces production of antibodies that knock out the virus before it can reach the central nervous system. A vaccinated animal or person should received a booster dose if bitten by a rabid animal.

Though bat-associated human rabies exposure is rare—usually only in those who handle sick or dying bats—rabies death of cattle from Mexico into South America is associated with the bite of rabid vampire bats that come at night to feed on cattle blood. Research has now revealed that these bats share food and actively groom their fellows. This habit has enabled selective control using the same blood anticoagulants which control rodents. Cattle can be treated with the anticoagulants at doses harmless to the cattle, but fatal to the predator. This treatment has such a devastating effect on vampire bat populations, that it need be applied only once every 3-8 years. Obviously, blanket bat-extermination efforts that attack bats at their roosts, are not appropriate.

[1]See page185. [2]Nat. Hist. 93(7): 7-12, 1984.

Appendix

Keeping Ripe Fruits & Vegetables

Apple grower Albert Eyck writing in *Fruit Grower Magazine* said, "Today it is easy to find people in their 20's who never eat apples at all. They tried a few of those dry, meal, bitter, gorgeous looking Red Delicious apples when they were six years old, and they believe that all apples are like that. They are definitely not interested in apples..."

Commercial fruit growers have strong motivation to ship fruit that can be expected to arrive without obvious blemishes. Often the poor taste of immaturity cannot be seen. Neither growers nor sellers are ordinarily penalized if inferior fruit is later discarded by consumers. On the other hand it's to the home grower's advantage to pick fruits and vegetables at the peak of perfection, and store them well for enjoyment later.

Two classes of fruit

Many of us assume that unripe fruits will soften and sweeten after picking. We've never been taught that some types of fruit don't behave that way.

Climactric fruits

Fruits with large pits (peaches, nectarines, apricots, avocados, plums, and mangos), with cores (apples, pears, and quinces), and a few others (bananas, kiwis, papayas, persimmons, and tomatoes)—which contain large nutrient stores of starches or oils, are known as **climacteric fruits**. *If picked at a slightly green but mature stage*, their *nutrient stores change to sugars as they ripen.* If picked too soon, however, they fail to sweeten and soften at all.

[1] Sustain. Agri. 6(2):8-9, 1994

Nonclimacteric fruits

It's different with cluster-fruits (berries, figs, pineapples, and pomegranates), small-pit fruits (cherries and grapes), melons, and citrus. They lack such starch reserves. These **nonclimacteric fruits** *won't get sweeter after picking,* though they eventually soften and decay.

Selecting & storing climacteric fruit

Obviously, you'll want to handle these two fruit types differently. Learn as much as you can about the fruits you raise so that you harvest at the optimum time for good taste—remembering that overripe may be worse than underripe. Don't be misled by color. Although yellow is a sign of succulent maturity in bananas and pears, *red color is of little help in selecting ripe apples, peaches, or nectarines.* Unless the flesh of a **peach** or **nectarine** gives slightly to the touch, and background color is appropriate to the type—yellow or white, not pale green—the fruit will never ripen.

Apple appearance cannot be trusted. Red skin often hides insipid flesh. Ignore red color, and keep tasting apples from the store until you learn which cultivars please you. You may be surprised at the possibilities. For optimum flavor, select apple at their peak ripening season. Often, they should be held at room temperature for about a week to complete ripening. So-called "dessert apples" do not keep more than a week or two. Favorite keeping apples mature during fall. For best flavor leave a few on the tree until completely ripe even though you'll share some with the birds.

Apples to be stored must be picked when mature, but slightly unripe. Be sure the fruits have begun to soften slightly. Dip them in a solution of 2 % calcium nitrate, air dry for a day at a cool temperature, and store in zipper plastic bags at 32° F. To ripen, remove to room temperature for a week or so. (The calcium nitrate helps prevent **bitter pit**, **corky spot**, and **water core**, and lengthens the time apples remain in good condition during storage). Ripening fruits consume oxygen and release carbon dioxide. The zipper bag retards ripening during storage by retaining the carbon dioxide and preventing the apples from obtaining more oxygen. The sugars in the fruit prevent the apples from freezing at the 32° which freezes water.

Pears make an ideal commercial fruit because they must be picked green and stored in the cold for a few weeks to develop quality. (Seckle pears can ripen on the tree, but should be picked a the mature green stage for storage). Pick pears when they reach mature size, and the stem snaps off easily when you lift the fruit. Place pears in the refrigerator at 28-32°F until a few days before you need them. (Do not use sealed zipper bags with pears or the other fruits which follow—they require dryer storage). When you want ripe pears, remove them to room temperature until they soften, then return to the cold until use. The favorite summer pear, Bartlett, is 'in season' from July through September. Use your Bartlett crop before October because a luscious-looking Bartlett in October can surprise you with a brown, mealy center. Asian pears must be picked before they start to ripen, or their flesh will also darken. Winter pears—D'Angou, Bosc, and Comice—are in season from October through February or March. They can be held in cold storage for weeks or months before removing to room temperature for ripening.

Apricots are one of our most delicate fruits. For immediate eating, pick well-colored, softened apricots. For canning or short-time storage, select orange but slightly firm apricots and chill immediately. They keep no longer than a week, and continue to ripen even in the refrigerator, though more slowly. Apricots for canning should be slightly firm when placed in the jar.

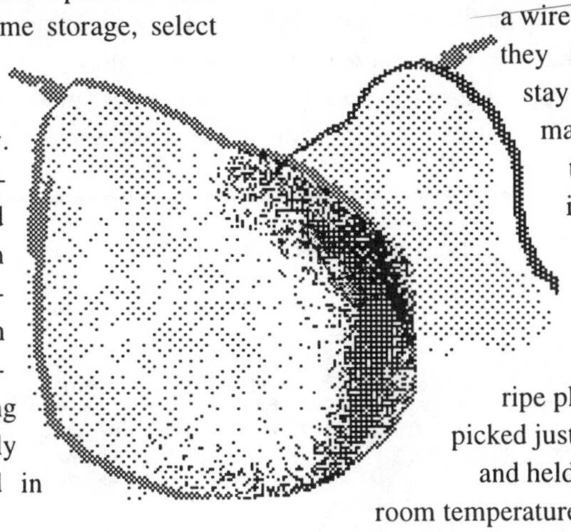

Plums do not ripen well if picked before they begin to soften on the tree, yet they often fall if left too long. The plums on a single tree ripen irregularly. One favorite, *Santa Rosa*, is a luscious purple-black when ripe, not the puckery-red fruit seen in markets. The delicious *Green Gage* must be picked just as it begins to soften, and can be stored in the cold no more than 2-3 days. (Green Gage makes an excellent canned fruit). *Frier* plums must not be picked too soon, or they never sweeten—yet they tend to fall readily when ripe. (Firm Friars make excellent jam). In general, European plums are good for fresh eating, canning, or drying—as prunes—and Japanese plums are best eaten fresh or cooked into jam.

Tomatoes harvested at the "green-ripe" stage have become the commercial norm. "Store-bought" tomatoes take the prize for insipid flavor—though the new biotech FlavrSavr* may be somewhat better. When you grow your own, wait until they're red or yellow before you pick them. Since cold ruins tomato flavor, *never place tomatoes in the refrigerator.* They keep for several weeks at room temperature if held in a wire basket so they breathe and stay dry. Tomatoes vary as to their keeping ability after harvest. In our experience, even green-ripe plum tomatoes picked just before frost, and held for weeks at room temperature—ripen well into winter, while most other tomatoes spoil before ripening. You might consider including an apple to supply that shot of ethylene gas which hastens ripening.

The American **persimmon** should be squishy-ripe before tasting, the flat, firm Oriental persimmon can be eaten out-of-hand like an apple. Well-colored persimmons will ripen at room temperature off the tree, or when stored in the freezer will be ready to eat when thawed. Well-colored, but unripe American persimmons can be pealed, sliced, and dried for a delicious natural snack. Warmly-colored, though firm **papayas** (pawpaws) and **mangoes** become reliably sweet after ripening at room temperature. An apple to your covered fruit bowl will release ethylene gas—a natural ripener—to speed the ripening of any of these climactic fruits.

Ripening & storage of nonclimacteric fruits

Possibly because their perishability prevents long-term storage or long distance shipment, excellent **strawberries**, **raspberries**, **blueberries**, **blackberries**, and **figs** are widely available even if you can't raise them at home. If they look bright and fresh, and are of ripe color, they should be fine—*but they won't get any sweeter, even at room temperature.* Purchase or pick only completely ripe nonclimacteric fruits. Remove plastic wrapping and baskets, and refrigerate *in wire baskets* to lower the humidity around them. *They should not be washed until they are used*—within two or three days.

Currently table **grapes** are often harvested at an unripe stage. This is unfortunate, since *grapes won't sweeten after harvest.* In the market, look closely to recognize these unripe grapes—or taste one. *Thompson Seedless* are yellow-green and translucent when ripe, but have a *dull opaque look.* when unripe. *Ripe Flame* and *Ruby seedless* are plum-red—not a pale raspberry. The season for domestic grapes is summer and fall. In the home vineyard, place maturing bunches in net or paper bags to keep birds and wasps away until they are sweetly ripe.

Only tree-ripened **cherries** from your own garden, or those picked ripe from a local orchard will supply quality cherry flavor and sweetness. To keep birds away, enclose your cherry tree in bird netting. Tie several nets together with twist ties so you can reach in to harvest the fruit. Do not pick until ripe. If rain threatens at harvest season, cover the entire tree with clear plastic to keep water off the the fruit. Wet cherries readily spoil. Cherries ripen unevenly, so several pickings will be required. Cherries will not keep for more than a few days even in the cold.

It's sometimes difficult to choose **melons**. Learn to recognize which are sweet and ripe. A prime **cantaloupe** (musk melon) will be round, and the stem will separate easily from the vine. Its straw-colored high netting should have no sun-burned smooth spots. The background color can be either pale green or tan. If you can hear the seeds rattle, or there are hollows on the surface, the cantaloupe is past its prime. The delicious **orange honeydew** is the most exciting new melon introduced in recent years. The rind of ripe honeydews will be slightly tacky —not smooth and slick like a bowling ball. **Green Honeydews** and other "winter" melons—**Crenshaws** and **Casabas** ripen in late summer and keep through autumn. They keep best at 45 to 50°F in humid, but not wet conditions—not in the refrigerator. Crenshaws have bright yellow background color with slightly tacky rind. Their flesh is orange. Casabas come in three varieties. ***Golden Beauty Casaba*** should be predominate dark gold, with pale green flesh. A ripe specimen will give slightly when pressed opposite the stem. ***Jaune Canari Casaba*** should be orange oval on the outside, and bright yellow within. The rind of a ripe ***Santa Claus Casaba*** has a bright yellow-orange ground between dark green streaks.

Citrus are easier. There's no advantage in choosing **oranges** by color, since some of the sweetest appear greenish. Prime citrus have smooth, shiny skins. *They should be heavy for their size.* Light-weight citrus with dry-looking skins are over-mature drying specimens. ***Navel oranges*** are in season from November into May. ***Valencias*** are prime from May to November. The flavor of **grapefruit** depends on its source. Grapefruit from Florida, Texas, and Arizona will usually be sweeter than specimens from California. Citrus can be stored under refrigeration for a few weeks though room temperature storage is acceptable for temporary care.

Only bright-red, plump **pomegranates** contain premium dark juicy fruitlets. Pomegranates are perishable, and should be used as soon as possible after picking or they will mold. To harvest the seeds without spattering juice, place the fruit into a bowl of cool water. Beneath the water, break open the fruit and pull out the seeds. The seeds sink and the pulp floats. Freeze the seeds, dry, for future use, or spin in a food processor to liberate the juice. After straining, this juice plus sugar makes **grenadine syrup**.

Choosing climacteric fruits

Name	Ripening	Color	Ripen/storage	In season	BestSources
Apple	Slight softening	R/G/Y	Rm T/Zipbag-cold	All year	Home, Farm
Apricot	Slight softening	O	Rm T/Frig<1 week	Summer	Home, Farm*
Avocado	Slight softening	G/Bla	Rm T/Frig	All season	Store, Home
Banana	Slight softening	Pale G/Y	Rm T/Rm T	All year	Store
Kiwi	Slight softening	Brown	Rm T/Frig w/air	All year	Store, Home**
Mango	Slight softening	Y	Rm T/Frig w/air	All year	Store
Pear					
Bartlett	Hard	Y/R	Rm T/Frig <1 mo	Jul-Sep	Store, Home
Winter	Hard	G/B	Rm T/Frig w/air	Oct-Mar	Store, Home
Papaya	Ripe color	O	Rm T/Frig w/air	All year	Store
Peach/Nect	Yellow base	Y	Rm T/Frig w/air	Summer	Home, Store
Plums	Soft	Dark	Rm T/Frig w/air	Summer	Home, Farm*
Persimmon					
American	Squishy	O	Rm T/Freeze	Winter	Home, Store
Oriental	Slight softening	O	Rm T/Frig w/air	Winter	Home, Store
Tomato	Bright red Color	R/Y	Rm T/Rm T w/air	Jun-Nov	Home, Farm

According to the University of California Wellness Letter, "Americans eat about one-third less fresh fruit per capita today than they did in 1048. This drop-off is unfortunate because fruit is good food—sweet but relatively low in calories, high in vitamin C and beta carotene—the precursor to vitamin A—yet nearly free

Choosing Non-climacteric Fruits

Name	Look for	Color	Storage	In season	Best Sources
Blackberry	Color	Solid Bla	Frig w/air, Freeze	Sum-Fall	Home,Farm,Store
Fig	Dark Color	Solid Bla	Rm T<3 days/ Frig	Spr/Fall	Home,Farm,Store
Blueberry	Color	Deep Blu	Frig w/air, Freeze	Sum-Fall	Home,Farm,Store
Cantelope	No stem/High netting		Frig w/air	Sum-Fall	Home,Farm,Store
Casaba					
Golden Beauty	Color	Drk gold	Frig w/air	Fall-Wint	Home,Farm,Store
Jaune Canari	Color	Drk Y	Frig w/air	Fall-Wint	Home,Farm,Store
Santa Claus	Color	Y-O Gr'nd	Frig w/air	Fall-Wint	Home,Farm,Store
Crenshaw	Tacky rind	Y Gr'nd	Frig w/air	Fall-Wint	Home,Farm,Store
Cherry	Dark color	P-Bla	Frig w/air	Spring	Farm, Home
Feijoa	Color	Pale G	Frig w/air	Fall	Home**, Store
Grape, seedless					
Thompson	Translucent	Light G	Frig w/air	Sum-Fall***	Home,Farm,Store
Flame	Dark color	Rasberry	Frig w/air	Sum-Fall***	Home,Farm,Store
Grapefruit	Heavy/Flat shape/origin		Frig w/air	Fall-Spr	Home,Farm,Store
Honeydew	Tacky rind/No Bruises		Frig w/air	Spr-Fall	Home,Farm,Store
Lemon	Heavy, shiny	Y	Frig w/air	All Year	Home,Farm,Store
Oranges	Heavy, shiny	O or G-ish	Frig w/air	All Year	Home,Farm,Store
Pineapple	Fresh-looking	Y-ish	Frig w/air	All Year	Store
Pomegranate	Color	Dark R	Frig w/air, Freeze	Fall	Home,Farm,Store
Raspberry	Color	Drk R	Frig w/air, Freeze	Spr/Fall	Home,Farm,Store
Strawberry	Color	Solid R	Frig w/air	Spr-Fall	Home,Farm,Store

Abbreviations: Blu=blue, Bla=black, Drk=dark, Frig=refrigerator, Frig w/air=Do not place in plastic bag, G=green, Gr'nd= Ground, O=orange, Spr=spring, Sum=summer, R=red, T=Temperature, Y=yellow, Wint=winter, W/=With.
Symbols: < =Less than, #Pineapple guava, *Do not purchase in store, **Sun belt, ***Available in winter from storage

of fat and sodium. Another of its attractions is its high fiber content, which helps reduce cholesterol in the blood, and may protect against colorectal cancer." As a home fruit grower, you need not follow this national anti-fruit trend.

Preventing post-harvest spoilage

Most commercial fruits are harvested in an unripe condition because *green fruit is less likely to spoil or be damaged mechanically.* Often a week or more passes before the product reaches the market. Even so, post-harvest spoilage is a source of considerable loss. Even worse, consumption of diseased foods can be a source of human illness. On way to prevent spoilage is to apply fungicides to newly harvested foods, even though the residues may still be present when the fruit is eaten. Indeed, several fungicides, believed to be animal carcinogens[1] have been withdrawn by the EPA for post-harvest use. *How can we prevent fruit and vegetable spoilage without use of conventional fungicides after harvest?*

Proper temperature control is the most important element in protection of produce. This is even more critical for vegetables than fruits. (See below for details on temperature conditioning for vegetables). Obviously bruising and other mechanical damage should be avoided. Humidity control is also critical. Several fruits require low humidity to prevent fungal growth—a wire basket in the cold, perhaps—while most vegetables thrive under high humidity.

Fruit Coatings— Many fruits are naturally coated with wax. (Some commercial fruits are coated artificially with waxes). A government-developed product, **Nature Seal***, contains methyl cellulose and food-grade shellac. **StaFresh 600*** contains food-grade emulsifiers and surfactants. **StaFresh 360*** is composed of alkali-soluble resins, denatured alcohol, food-grade surfactants, and silicone antifoam. All of these coatings reduce oxygen exchange and inhibit ripening while protecting fruits from fungal penetration. [Methyl cellulose is on the USDA Generally Recognized As Safe (GRAS) list]. Fruits treated with these coatings have a higher level of carbon dioxide and a lower level of oxygen than uncoated fruits.[1] [This is the same situation which is found in fruits placed in **"controlled atmosphere"** (CA) **storage**. In CA storage, the level of carbon dioxide is raised and the level of oxygen lowered to slow ripening. Some apples and pears keep for months when held in the cold under long-term CA storage]. When fruits are covered with any of these coatings, experimental evidence suggests that insects feeding in the fruits are likely to be killed.[2] This would be helpful in preventing the transport of pest insects in the fruits.

In the near future several **microbial antagonists** may be available to help prevent post-harvest spoilage. Most of these microbes were discovered on

[1]Cancer-causing substances. [2]J. Econ. Entomol. 87:752-757, 1994

the foods they protect. They wash off of the surface when the produce is cleaned, causing more spoilage than would occur with an unwashed product.

The ideal microbial antagonist for fruit protection should colonize the surface, grow under the same conditions as the pathogens, and be safe to both plants and animals. These protective microbes will be applied in dips or sprays.

Promising candidates are bacteria, *Bacillus subtilis*—which secretes iturin, an antibacterial chemical which protects citrus, strawberries, apples, peaches, pears, cherries, and other stone fruits, and several *Pseudomonas spp.* which protect apples, pears, and citrus. A yeast, ***Pichia guilliermondii,*** and other spoilage biological control agents to be available in the near future. In addition, a paper wrap around each fruit, helps isolate spoilage.

Vegetable harvest & storage

Many of us assume that all vegetables should be stored in a plastic bag in the refrigerator. Not necessarily true. Certain vegetables exhibit chilling injury symptoms and loss of quality when stored at typical refrigerator temperatures—between freezing and 50-55° F. Symptoms can include pitting, discoloration, water-soaking, internal breakdown, off-flavor, and tissue weakening, leading to spoilage.

Temperature conditioning

If you want to store vegetables more than a few days they should be *"temperature conditioned"*— held at a slightly higher temperature than the indicated temperature on the chart for two days, transfer them to ≈ 40° F for a longer period without chilling injury.

Temperature Conditioning for Summer Vegetables[1]

Vegetable	Chill no lower than	Or else they'll show
String beans	45° F	Pitting & russeting
Cucumbers	45° F	Pitting, water-soaked spots, decay
Eggplant	45° F	Surface scald, blackened seeds Alternaria rot
Okra	45° F	Discoloration, water-soaked spots, pitting, decay
Peppers, sweet	45° F	Pitting, Alternaria rot, darkened seeds
Summer squash	45° F	Pitting, Alternaria rot
Sweet potatoes	55° F	Decay, pitting, internal discoloration, hardcore, bad flavor
Ripe tomatoes	45° F	Water-soaked & softening

1 Based on Amer. Vegetable Gardening 9/93, p 23.

Harvest timing

The idea of "tender baby vegetables" has been pushed relentlessly by the media. *This may be fine for lettuce, corn, beets, or squash, but not for carrots or tomatoes.* If you want small carrots, plant a small variety. And wait a while after your carrots reach full size before you pull them. That extra time will be used to develop the sugars which which make **carrots** sweet. Young carrots have a bitter taste. For best luck in raising carrots, plant for fall harvest so the carrots reach full size when days are warm and nights are cool. Wash immediately and store in plastic bags in the refrigerator for up to 6 months.

Keep **lettuce** growing rapidly by applying plenty of water during mild weather. To prevent bitterness, harvest when the leaves are small or cut the entire head just as the leaves reach full size.[1] Leaf lettuce is much more nutritious than head lettuce. Wash lettuce in clear water, spin dry, and store upright at 95° humidity for a week or two. **Broccoli** does not store well, so harvest throughout the season, or import from mild climates during winter. **Cabbage** can be stored in plastic

1 Commercial lettuce (J. Econ. Entomol. 86:1781-1785, 1994) & broccoli are often sprayed with insecticides to control aphids. Since these are applied at frequent intervals, they may leave detectable residues. If your lettuce or broccoli attract aphids, cover seedlings with row covers. Newly harvested vegetables that have aphids can be swished in water containing a drop of liquid detergent. The aphids will fall away. Then rinse with clear water and drain before storage.

bags in the refrigerator or wrapped in newspaper in a root cellar for several months.

Summer squash should be picked in the morning and stored in plastic bags in the refrigerator or used immediately. Do not leave out at room temperature. Winter squash should be kept dry and held on the vine until the fruit colors and the stem dries. They will keep in dry storage at room temperature for several months.

Corn should be picked when the kernels are full size, but the juices run clear. It is best cooked immediately but can be stored in the refrigerator for a day. **Beets** prefer cool growing weather. They are tasty at any time during growth, and some varieties can be held in the ground during winter or stored in the cold at high humidity. They're not fool proof, however. If they bolt, texture becomes woody.

Though **mushrooms** are neither fruits nor vegetables their storage is critical. They must be kept dry or they will spoil and become slimy. Keep them in the refrigerator in open storage such as an open paper bag or wire basket. If they dry out, reconstitute them in boiling water for a few minutes.

Jerusalem artichokes can be held in the ground until harvest or stored in the refrigerator at high humidity for a month or two. **Sweet potatoes** are dug in the fall after the vines begin to dry. They are spread out to cure in a dark, warm (≥80°F) place for two weeks before placing them in final storage in the dry, dark at ~60°F.

Newly dug **potatoes** should undergo a sequence of temperature changes to cure them for storage.

Obviously the "old fashioned" root cellar dug deep in the ground, or similar conditions, are a good idea for storage of potatoes and other vegetables and fruits with similar requirements. A fan will ensure that plenty of oxygen is available.

Fall & winter storage

Vegetables are best harvested at optimum flavor and maturity, so plan to harvest mature storage vegetables in fall. Store them in the dark. Large piles of produce generate heat, so keep volume moderate.

Harvest **garlic** and **onions** as soon as the tops begin to yellow. Dig garlic immediately and cure in the sun for 3-4 days. Leave onions to dry in the ground for a week, then dig and cure in the sun. Both of these vegetables should be stored in the dark in a cool, dry basket. *Do not store garlic or onions in the refrigerator.*

Ideal temperature/humidity for storage

Storage conditions	Vegetables & Fruits
32-40° F, 90-95% humidity [1]	beets,carrots, Jerusalem artichokes, turnips, rutabagas, apples
32-40° F, 80-90% humidity [2]	potatoes, cabbages, pears, quinces
32-50° F, 60-70% humidity [3]	garlic, onions, garlic, mushrooms, berries
50-60° F, 60-70% humidity [4]	sweet potatoes, pumpkins, winter squash, tomato

[1] Plastic bag in refrigerator [2] In refrigerator crisper, in wire basket [3] In wire basket in refrigerator for cold, in basket at normal humidity in unheated room. [4] Normal conditions in warm room
None of these dry-storage products should be piled or placed in a closed container. Some can be layered in sawdust or wrapped in paper

A discussion which includes varietal names of good storage varieties of fruits and vegetables can be found in the August/September 1993 issue of *Mother Earth News.*

Introduction to Pesticides

Pesticides are chemicals used to kill living organisms, or affect their growth or development in order to control them. In the United States, pesticide use is regulated by the Environmental Protection Agency (EPA), though the State of California has even stricter laws which prohibit some pesticides from registration there.

The Federal Insecticide, Fungicide, and Rodenticide Act (FIFRA) requires that the EPA balance the risk and the benefit of each pesticide. The primary tool to regulate pesticide use is **the label**. *The EPA assumes that if directions on the label are followed, the product will not cause unreasonable harm to humans or the environment.*

The label may require that an acutely toxic product be diluted and mixed in a sealed container, that the applicator be protected by an air-conditioned vehicle, that no one enter the sprayed area until the toxins have time to degrade to harmless levels. If evidence shows that a pesticide is causing unacceptable damage to people or the environment when properly applied and risk is greater than economic damage, the EPA can cancel it, though the process usually takes a very long time. California law does not require consideration of economic benefits, and does not allow registration of products with significant adverse effects.

Pesticides are not the only chemicals

Perhaps you're afraid to use 'chemicals' for pest control. Unless you use only cultural means, barriers, or natural enemies, this is not possible, so don't be afraid, be educated. Everything in the world is composed of chemicals. 'Synthetic' substances are not the only chemicals. Foods, plants, and animals are made of chemicals—either **elements** or **compounds**. All of the components—the atoms—in an element such as sulphur, iron, oxygen, or nitrogen are alike. When any two or more different elements combine, they form a *compound.*

Perhaps you plan to use only pesticides which are composed of 'organic chemicals.' That's not easy. Elements and compounds which contain carbon are **organic**, regardless of their origin. Substances without carbon are dubbed **inorganic**. The composition of each substance is described by a **chemical formula** showing the atoms which make up the structure. For example, H_2O is the chemical formula for water. It shows that each molecule of water is composed of two atoms of hydrogen and one atom of oxygen. Similarly, C_6H_6 is the chemical formula for benzene. Each molecule of benzene consists of six atoms of carbon and six atoms of hydrogen. Obviously, *water is inorganic,* and *benzene is organic.* Its atoms form the benzine ring, a common component of many pesticides.

H H O water

benzine

What is toxicity?

The vast majority of the chemicals we contact are 'natural'. And every natural or synthetic chemical—even water—is toxic if *its concentration is large enough.* And the daily exposure to naturally toxic chemicals in foods is tens of thousands of times higher than the typical dietary dose of pesticide residues. You've no doubt heard that plant or animal-based chemicals are not a problem under 'natural' concentrations because our bodies have evolved mechanisms for breaking them down and getting rid of them. Most synthetic chemicals are dealt with in the same manner; since our detoxification defenses are of a general nature, readily induced by exposure to almost any toxic substance.

A few pesticides and industrial chemicals fail to degrade readily either in the body or in the environment. *You should be concerned about consuming or breathing in residues of such persistent materials—many of which contain bromine or chlorine—and certain heavy metals because they bioconcentrate in food chains.* When a chemical cannot be degraded and/or eliminated from the body, animals often tuck it out of the way in body fat. Thus, you can get a double exposure; when you directly contact a chemical in the environment and then consume it along with animal fat in your diet. This accumulation effect ultimately makes even tiny exposures large since residues will concentrate in your body.

Constant or frequent exposure to less persistent toxins has similar effects. This is why certain life-style decisions such as smoking, alcoholism, and consumption of fatty foods provide the greatest health risks. In addition, the air of most homes contains toxic vapors which should be cause for concern.[1]

Several factors should be considered in choosing and regulating pesticides. When we consider whether a chemical has potential to "poison" an individual, a population, or a city, ask, *"What is its dose?"* "*What is* • *the method of exposure?* • *the length of exposure?* • *its persistence?"* We might even ask, *"What is poisoning?" "What is meant by toxic?"*

Is toxicity • lethality? • debilitating injury? • tumorogenesis? • damage to an embryo, or a reproductive system? • behavioral changes? • environmental damage?

[1] Nonoccupational pesticide exposure study, EPA/600/3-90/003, 1990.

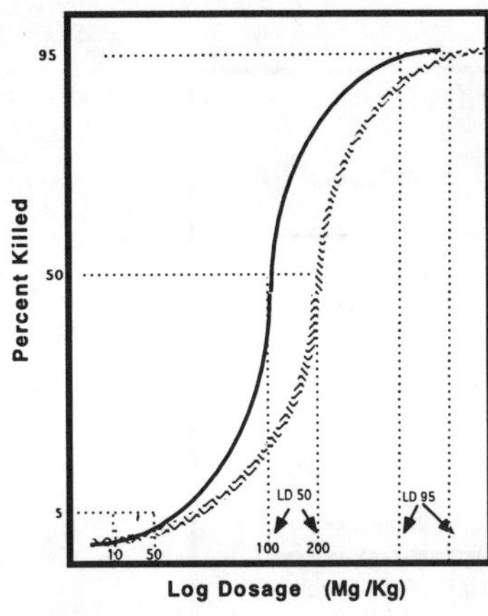
95
50
5
Percent Killed
LD 50
LD 95
10
50
100
200
Log Dosage (Mg /Kg)

If these define toxicity, how do we evaluate injury, and how can we reach consensus as to hazard?

Chemicals enter the body via oral, dermal, or inhalation routes—by mouth, through the skin, or by breathing vapors. The EPA designates *acute pesticide toxicity by lethal dose* (LD_{50}) —the concentration in milligrams per kilogram (mg/kg) that will rapidly kill 50% of an experimental small animal population. These doses are large enough to overcome the natural detoxification systems.

The most commonly reported toxicity of a pesticide is the rat oral LD_{50}—even though the typical person who applies pesticides is at greater risk from exposure through the skin or even lungs. The LD_{50} is not always an accurate measure of acute toxicity, especially when effects of the more frequently applied LD_{95} is considered. The EPA requires that tests on mammals, birds, fish, and crustaceans measure the oral, dermal, or inhalation LD_{50} for each 'active ingredient' in a pesticide.

Measures of pesticide hazard

While an • **acute** test estimates the hazard from a single large dose, it provides no information on chronic effects, depilation, reproductive injury, tumorogenesis, behavioral effects or environmental hazards. A •sub-chronic test estimates hazard from repeated small doses during one tenth of a life span. It describes certain long term effects to a single end point, but yields little information on depilation, behavior, or tumorogenesis.

• **Chronic** effects are determined after using repeated small "no effect" doses over an entire life span to determine which compounds are carcinogens, teratogens, or mutagens.

• **Carcinogens** are cancer-causing agents. Usually they also cause mutations—are **mutagens**. Any substance that can mutate or change DNA—the molecules which form genes—may cause cancer. Materials which cause the greatest damage to DNA are believed to be the most potent carcinogens.

• **Teratogens** induce defects in the developing embryo, or damage ovaries or testes. Currently, such injuries are recognized when offspring of experimentally exposed test animals exhibit obvious physical abnormalities at birth. The complete array of tests on many older pesticides have not been completed and they must be re-registered.

EPA Classifcation of Carcinogens

Group A: Human carcinogen—sufficient evidence from human epidemiological studies

Group B: Probable human carcinogen—

B_1 limited evidence from human epidemiological studies
B_2 sufficient evidence from animal epidemiological studies

Group C: Possible human carcinogen—limited evidence from animals; no human data, including malignant tumor response in one well-conducted experiment; or tumor responses of marginal statistical significance in studies with inadequate design; or benign tumors where mutagenicity tests were negative; or responses of marginal significance with untreated controls showing many cancers

Group D: Not known to be a human carcinogen—**data inadequate, or no data**

Group E: Not a human carcinogen in two adequate animal tests on different species, or adequate evidence from both epidemiological and animal studies

The EPA does not require tests to measure nerve or behavioral effects, even though many pesticides are known to act on the nervous system. Yet it is increasingly apparent that certain persistent chemicals which mimic natural hormones are a health hazard to humans and wild animals. Unfortunately, several of these which are pesticides are still registered for use here, and others banned in the U. S. are available elsewhere. Fish living in polluted waters often contain residues of chlorinated pesticides and heavy metals which have bioaccumulated in their food chains. Toxic residues are again increasing in birds and bats at the top of food chains. Many of these come from untested **chlorinated industrial compounds.**

As mentioned above, all animals have enzymes which can metabolize low doses of toxic substances. This is fortunate since many plants synthesize toxic substances. In general this metabolism is faster in smaller, than in larger animals. As in insects, vertebrates with the most varied diets are preadapted to degrade toxics readily, plant-eating animals are next, and predators are least able to tolerate toxics. Mammals handle poisons better than birds, and fish are most sensitive, perhaps because they are exposed through their moist skins.

The EPA allows tiny pesticide residue 'tolerances' in foods which are 1000 times lower than acute no-effect levels determined by animal experiments. Some individuals question the validity of allowing any tolerances since they do not take hormonal effects of pes-

[1] Amer. Veg. Grow. 41(12):37-39, 1993

PESTICIDE TOXICITY RELATIONSHIPS*

Category	Toxicity	Signal word	LD50oral dose (mg/kg)**	LD50dermal dose (mg/kg)	Irritation potential	Averdupois
I	high	DANGER POISON***	≤ 50	≤200	Corrosive	a few drops to 4 teaspoons
II	moderate	WARNING	>50-500	>200-2000	Severe irritation	>4 teaspoons to 4 ounces
III	slight	CAUTION	>500	>2000	Moderate irriation	>4 ounces
IV	v. slight	CAUTION	>5000	>5000	Slight irriation	>12 ounces

* Based on Common Sense Pest Control, Fall 1984. **Milligrams active ingredient per kilograms body weight (A 150 pound man weight ~43 kg—3100 mg/ounce. ***POISON along with a skull & crossbones is on labels with low oral LD50. DANGER alone means that either dermal LD50. is low, or other acute hazards are evident.

ticides into account, but it is very difficult to remove every molecule. Obviously even trace amounts of persistent pesticides which do not easily metabolize in the body should be eliminated. The situation has improved recently. Most newer pesticides labeled for food use degrade in the environment to harmless molecules in days or weeks. Most residues are washed off before foods reach the market. A recent FDA study found that 68.9% of vegetables in the market contained no detectable pesticides (in parts per trillion), while 29.4% had residues lower than the tolerance levels. A few samples of lettuce and peas—1.7% of the vegetables tested—had residues above the tolerance.[1] These crops are often treated with a pesticide in the last days before harvest to eliminate aphids or thrips.[1] *This enables the product to comply with government and industry standards which prohibit insect contamination.* You may wish to carefully wash all purchased vegetables, or grow your own, or even support changes in the legislation concerning insects on vegetables.

Deciding to use a pesticide

Those who apply pesticides are likely to be exposed through the skin and the air. Before you use a pesticide think • Do I really need a pesticide? • Are other control methods available? • How many pests are present? • Are they likely to cause serious damage? • Are natural controls operating? • Will this pesticide be effective? • Will its use cause environmental hazard? *If the decision is to proceed, use the least toxic, least persistent effective compound available.*

Reading the pesticide label

A government report notes that few of us read pesticide labels. If you're one of these, we can empathize. Perhaps you find it difficult to wade through the tiny print, or you haven't found the long words and unfamiliar terms very helpful. One scientist[2] found the print size too small to be read by millions; the text too difficult for 40% of us. Don't give up. The label is important. A few tricks and a little know-how will put you in control.

Federal laws make the label a legal document. Certain information must be located on the front panel, and a minimum print size is stipulated. *It's against the law for any pesticide to be labeled as "safe", and statements about hazard must be included.* **Signal words** based on toxicity data give a cue to product hazard.

- **Danger-Poison—Toxicity Class I** —if skull & crossbones = acutely toxic. Danger (without skull & crossbones) = a potent skin or eye irritant
- **Warning—Toxicity Class II** — moderately toxic
- **Caution—Toxicity Classes III or IV** slightly toxic (class III) to relatively non toxic (class IV)

Each **active ingredient** has several names. The label must include the **chemical name** and the **common name** for each of them, and a trade name for the product. For example, Isopropyl (E,E)-11-methoxy-3,7,11-tri-methyl-2,4-dodo-cadienoate is the chemical name for the insect growth regulator with the common name *methoprene*. The trade names Altosid, Kabat, Pharorid, Precor, Minex, Diacon, Dianex and Apex denote products containing formulations of this *active ingredient.*

Common names of insecticide active ingredients are selected by the Entomological Society of America, herbicides by the Weed Science Society of America, and fungicides by the American Phytopathological Society. Common names avoid confusion from the use of multiple trade names. *Common names are easier to remember the active ingredients in each product.*

Sometimes the same trade mark is used on an entire pesticide line. Ortho, Black Flag, Zodiac & VetKem, Dexol, Safer, and Chacon are examples. Occasionally the trade name of the active ingredient—Enide, Dipel, Thuricide—or the main use—Flea Stop—carry the message. The trademark name on the front section of each label is usually followed by a short phrase which describes the major purpose of the product.

[1] J. Econ. Entomol. 86:1781-1785, 1994. [2] Health 8(3):11, 1994.

FLEA STOP®
Zone Control™ for pets
DIP for dogs, cats,
puppies and kittens
Citrus sent formula

BLACK FLAG®
HOUSE & GARDEN INSECT KILLER
KILLS BUGS FAST
FAST KNOCKDOWN
KILLS FLEAS
FAST KILL

The chemical names of active ingredients must be on the front panel. The common names must appear on the label, but sometimes they're not found in the ingredient statement. If you don't find a common name there, look for it in the front panel near the main trademark name (e.g. contains methoprene). Common names are in normal print, chemical name are in parenthesis. They are followed by the percent volume of this ingredient. *Focus on common names.*

As you become familiar with common names, you'll be able to compare ingredient lists and select the least toxic or least persistent products. Articles and news reports which mention pesticides often use common names. If a trade name is used, look in our tables to find the common name.

FLEA STOP	
d-Limonene	78.2 %

FLEA STOP's only active ingredient is d-Limonene

HOUSE & GARDEN INSECT KILLER

Resmethrin (5-(phenylmethyl) -3-furany 2,2-dimethyl-3- (2-methyl-1-propenyl) cyclopropanea-caroxylate)	0.10%
Related compounds	0.01%
d-trans allethrin (allyl homolog of Cinerin I)	0.20%
Related compounds	0.015%
Piperonal butoxide technical [equivalent to 0.64% or (butylcarbityl)(6-propyl-piperonyl) ether & 0.16% related compounds]	0.80%
Aromatic petroleum solvent	1.133%

HOUSE & GARDEN INSECT KILLER contains two synthetic pyrethroids—resmethrin and d-trans allethrin—with "related compounds"—and a synergist,[1] piperonyl butoxide, all dissolved in aromatic petroleum solvents (no scientific name here).

Organic solvents such as xylene or petroleum distillates should be considered 'active ingredients' because our lungs are sensitive to the fumes from these materials, and their accidental swallowing can lead to a chemical pneumonia. In addition, some solvents are toxic—a few are even suspected of causing cancer. Some can even dissolve the gloves you use to protect your hands. It's prudent to choose pesticides with less than 5% organic solvent content.

Usually the major portion of the pesticide product is composed of **'inert ingredients.'** Inerts can include soap-like spreader-stickers which help the compound adhere to waxy leaves, or a mineral dust to adsorb an 'active' which will not dissolve in water. Many liquid formulations contain toxic preservatives such as formaldehyde.

The manufacturer's name, the net weight, and EPA registration and establishment numbers must appear on the front panel. It's illegal to market a pest control chemical which does not show this information.

Label Limitations—Pesticide labels tell nothing about the possibility that the product can cause cancer, birth defects, hormonal changes, or genetic mutations. Information about persistence is not included either. Data about persistence and these adverse effects is now required for registration. Older pesticides with "data gaps"must be re-registered or banned in the next few years. Because of acute risk it is unusual for a Category I 'active' to be registered for home use, but exceptions occur. Many rodenticides are Category I, for example, so keep your eyes open. All things being equal it is best to choose products with the signal word CAUTION, but check the concentration of the 'active ingredients', and find out about persistence. It's best to use materials which degrade to harmless compounds within days. Common names help you locate this kind of information.

Let's see how this might work in our examples. The signal word WARNING on the FLEA STOP bottle ordinarily should give us pause. We note, however, that 78.2% of its contents are composed of the active ingredient, d-Limonene, rather than the less than 5% which is a typical concentration for an 'active'. FLEA STOP is a *concentrate*, designed to be diluted at the rate of 1.5 to 5 tablespoons pesticide per gallon of water—a dilution which obviously reduces the risk. Just as obviously, care should be exercised during the dilution phase. You should wear protective clothing, gloves, and eye protection.

HOUSE & GARDEN INSECT KILLER features the signal word, CAUTION a sign of minimal hazard. We have little information about the toxicity of the active ingredients, however, which constitute only 3.39% of a product which is *used without further dilution.*

[1] Synergist = A substance which increases the effectiveness of the active ingredient

We remember, however, that aerosols such as this, are dangerous if inhaled. *The concentration differences we found in these products, highlight the importance of following dilution directions carefully.* Occasionally individuals have applied concentrated materials without dilution—with tragic results. Failure to dilute as directed is not only dangerous to you and other non-target animals, but may injure plants. Be aware that all labels include disclaimers: 'Buyer assumes all responsibility for safety and use not according to directions.' Or, 'It is a violation of Federal Law to use this product in a manner inconsistent with its labeling.' Here are other precautionary statements found on the labels of our examples:

Flea Stop

HAZARDOUS TO HUMANS AND DOMESTIC ANIMALS

WARNING: May cause eye injury Do not get in eyes or on clothing. Wear eye protection when mixing concentrate with water. Harmful if swallowed. Wash thoroughly with soap and water after handling. Use with caution on nursing animals. Do not use on puppies or kittens under 6 weeks of age. Some individuals may be sensitive to this product. If irritation develops, discontinue use.

House & Garden Insect Killer

CAUTION—Cover or remove exposed food before spraying. Remove pets, fish bowls and bird cages from rooms being sprayed. Press button firmly to spray.

WARNING—Contents under pressure. Do not store or use near heat or open flame. Do not puncture or incinerate container. Exposure to sunlight or temperatures above 120°F may cause bursting. Avoid freezing.

Most labels include information about anecdotes. Should a pesticide accident occur, consult the label first, even before you call the doctor so you can supply information about ingredients and treatment recommendations.

Use your own judgement

Sometimes directions seem to promote unnecessary hazard. House and Garden Insect Killer states: "To clear a room, close doors and windows: spray upward until room is filled with mist (6 to 8 seconds). Do not remain in treated areas. Keep room closed then let air circulate before reentering. Sweep up fallen insects." If you follow these suggestions you'll receive significant respiratory exposure and contaminate all objects in the room with pesticide. *Use common sense. Apply the minimum amount of pesticide which will solve the problem—spot treat if possible.* If you can think of a safer, more selective control method, use it.

Pesticides readily penetrate unbroken skin

Those happy sprayers in the ads wearing shorts and sandals, are taking unnecessary risks. Researchers have recently reported six times greater risk for non-Hodgkin's lymphomas—a cancer—among farmers who applied phenoxy herbicides, especially 2,4-D, more than 20 times a year.[1] (Risk for this cancer for farmers is about 3 times that for non-farmers). Dogs, too, have increased risk of cancers of the lymph system in situations where this herbicide is used. Yet 2,4-D—an organochlorine—has only moderate acute toxicity.

Pesticide exposure is effected by clothing. When gauze pads were placed at key areas on the body under several different clothing regimes, dusts caused the greatest exposure, and wettable powders diluted with water, the least. Not surprisingly, the amount of exposure decreases as the coverage of clothing increases. The dermal acute lethal dose of carbaryl is 4000 mg/kg, the maximum exposure during a 15 minute spray test was only 10 mg. Obviously the exposure would be multiplied if spraying continued? Even this tiny exposure may not be appropriate, since carbaryl is an estrogen mimic. Nevertheless, the small exposure found indicates the safety advantage of pesticides with a large dermal LD_{50}, since it takes a lot of these to cause harm. Minimize all exposure by wearing **protective clothing.**

To some extent all clothing is protective, but clothing made of woven cloth does not necessarily provide adequate protection. If you use only low toxic pesticides, you obviously reduce risk, but *barriers are still appropriate.* Leather or fabric gloves and shoes readily absorb chemicals. T-shirts, and nylon, acrylic, and polyester fabrics wick liquids directly to the skin. A soil-repellent finish applied to 100 percent cotton or 50/50 or 65/35 polyester-cotton work clothing makes them protective. Long pants and sleeves, rubber boots and rubber gloves make up a prudent sprayer's wardrobe. Always shower after pesticide use, and wash clothing separately.

Learn to measure

In a study of home garden spraying, *most volunteers did not measure very well.* When they tried to measure one tablespoon of a liquid, the actual volume ranged from 4 to 15 grams, when the actual measurement should have been 15 grams. Similar errors were made with a wettable powder, except that some added more than twice, and others less than half of the proper dose. The applications of a dust were even more variable, the amount applied to beans ranged from 23 to 680 grams, with some making the leaves white, and others applying a thin film.

---

[1] J. Nat'l Cancer Inst. 78, 1986, Cancer Res. 52: :2447-2455, 1992

In the U.S. we use the avoirdupois system of measure. Learn the conversion factors for avoirdupois measures. You'll need a spoon set— one tablespoon to 1/4 teaspoon—cup, pint, quart, and gallon containers dedicated to pesticide use. *Fill just to the top—no more no less.* Use a straight edge to level powdery ingredients. When full, liquids will curve up a little above the top. Always wear rubber household gloves and eye protection when measuring pesticides.

Measurement equivalents

3 teaspoons	= 1 tablespoon	= 1/2 fluid ounce
16 tablespoons	= 1 cup	= 8 fluid ounces
2 cups	= 1 pint	=16 fluid ounces
4 cups	= 1 quart	= 32 fluid ounces
4 quarts	= 1 gallon	= 8 pounds (water)

Pesticide formulations

The substances in pesticides which cause the desired effects, the **active ingredients**, are never sold as pure compounds. They are '**formulated**' by being combined with 50% or more **carriers** or **inerts**—water, organic solvents, preservatives, or powders. The user usually dilutes the pesticide product even more by mixing it with water. A typical diluted spray or dust may contain only a fraction of 1% of the active ingredient (**AI**). In theory, inerts have no effect on either pests or the environment. Unfortunately, they may be neither safe nor inert. The EPA is only now investigating the effects of such common 'inerts' as organic solvents and formaldehyde which have obvious potential for harm.

The herbicide Roundup® is formulated as an solution containing 41% of the glyphosate active ingredient dissolved in 59% 'inerts'. Before use to eliminate weedy bermuda grass, it is further diluted 98% with water to yield final spray containing 0.42% of the active ingredient. Safer® Insecticidal Soap Concentrate is formulated with 49% potassium salts of fatty acid active ingredients and 51% 'inerts'. Before use 5 tablespoons of this emulsion are added to each gallon of neutral—pH 6-7—water for a final dilution of 99.18% inert ingredients in the spray

Safe pesticide use

Mixing and diluting a pesticide presents potential risks. Unless the mixer wears protective clothing, inevitable tiny spills cause exposure to the undiluted technical material. More than 75% of the pesticides we use are applied as sprays—usually water emulsions of **emulsible concentrates (EC)**. In these, concentrated solutions of technical grade active ingredients are dissolved in organic solvents with enough detergent-like emulsifier to disperse the the oily solution in water, giving it a milky appearance. Most ECs have a shelf life of about three years.

Wettable powders (WP) contain concentrated technical active ingredients mixed with talc or clay. After dilution with water, most WPs readily sink to the bottom of spray tanks unless they are continuously agitated. If not filtered before use, some readily clog spray equipment. A very few powdery formulations contain **water-soluble powders (SP)**. These and the similar **flowable** formulations (**FL**) form true solutions in water—thus do not sink to the bottom.

You must adhere to the pesticide label—but failure to use the proper dilution is dangerous to you, and other organisms, including plants. You cannot legally use a pesticide unless the target pest, its location, or a particular plant is included on the label. For example, if the label states only, "For use on ornamentals," you cannot use this product on a food crop.

Use good sense— The EPA allows you to use a *lower concentration* of a pesticide if you have knowledge that less will do the trick in your situation. Similarly, you need not treat the entire garden or the entire room *even if the label allows you to do so.* • *Apply the minimum amount which will solve the problem.* • *Spot treat if possible.* • *Choose the least toxic active ingredients available, and the least toxic formulations.*

When compounds of the same LD50 are compared, WPs are generally less toxic to the applicator than ECs, and liquid sprays are safer than dusts. Synthetic organic pesticides are not necessarily more harmful than those of natural origin. Such factors as persistence, toxicity, presence of chlorine, and selectivity should influence your choices. • Avoid broad-spectrum, persistent products, and Class A or B carcinogens and teratogens. • Avoid highly chlorinated structures which tend to be persistent estrogen mimics. Unfortunately, *not everything has been tested for chronic effects.*

• Never apply pesticides on windy days. Large droplets are less likely to drift or be breathed into the lungs.
• *Keep children and pets away at least until residues dry or stricter labels precautions have been met.* After accidental spills of hazardous chemicals, children and pets are affected first. Small animals have high surface to volume ratio, and they're more likely to crawl through vegetation or lay on the ground where residues are concentrated.

Household hazards ?

There is good evidence[1] that household use of persistent pesticides can cause harm. Brain cancer and acute lymphocyte leukemia in children are

[1] J. Natl Cancer Instit. 79:39-46, 1987. Arch. Environ. Contam. Toxicol. 24: 87-92, 1993.

linked to dermal or respiratory exposure to **chlordane** (for ants and termites), **lindane** (gama BHC)—still registered as Kwell® for head lice—**diazinon**, **carbaryl**, and **dichlorvos** (in flea collars and pest strips).

In a household where **chlorpyrifos** was applied repeatedly to control roaches, caged birds died.[1] The persistent chlorpyrifos, an organophosphate insecticide with a high chlorine content, evaporates readily so that all household members are exposed after it is applied indoors. This is one of the most common compounds currently favored by pest control companies for routine 'pest control'. Better a few insects than continuous respiratory exposure to such a questionable product. In addition, soil applications of any pesticide potentially leach into water.

Will I ever use pesticides?

You may believe that you will never use a pesticide. A 1992 EPA survey of 2000 households in 29 states found that 85% of these homeowners were storing at least one pesticide, and most had between one and five. *About 75% of these households stored these products in unlocked cupboards within easy reach of children.* Half of the families with small children, stored pesticides within four feet of the ground where they were easily available to children.

Even though we believe that a primary pesticide risk is dermal and respiratory exposure during and after application, it's obvious that consuming a concentrated pesticide, can be hazardous. Even though monitoring of pesticide-related accidents is completely inadequate in this country,[2] in 1992 an ongoing annual national survey of hospitals, found 58% of pesticide-related cases in emergency rooms involved children under the age of five.[2] Even though you do not have children, all pesticides—and other toxic household products such as bleaches—should be stored only in high cupboards. According to the EPA *about 13% of poisoning incidents among children take place outside the child's own home.* Take seriously the admonition on all pesticides,

"Keep out of the reach of children".

In summary

- **Be sure you need a pesticide**
- **Use only selective materials with low toxicity**
- **Avoid persistent compounds**
- **Read directions carefully**
- **Wear protective clothing**
- **Use precise dilutions**
- **Treat the target only**
- **Avoid drift**
- **Keep pesticides away from children**

How 'Circle of Poison' Affects Food Supply

Though much effort is made to assure that our diets contain minimal pesticide residues, the so-called "Circle of Poison" phenomenon is a potential problem.

A 1993 report to the U.S. Senate from the General Accounting Office (GAO) identified 27 unregistered food-use pesticides that were manufactured here for export. Nineteen of these were never registered for food use, including 6 that the Food & Drug Administration(FDA) *did not know existed.* The Food-use registration for the other 8 had been canceled. In 1989-1991 the FDA tested our food supply for 14 of these pesticides and found 4 illegal pesticides. One, monocrotophos, (an organophosphate) (OP) was responsible for ≈3/4 of the violations since it was used on vegetables in Mexico. The FDA did not test for the remaining 13 low toxicity pesticides, because they were not believed a risk.

Of the 4 illegal pesticides found, 3 were OPs and one, heptachlor, an organochlorine (OC), moves in the food chain, has been found in human milk, is a known cancer-causing substance.

The manufacture of this and other OC for export is not regulated in the United States, even though these illegal substances threaten world food supplies and the environment. To order GAO/ RCED-94-1, GAO, PO Box 6015, Githersburg, MD 20884-0615, 202-512-6000, fax 301-258-4066

[1] Proc. Assn. Avian Vet. 1990:112-114. [2] GAO/PMED-94-6 (address in box).

Classification of Garden Pesticides

Organic pesticides

Organic pesticides— compounds containing carbon—are the most common active ingredients in pest control substances.

Insecticides

Insecticides attract, repel, interfere with development, or kill insects. They are classified chemically and by mode of action.

Botanical & fungal insecticides contain active ingredients which are obtained from living organisms. Most have nervous system, muscular, genetic, or respiratory activity which is similar to that of synthetic organic pesticides. Most degrade readily in the environment, but many have not been adequately tested for long term adverse effects.

Abamectin is derived from the fungus *Streptomyces avermitilis.* Some other compounds from this fungus are active against parasitic worms. *Abamectin causes muscular paralysis by stimulating release of GABA, an inhibitory neruotransmitter.* Products containing abamectin include Avid* registered to control **mites** and **insects** and Affirm* which controls **fire ants.**

Several insecticides are derived from the **neem tree,** *Azadirachta indica.* The most common active ingredient, **azadirachtin**, is an *insect feeding deterrent, sterilant, and growth regulator.* Margosan-O*, Bioneem*, and Azatin*, are registered for use on ornamental plants to **control leafminers, caterpillars, or bugs.** Neem oil also inhibits **some plant diseases.** *These products have very low acute toxicity and produce no long term adverse effects on mammals. They are non-toxic to most beneficial insects because they are not exposed in the juvenile stages.*

Nicotine sulphate is a very toxic tobacco extract with broad-spectrum activity, which belongs to the group of plant-derived *bioactive chemicals* **—alkaloids.** Other well known alkaloids are caffeine, quinine, morphine, cocaine, strychnine, and LSD. Nicotine mimics acetylcholine at the neuromuscular junction. High doses cause twitching, convulsions, and death.

Pyrethrins *are extracts of the flowers of chrysanthemum. They disrupt normal nerve functions.* They are often incorporated in space sprays to *control flying insects.* In this use they are usually combined with **piperonyl butoxide**, a plant-based synergist which inhibits the action of *mixed function oxidases*—enzymes which rapidly degrade pyrethrins. This synergist helps prolong pyrethrins activity, preventing insect recovery after initial knockdown.

Pyrethrins are effective at low doses, have low mammalian toxicity, simple structures, and *broad-spectrum activity.* Because of these favorable characteristics, **pyrethroids—**pyrethrin analogues with similar structure and activity—have been synthesized. The earliest pyrethroids—**tetramethrin, resmethrin, bioresmethrin,** and **phenothrin**—are more effective than the natural pyrethrins, but rapidly degrade in sunshine.

Several more stable pyrethroids with moderate acute mammalian toxicity, **cypermethrin** (Cymbush*), **fluvalinate** (Mavrik*), **bifenthrin** (Talsar*), **permethrin** (Pramex*), **tetramethrin**, etc. are registered for ornamentals and/or food crops. In general, their persistence is increased by the addition of chlorines on the molecules. The most selective of these, fluvalinate, has low toxicity to honeybees, and its significant mite activity prevents the secondary pest upsets triggered by other pyrethroids. *Because of their tendency to irritate skin, no pyrethroid should be used without protective clothing.* In general, insect populations which are resistant to organochlorines, are also resistant to pyrethroids.

Rotenone is an extract of *Derris* and *Cubé* roots—plants in the bean family. It is often recommended for **beetle** control, though it kills a wide variety of insects. *Rotenone inhibits respiratory pathways, and is unusually toxic to fish.* It persists on foliage for several days, and has caused tumors in rats, but not in mice.

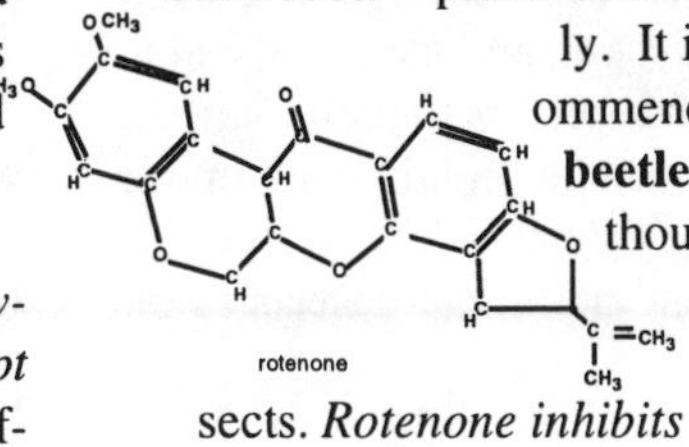

rotenone

Ryania, from *Ryania speciosa* is registered to control **codling moth** and **corn borer**. It has low contact activity on natural enemies because it is a food poison. This complex chemical, which has not been synthesized structurally, is known to interfere with muscle contractions.

Sabadilla is a mixture of alkaloids derived from the seeds of *Schoenocaulon officinalis.* It is not very toxic to mammals, but is a skin irritant. It's useful activity on **thrips, bugs** and **beetles**, must be balanced by its hazard to honey bees

Pheromones are specific insect signal odors. A variety of female insect *sex pheromones* (attractants) are available for placement in traps. These are marketed as Pherocon* and Biolure* to trap males and monitor population size and timing of the life cycle of over 70 insect species.

Sometimes insect pheromones are formulated to confuse males and disrupt the insect mating process. These confusion formulations are not effective

* Trade names

in home gardens because they work best in larger plots. For more information, see pheromones.

Synthetic organic Insecticides

Insect Growth Regulators

(**IGR**) alter growth or development of insects by mimicking or inhibiting their hormones or enzymes. They are effective in ultra-low concentrations. They do not directly kill insects, but effect them at a later stage of their development. JHA are *very selective* and essentially non-toxic to birds and mammals, but the persistent cuticle inhibitors among them may interfere with crustaceans in the water and non-target insects in the soil.

After treatment with **juvenile hormone analogues (JHA)**, *larval insects stop development at the pupal stage, or become sterile adults*. JHAs control by being present at a time when larval insects cannot tolerate their natural juvenile hormones. JHAs are short-lived in sunlight, but late day applications on ornamentals allow outdoor use of the very effective **kinoprene** (Enstar*) for whitefly, scale, or mealybug control. **Methoprene** is registered under several trade names

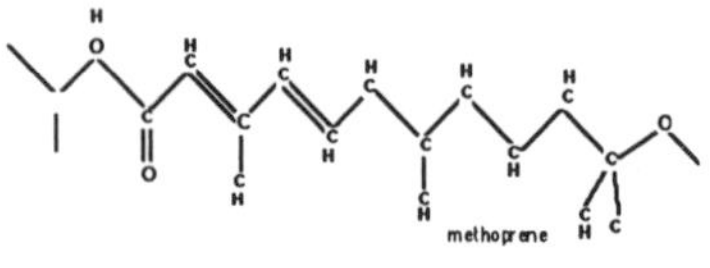

methoprene

for mosquito, flea, or whitefly control **Hydroprene** (Gencor*) sterilizes cockroaches. **Fenoxycarb**, a carbamate JHA with low toxicity, is formulated as Insegar* for control of caterpillars, psyllids, and scales on fruits and ornamentals.

Cuticle inhibitors (**CI**) are IGRs which interfere with chitin synthesis—insect cuticle contains chitin and protein. *CI-treated larvae die at the next molt because their newly-synthesized cuticle is weak.* CIs also affect predatory arthropods, especially in water and soil. **Diflubenzuron** (Dimilin*) is registered for forest use against gypsy, Nantucket tip and Douglas fir tussock moths. It is persistent on foliage, and is readily taken up by soil arthropods. **Cyromazine**—Trigard*, a restricted use insecticide, is used for leafminer control in vegetables and ornamentals. Larvadex* incorporated in the food, controls fly development in poultry droppings. **Flufenoxuron** (Cascade*) is registered for control of mites and insects. **Chlorflurazuron** (Atabron*), **teflubenzuron** (Nomolt*), and **triflumuron** (Alsystin*) effect caterpillars and the latter two control weevils and mosquitoes as well.

In **organochlorines** (OC) or chlorinated hydrocarbons—carbon, hydrogen, and chlorine are bound to one or more phenyl rings. *Several OCs upset salt balance inside nerves, causing tremors, convulsions, and death.* OCs are insoluble in water but soluble in fats. Certain OCs magnify in food chains because they are stable and concentrate in body fat. The half life[1] of DDE—a toxic metabolite of DDT—is about 60 years.

The most notorious—**DDT**, **dieldren**, **aldren**, **declorane** (**Mirex***), **chlor-decone** (**Kepone***), and **chlordane** are banned because of their potential to cause cancer or birth defects, but residues of one or more of these substances are still found in body fat of virtually all animals on earth. Unfortunately, many of these are still being applied in the third world. Residues of these OCs as well as residues of the agricultural OC, **endosulphan,** and other pesticides and industrial chemicals with estrogen-like activity are linked to human breast cancer and disruption of reproductive activity of humans and other animals. (see Endochrine Disrupters) On average, residues of these OCs are significantly higher in women with breast cancer, than in similar women without cancer.[2]

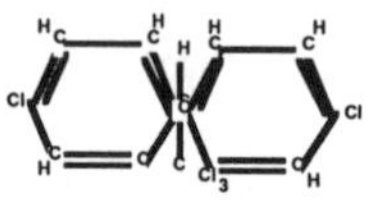

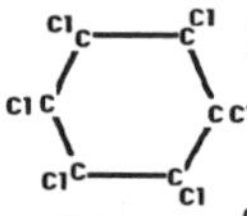

DDT structure

The OC **lindane** (gama BHC), sometimes prescribed to treat head lice—though less effective and more hazardous than pyrethrins for this use—is also linked to breast cancer[2] and endocrine disruption. Because of its persistence and high vapor pressure, lindane is also registered to control wood-boring insects and treat seeds. *Gama BHC is believed to block GABA transmission in the central nervous system.* OCs affect many kinds of insects, so have *broad spectrum activity*. **methoxychlor** is the last OC insecticide available for home use, and **dienochlor** (Pentac*) the last mitecide.

lindane

Organophosphates (OP)—

are derivatives of phosphoric acid. Many OPs are extremely toxic to mammals and other vertebrates, but readily degrade in the environment unless they are chlorinated. *OP are broad-spectrum acetylcholinesterase (AChE) inhibitors. (AChE is an essential enzyme at nerve junctions).* Such OPs as **methyl** and **ethyl parathion**, **dichlorvos**, and **dimethoate** have been restricted or banned by the EPA because of acute toxicity and chronic effects. OP poisoning can result from inhalation, dermal exposure, or consumption in foods. *Even worse, AChE inhibition caused by OPs accumulates during chronic exposure, so that farm workers can die after multiple small exposures as this essential enzyme is depleted.*

OPs available for home use are relatively non-toxic, but **malathion** and **acephate** (Orthene*) are not recommended for IPM because *their broad-spectrum activity triggers secondary pest upsets.* Malathion rapidly degrades in the environment. Acephate is a moderately persistent systemic compound—it moves into plants to kill sucking insects. The EPA has banned **diazinon**

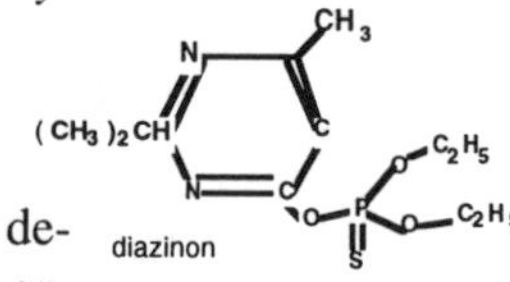

diazinon

[1] Length of time for half of compound to degrade [2] J. Nat. Cancer Ins. 85:649-652, 1993

granules from golf courses and sod farms because of its propensity to kill ground-feeding birds. Diazinon has been found in ground water, birdbaths, rivers, streams—even fog. It presents neurotoxic and ocular risks. In spite of its moderate toxicity, it is the source of a large number of home poisonings, perhaps because it is so widely used. There is some evidence that it is a teratogen. Two other commonly applied turf products, **isofenphos** and **trichlorfon** are acutely toxic insecticides. Both have been detected in ground water, and obviously neither is a suitable choice if you're looking for a safe environment.

Chlorpyrifos (Dursban*) a chlorinated OP has replaced chlordane as a major termitecide. Because of significant persistence, both Dursban and its toxic metabolite, TCP, can be detected in the air of treated homes and yards, so *the occupants of these homes are chronically exposed to low levels of these toxins.* The EPA is investigating possible risks of acute toxicity to children from its residues. There are less toxic methods available for most of its uses. **Phosmet** (Imidan*) is useful in control of certain beetles and moths on fruit trees and ornamentals. It persists on foliage for a week or two without causing secondary pest upsets. It is rated as a Class C (possible) human carcinogen.

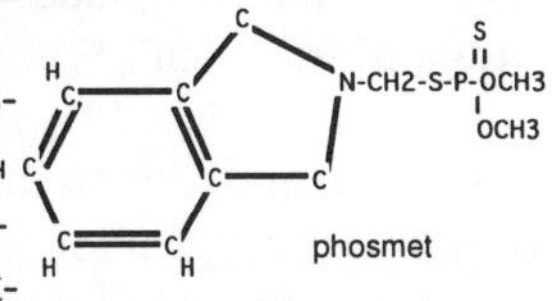

phosmet

Carbamates (CB)—from carbamic acid—also have anti-AChE activity. *Though most CBs are extremely toxic to mammals, their chronic toxicity is less than that of the OPs, because their antiAChE activity is reversible.* **Carbaryl** (Sevin*) is the CB least toxic to mammals, but it is rather persistent, and is known to be an endocrine disrupter. It also is *extremely hazardous to beneficial hymenopterans* (miniwasp parasitoids, large wasps, and bees). After carbaryl kills these natural enemies, populations of spider mite secondary pests increase. In baits, carbaryl is useful for earwig or sowbug control, but these baits should be carefully and selectively applied, because ground beetles and other important predators may also be attracted and killed.

carbaryl

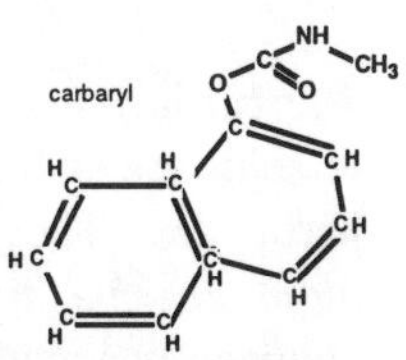

Other organic insecticides

Hydramethylnon (Amdro*) is a unique stomach poison available in selective baits for cockroach and fire ant control.

Surfactants—are oils or soaps *which interfere with arthropod respiration and membrane function.* Their low toxicity to parasites and predators is related to lack of contact activity after residues dry. They include **narrow range oils** (Sunspray*, Volck Supreme*) which also have limited repellent action against sucking insects, and deter them from penetrating leaf surfaces. **Insecticidal soaps (IS)**—potassium salts of fatty acids—provide *selective insect and disease control* without vertebrate toxicity. Dilute IS solutions interfere with the water management of soft insects such as aphids, spider mites, mealybugs, and whiteflies. At higher concentrations they kill insects which have thicker cuticles like fleas and earwigs. Sulphur increases IS fungicidal activity.

Microbial insecticides

Most insect bacterial, viral, and fungal diseases are unique to insects, and are harmless to mammals. (Some fungal diseases are mammalian irritants or allergens, and currently no fungus is registered for insect control)

Bacterial insecticides—The first isolates of the important insect bacterial disease, ***Bacillus thuringiensis* (Bt)**, produced a ß-exotoxin which affected mammals. *All current products containing Bt are guaranteed free of this exotoxin.* Each Bt product contains an endotoxin which selectively binds to the stomach wall of the target insect. There are several commercial strains of Bt. ***Bt. kurstoki*** (Javelin*, Thuricide*, Dipel*, Caterpillar Attack*, etc.) *controls caterpillars.* ***B.t. isreaelensis*** (Teknar*, Mosquito Attack*) *affects mosquito and black fly larvae.* ***B.t. san diego*** (M-Cap*) and ***B.t. tenebrionis*** (Trident*) are registered for *Colorado potato and elm leaf beetle control.* Bts have a half-life of about 2-3 days outdoors.

B. popilliae (Doom*)— Milky Spore Disease—is purported to provide permanent control of *Scarab beetle larvae* which live on the roots of grasses. Several recent tests suggest that the marketed products may be minimally effective. In any case this disease takes several years to provide useful control.

Protozoan insecticides— The protozoan ***Nosema locustae*** (Noloc*, Grasshopper Attack*) is marketed in spore form for control of *grasshoppers and Mormon crickets.*

Viral insecticides— ***Heliothis* NPV** (nuclear polyhedral virus) is registered as Elcar* for *Heliothis sp. caterpillar control.* Sertan*, polyhedral inclusion bodies of ***Nucleopolyhedrosis sertifer*** virus are conditionally registered to control *European pine sawfly.* Decyde* the **NPV of the codling moth** is under experimental review for control of this apple pest. The **alfalfa looper NPV**, is registered as Gusano* for control of armyworms, *Heliothis sp.*, loopers, corn borer, and several other pest moths. All viral insecticides kill slowly, so egg-laying should be monitored and spray applied just before maximum hatch.

Entomopathogenic nematodes
Steinernema carpocapsae, S. feltiae, and ***Heterohabditis sp.*** —are minute worms which control *soil-living insects* such as beetle larvae. The nematodes penetrate insect prey and release a bacterium which kills the pests and provide food for the little nematodes. Efforts are under way to improved the searching efficacy of these safe and selective predators.

Inorganic insecticides—
contain no carbon.

The **heavy metal insecticides**—**lead**, **mercury**, and **tin**—are now banned because of toxicity, carcinogenicity, and biomagnification.

There are several useful **mineral insecticides. Cryolite** (Kryocide*), sodium fluoaluminate, is a *stomach poison* which affects **beetles** and **caterpillars** is replacing more toxic materials for some agricultural applications.

Sulphur—in a wettable formulation—safely controls mites and such **soft-bodied insects** as aphids, scales, and thrips. Sulphur is also active on leafhoppers, asparagus and **flea beetles**, and some bugs, as well as several **foliar diseases.** Its mode of action is unknown.

Diatomaceous earth (DE)—shells of fossil diatoms—high purity amorphous silica of uniform small particle size—are registered for insect control, and included as 'inactive' diluents in pesticidal dusts. *DE absorbs cuticular oils and waxes leading to dehydration and death of insects and other invertebrates.*

The most effective insecticidal DEs (e.g. Diafil*, PermaGuard*, Organic Plus*) are composed of *fresh water diatoms* with excellent oil absorptive qualities. They are non-toxic to mammals that ingest them. They are useful to control **stored grain insects**. For **household insect control**—cockroaches, ants, fleas, etc.—the repellency of pure DE is best overcome by adding a food attractant (Shellshock*). Although DE is widely used in agriculture, *it cannot be recommended for garden insect control because its absorptive qualities are more effective against parasitoids than against larger plant-eating pests.* (Crystalline salt water diatoms are available for water filtration (Celite*). Careful! *Breathing dust of this crystalline material can cause silicosis lung disease).*

Non-toxic pulverized **amorphous silica** or **silica gel** (SG) available in Dri-Die 68* dehydrates cockroaches, ants, silverfish, drywood termites, and fleas by *absorbing water-protective oil from the cuticle*—the thinner the oily layer, the more rapid the kill. Because SG tends to readily float in the air, it is often combined with ammonium flosilicate (**DriDie 67***). This product is moderately toxic, but its static electric charge causes the dust to adsorb to surfaces and insects. *It is more effective against drywood termites than chlordane*, and it continues to work well even in areas with high humidity. This DriDie 67* also repels insects, so is best used as a desiccant in attics and wall voids to prevent termite invasion.

SG *helps protect pyrethrins from decomposition*. Products containing SG plus pyrethrins (Dione*, Perma-Guard*) retain activity for months when applied in wall voids to control **household insects**. Liquid formulation (Revenge*, Pursus*) are useful as repellants. **Boric acid** (Roach Pruf*, Perma Proof*) applied in a similar manner, gives *long lasting non-repellent control of cockroaches.* Roaches ingest this stomach poison as they groom themselves.

Applicators using dusts should always wear a mask

Herbicides

Herbicides are designed to penetrate a plant's surface layer—usually a waxy cuticle to control plant growth. As wax increases penetration declines, and control becomes more difficult. Herbicides are the most commonly used pesticides because they are so useful in controlling difficult weeds without much work.

They reduce the erosion triggered by cultivation, but *may pollute the soil, stunt growth of desired plants, or move into the water table.* Mulches, on the other hand, can reduce herbicide use while enriching the soil.

Herbicides are classified as either **post-emergent**—applied to foliage of growing plants—or **pre-emergent**—applied to the soil to prevent seeds from sprouting. **Systemic** herbicides move in plant's conducting system.

Inorganic Herbicides— composed of inorganic substances such as **lead**, **arsenic**, **borax**, **salt**, and **copper** *have been banned for herbicide use because of persistence, toxicity, or carcinogenicity.*

Organic Herbicides—
contain carbon. Many plants secrete substances which prevent the growth of competing vegetation. Until recently none of these compounds were available for use as herbicides. Recently **maize corn gluten meal** (Amazing Lawn*), a byproduct of corn starch and corn syrup manufacture, was registered as a broad-spectrum pre-emergent herbicide. Its *mode of action is unknown*, but it eventually breaks down to provide nutrients for existing vegetation.

Another new herbicide, **glufosinate-ammonium** (Finale*), is a metabolic compound produced by a soil-inhabiting *Streptomyces* bacterium. Applied to growing vegetation, this product moves systematically to kill the plant within 4 days. *Glufosinate-ammonium inhibits activity of the plant enzyme glutamine synthetase, causing ammonia to accumulate in treated leaves and green stems.* It degrades rapidly in soil to non-toxic compounds.

Aliphatics—sodium salts of aliphatic acids are stable heavily chlorinated herbicides. They are believed *to alter plant enzyme structures, leading to changes in metabolism.* Several applications of **dalapon** will control perennial grasses.

Amides are pre-emergent herbicides which *inhibit sprouting of seeds* in established plantings. *They inhibit root elongation by interfering with RNA synthesis*. The corn herbicide, **alachlor** (Lasso*), leaches into soil water, and is rated a Class B carcinogen and an estrogen mimic. Moderately persistent, **diphenamid** (Enide*) and **naprophmide** (Devinol*), are used in ornamental borders. These amides must be incorporated into the soil via moisture or cultivation. Unfortunately they also move in water.

Benzoic acids are *pre-emergent compounds with auxin-like growth effects.* Their mechanism of action is unknown. **Dicamba** (Banvel*) is used for long term control of broadleaved weeds in turf. **DCPA** (Dachthal*) provides less persistent control of annual grasses—crab grass, fox tail—and some broadleaved plants in established plantings. Impurities in the manufacturing process are cause for concern. DCPA is highly chlorinated. These herbicides have been found in ground water.

Dinitroanilines—oryzalin (Surflan*) applied to soil provides 8 months *pre-emergent control* of sprouting weeds among permanent plantings. A less persistent product with similar activity, **trifluralin** (Treflan*) is restricted by the EPA. **Pendimethalin** (Prowl*) and oryzalin are sometimes applied to turf to inhibit sprouting weeds. All dinitroanilines have been detected in ground water, and several have been shown to affect the endocrine system.

Heterocyclic Nitrogens are persistent herbicides with pre-emergent activity. **Triazines** *block the CO_2 fixation step of photosynthesis, and may interfere with other plant metabolic processes*. **Simazine** (Princep*) and **atrazine**—an important corn herbicide—can damage non-target shrubs, and at high doses simizine prevents growth of new plants for several years. These chlorinated heterocyclic nitrogens *readily move* into the water supply. Atrazine causes mammary cancer in laboratory animals. The related **aminotriazole** (Amitrole*)—*inhibits a critical component of protein synthesis in plants.* It is active as a foliar spray, and decomposes rapidly in warm moist soils. It is often combined with simizine in a product called Amazine*. Triazines and triazones are rated as Class C carcinogens and estrogen mimics.

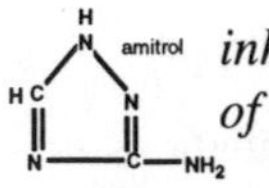

Organic Arsenicals— cacodylic acid (Phytsr*) **MSMA** (Ansar 170*) and **DSMA** (Ansar 8100*) are used for systemic *post-emergent control of annual grasses in turf* and stubborn perennial weeds, especially Johnsongrass and nut-sedges. *They inhibit plant growth by interfering with phosphorus metabolism.* They also kill beneficial insects, such as honey bees. *Repeated use of arsenic containing products will result in arsenic buildup in the soil.*

Petroleum oils—are surfactants used post-emergence to *knock down top growth via dehydration.* They do not effect roots of perennial weeds.

Phenoxys are systemic hormone-like herbicides which give post-emergent *control of broadleaved perennial weeds* in turf and unwanted shrubs and trees in coniferous forests. *They interfere with normal maturation of plant cells, producing tumorous tissues and excessive bud or root initials.* They have greater acute toxicity than most herbicides, and have been shown to disrupt the endocrine system of animals. All are highly chlorinated. The phenoxys **2,4,5-T** and **2,4,5-PT** (Silvex*)—a component of Agent Orange —are banned because of **2,3,7,8-TCDD** dioxin impurities and carcinogenicity. And **2,4-D**, though still available, may also cause human cancer .

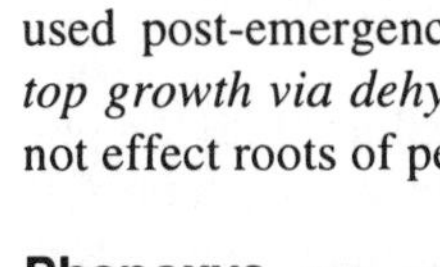

2,4-D

Substituted ureas *interfere with an energy step in photosynthesis.* They have persistent pre-emergent activity. **Diuron** (Karmex*) is the most persistent, **linuron** (Lorox*) less so. They are rapidly absorbed by the roots and translocated to the top of the plant. The EPA has rated linuron a Class C carcinogen.

Thiocarbamates are carbamic acid based compounds which contain sulphur. Some are active against plants, others insects. Most are restricted to agricultural use. The material involved in a serious California spill into the upper Sacramento River, **metham-sodium** (Metham*, Vapam*), though nominally a herbicide, is really a *non-selective biocide.* When this material contacts moisture, it decomposes, releasing toxic vapor which kills **fungi, bacteria, nematodes, insects, plants, and seeds**. It is used to fumigate seed beds before planting to kill existing plants, seeds, nematodes and soil fungi. In case you think this is a good idea, read the section on soil.

More organic herbicides and growth regulators

Fluazifop-butyl (Fusilade*) and **sethoxydim** (Poast*) *control annual and perennial grasses*—including Bermuda and Johnson grasses—in established plantings without harm to broadleaved plants. **Glyphosate** (Roundup*) also controls these grasses, but kills broad-leaved plants as well. It is very effective against difficult deep-rooted perennial grasses such as Bermuda. **Oxadiazon** (Ronstar*) is a *selective pre-emergent*, moderately-persistent herbicide registered for use on ornamentals and turf. It must be incorporated with moisture. Oxadiazon does not harm existing plantings. **Maleic hydroazine** (MH or Slo-Gro*) is a *growth regulator* which retards terminal growth and increased lateral growth in established plantings. It inhibits cell division at the shoot, but does not effect cell enlargement. **Potassium salts of fatty acid** products (soaps) marketed for insect control are produced to control annual weeds. These provide non-toxic, but also non-selective ways to control weed seedlings and knock down top growth.

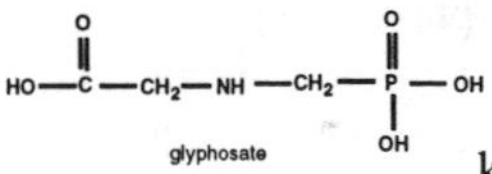

Molluscicides

Molluscicides are designed to kill mollusks—snails and slugs. Obviously compounds which kill problem mollusks also kill their relatives, many of which live in the water.

Certain snails and slugs are important garden pests which are resistant to toxic compounds which readily kill insects. **Metaldehyde** a complex aldehyde has *contact and stomach action against mollusks.* After eating the typical bran bait formulation, snails and slugs stop feeding and lose fluids. Fresh water **diatomaceous earth (DE)** products will also dehydrate snails and slugs *when puffed directly on them* or used as a barrier on dry soil. DEs are not active when applied to plants, where they also threaten beneficial insects on the foliage.

Fungicides & bactericides

Fungicides kill fungi which attack living plants, and fruits and vegetables after harvest. Some are **protective**—preventing the invasion of disease—others **cure** existing disease. Many effect only the tissues where they are applied, but others are **systemic**, moving throughout the plant. **Bactericides** have many of the same classifications as fungicides, but kill bacteria. In any case, if disease-resistant plants are available, fungicides and bactericides can be eliminated.

Inorganic fungicides— are mostly purely protective and residual.

Sulphur—the earliest fungicide was know by the Greeks. It controls powdery mildew, scab and brown rot of peaches or cherries by *interfering with an energy conversion step in cell metabolism.* Applied to soil, sulphur changes the pH toward the acid range. enabling control of *club root of crucifers.* A mixture of compost and sulphur helps reduce *potato scab.*

The flowable sulphur formulations or **soap-sulphur** products are more effective against diseases and less likely to burn foliage than common dusting sulphur. These mixtures do not harm predatory mites—are compatible in IPM control of powdery mildews or black spot. **Lime sulphur** is useful against *peach leaf curl and other diseases* in dormant sprays—but be careful, it is very irritating. **Bordeaux mixture** (copper sulfate plus limestone) is also active against peach leaf curl. *Sulphur injures some melon varieties and apricots. It should never be mixed with oil or used for 30 days after oil has been applied.* **Fixed copper compounds** such as cuprous oxide applied in early spring will control *brown rot* and other plant *bacterial diseases*—e.g. fire blight. *Residues of copper remain in the soil, so its use should be minimized as much as possible.*

A mixture of **sodium bicarbonate** (baking soda) **and oil** is effective against powdery mildews or black spot. Unlike most inorganic herbicides, it seems to have some curative powers. Registration is being pursued.

Mercury and **tin** fungicides have been banned due to either adverse toxicity or carcinogenicity.

Organic fungicides—are divided into **surface acting** and **translocating** materials, most of which move in the xylem from roots to shoots. Conversely, they can also be classified as **protectant**, **eradicant**, or **curative**.

Aromatic hydrocarbons — (AHC) *have diverse imodes of action.* All are heavily chlorinated old-style pesticide with data lacking on long term effects. At least one, **hexachlorobenzine**, is a known estrogen mimic. **Pentachloronitrobenzine (PCNB)** is used in the soil to prevent root rots, and as a seed protectant. The extremely toxic carcinogen **Pentachlorophenol (PCP)** is a wood preservative. **Chlorothalonil** (Bravo*, Daconil*), a protectant fungicide, is registered for use on a variety of vegetables and on turf.

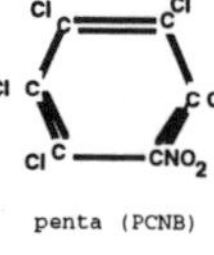
penta (PCNB)

When used before the fact, the chlorinated **dicarboximides (DCM)**, *prevent fruit and foliage diseases.* Residues of the DCM, **captan**, previously used in home gardens, readily wash away, but captan is now known to be carcinogenic and mutagenic. **Folpet** has been cancelled for similar reasons. Use of newer DCM fungicides, **iprodione** and **vinciozolin**, should be restricted to prevent resistance buildup. DCMs affect growth of *Botrytis cinerea* (grey mold) and *Sclerotinia* and *Alternaria* wilt and stem diseases. Careful sanitation helps prevent such diseases. DCM *fungicides interfere with protein and amino acid synthesis.*

A popular **dinitrophenol** fungicide **(DNP)** with mite-suppressing activity, **dinocap**, formerly used on powdery mildews, is now restricted by the EPA because it causes birth defects. *Dinitrophenols interfere with normal cell metabolism.*

EBDC (ethylene bidithiocarbamates) *protectant,* broad spectrum fungicides, were widely used on fruits, vegetables, nuts, ornamentals, and grains. When studies revealed that their major breakdown product, **ethylenethiourea** (ETU) causes thyroid and liver tumors, birth defects and mutations in rats, the EPA responded by restricting some uses and cancelling others. A market basket survey found that produce has low EBDC residues, because they wash off readily during cleanup. Those who apply EBDCs risk cancers and endocrine problems. Pregnant women should stay away! The EBDC fungicides include **mancozeb**, **maneb**, **nabam**, **tetiram**, and **zineb**. *They interfere with cell protein synthesis and metabolism.* When applied to the soil, manicozeb has been shown to significantly reduce earthworm numbers.

Benzimidazoles (BZZ) move into the host plant to inhibit infection, and travel to untreated areas with *long-term preventive or curative effects.* BZZ uptake through the roots is more efficient than foliar treatment, but soil applications are impractical because they degrade in soil. In addition, soil application could potentially cause adverse effects on non-target soil animals.

Although, BZZs interfere with fungal cell division, they cause few undesirable responses in plants; even boost cereal yields. However, many diseases are now resistant to these widely used broad-spectrum carbamate fungicides. The BZZ, **benomyl** (Benlate*), is registered for home use even though it is linked to severe birth defects in humans, and birth defects and lowered sperm production in test animals. *It persists in soil for up to 12 months, and its residues can't be washed off of foods.* It is known to be detrimental to earthworms, and to kill predatory mites and ladybird beetles, as well as several parasitoids including *Encarsia formosa*, the parasitoid which controls certain white-flies. *Recently, Benlate's manufacturer dropped its registration for ornamentals.*

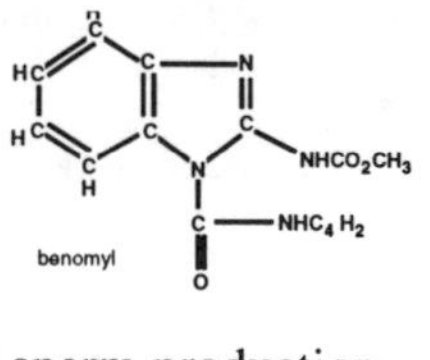

Carboxins (**carboxin** and **oxycarboxin**) move systemically upward in the plant to control *rusts and smuts* in cereal grains, vegetables, and ornamentals. They also stimulate plant growth. *Carboxin fungicides interfere with succinate oxidation in fungal (and mammalian) mitochondria*[1]*, and rap-idly degrade in the environment.*

Morpholines act systematically on *powdery mildews.* **Dodemorph** is used on fruits and ornamentals, and **tridemorph** on legumes, curcubits, and cereal grains. *Morpholine fungicides interfere with sterol biosynthesis* (**SI**) in fungi, some bacteria *(Bacillus subtillus, Streptococcus lacis, S. faecalis* and *Myucobvacrium phleii,* and green plants—though perhaps through different mechanisms.

Neem Seed Oil and **Neem Wax** (see insecticides) show activity on *black spot and powdery mildew.*

Triazoles—triforine (Funginex*), **triadimefon** (Bayleton*), and **mylcobutanil** (Systhane*, Nova*, Rally*) provide simultaneous protective and curative control of economically important diseases such as powdery, mildew, apple scab, brown rot, black spot, and cedar apple rust via systemic and vapor activity. *They inhibit ergosterole biosynthesis.* **Tebuconazole** (Folicur*) controls several diseases of fruits and cereals. Higher rates of triazoles must be used when disease pressure is high or cure is desired. They are weak against rot diseases, so must be combined with other fungicides when rots are anticipated.

Piperazines, pyridines, pyrimidines and **azoles** *inhibit sterol biosynthesis by a different mechanism.* Their curative power on existing diseases is a plus, but some interfere with the growth of broadleaved plants. Resistance has developed rapidly, perhaps because they must be applied frequently. Newer products are reported to be safer to broadleaved plants, but must be applied under dry conditions to be effective. **Fenarimol** (Rubigan*) is registered for use control of scab, rusts and powdery mildew of fruit trees and ornamentals.

Phenylmides (PNM) control oomycete fungi (*Phythium, Phytophthora,* downy mildews). **Metalaxyl** is the most active, versatile, and broadly used compound of this class. It has good persistence and systemic protective toxicity against these fungi. It controls soil-borne *Phythium* and *Phytophthor* downy mildews and potato late blights. Root and crown diseases of several fruits are controlled by **fosetyl-al.** **Furalaxyl** has a similar function on ornamentals. Fosetyl-al degrades on the host to phosphoric acid which is directly toxic to these fungi. The PNMs interfere with ribosomal RNA synthesis in this one group of fungi, allowing the antifungal defense reactions of the plant to operate. In most products metalaxyl is mixed with **hymexazol**, and fosetyl-al is combined with other fungicides. Such practices extend activity, at the expense of selectivity.

The **2-Aminopyrimidines (AP)** are structurally related to the insecticide diazinon. Several are active against *powdery mildews* in cereal grains, though sulphur and benomyl often show better activity. When applied within 8 hours after an infection triggering event—a warm rain—these fungicides interfere with enzymes which facilitate the ability of powdery mildew to penetrate leaves. **Bupirimate** (Nimrod* is useful in IPM programs because it is *protective against powdery mildews* on woody plants *without affecting predatory phytoseid mites or the fungae* which kill aphids. However, they should not be used on grains because other harmful fungi often increase after their use. They possibly inhibit certain cereal disease-resistant mechanisms.

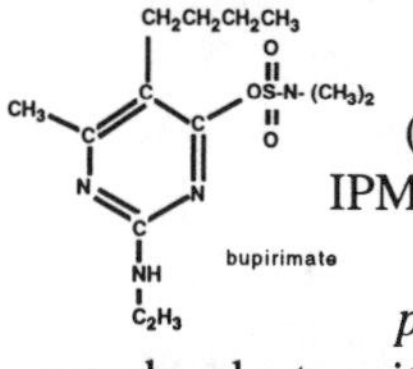

Fungal fungicides— contain harmless fungi which colonize plant sites preventing the infection from harmful fungi. The fungus ***Trichoderm sp*** (BinabT*) is registered to suppress both wound-infesting fungi and *Botrytis, Fusariium, Phthium, Rhizoctonia solani,* and *Scloetinia sp.* disease on fruits and vegetables. Several soil microbes can be added to prevent soil pathogens. ***Ampelomyces quisqualis*** (**AQ**^{10*}) a fungal parasite of powdery mildew fungus (a hyperparasite) is applied after an initial sulphur spray to grapes to prevent powdery mildew. **Bio-Save*** utilizes naturally occurring yeast and bacteria to prevent decay from *Penicillium expansum* (blue mold), *Botrytis cinerea* (grey mold) and *Mucor piriformis* (Mucor rot) after harvest of apples, pears, and citrus.

[1] mitochondria are cell organelles which control essential cellular respiration

CHARACTERISTICS OF URBAN PEST CONTROL AGENTS

Names: Common	Names: Trade	Uses	Benefits/Restrictions	Dermal LD50[1]
Attractants/Repellents/Traps				
DEET	Delphene, Off	"mosquito repellent" repels insects/ticks	Preferably use push-spray on clothing, not skin Avoid high concentrations—≤30% best	low
Eggs (spoiled)	Big game repellent	Sprinkle on moist foliage	Repels deer, elk	NT
Food attractants	BugPro, Entice	Feeds beneficial insects	Spray where needed	NT
Pheromones (natural insect)	Curlure, Dispalure Pherocon, Codlelure	Attract male insects to traps, or confusion prevents mating—	Monitor life cycle, population size Selected species only	Vapor >10,000
Repellents	Hinder, Deer-Away	Repels rabbits/deer	Spray on foliage	NT
Sticky coating	Tanglefoot	Coats sticky traps	Vegetable oil is solvent	NT
Traps—yellow	Pherocon AM, etc.	Attracts aoft-bodied insects	Monitor populations, Some control possible	NT
Traps—pale blue		Attracts thrips	As above	NT
Traps—white		Attracts flea beetles	As above	NT
Barriers				
Apply over beds to control weeds, heat soil, help prevent soil-borne foliar diseases				
Landscape fabrics		Air/water penetrates controls weeds	Heating moderate, long lasting under mulch	NT
Plastic—black		Air/water barrier, controls weeds	Heating moderate, moderate life	NT
Plastic—blue		Air/water barrier, controls weeds	Moderate life	NT
Plastic—clear		Solarization, high heat,	With moisture, kills weed seeds, soil borne diseases, root nematodes	NT
Protects against insect/disease/animal attack or frost				
Anti-transpirants	VaporGard, WiltPruf, Cloud Cover, Folicote, StayFresh,	Lowers water evaporation	Barriers to fungal invasion	NT
Bird netting		One inch plastic mesh	Prevents bird or mammal access to crop	NT
copper—sheet	Snail Barr	Around tree trunk/planting bed	Snails cannot cross copper	Can girdle
Frostgard*	Spray on foliage	Mutant bacteria colonize plant/prevent frost		NT
Nature Seal*	Methyl cellulose + shellac		Fruit coating—prevents disease, slows ripening	NT
Sta-Fresh 360HS	(resins, alchol, surfactanst, silicone antifoam)		Fruit coating—prevents disease, slows ripening	NT
Sta-fresh 600	food-grade emulsifiers & surfactants		Fruit coating—prevents disease, slows ripening	NT
Row Covers	Floating, Remay	Place over seedlings	On leaf crops, can remain till harvest	NT
Tree wrap	Sure Fire, Stiky Tree Guard	Wrap trunk	Stops borers	Can girdle
Pest diseases, parasites, predators				
*Agrobacterium radiobacter*K-84	Gallitrol-A Gallex, Norbac 84-C	Controls crown gall of roots		NT
Ampelomyces quisqualis	AQ[10]	Controls powdery mildew	Hyperparasite of *Erysiphaceae* fungi.	NT
Autographa californica NPV	Gusano	Controls many caterpillars	Apply to eggs, with spreader-sticker	NT
Bacillus. popilliae	Doom. Milky spore	Scarab beetle larvae	Apply to soil (grass)	>10,000
B. subtilis-A13/GB03	Quantum 4000 HB	See inoculant for legumes	Controls *Rhizoctonia* root rot	NT
B. subtilis M31600		Gustofson	Antifungal seed treatment	NT
B. thuringiensis				
kurstoki	Javelin, Thuricide,	Controls caterpillars		
	DiPel, Attack, Agree	Controls caterpillars	Safe for natural enemies (NE)	>10,000
israelensis	Tecknar, Novar Nordrisk	Controls mosquitoes	Safe for NE	>10,000
san diego= tenebrionis	M-Trak Trident	Colorado potato & Elm Leaf beetles	Safe for NE	>10,000
H-14	Gnatrol	Controls fungus gnats	Houseplants, green houses	>10,000
Beneficial insects	parasitoids, lady beetles, lacewings, etc.	Timing, species, important Call suppliers for help	Parasitoids very selective, predators less so	NT
Entomopathogenic nematodes	Biosafe, Bioflea,Bioquest	Soil insect predators	Moisture essential.	>20,000
*Gliocladium virens*GL 21	Gliogard	Control *Pythium* & *Rhizoctonia* root rots of ornamentals		NT
Glomus intraradices	Mycori-Mix	Fungus helps phosphorus absorption	Add to planting mix	NT
Heliothis NPV	Elcar	Viral disease *Heliothis sp.*	Safe for NE	>10,000
Nosema locustae	Noloc, Semaspore	Grasshopper protozoa disease	Safe for NE	>10,000
Phlebia gigantea	Rotstop		Add to planting mix	

Names: Common	Trade	Uses	Benefits/Restrictions	Dermal LD$_{50}$[1]

Pest diseases, parasites, predators (continued)

Common	Trade	Uses	Benefits/Restrictions	Dermal LD$_{50}$[1]
post harvest fungicide		Bio-Save 10	prevents post harvest spoilage	Dip fruit
Pseudomonas celpacia		Intercept	Controls rhizoctonia, fusarium, pythium	Add to planting mix
Pseudomonas fluoresces	Dagger	Seed treatment		
Soil microbes	Bioturf, Soil Aid, Lawn Restore, Dispatch, etc.	Microbial soil amendments	Attack some soil pathogens	NT
Streptomyces griseoviridis.	Mycostop	Prevents damping off disease, pythium, phytophthora	Add to potting soil (HydroGardens)	NT
Streptomicin	Agrimyucin	pear, apple fire blight	See text for timing	
Terramyucin	Mycoshield	pear fire blight, peach bacterial spot	See text for timing	
Trichoderma sp	BINAB T	Prevent tree wound disease	harmless, colonizes wounds to compete with	NT
Trichoderma sp	F-Stop	Control damping off of peas, beans, corn		NT

Pesticides

When using pesticides, avoid "combination-products". Although some of these contain selective 'active ingredients', when combined they are no different than broad-spectrum pesticides. If you wish to apply an insecticide and a fungicide in the same application, combine appropriate materials yourself.

Insect Growth Regulators (IGR)

Common	Trade	Uses	Benefits/Restrictions	Dermal LD$_{50}$[1]
cyromazine	Trigard	FleFlyMosq	Triazine Cuticle Inhibitor	>3100
flufenoxuron	Cascade	Mites & insects	Cuticle inhibitor, Toxic aquatic invertebrates	>2000
hexaflumuron	Recruit	Termite baits	Cuticle inhibitor, Toxic aquatic invertebrates	>2000
hydroprene	Gencor	Cockroaches	JHA nymphal roaches	34,000
	Gentrol	Stored product insects	Cracks & crevices in food areas	34,000
kinoprene	Enstar	Whiteflies, mealybugs, scales	Short HL JHA	9000
methoprene	Altosid Briquettes	Mosquitoes	Short HL JHA	>36,000
	Minex	Leafminer flies	Greenhouse JHA	>36,000
	Pharorid	Pharaoh's ants	Indoor baits	>36,000
	Precor	Fleas	Larval fleas JHA	>36,000
	In mixtures	Aphids, Whiteflies	Houseplant JHA	LT
tebufenozide	Mimic	Caterpillars, some scales	Ecdysone agonist, protects beetles	*

Plant/Fungal-based Pesticides

Common	Trade	Uses	Benefits/Restrictions	Dermal LD$_{50}$[1]
abamectin	Avid	Miticide	Ant bait of spray, fungal product	>2000
glufosinate-ammonium	Finale	Broad spectrum herbicide (BS)	Systemic post emergent	>4000
d-limonene		BS insecticide	citrus peel oil insecticide	*
maize gluten meal	A-Maizing Lawn	Pre-emergent herbicide	Apply before seeds germinate, water, allow to dry	NT
neem, azadirachtin	Margosan-O	Leafminer, aphids, bugs, fungi	Anti-feedant/sterilant/IGR	Mod
0.3% azadirachtin	Bioneem	Caterpillars, beetles, sawflies	Anti-feedant/sterilant/IGR	>2000
3% azadirachtin +	Azatin	Gypsy moth, whiteflies, fungus gnat	IGR, Anti-feedant	Low
pyrethrins	Bug Buster-O etc.	Flying insects, ants	Broad spectrum, Short HL, Toxic bees/fish	1800
Chrysanthemum cinerariaefolium flowers		often combined with synergists such as piperonyl butoxide or MGK-264		
rotenone	Rotenone	Beetles, many others	Very toxic to fish, not recommended	>1000
ryania	Ryania	Caterpillars on corn/apples	Selective stomach poison, Moderate HL	4000
sabadilla	Sabadilla	BS thrips, bugs, beetles	Toxic bees	4000

Synthetic Organic Pesticides

Common	Trade	Uses	Benefits/Restrictions	Dermal LD$_{50}$[1]
acephate	Orthene	Aphids/ BS insecticide	Systemic, Moderate HL, Toxic bees	>10,250
antitranspirants	Forever Green, Cloud Cover, Vapor Guard	Fungal barriers	Prevent fungal penetration, reduce water loss	NT
carbaryl	Sevin	BS insecticide—Use baits only	V toxic bees/ parasitoids.	2000
clofentezine	Apollo	Mite ovicide on tree fruits	Good for IPM, non-toxic to parasitoids	2400
fenarimol	Rubigan	Sterol-inhibitor fungicide	Inhibit fungal development	>2500
fluazifop-butyl	Fusilade	Selective herbicide	Post-emergent grass control in borders	2420
glyphosate	Roundup, Cleanup	BS herbicide	Systemic post emergent	4300
hydramethylnon	Amdro	Cockroach, fire ants	Baits	>5000
K salts fatty acid	Safers Superfast	Kills annual weeds	Safe for NE, no toxic residues	NT
K salts fatty acid	Safers Insecticidal Soaps	Soft-bodied insects	Safe for NE, no toxic residues	>10,000
K salts FA+sulphur	Safers Fungicidal Soap	Powdery mildew, Black Spot	Safe for NE, no toxic residues	>10,000
malathion	Malathion	BS insecticide	Short HL, broad spectrum	4100

Names: Common	Names: Trade	Uses	Benefits/Restrictions	Dermal LD_{50}[1]
metaldehyde	Metaldehyde	Snail/slug baits	Use selectively only	250
oil, dormant	many	Scales, overwintering insects	Use only on plants without green foliage	NT
oil, superior	Sunspray	Soft bodied insects	Contact activity for 5 days	NT
oxadiazon	Ronstar	BS herbicide	Pre-emergent broad spectrum	>5000
phosmet	Imidan	Beetles, caterpillars	Moderate HL, Toxic bees	>4640
fluvalinate	Mavrik	BS insecticide, Long HL	Dermal irritant, Non-toxic bees, miticide	3100
resmethrin	Chryson	Pyrethroid insecticide	Dermal irritant	3040
sethoxydim	Poast	Selective herbicide	Post emergent	>5000
tebuconazole	Folicur	Sterol-inhibitor fungicide	Inhibit fungal development	5000
tetramethrin	Tetramethrin	Pyrethroid insecticide	Dermal irritant, Toxic to bees	4640
triadimefon	Bayleton	Sterol-inhibitor fungicide	Inhibit fungal development	>2000
triforine	Funginex	Sterol-inhibitor triazole fungicide.	Protectant, eradicant activity	>2000
warfarin/diphacinone	d-Con, etc.	Rodent baits	Anti-coagulant rodenticides	25

Inorganic Pesticides

Common	Trade	Uses	Benefits/Restrictions	Dermal LD_{50}
boric acid	Roach prufe, BoraCare	Cockroaches, Termites, Fungi	Do not breathe, slippery. Apply to wood	low
copper sulfate + Ca	Bordeaux solution	Fungus diseases	Dormant season spray. Skin irritant	Irritant
cryolite	Kryocide			
Na alumo fluoride		Caterpillars, beetles	Stomach poison. Do not breathe	>10,000
diatomaceous Earth	Organic Plus, Diafil	Slugs, household pests/repellent	Insect Desiccant/Kills NE on foliage	NT
+ food	Shellshock	Cockroaches	Insect Desiccant, Do not breathe	NT
Na bicarbonate	Baking soda+oil	Foliar fungicide	Use oil as sticker	NT
DOT	BoraCare, Tim-Bor	Wood fungi & insects	Paint on unfinished damp wood	low
sulphur	Many	Soft insects/mites/fungus	Aqueous suspension best	Irr
sulphur-soaps	Safers	Foliar fungus	Do not apply in hot weather or with oil	NT
silica gel	Dri-Die 68	Household pests/repellent	Desiccant, Do not breathe	NT
+ pyrethrins	Drione, PermaGuard	Termites, ants, cockroaches	Desiccant, Do not breathe	low
+ pyrethrins	Revenge, Pursue	Repels ants, spot treat	Liquid spray	low
+ Ammonium fluosilicate	DriDie 67	Drywood Termites, roaches	Insect Desiccant, Do not breathe	low

Nematocides

Common	Trade	Uses	Benefits/Restrictions	Dermal LD_{50}
Organic matter (compost) in soil		Helps reduce nematodes	Nourishes natural enemies	NT
chitin/protein urea	Clandosan	Till into soil	Nourishes natural enemies. High in nitrogen	NT

Synergists

Common	Trade	Uses / Benefits/Restrictions	Dermal LD_{50}
MGK 264	n-octyl-bicloheptene dicarvboximide	Inhibits MFO which degrade pyrethrins, allethrin, rotenone in the body	> 4980
piperonyl butoxide	Butacide	Inhibits MFO which degrade pyrethrins, allethrin, rotenone in the bocy	>7500

Miscellaneous Household Chemicals

Common	Trade	Uses	Benefits/Restrictions	Dermal LD_{50}
aspirin	Aspirin	Pain/inflammation, heart	Stomach irritant	3838
formaldehyde	Many	Fungicide, disinfectant	In particle board, plywood, fabrics—vapor	500
naphthalene	Moth balls/flakes	Repel/kill pests	Use only in garment bag—vapor danger	low
paradichlorobenzine	PDB Moth balls	Repel/kill pests	Use only in garment bag—vapor danger	2000
Na hypochlorite	Household bleach	Bactericide, Fungicide	Irritant	>3000

[1] **Abbreviations: Dermal LD_{50}** = acute dermal lethal dose for 50% of a test rabbit population, **AI** = active ingredient, **Ca** = calcium, **BS** = broad spectrum, **DOT** = disodium octaborate tetraborate, **IGR** = insect growth regulator, **K** = potassum, **MFO** = mixed function oxidases, **Na** = sodium, **NE** = natural enemies, **HL** = half life, **NT** = non toxic.

COMMONLY ENCOUNTERED PESTICIDES

Names			Characteristics and Modes of Action[2]				
				Oral	Dermal	Important Effects[6]	
Common	Trade	Uses[1]	Type[2]	LD$_{50}$[3]	LD$_{50}$[4]	Data Gaps[7]	Persistence[8]
			INSECT GROWTH REGULATORS				
buprofezin	Applaud	Whitefly larvae	CSI	2198	*		long
cyromazine**	Larvadex	Leafminers	CSI/TZO	3387	>3100	DCar/feto tox/ to melamine	*
diflubenzuron**	Dimilin	Broad Spec	CSI	4640	10,000	AD	≥ 1 y fol, soil
fenoxycarb	Insegar, Logic	FleaCockroach	CB/JHA	16,800	> 2000	Non-selective on foliage	≥ 28 d fol
hexaflumuron	Recruit	Cockroach bait	CSI	≥5000	≥2000	Toxic aquatic invertebrates	stable
hydroprene	Gencor, Gentrol	Cockroach	JHA	>10,000	4550	Vapor	≈4 w wood
kinoprene	Enstar	Whiteflies, aphids	IGR	4900	9000	Product not available	≤ 1 d sun
lufenuron	Program	Oral flea control	CSI	?	?	Registered as drug	>1 mo
methoprene	Precor, Altosid	FleFlyMosq	JHA	34,600	>5000		1 d sun, ≤ 10 soil
neem, azadirachtin	Margosan-O,	caterpillars, bugs. &	IGR, AF	>5000	>2000		3 d
	Biomeem, Azatin	whitefly nymphs	IGR, AF	>13,000	>2000		3 d
tebufenozide	Mimic	Caterpillars only	EcAg	*	*	Registration pending	*
			INSECTICIDES				
Alfalfa looper NPV	Gusano	pest caterpillar disease	Disease	NT	NT	broad-spectrum, slow kill	≤ a3 d fol
abamectin**	Affirm, Avid	Ants, Mites	ONT	650	>2000	Primarily stomach poison	≈ 2 w fol
from *Streptomyces avermitilis*							≈ 7 d fol
acephate**	Orthene	Plants, Systemic	OP	866	2000	C Car	≈ 2 w fol
aldrin***	Aldrin	SoilPest	OC	38	98	Car/Per/Air/water/MFC	≈28-40y
aldicarb***	Temik	SoilSys/ leaches	CB	1	5	tox/MFC/Immune suppress	>1 y/acidsoil
allethrin**	Pynamin	HousePests	PR	6800	11200		≈ 1 d
azinphosmethyl**	Guthion	AgrFruit	OP	13	220	DCar/tox/leaches	14 d/fol
Bacillus popuilliae	MilkySporeDisease	Soil beetle	Disease	NT	NT	*Data	Soil microbe
B. thuringiensis							
aizawai	DiPel Bta	Diamondback Moth	Disease	NT	NT	stops feeding	≤3 d fol
thuringiensis	Thuricide	Caterpillar Disease	Disease	NT	NT	stops feeding	≤3 d fol
kurstaki	DiPel, Attack	Caterpillar Disease	Disease	NT	NT	stops feeding	≤3 d fol
israelensis	Bactimos, Teknar	MosqLarvae	Disease	NT	NT	stops feeding	≤3 d fol
san diego=	M-Cap, M-Track	CO potato &	Disease	NT	NT	stops feeding	≤3 d fol
tenebrionis	Trident	Elm leaf beetles	Disease	NT	NT	stops feeding	≤3 d fol
boric acid	Roach Pruf	CockrAnt	IN	4500	low	ECar/Do not breathe	stable
carbaryl	Sevin,Sevimol	Plant Eaters	CB	307	2000	Ter/V tox hymenoptera, ED	>6 w, adsorbs soil
carbofuran**	Furadan	Broad Spec Inst/Nem	CB	8	3000	tox/MFC/birds/Data	≈2 -6m
chlordane***	Chlordane	Termites, ants	OC****	283	580	B_2Car/Neur/MFC/ED/MIE	25 -40 y
chlordecone***	Kepone	Fire Ant	OC	95	114	Car/Per/Neur/Ter, MFC	persistent
chlorpyrifos	Dursban, Lorsban	House/Borers	COP	97	2000	ECar, toxBrds/erthwms	4 m soil, water
cryolite, Ca_3AlF_6	Kryocide	FruitVeg	IE	>10000	NT	Mineral	stable
cyfluthrin	Tempo	Broad Spec	PR	826	>5000	Eye irritant	3 w
DBCP***dibromochioropropane		Soil Fumigant/Nem		170	1420	Car/Male Sterilant/ED	stable
DDT***	DDT (toDDE)	Broad Spec	OC****	87	113	B_2Car/Per/Ter/Rep,MFC,ED	≈40 y
declorane***	Mirex (to Kepone	Ants	OC****	235	800	CarNeur	≥ 12 y
diatomaceous earth	Diatomite(silica)	Slugs, Cockroach	AntIE	3160	NT	Do not breathe	stable
diazinon**	Diazinon	Broad Spec	OP	300	3600	tox /MFC/Brds/Air/Water	≈3-6 m
dichlorvos	DDVP,Vapona,NoPestStrip	GenFumig	OP	25	59	CCar/Ter/Neu/i/Air	months
dieldrin***	Dieldrin	Broad Spec	OC****	40	65	B_2Car/Per/Rep,MFC/ED/Air	>33 -40y
d-limonene	Flea Stop etc	Broad Spec	UN	low	NT	Registration pend. Ter*	*
d-trans allethrin,	Bioallethrin	HousePests	PR	1100	11,200	*Data	≈ 1 d
endosulfan**	Thiodan	Broad Spec	OC****	18	74	ECar/tox,MFC,ED	long
fenvalerate**	Pydrin,Sumicidin	Broad Spec	PR	451	2500	irritant*Data, ED	3 w
fluvalinate	Mavrik	Broad Spec	PR	260	>20,000	irritant*Data, ED	3 w
heptachlor***	heptachlor	termites	OC****	147	>2000	B_2Car/Per/Neur/MFC/ED/Air	>28 y/soil
hydramethylnon	Amdro	ants, cockroach bait	Amid-hy	5000	>5000	C Car/AD	3 w
imidacloprid*	Premise, Admire	soil applied systemic	ClAK	450	<5000	Nicotine analog	stable

Names: Common	Names: Trade	Uses[1]	Type[2]	Oral LD$_{50}$[3]	Dermal LD$_{50}$	Important Effects[6] [4]Data Gaps	Persistence[8]
isofenphos**	Oftanol	Soil Insects, termites	OP	20	70	tox, Delayed neurotox	>12 m
K salts of FA (soap)	Safer's, Attack	Soft Insects	FA	>5068	NT		none
lindane** gamaBHC	Lindane/gama HCH	borers, head lice	OC****	76	500	B_1Car/Fet/tox,MFC,AD/ED/Air	30-40 y
malathion	Malathion	Broad Spec	OP	885	4000	DCar/Ter/Air/*Data	1-3 d/soil
methomyl**	Lannate	Broad Spec	CB	17	5880	tox/C Car/Vap	1 w
methoxychlor	Methoxychlor	Broad Spec	OC	5000	>5000	DCar, MFC, ED	≈ 3 w
mevinphos**	Phosdrin	Broad Spec	OP	3	51	tox/Vap	5 d
nicotine**	Black Leaf 40	Broad Spec	AK	50	50	tox/Ter/*Data	short
Nosema locustae	Semaspore	Grasshopper	Disease	NT	NT		
oil, superior	Sunspray	Soft Insect	Hy	NT	NT	contact activity for 5 days	3 w
ofm pheromone	Isomate-M	Control oriental fruit moth	PH	>20,000	>2000	Air	weeks
oxydemeton methyl	Metasystox-R	Suck Insect	OP***	65	100	tox/Ter/Rep	days
permethrin **	Pounce	Broad Spec fruits	PR	4000	>2000	CCar/irritantAD/ED	>2 w
phosmet	Imidan	Broad Spec fruits	OP	147	4640	CCar/leaches	20 d fol
propoxur	Baygon	HousePests	CB	95	1000	B_1Car/Air/*Data	long
pyrethrins	Bug Buster-o	Broad Spec	PR	1500	>300	* Data	<1 d
resmethrin	Resmethrin	HousePests	PR	1500	3040	* Data	1--2 d
rotenone	Derris,sp	Broad Spec spec	DR	132	940	DCar/Ter	≈ 4 d
ryanodine	Ryania *Ryania speciosa*	Codling Moth	CT	1200	1200	* Data	≈ 1 w
sabadilla	*Schoenocaulon officinale*	Bugs, broad spec	CT	4000	>4000	Do not breathe, * Ter	≤ 1 d
silica gel/aerogel	DriDie	HousePests	IN	3160	NT	Do not breathe	stable
sulphur	sulphur	selectiveSuckInsect	UN	1700	NT	irritant allergen	until rain
temephos	Abate	Mosquito	CB	2330	1300	AD	2 w water
tetramethrin	Tetramethrin	Broad Spec	PR	>5000	4640	CCar,ED	≈ 6 w
toxaphene***	toxaphene	SoilPest	OC	40	69	B_1Car/Per, MFS,ED	25-40 y
trichlorfon	Dylox,Dipterex	Broad Spec	OP	150	2000	Car	≈2 m

ACARICIDES (Miticides)

Common	Trade	Uses	Type	Oral LD$_{50}$	Dermal LD$_{50}$	Important Effects / Data Gaps	Persistence
clofentezine	Apollo	ovicide on tree fruits	ClTetrazine	3200	2400	Good for IPM	≈2 m
cyhexatin***	Plictran	Selective	OT	180	2000	Car, ED	≈ 3 w
dicofol**	Kelthane (part DDT)	FruitVeg	OC	575	2100	C/BjCar,MFC,ED	40 y as DDE
dinocap**	Karathane	Prot/Erad	DIP	980	irritant	Ter/*Data	months
fluvalinate	Mavrik	Broad Spec mites/insects	Py	260	>20000	irritant	3 weeks
hexythiazox	Savey	ovicide on tree fruits	OS	>5000	>5000	Protects beneficials	2 m
ovex	Ovotran	Broad Spec mites	OS	2000	NT	Selective	weeks
oxydemetonmethyl	Metasystox-R	SuckInsects/mites	OP	65	150	tox	≥7 d
progargite**	Omite	Broad Spec fruits	OS	4029	2940	Inhalation, irritant	weeks
sulphur	sulphur	Broad spec	UN	1700	NT	irritant allergen	stable
tetradifon***	Tedion	Larvicide, ovicide	OC	>10,000	<10,000	Long term tox.	25-50 y

REPELLENTS

Common	Trade	Uses	Type	Oral LD$_{50}$	Dermal LD$_{50}$	Important Effects / Data Gaps	Persistence
citronella	*Cylmbopogon nardus*	Mosquito	UN	*	*	*Data	≈1-2 h
diethyl toluamide	DEET, Delphene, Off	Broad Spec insect	UN	2000	≈2000	Avoid high concentrations	≈ 4 h skin
dimethyl phthalate	DMP	Broad Spec insect	UN	8200	*	Plasticizer	*
methyl nonyl ketone	MGK Repellent 326	Dogs, cats OC	5000	*	B_1Car	Stable	

HERBICIDES

Common	Trade	Uses	Type	Oral LD$_{50}$	Dermal LD$_{50}$	Important Effects / Data Gaps	Persistence
alachlor**	Lasso	FieldCr/PE	CSAm	1200	5400	B_1Car/leaches/ED	1-2 m soil
aminotriazole	Amitrol	Broad Spec/Sys post	TZO	1100	>10000	B_1Car/disease, ED	3 m
atrazine**	Atrazine	FieldCr/PE	TZI	1780	780	CCar/Mut,leaches,ED	2 y
benefin	Balan	Select/PE	DNP	10,000	>10,000	AD	≥ 1 y
bromacil	Bromacil	Brush/post	Ur	5200	5200	CCar	10-18 m
cacolylic acid	Phytar 560	Broad Spec/post	Ars	700	700	Per/*Data	≥ 2 y
chlorsulfuron	Glean, Telar	Post/syst ornamen	SulfUr	>5000	>2000	Drift, leaches	stable
DCPA	Dacthal	Select/PE/ to DCPA acid	OC	>10,000	>10,000	DCar/acid/AD	6 mo
dicamba	Banvel	Broad Spec/post, grains	BZHOC	1040	2000	Leaches/Dat	≈12 m
diphenamid	Enide	Select/PE	SAm	1000	1000	*Data	8 m
diquat	Diquat	Broad Spec post	Bi	231	400	*Data	> 1 y
diuron	Diuron, Karmex	Broad Spec/pre/post	Ur	2900	3400	DCar/AD	≥ 1 y
K salts FA	Safers Superfast	Post, Annuals	FA	low	low	Surfactant	none

Names: Common	Trade	Uses[1]	Type[2]	Oral LD_{50}[3]	Dermal LD_{50}[4]	Important Effects[6] Data Gaps[7]	Persistence[8]
DSMA	Ansar DSMA	Grass/post	Ars	600	10,000	Per/*Data	months
fluazifop-butyl	Fusilade	Grass/post	UN	1490	2420	Controls grass/AD	4 w
glufosinate-ammonium	Finale	Broad Spec/Post	IGS	2000	≥4000	Bacterial product	7-20d
glyphosate	Roundup, Cleanup, Rodeo	Brod Spec/post/Sys	AAB	5600	>5000	ECar/ADe	short
mineral spirits	Stoddard Solvent	Broad Spec/post	Hy	vap	100		non
maize gluten meal	A-maizing lawn	PE on lawn	UN	NT	NT	High dose required, fertilizer*	
MSMA	Ansar	Grass/post	Ars	700	700	Per	≥ 1 y
nicosulfuron	Accent	Post/Barnyard grass in corn	SulfUr	>5000	>2000		> 1 yr
oryzalin	Surflan	Select/pre ornam	Dna	10,000	*	CCar/may leach	≥4 m
oxadiazon	Ronstar	Broad Spec/PE	TZO	3500	>2000	CCar	3-6 m
oxyfluorfen	Goal	PE/post apples, potatoes	DPE	5000	10,000	CCar/Warning	non per
paraquat**	Paraquat	Broad Spec/post	Bi	20	150	ECar/tox/Ter/Mut	> 1 y soil
pendimethalin	Pendulum,Prowl, Stomp	Select/PE	Dna	2679	226	0CCar/dust/color	3-6 m
picloram**	picloram	Systemic brush	CHCN	8200	*	DCar/irritantTer/Repro/AD	≥6 m
pronamide**	Kerb	PE/post/selective	CSAm	8350	*	B_2Car/leaches	30 d
sethoxydim	Poast	Select/post	UN	3200	>5000	Against grass/ may leach	short
sulfometuron methyl	Oust	Select/post/syst	SulfUr	>5000	>2000	Drift, leaches/AD	>30 d
soap, fatty acid	Superfst WeedGrassKiller	Annual weeds	FA	NT	NT		2 d
simazine**	Simazine,Princep	Broad Spec/PE	TZI	5000	>3100	CCar/Per/leaches/ AD	≥ 8-22 m
triclopyr	Garlon 4	Systemic brush	CHCN	1847	2000	Caution/irritant	6 m
	Garlon 3A	Systemic brush	CHCN	630	*	Danger/irritant	6 m
trifluralin**	Trifluralin,Treflan	Select/PE	Dna	>10,000	>10,000	CCar/Ter/leaches, AD/ED	1 y
2,4-D**	Weedone	Select/post	POx	375	*	ACar/leaches, ED	≥2 m
2,4,5-T***	Fruitone,Weedar	Select/post	POx	300	500	Car/Per/Ter, ED	≥ 1 y

PLANT GROWTH REGULATORS

Common	Trade	Uses	Type	Oral LD_{50}	Dermal LD_{50}	Important Effects Data Gaps	Persistence
alpha-naphthylacetic acid	NAA, fruitone	Stop fruit drop	UN	1000	≈8,000	*Data	
daminozide***	Alar , Aminozide	Retard/Ornam	UN	8400	>5000	B_2Car/Ter to persistent UDMH	
ethephon	Florel	Causes fruit drop	OP	4229	≈8,000	Releases ethylene gas	short
indole-3-butyric acid	IBA, Rootone	Induce Roots	UN	low	*	*Data	short
meleic hydraazide	Retard	Retards cell division	HZ	6950	*		short
1-naphthaleneacetic acid	NAA, Rootone	Induce roots/stop fruit drop	UN	2520	>2000	Serious eye irritant	*
PMP + gibberellins	Accel	Thins certain apples	UN	NT	NT		short

FUNGICIDES and BACTERICIDES

Common	Trade	Uses	Type	Oral LD_{50}	Dermal LD_{50}	Important Effects Data Gaps	Persistence
Agrobacterium radiobacter	Norbac 84C Galltrol-A	EP	NT	NT		Controls Crown Gall	season
Ampelomyces quisqualis	AQ[10]	p. mildew hyperparasite	Disease	NT	NT	biofungicide	season
antitranspirants pinoline	VaporGard, WiltPruf, Folicote, StaFresh, CloudCover	Polymers + wax	NT	NT		Protect from diseases blackspot, powdery mildew @ 4%	≈2 w
lime+coppersulfate	Bordeaux Mix.	Dormant spray	IN	2660	>1000	irritant	≈ 2 m
B. subtilis-	MBI 600	Cotton, grains	EP	NT	NT		
A13/GB03	Quantum 4000 HB	Legume seed inoculant	EP	NT	NT	Controls *Rhizoctonia* root rot	short
benomyl**	Benlate	Systemic fruits, rice	BZZ	>10,000	low	CCar/Ter/leaches/*Data, ED	≥ 7 d
bupirimate	Nimrod	Systemic	AP/OP	>4000	*	Not on grains	*
calcium polysulfides	Lime Sulfur	Dormant spray	IN	low	M	irritant	≥ m
captan**	Captan	Protect fruits, veges	DCM	9000	9000	B_2Car/Mut/Ter/Feto	15 d
chlorothalonil**	Bravo, Daconil 2728	Prot potatoes, turf.	Cl BZZ	10,000	≥10,000	B_2Car/Eye/leaches/AD	≈ 6-12 m
copper-fixed**		Bacteri/Fungicide	IC	1000	1500	Burns leafy vegs	≈ 2 m
cuprous oxide		Bacteri/Fungicide	IC	470	8000	PerSoil	≈ 2 m
copper napthenate	Cuprinol	Wood Fungi	IC	6	*	toxic	stable
copper sulfate**	Bluestone	Algicide	IC	472	Eye irritant	PerWater, tox fish etc.	stable
dinocap**	Karathane	Prot/Erad powdery mil	DNP	980	980	Ter/irritant	short
Glomus intraradices	Mycori-Mix	K absorption aid	EP	NT	NT	Fungus colonizes roots	Persistent
DOT disodium octaborate tetrahydrate	BoraCare, Tim-Bor	Wood fungi/insects	IN	5560	low		stable
fenarimol	Rubigan	Prot/Erad	SIF/PY	2500	>2000	Systemic/leaches/AD	≈ 2 m
folpet	Folpet,Phaltan	Protect fruits, veg.	DCM	10,000	>10,000	B_2Car/irritantTer	short
fosetyl-al**	Aliette	Prot/Erad	PNM	5800	>2000	C Car, Not in U.S.	*
furalaxyl	Fongarid	soil fungicide	PNM	940	>3100	Not in U.S	short
Gliocladium virens	GL 21	Control *Pythium*	EP	NT	NT	Quantum 4000 HB& *Rhizoctonia* root rots	
hexachlorobenzene**	HCB	Seed protectant	HAH	40,000	*	Car/Repro/Ter/AD	Persistent
iprodione	Roval	Protect	DCM	>4400	>2000		≈ 2 m

Names: Common	Trade	Uses[1]	Type[2]	Oral LD_{50}[3]	Dermal LD_{50}	Important Effects[6] [4]Data Gaps	Persistence[8]
maneb**	Maneb to ETU	Protect fruit/vege	EBDC	7990	7100	B_2Car/Ter/Neuro/AD/ED	≈ 2 m
metalaxyl	Subdue, Ridomil	Soil—*Phytophthora*	PNM	669	>3100	ECar	2-3 m soil
myclobutanil	Nova, Systhane	Prot/Erad broad spec	SIF/TZO	1600	>5000		≈ 2 m
nuarimol**	Trimidol	Prot/Erad broad spec	SIF/PY	2500	1250	Not in U.S.	*
thiram**	Thiram to ETU	Seed, latex products	EBDC	780	780	B_2Car/Ter/leaches, ED	≈ 2 m
sodium bicarbonate	fungicide	Prot/Erad	UN	NT	NT	* Not currently registered*	
Streptomyces sp	Mycostop	Controls damping off	EP	NT	NT	Add to potting mix	season
Streptomycin sulfate	*Streptomycein*-based antibiotic		AB	9000	irritant		≈ 30 d
sulphur	sulphur	Prevent	UN	1700	irritant	irritant/allergen	≤ 14 d
tebuconazole	Folicur	Syst/Prot/Erad	SIF/TZO	4000	5000		*
triadimefon**	BayletonSyst	Prot/Erad fruits	TZISIF/TZO	1000	>2000	CCar	≈1-2 m
Trichoderma sp	BINAB T	Prevent tree wound disease	EP	NT	NT	competes w/ diseases	season
Trichoderma sp	F-Stop	Control damping off	EP	NT	NT	of peas, beans, corn	season
triforine	Funginex	Prot/Erad	SIF/PZ	16,000	>2000	irritant/may leach	≈ 3 w soil
zineb***	Zineb to ETU	Citrus/Fru	EBDC	5200	>6000	irritant/Car/Ter,ED	≈ 2

MOLLUSCICIDES, NEMATICIDES, PICICIDES (Fish Killers)

Common	Trade	Uses	Type	Oral LD_{50}	Dermal LD_{50}	Important Effects / Data Gaps	Persistence
clandosan	crustacean exoskeleton	Stimulates NA in root nematodes		NT	NT	Incorporate in soil	1 y
codusafos	Rugbly	Nematodes potatoes	OP	679	143	ECar	2 m
fenamiphos	Nemacur	Nematodes/ fruits, veges	OP	3	200	ECar	short
dichloropropene**	Telone	Nematodes preplant	OC	127	333	B_2Car,MFC, ED,tox	short
ivermectin	*Streptomices avemitilis*	InternalWrms	GA	650	>2000		
metaldehyde	Metaldehyde	Snail/Slug Bait	OP	630	*	*	≈ 1 w
methiocarb C*	Mesurol	Snail Bait, Bird repel	CB	130	2000	DCar	long
rotenone	*Derris sp*	Fish	DR	132	1000	DCar/Tumorigenic	≈ 4 d

RODENTICIDES

Common	Trade	Uses	Type	Oral LD_{50}	Dermal LD_{50}	Important Effects / Data Gaps	Persistence
cholecalciferol	Armarmentarium	Rodent Bait	ST	low	low	Danger dogs	*
coumafuryl	Fumarin	Rat/Mouse	AC	25	*		*
diphacinone	Diphacin	Rodent Bait	AC	1.86	*		V long
gas cartridges	Na/K nitrate+C or S	Gas in burrows	IN	3700	≤2000	Burn, Inhale, Nontarget	None
Na fluoroacetate***	Compound 1080	Broad spec	CM	0.22	*	tox/Non-target	V long
Strychnos nuxvomica	Strychnine**	Broad Spec	AK	30	*	tox/*Data/Non-target	Long
Urginea maritima	Red Squill	Rats	CHM	0.7	*	*Data	
warfarin	Warfarin	Rat/Mouse	AC	3	*	Ter	*
zinc phosphide**	Phosvin	Rodents	IM	46	*	toxic dust	Stable if dry

SYNERGISTS

Common	Trade	Uses	Type	Oral LD_{50}	Dermal LD_{50}	Important Effects / Data Gaps	Persistence
n- octyl-bicloheptene dicarboximide	MGK 264	IMFO	> 4980	*	*	*	
piperonyl butoxide	*Ocotea cymbarium* Buticide	IMFO	7500	<2000	*Data	Short	

HOUSEHOLD COMPOUNDS*

Common	Trade	Uses	Type	Oral LD_{50}	Dermal LD_{50}	Important Effects / Data Gaps	Persistence
acetone	nail polish remover	solvent airplane glue	Ketone	low	low	Liver	Short
aspirin	aspirin	pain/inflammation		750	3830	Stomach irritant	Short
bleach	sodium hypochlorite	chlorine disinfectant	IN	192	>3000	* Skin irritant	Short
creosote oil**	Coal Tar	wood protection	Hy	tox	tox	ACar/Mut/*Data	Persistent
ethanol**	ethyl alcohol, booze	beverage, fuel	OH	mod	Mod	Ter, heart, liver, nerve	Hours
gossypol		plastic stabilizer		*	*	Ter/Sterilant	*
naphalene	moth balls, toilet deodorize	broad spectrum	Ph	med	tox	Ter/tox*/MFC	m in bag
nickel	Ni	stainless steel, jewelry, hair spray	IM	low	Allergen	essential nutrient, MFC	Stable
Ni carbonyl, Ni subsulfide**		tobacco, occupational	IM	tox	tox	ACar/MFC	Persistent
nitrates	NO_3	fertilizer, vegetables	IN	low	low	essential nutrient	Moderate
nitrites	NO_2	cured meats, formed in mouth	IN	med	med	precursors of nitrosomides	
nitrosomides	NO_2 + proteins	In stomach, burning		tox	tox	BCar, Anti-oxidants prevent formation	
Pheylphenol	Lysol	disinfectant	Ph	*	*	*Ter/Car/Rep	
paradichlorobenzine	PDB mothballs	stored products	OC	vap 500	2000	CCar/Mut/MFC	m in bag
pentachlorophenal**	PCP, Penta	termite/wood rot	OC	50	*	ACar/Ter/tox,MFC,ED	Persistent
selenium	Se	essential element meat/grains	IM	low	low	Antioxt/high dose tox	Stable
sodium hydroxide	lye, caustic soda	drain/oven cleaners	IN	tox	tox	Burns skin, eyes	Stable
table salt	sodium chloride	seasoning, preservative	IN	3320	NT		Stable

Commonly Encountered Pesticides (continued)

vinyl chloride**	precursor PVC	chlorinated plastic	OC	*	vap	BCar/Ter/tox,MFC,ED	Stable
vitamin A**	fat soluble	essential nutrient	FSV			Ter/high dose toxic	Persistent
zinc	Zn	essential element meat/grains	IN	low	low	high dose toxic	Stable
ALL PURPOSE KILLERS and ENVIRONMENTAL CONTAMINANTS*							
carbon monoxide**	CO	smoking, autos, burning	CM	high	high	Ter/Neur	Short
CFC	chlorofluorocarbons	refrigerant, propellant, foam	CFC	low	*	MIE/destroys ozone	Stable
chloroform	Freon 20	solvent, paper bleach	mod	low		B_2 Car/MIE/in fat	Persistent
CCA	chromated copper arsenate	wood preservative	IN	high	high	* Seal treated wood	Stable
creosote	mix. phenol, cresol, creosol	preservative	PH	tox	tox	B_1Car/corrosive	Persistent
dichloromethane**	methylene chloride	organic solvent OC	high	vap 400		ACar/Mut/tox/Mem/MFC	Years
dioxin***	2,3,7,8-TCDD	air, food, water	HAH****	0.2	2.5	Car/Mut/Ter/Feto,MFC,ED	2 y
EDB***	ethylene dibromide	fumigant (in water/ food)	HAH	146[5]	vap 200	B_2Car/Ter/Rep/tox/ED/AD	>20 y soil
EDC**	ethylene dichloride	fumigant	HAH	670	vap 1000	Car/*Data	Short
ethylene glycol	EtO	antifreeze, polyester etc	OH	mod	tox	Air	Persistent
ethylene oxide***	EtO	sterilant/fumigant	UN	flam	vap 50	B_1Car/Mut/Ter/Sterilant*	Short
formaldehyde**		fabrics, plywood, pesticides	AAM	tox gas	tox gas	B_2Car/irritant	V long
hydroquinone	D-76	photo developer, bleaching cream	PH	mod	low	Car/Mut/MIE	*
lead***	Pb	water, food, paint, crockery	IM	tox	low	neurotoxin, blood effects	
		moves from soil to plants/food	MFC,ED			max dose≥10μg/dl	Stable
metham-sodium***	Vapam	soil fumigant	Th	450	tox	Ter, Mut, leaches	≤ 60 d
methyl bromide**	MB	broad spec fumigant	HAH	vap 200	2700/30 m	Ter, destroys ozone ≈3 y	≤ 2 w soil
Na arsenate/ite***		Kill All—if ingested	IM	10	low	A Car/tox/Neuro	Stable
osmose**	CCA copper,chromium, arsenic	wood treatment	IM	tox	low	Car/tox/irritant	Stable
phthalates	plasticizers	in plastic, oily foods	PH	mod	low	liver damage/MIE/ED	Long
PBB***	polybromilated biphenyls	fire retardants, TV	HAH****	tox	tox*	Ter/Car/Rep	*Long
PCB***	polychlorinated biphenyls	fire retardants, plasticizers	HAH****	≈250	tox*	Ter/Car/Rep/MFC,ED	≥ 25 y soil
sulfuryl fluoride**	Vikane	termite fumigant	IN	5	10	tox	Short
tobacco smoke		>14 toxicants	AK/Tar	mod	low	ACar/Ter/Neur/Cardiov/ED	Short
toluene**		organic solvent	AH	low	low	Ter/Neur	Short
xylene		solvent pesticides, oil paints, glues etc.	AH	tox	tox	MIE/in fat/ Air	Persistent

Definitions & footnotes:

[3] **Oral LD_{50}**—Amount of compound—*in milligrams per kilogram of body weight* (mg/kg)—which killed 50% of a group of test rats which ate it. **Note that *smaller values are more toxic*.**
NT = essentially not toxic assumes ≥10,000 mg/kg.

[4] **Dermal LD_{50}**—Amount of compound—*in milligrams per kilograms of body weight* (mg/kg)—which killed 50% of a group of test rabbits (usually) when it was applied to the shaved skin. This is a measure of the ability of the pesticide to penetrate unbroken skin—*smaller values are indicative of the more toxic materials.* **irritant** = skin or eye irritant

[5] **Vap LD_{50}** —amount—*in parts per million* (ppm)—of the substance mixed with air which killed 50% of test animals which breathed the mixture—*smaller numbers are indicative of the more toxic materials.*

[6] **Important effects—Car** = carcinogen (cancer causing), **Carcinogen Rankings: Class A** = Human Carcinogen, **Class B** = Probable Human Carcinogen, **Class C** = Possible Human Carcinogen, **Class D** = Data not available, **Class E** =Not carcinogenic—See chart. *Class A & B carcinogens are here considered of greatest concern, because data for others are often equivocal.* **Fet** = Fetotoxic (toxic to the fetus), **Mut** = Mutagen(Causes mutations), **Neur** = Neurotoxic (stable nerve damage), **Onc** = oncogen (tumor causing), **Per** = Persistent in environment, **Rep** = reproductive toxicant, **Ter** = teratogen (fetal deformation), **tox** = toxicity (acute toxicity to humans or wildlife)

[7] **Data Gaps**—Either the EPA or the State of California have called for more data on this product.

[8] **Persistence in the environment**—Stable and persistent compounds are usually not recommended

* **No data** *does not* indicate no hazard—but likely inadequate testing.

** Restrictions to use by EPA

*** Bans or Suspensions by EPA often for persistence, A or B carciogenicity, toxicity, leaching

**** Bioconcentrates in food chain from air, soil, fats

Commonly Encountered Pesticides (continued)

1 **Abbreviations**: **AAB** = amino acid biosynthesis in plants, **AAM** = amino acid metabolism, **AB** = antibiotic, **AC** = anti-coagulant, **AD** = adsorbs to soil particles, can leach out later into water, **AF** = antifeedant, **AH** = aromatic hydrocarbon, **Air** = found in household air, **AK** = alkaloid, **Amid-hy** = amidinohydrazone, **Ars** = Arsenicals, **Bi** = bipyridylium herbicides, **Broad Spec/ broad spectrum** = kills most plants or kills most insects/mites (usually undesirable), **Brush** = kills shrubs/trees, **BZZ** = benzimidazoles, **CSAm**= chlorinated substituted amides, **Car** = A or B carcinogen, **CCar** = possible carcinogen, **CB** = Carbamates, **CFC** = chlorofluorocarbons, **CHM** = carbohydrate metabolism, **ClAK**= Chlorinated alkaloid, **CHCN** = chlorinated heterocyclic nitrogens, **COP** = Chlorinated organophosphate, **CM** = carbon monoxide, **CSI** = chitin synthesis inhibitor, **CT** = calcium transport, **d** = day, **DCM** = dicarb-oximide fungicides, **Disease** = disease of pest, **dl** =deciliter of blood, **Dna** = dinitroaniline herbicides, **DNA** = deoxyribonucleic acid— structure of genes, **DNP** = dinitrophenol, **DPE** = diphenyl ethers, **DR** = depresses respiration, **Dormant** = apply only in the dormant season, **EBDC** = bidithiocarbamate fungicides, **EcAg** = Ecdysone Agonist, **ED** = endocrine disrupter, **EP** = ecological preventative, colonizes space & prevents disease, **ETH** = ethylene gas is released from ripening fruits, **ETU** = ethylene thiourea (a carcinogen, mutagen, skin sensitizer, & thyroid poison which penetrates plants), **FA** = Fatty acids, **Fieldcrops** = used only in agriculture, **FleFlyMosq** = fleas, flies or mosquitoes, **fol** = foliage, **Fruit/Veg** = fruits/ vegetables, **FSV** = fat soluble vitamin, **GA**= gaba, **GrowthRetard** = slows plant growth, **HAH** = halogenated aromatic hydrocarbons, **Hy** = hydro-carbons, **HZ** = hydrazide, **IBA** = indole-3-butyric acid, **IGR** = insect growth regulator, **IGS**= inactivate glutamate synthetase, **IE** = inactivate insect enzymes, **IM** = inorganic heavy metal, **IMFO** = inhibit mixed function oxidases, **IN** =inorganic, **InduceRoots** = stimulates root growth, **Internal** wrms = eradicates round worms in mammals, **K** = potassium, **JHA** = juvenile hormone analog, **LD** = lethal dose, **m** = month, **MdP** = methylene doxyphenyl, **Mem**= memory loss, **MFC** = magnifies in food chains, **MIE** = moves in environment, **NAA** = naphthaleneacetic acid, **NAD** = naphthalene acetamide, **NT** = not toxic , **ofm** = oriental fruit moth, **OC** = organochlorine, **OH** = alcohols, **OP** = organophosphates, **OS** = organosulphur, **ONT** = octopamine nerve transmission, **PCHT** = polychloro-terpene, **Ph** = phenol, **PH** = pheromone, **PhPy** = phenyl pyrazole, **PMP** = N-(phenylmethyl)-1H-purine 6-amine, **POx** = phenoxy, **PlantEat** = plant eating insects, **PNM** = phenyl-amide fungicides, **PE** = pre-emergent herbicide, apply before growth begins, **PrevFrutDrop** = prevents premature fruit drop, **post** = post-emergent herbicide, apply during active growth, **PP** = both pre & post emergent herbicide activity, **Protect** = protects against fungi, will not eradicate an existing infestation, **Prot/Erad** = protectant/ eradicant fungicide, **PY** = pyrimidines, **PR** = pyrethroids, **PZ** = piperazines, **Rep**= reproductive effects, **SAm** = substituted amide herbicides, **Select** = kills only a few types of plants of insects (desirable), **SIF** = sterole inhibiting fungicides, **SoilPest** = Controls soil dwelling insects, **SoilSys** = moves from soil into plant to kill insects, **Sub Arom**= substituted Aromatics, **Suckinsect** = used against insects which suck plant juices, **SulfUr**= sulfonyurea herbicides; **Sys** = systemic (moves in plant circulation), **ST**=steroid, **TZI** = triazine, **TZO**= triazole, **Ur** = urea, **w**= week, **WoodFungi** = prevents growth of fungi in wood, **y** = year

---

* For more information about household compounds & environmental contaminants see Hart, et al. Toxics A to Z, U. Cal.

2 **Modes of actions**:

Pesticides effecting acetylcholene nerve transmission:

1. **Inhibit acetylcholenesterase**—repetitive nerve firing, blockage of nerve transmission—**CB** = carbamates & **OP** = organophosphates *Causes excessive release of acetylcholene*
2. **Bind to the acetylcholene receptor**—trembling, convulsions, paralysis—**AK** = alkaloid—(Nicotine sulfate, imidacloprid)

Other nervous system effects

1. **Sodium-potassium balance of neurons**—violent trembling,convulsions, paralysis— **OC** = organochlorine (aldrin, chlordane, endosulphon, DDT, dieldrin lindane), **PCHT** = Polychloroterpene (toxaphene), & **PR** = pyrethroids
2. **Slows nervous transmission**— **OC** = organochlorines (methoxychlor)
3. **Interferes with GABA-mediated nerve transmission**—**GA** = products derived from *Streptomyces avermitilis*

Commonly Encountered Pesticides (continued)

PhPy phenyl pyrazones (fipronil) more specific for insect receptors than mammalian receptors

4. Interferes with gamaminobutyric acid-gated chlorine channels, altering steroid levels—OC =(dechlorane)

5. Octopamine nerve transmission (ONT)

antagonizes octopamine—(chlordimeform) slows activity

inhibits octopamine—(abamectin)—paralysis by interfering with glutamate receptors on chloride channels

Pesticides which:

1. Interfere with membranes

—*of insects*—**FA** = Fatty acids (soaps), **Hy** = superior oil, **IN** = inorganic dusts

—*of plants*— **Hy** = hydrocarbons (cold tar, mineral spirits)

— *calcium transport, preventing muscle contraction*—**CT** = calcium transport (ryanodine, *sabadilla* both alkaloids)

—*binds to membrane receptor to synthesize toxic metabolite*—Sulphur, **HAH** = halogenated aromatic hydrocarbons (dioxin, interferes with cytochrome P450 system)

2. Interfere with cellular respiration

—*progressive inactivity*—**IM** = inorganic heavy metal (inorganic copper/ tin/mercury)—**Bi** = bipyridylium herbicides, —**EBDC** = dithicarbamate fungicides

—*binds to hemoglobin & prevents oxygenation of blood* **CM**

—*enzyme inhibitor (between NAD+ & Coenzyme Q)*—**DR** = (Rotenone),

—*increases respiration until death- plants & animals*—Ph = phenol—(pentachlorophenyl)

—*increased oxidation*—**OC** = organocoppers

—*Uncouple oxidative phosphorylation*—**DNP** = (dinoseb, dinocap)

—*Uncouple photophroylation*—**DPE** = diphenyl ethers (oxyfluorfen)

3. Interfere with cell division:

—*fungal cell division*—**BZZ** = benzimidazoles—**EBDC/ETU** = ethylenebisdichiocarbamate fungicides

—*plant cell division*—**SAm** = substituted amide herbicides, **Dna** = dinitroaniline herbicides

4. Interfere with normal development:

—*influence the pattern of messenger RNA in insects*—**JHA** = juvenile hormone analog (methoprene, hydroprene)

—*interfere with insect chitin synthesis*—**CSI** = Chitin Synthesis inhibitor(diflubenzuron)

—*substitute for phosphates in cell metabolism*—**Ars** = arsenicals

—*interfere with normal growth*—**IGR** = Insect growth regulator—ecdysone analog (azadirachtin)

—*insect antifeedant*—**AF** = (*azadirachtin*)

5. Cause diseases in certain insects or fungi

—*Selective Bacterial, fungal, protozoal, or viral diseases*—**Disease** = disease of pest

6. Interfere with blood clotting

—**AC** = anti coagulants

7. Mimic the plant growth hormone, auxin

—*causing persistent disorderly growth*—**POx** = phenoxy & **BZH** = benzoic acid herbicides

8. Interfere with normal biosynthesis

—*ribosomal RNA synthesis* —**PNM** = Phenylamide fungicides

—*amino acid biosynthesis*—**AAB** = in plants (by depletion of phenylalanine) (glyphosate) —**DCM** = dicarboximide fungicides (by inhibition of —SH radical synthesis)

—*of heme (oxygen-carrying element of blood)*—lead

—*interferes with plant photosynthesis*—**DNP** = dinitrophenol, **MdP** = Methylene doxyphenyl, **NPh** = nitrophenols, **TZI** = triazines **Ur** = urea

—*of carotenoids,* bleaches leaves—**TZO** = triazole

—*of proteins*—**AB** = via ribosomes, **CHCN** herbicides

Commonly Encountered Pesticides (continued)

—*of sterols (essential carbohydrates)*—**SIF** = sterol inhibiting fungicides, **TZO** = triazole

8. Interfere with normal biosynthesis (continued)

—*of thyroid gland hormones* = **ETU**

9. Inactivate enzymes

—*by release of fluoride*—(cryolite) **IE** = Inactivate enzymes containing iron, calcium, & magnesium

—*liver*—**IN** = (DOT boron products)

—*plant enzymes*—**CSAm** = chlorinated substituted amides, **IM** = inorganic heavy metals, (mercury/copper)

—*bind with or inactivate enzymes containing SH groups*—IM = inorganic heavy metals, (*mercury/copper*, arsenate ion), **SubAro** = substituted aromatics

—*inhibit mixed function oxidases which metabolize foreign compounds*—**IMFO** = (piperonyl butoxide)

—*inhibit glutamate synthetase causing buildup of ammonia in plant tissues*— **IGS** = (glufosinate-ammonium)

—*inhibit acetolactate synthase (* ***ALS*** *) required for plant cell growth* **SulfUr**= sulfonylurea herbicides (sulfometuron methyl)

10. Interfere with metabolism of

—**amino acid (AAM)** *competes with DNA formation possibly triggering cancer* (eye & mucus membrane irritation) (formaldehyde)

—**carbohydrate (CHM)**—in the heart (red squill*)

—**calcium**—(cholecalciferol)

11. Paralyze muscles —Strychnine, *effects breathing*

12. Coagulate proteins = **Ars** (arsenate & arsenite ions)

13. Absorb cuticle waxes =(boric acid, silica gel)

14. Pesticides with unknown mode of action

—**UN**—(lime sulphur, boric acid,)CBetc

Endocrine Disrupters threaten health

Increasing evidence indicates that human and environmental health are threatened by toxics. In 1991 alone, manufacturers released into air, water, and soil more than 3.38 billion pounds of the 320 toxic chemicals for which the EPA requires emission-level reports. Adequate toxicology exists for only only 2-3 percent of the chemicals used in commerce. More than 60,000 have never been studied for hazards, and these make up 99.9% of the total tonnage manufactured in the U.S. today. [1]

Many industrial compounds contain chlorine, an element which tends to increase their persistence. A portion of these ≈15,000 chlorinated compounds are released into water, soil, and air every day. *At least 177* of these *have been identified in the blood and fat of U.S. citizens.*[2] Though these organochlorines (OC) are likewise not well studied, 59 have been linked to cancer—19 specifically to mammary cancers.

The **polychlorinated biphenyls**, (PCBs), were introduced in the 1930s as insulating fluids in electrical transformers, but were also incorporated in plastics, paints, lubricating oil, and dyes. PCBs are now known to magnify in food chains, and they are currently ubiquitous in the environment. Their manufacture was stopped in the 1970s because of their evident toxicity and carcinogenicity, but they are still leaking from transformers, warehouses, and landfills.

Other chlorinated industrial bad actors include **plastics: [vinyl chloride** (VC), **ethylene dichloride** (EDC), **polyvinyl chloride** (PVC), and VDC —a precursor for saran wrap], **fumigants: [dibromochloropropane** (DBCP) and **dichloropropane]** and the industrial **solvent: dichloromethane** (DCM).[2] VC, EDC, VDC, and DCM are widespread in air and drinking water. VC and VDC leach out of jars and wraps into foods and drinks. (Some cooking oils are even marketed in PVC bottles—see recycling, next page). DCM is found in blood and mother's milk of U.S. women.[2] Though banned for use as a fumigant, DBCP is a contaminant of chlorinated solvents and chemicals. In addition, other chlorinated solvents used by the dry cleaning, metal finishing, and electronic industries escape into the atmosphere and groundwater. Solvents, resins, and glues have been implicated in testicular cancers and other disorders of the male employees at Lockheed.[1]

In 1992, both the International Joint Commission— environmental watchdog for the Great Lakes—and the Paris Commission—which oversees pollutant emissions in the northeast Atlantic— called for a gradual phaseout of chlorine and chlorine-containing compounds in industrial processes.[3] Greenpeace[2] and the Sierra Club—believing there is neither time nor money to study these chemicals individually—advocate total elimination of chlorine compounds because of their potential hazard. On the other hand, the Chlorine Institute advocates study on a compound by compound basis. The Clean Air Act requires companies to conduct hazard assessments of their compounds, but EPA has not drawn up rules.[1] There *is* progress, however. Several companies have begun to reduce chlorine use, and ozone depleting **chlorofluorocarbons** and **methyl bromide** are due to be phased out worldwide by the year 2001.

Most Known Endocrine Disrupters
are *heavy metals* or organochlorines

Herbicides
- alachlor
- aminotriazole
- atrazine
- 2,4-D
- nitrofen
- 2,4,5-T
- trifluralin

Fungicides
- benomyl
- dithiocarbamates
- hexachlorobenzine
- mancozeb
- maneb
- *tributyltin*
- zineb
- ziram

Insecticides
- carbaryl
- chlordane
- dicofol
- dieldrin
- DDT & DDE
- endosulfan
- BHC
- heptachlor & hepoxide
- lindane (gama HCH)
- methomyl
- methoxychlor
- declorane (mirex*)
- oxychlordane
- parathion
- synthetic pyrethroids
- toxaphene

Nematocides
- aldicarb
- dichloropropene

Misc. Chemicals
- *cadmium*
- *lead*
- *mercury*
- polybromilated biphenyls
- PCBs (≥100 compounds)
- pentachlorophenyl(PCP)
- penta to nonylphenols
- phthalate
- styrenes
- 2,3,7,8-TCDD [dioxins (≥100 compounds)]

Endocrine disrupters

Some OCs are known to be estrogen mimics. **DDT**, **methoxychlor**, **mirex** and some **PVCs** bind to cellular estro-

---

[1]Sci. Amer. 273(1):22, 1995, [2]*Chlorine, Human Health & the Environment, the breast cancer warning,* Greenpeace USA, 1436 U St. NW, Washington, $5. C&E News 1/31/94, p. 19-23. [3]C&E News, 4/19/93, p. 11-20. [4]di(2-ethylhexyl) phthalate is a plasticizer for polyvinyl chloride & other phthalates are toxic plasticizers in other plastics. Chem Reg. Report. 3/11/88, p.1899-1900.

gen receptors, speeding the growth of mammary tumors induced by other causes. *Even though estrogen is a natural hormone, high or sustained estrogen levels beyond the normal, increase risk of breast cancer.* Since low levels of estrogen are found in males, too much estrogen, or its presence at the wrong time can trigger reproductive anomalies in either sex.

Several **dioxin** contaminants synthesized during production or incineration of chlorinated compounds move in food chains. People usually ingest dioxin from meat, whole milk, eggs, and fish. The most toxic—**2,3,7,8-TCDD dioxin—** reduces the number of estrogen receptors by disturbing natural regulation of estrogen synthesis, as well as synthesis and metabolism of other sex hormones. Dioxin exposure can cause fat loss, immune suppression, feminization and increased hairiness. In female rats, it causes reproductive failure and mammary tumors. The average concentration of dioxin-like substances in humans is now 9 ng/kg (1 nanogram = 1 billionth of a gram). At 13 ng/kg dioxin, sex hormones decline in men; at 47 ng/kg, children's growth slows.[1]

Unfortunately, elimination of chlorine cannot solve all pollution-based endocrine problems, since several estrogen mimics are not OCs. Bromine is another problem element. And certain heavy metals and non-chlorinated chemicals—including alkylphenol ethoxylates (in detergents and household products), and spermicides (in sewage effluents) are also estrogenic. **Estrogen disrupters** can bind to estrogen receptors, mimicking or blocking the action of natural estrogen, or interfere with the normal metabolism of estrogen. Many are persistent, fat-soluble compounds. Most cross the placental barrier to reach the developing fetus. Chlordane and its metabolites have these effects. At concentrations found in U.S. citizens, these estrogen disrupters caused masculization of male and female rats which were exposed during gestation.

Recycling Numbers are Key to Plastics Which Contact Your Foods

1 = PET or PETE (polyethylene terephthalate)—used for peanut butter, mouthwash, & soda bottles

2 = HDPE (high-density polyethylene)— millk jugs, detergent bottles, motor oil —65% of plastic bottles

3 = PVC (polyvinyl chloride)—shampoo, cooking oil, & water bottles—5% of plastic packaging but also baby mattresses, plastic pants, etc.

4 = LDPE (low-density polyethylene)—shrink wrap & plastic bags

5 = polypropylene—lids, drinking straws, yogurt & cottage cheese containers

6 = polystyrene & polystyrene foam—food containers, cups, packing peanuts, meat trays. Clear clamshell containers are polystyrene

7 = mixed plastic—sandwiched or mixed together. Squeeze bottles (like fudge or ketchup bottles)

Residues increasing

These studies suggest that *environmental residues of persistent estrogen disrupters are high enough to interfere with the hormonal systems of wildlife and humans.* **PCB**s are the major problem pollutants in Great Lakes waters. Other toxic substances in Great Lakes fish are **mercury** and other heavy metals which also bioaccumulate in the environment.[2] Almost 100% of mature Great Lakes salmon have enlarged thyroids, indicating a disturbed endocrine system. Some of these salmon species cannot reproduce in the wild.[3]

Even though many OCs—**DDT**, **aldrin**, **dieldren**, **mirex**, **kepone**, **chlordane**, and **lindane**—have been long banned or restricted in the U.S., they are are still with us in the environment and in the body fat of each of us. Residues of **DDT** and **mirex** have even begun to rise again, and concentrations of several other OCs are no longer declining. *Most of these restricted insecticides are available elsewhere in the world.* According to the Los Angeles-based Foundation for Advancement in Science & Education, almost 4.1 million pounds of these pesticides were exported from the U.S. in 1991.[3] They return to us via air, migratory animals, and possibly in foods. (Box page. 208) They also devastate wildlife and the lives of people in importing countries. By the early 1980s, with DDT residues in Central American farmers 11 times higher than those in the average American,[3] President Carter signed an order to prevent export of banned pesticides. Later President Reagan revoked the order. The U.S. is still a major source of banned pesticides in other countries.

DDE residues and thinning eggshells have again been found in Bald Eagles on the Columbia River.[4] More horror stories abound. The banned tin compound, **tributyltin**, causes alterations in sexual and functional development in fetuses exposed at levels found in the environment. Chlorinated herbicides such as **atrazine** are banned in much of Europe, but are still widely used here, even though they move readily into water supplies and turn up in midwest wells.

Ovarian, uterine, prostate, and testicular cancers and reduced sperm counts are related to OC residues in humans, and linked to a 1-2% annual

[1]Toxicol. Appl. Pharmacol. 126:326-337, 1994. [2]Sierra 79(5):41-45, 75-76,1994. [3] C&E News, 4/19/93, p. 11-20. [4]Sierra 66(5) 1981, p, 63-67.

increase in breast cancer almost everywhere. (In Israel where certain persistent OCs were phased out in the 1970s breast cancer is declining). Some suggest dioxin may be the cause of a recent increase in endometriosis.

Residues threaten infants

Young children are believed to be especially sensitive to hormonally-active pollutants. During prenatal and early postnatal development, specific sex-related ratios of estrogen to male hormones is necessary for normal sexual differentiation and proper formation of the reproductive organs of each sex. During these critical stages tiny increases in estrogen can have permanent effects on endocrine, reproductive and central nervous systems. *Prenatal and postnatal exposure to persistent OCs is now universal since OC residues in the woman's body are passed across the placenta and via mother's milk.* Exposure to even non-persistent endocrine disrupters may be a problem if a pregnant woman contacts such a substance during her pregnancy. The effects of these prenatal and early infant exposures may not be manifested until adulthood.

In adulthood, these exposed males may exhibit reduced sperm counts, reproductive tract abnormalities, and testicular cancer. Exposed females may exhibit defeminization, masculinization, oestrous irregularities, and infertility. These exposures may related to the fact that in the last 50 years sperm counts in the industrial nations have fallen 50%, and testicular cancer has risen 2-4 times.

In addition, lead ingested from flaking paint and drinking water—from lead soldered copper pipes and faucets—can cause behavioral impairment in young children at minute doses, and irreversible brain damage at higher doses. Bottled water is not the answer, since it does not contain needed fluorine to protect dental health. Use first-draw water[1] for other things than cooking and drinking, wash old paint with soap,[2] *and* keep smiling.

[1] First draw (first morning) water contains lead absorbed from pipes and taps overnight. [2] As described in Consumer's Reports, July, 1995.

POSSIBLE ENVIRONMENTAL POLLUTANTS[1]

Cigarettes	Air	Water	Food	Packaging	Cosmetics
arsenic	benzo Apyrene	benzo Apyrene	cadmium	chloroform	ethylene glycol
asbestos	ozone	asbestos	chloroform	dioxin	formaldehyde
benzo Apyrene	arsenic	arsenic	DDT (fish)	DEHP (wrap)	hydroquinone
cadmium	carbon monoxide	cadmium	dioxin (fish)	formaldehyde	saccharin
carbon monoxide	chloroform	carbon tetrachloride	DEHP	styrene	vinyl chloride
chloroform	DDT → DDE	chloroform	EBDC → ETU	vinyl chloride	
chromium	dioxin	DEHP → PVC	dyes	vinylidene chloride (wrap)	
cyanide	DEHP (inside)	EDB/EDC	heptachlor (milk)		
ethylene oxide	ethylene glycol	lead	lead		
formaldehyde	ethylene oxide	lindane/BHC	lindane/BHC (eggs)		**Formaldehyde**
nickel carbonyl	formaldehyde (in)	mercury	methyl mercury (fish)	**Ozone Depleters**	paints
nitrosomides	naphthalenenicotine	naphalene	nitrate/nitrite	carbon tetrachloride	textiles
toluene	nicotine	nitrates	nitrosomides	methyl bromide	rugs
vinyl chloride	nitric acid NOX	PCB (fish, eggs, milk)	CFC	plywood	
	nitric oxide NOX	PCB/PBBs	saccharin	halons	particle board
	nitrogen dioxides	naphthalene	strontium 90 (milk)	TCA	foam mattresses
Fires	PAN peroxyacelyl nitrate	Cl naphthalene	styrene		dinnerware
carbon monoxide	hydrogen peroxide	Cl dibenzofurans	sulfites		cosmetics
dioxin	nitrous acids	sulfuric acid	TCE	**Cosmetics**	plastics
formaldehyde	PCB	PERC	vinyl chloride	ethylene glycol	air
sulphur dioxide	PCE	toluene		formaldehyde	auto exhaust
	plutonium	TCA		hydroquinone	smoke
	radon (inside)	TCE		saccharin	urea foam
	styrene			vinyl chloride	pesticides
	sulphur dioxide		**Breast Milk**		
	TCA		DDT	**Paint**	
	vinyl chloride		dioxin	formaldehyde	
	xylene		EDB	toluene (oil)	
			heptachlor	xylene (oil)	
			PCE		

Abbreviations: **BHC** = benzine hexachloride, **CFC** = chlorofluorocarbons—ozone depleting refrigerants, **DEHP** = di(2-ethyl hexyl) phthalate plasticizer, **EBDC** = ethylenebisdithiocarbamate fungicides, **EDB** = ethylene dibromide, **ETU** = toxic, carcinogenic breakdown product of EBDCs, **PAN** = toxic peroxyacetyl nitrates formed in sunlight from aldehydes & nitrogen oxides, **PCB** = polychlorinated biphenyls, **PCE** = perchloroethylene, **PBB** = polybrominated biphenyls, **PVC** = polyvinyl chloride—rigid plastic, **TCA** = trichloroacetate—industrial solvent & precursor of vinylidene chloride, **TCE** = trichloroethylene

[1] Based on Harte, et al. 1993. *Toxics A to Z.* U. Cal.

Mail Order Sources for Ecological Gardening Products

These can readily change through time

Product	Use	Sources
Barriers		
Bird netting	Protect tree fruits	4,9,11,13,14,15,16,17,18,20,24,25,26,29,30,46
Brassica Collar	Tarpaper collar to prevent root maggots	14,15,29
Gypsy moth, Slick'n Stick*	Stops larvae on trunk	13
Protective clothing	Goggles, respirators, gloves	4,9,13,16,17,25,28
Row Covers, floating	Keep insects off plants	9,13,14,15,16,17,18,22,24,25,26,28,38,46
Shade cloth	Shades plants	9,17,25
Snail Barr*	Copper strip to keep snails from trees	7,9,17,27,29,36,45
Stickem Special*	Sticky barrier	9,17
Tanglefoot*, tangletrap*	Sticky barrier	4,9,13,18,17,20,24,25,28,29,30,45
Tree shields,skins, wraps	Wrap tree trunks, prevent rodent feeding, borers	4,11,14,16,17,18,24,25,26,29,30,38
Weed control fabric	Black woven mat—air & water penetrates	4,9,11,13,14,16,17,24,25,26,28,30
Beneficial—living organisms		
Aphid midge	*Aphidoletis aphidimyza* controls aphids	19
Agrobacterium radiobacter-K84	Crown Gall Disease control, Norbac*, Galltrol-A*	13,21
AQ-10*	Fungal antagonist for powdery mildews	17
Bacillus subtillis	Kodiac* Seed treatment	**49**[1]
Bumblebee colonies	Potential pollinators for fruits	6,7
Bt israelensis	Mosquito Dunks* Teknar* Bactimos* Controls mosquitoes	12,14,15,17
Bt baits	European cornborer, armyworm	13
Decolate Snails *(Rumina decollata)*	Snail predators (not to N. CA)	34,45
Entomopathogenic nematodes	Attacks insects	8,9,12,13,14,16,17,19,20,22,24,25,26,28,29,30,34
Gliocladium spp	Gliogard* in potting soil interferes with *Pythium & Rhizoctonia*	**50**
Glomus intraradix	Mycori-Mix* in potting soil interferes with *Pythium & Fusarium*	**51**
Green Magic*	Nutrients/benef microbes to control necrotic ring spot in turf	3
Insects or mites	Parasitoids/predators for release	7,12,13,17,18,26,**27**,28,29,**32**,**34**,45
Microbial Insect diseases	(Bt, milky spore, virus etc)	13,14,16,17,18,22,24,25,28,29,30
Mosquito Fish	Controls mosquitoes in ponds & ditches	26
Phlebia gigantea	Rotstop*	
Pseudomonas fluorescens	Dagger* Seed treatment	48
Promot*	*Trichoderma sp* retards growth of harmful soil fungi	17
Restore*	Benef microbs to control necrotic ring spot in turf	29
Strengthen & Renew*	Nutrients/benef microbes to control necrotic ring spot in turf	3
Streptomyces griseoviridis	K61* Mycostop* control damping off, *Pythium, Phytophthora*	17,19,29
Trichoderma spp	BINAB-T* (wound rots), F-Stop* (controls damping off)	13
Fertilizers		
Ca Nitrate/Chelate	Prevent watercore, cork spot, bitter pit in apple/pear fruits.	17,24,41
Charcoal	Remove soil impurities	17
Mycori-Mix*	*Glomus intraradices* helps roots absorb K	42
Trace Minerals	Chelates of calcium, zinc, iron, boron	4,14,17,24,28
Insect food		
Good bug blend/Insectary blend	Seeds of plants which feed beneficials	17,28, 29
Bug Pro	Feed Green Lace Wings	13
Pred Feed*, Wheast*	Feed predatory insects	8,9,13,16,17,29,34
Rescue!*	Soldier bug	7,37
Repellent pesticides		
Deer repellent	Contains putrid egg solids	11,14,17,18,22,25
Deer repellent	soap/bitter	11,13,17,29
DEET (Off!*)	Push spray, Repels mosquitoes & other biting insects	11,2

Product	Use	Sources
Hinder*	Soaps of fatty acids, repels mammals	4,17,20,28,45
No-See-Um* lotion	Same ingredients as Skin-So-Soft*— reported to repel insects	11
Scare eyes balloon/flash tape	Keep away birds from fruit	11,13,14,16,17,18,20,29,30,31,45,46
Selected pesticides		
abamectin	Affirm*Fire Ant control, Avid*	17,28
A-maizing lawn*	Corn syrup extract pre-emergent herbicide	13
boric acid	Ants, Cockroaches	17,28
boric acid baits	Cockroaches, ants, Liquid Ant Killer*	9,13,14,16,17,23,28,43,45
Bordeaux mixture	Disease control	13,24,25,28
Clandosan*	Controls root-knot nematodes (chitin & urea)	13,28
Cloud cover*	Anti-transpirants	17,25
copper	Fungal & bacterial diseases	9,13,14,17,22,24,25,28
cryolite	Caterpillar, beetle desiccant	12,25
diatomaceous earth	Slugs, some insects	9,13,14,15,16,17,24,25,20,45
Frostgard*	Help protect plants from freezing 25-32° F	24
gas cartridge	Kill gophers	14,25,43
d-limonene	Flea Stop* flea soap	13,24
hydramethylnon	Combat* roach & ant baits	13,16
lime sulphur	Peach leaf control	17,18,24,25,28
kinoprene (Enstar*)	Aphid, whitefly control	24,**35**
methoprene	Gencor* roaches, Precor* Bioflea* Petcor* spray dogs/bedding	9,16,24,28,**35**
neem	Ornamentals many insects, Margosan-O* , Bioneem*, Neemex*	9,13,14,17,19,25
Nematrol*	Nematicidal sesame product, kills root nematodes	17
oil, dormant	Preventive insect control on leafless trees	13,14,17,18,24,25,28
oil, superior	Aphid, mite, psyllid control, whitefly control	13,17,18,19,24,25,28,29,30
phosmet (Imidan*)	Codling moth, plum curculio control	13,24
Permanone*	Permethrin treatment for clothing to repel ticks	11
Permethrin*-laced mouse nesting matl	Control Lyme disease ticks	17
pyrethrins	Effects many insects	9,14,17,22,24
rotenone	Effects many insects	13,14,27
ryania	Codling moth control, Ryan 50*	13,14,17,25,27
sabadilla	Effects many insects	8,13,14,15,17,18,22,24,27,28
silica aerogel	Household ants, termites (some with pyrethrin)	17,39
soap, fatty acid (insect, weed, fungus)	Insecticidal*. M-Pede*, Superfast*	8,9,13,14,15,17,18,19,20,24,25,27,28,29
Streptomycin	Fire blight	17,24
sulphur, wettable or with soap	Several diseases, mites	13,17,19,24,28
Wilt-Pruf*, Crop Life*	Anti-transpirants	4,19,24,25
Tools, instruments		
Bat Houses	Large sizes are best	13,14,15,17,25,31,43
Bird houses, wood crete	Predator proof	23
Books	IPM information	9,14,17,22,28,44,45,47
Compost bins		4,9,13,15,16,17,25,28
Drip irrigation equipment	Compatible open stock parts	4,17,19,24,25,45,46
Insect sweep nets	Sample insects	5,11,23,30
Goatskin gloves	Long lasting, non-bulky. Best for garden use	4,11,17,45
Magnifiers, lenses	Pocket	4,5,11,17,23,29,30
Propagation mats	Underheating for seedlings	4,14,15,26
Pruners, pole	Extension telescoping	4,11,45
Rain gauge	U.S. Weather Bureau	11,30
Soil test kits		9,13,14,17,22,28,45
Spiked lawn aerator sandals	Aerate lawn, White grub control	10,14,15,21,25,45,43

Product	Use	Source
Syringe, garden	Inject plants	13,15
Thermometers, Max-Min	Keep track of temperatures to monitor insects, diseases	4,11,14,15,17,19,22,23,24,25,26,45
Thermometers, Soil	Determine soil temperature	4,9,11,14,16,17,23,24,25,28,46
Weed burner, propane	Burning weeds	11,14,16,17,18,25,31,45
Traps & attractant baits		
Ball, red	Attract apple maggot	9,13,14,15,17,18,25,26,28,29,46
Bee swarm trap	Capture swarms	30
Black light (UV)	Attract insects at night	20,39
Colored cards	Attract certain small insects	8,9,13,16,17,21,22,25,28,29,30,45
Eugenol	Attract cucumber beetles, mix with poison bait	29
Entice*	Mix with Bt to stimulate caterpillar feeding	13,14,28
Flea trap	Traps adult fleas	13,17,25,43
Insect bait stations	Kill ants, cockroach, Japanese beetles	4,9,13,15,17,20,25,28
Live catch traps	Mammal	5,9,11,13,14,16,17,18,25,26,28,31,43
Mosquito trap	Carbon dioxide-based	39
Pheromone	Attract insects to monitor populations	13,14,17,20,28,29,30,37,45,46
Mating disruption	Pheromone point sources to confuse males	28,29,30
Slug/snail traps	Attracts mollusks	13,14,15,17,22,28,29,39
Sticky roach*	Monitoring roaches	13,20,24
Wasp trap	Add food to attract	17,25,43,4

* Registered products [1]Bold numbers represent producers

Sources

3. Agro-Chem, 11150 W./ Addison St. Franklin Park, IL 60131	708-455-6900
4. A.M. Leonard, Inc. O.O. box 816, Piqua, OH 45356-0816	800-543-8955
5. BioQuip, 17803 La Salle Ave., Gardena, CA 90248-3602	310-324-0620
6. Bees West, Inc. P.O. Box 1378, Freedom, CA 95109	408-728-3325
7. Biobest Biological Systems, Beneficial Resources, Inc. P.O. Box 34, Turbotville, PA 17772	717-649-6289
8. Bozeman Bio-Tech, P.O. 3146, Bozeman, MT 95772,	800-289-6656
9. Ecology Action, 5798 Ridgewood Rd., Willits, CA 95490	
10. FAR, 510-1/2 West Chase Dr., Corona, CA 91720	714-371-0120
11. Forestry Supplies, Inc., P.O. Box 8397, Jackson, MS 39284-8397	800-647-5368
12. Four Winds Farm Supply, Route 1, Box 206, River Falls, WE 54022	715-425-7037
13. Gardens Alive! P.0. Box 149, Sunman, IN 47041.	812-623-3800
14. Garden City Seeds, 1324 Red Crow Rd., Victor, MO 59875-9713,	460-961-4837
15. Gardeners Supply, , 128 Intervale, Rd. Dept. GRSM, Burlington, VT 05401	800-863-1700
16. Gurneys Seed & Nursery Co., 110 Capital St., Yankton, SD 57079	605-665-1930
17. Harmony Farm Supply, 3244 Gravenstein Hwy. N., Sebastopol, CA 95472,	707-823-9125
18. Henry Fields, 415 N. Burnett, Shenandoah, IA 51602	605-665-9391
19. Hydro-Gardens, P.O. Box 9709, Colorado Springs, Co 80932	800-634-6362
20. Insects Limited, 10540 Jessup Blvd. Indianapolis, IN 46280-1451	800-992-1991
21. IPM Labs, P.O. Box 300, Locke, NY 13092-0300	315-497-3129
22. Johnny's Selected Seeds, Foss Hill Rd, Albion, MA 04910-9731	207-437-4301
23. Kinsman Co. River Rd., Point Pleasant, PA 18950	800-733-5613
24. **Many local suppliers, garden, grocery, feed, pet stores**	
25. Mellingers, Inc., 2310 South Range Rd. North Lima, OH 4452-9731	216-549-9861
26. Monterey Lawn & Garden Products, Box 5317, Fresno	209-255-4770
27. Natural Pest Controls, 8864 Little Creek Dr. Orangevale, CA 95662	916-726-0855
28. Necessary Trading Co, 1 Natures Way, New Castle, VA 24127.	703-864-5103

Sources

29. Peaceful Valley Farm Supply, 11173 Peaceful Valley Rd., Nevada City, CA 95959.	916-265-3276
30. Pest Management Supply, P.O. Box 938, Amherst, MA 01004	800-727-7672
31. Plow & Hearth	800-627-1712
32. Praxis, P.O. Box 360, Allegan, MI 49010	616-673-2793
51. Premier Enterprises, 326 Main St., Red Hill, PA 18076	800-424-2554
33. Real Goods, 966 Mazzoni St. Ukiah, CA 95482-3471	800-762-7325
34. Rincon-Vitova, P.O Box 95, Oak View, CA 93022	800-643-5407
35. Sandoz Crop Protection, 1300 E Touhy Ave. Des Plaines, IL 60018	800-553-4833
36. Snail Barr, Box 4939, Ventura, CA 93004	805-647-1652
37. Sterling International, Inc. 15916 E Sprague Ave, Veradale, WA 99037	800-666-6766
38. Stokes, P.O. Box 548, Buffalo, NY	716-695-6980
39. Target Specialty Products, 1280 North 10th St. San Jose, CA 95112 408-293-6032	800-767-0719
40. Trecé, 635 S. Sanborn Rd., Suite 17, Salinas, CA 93901.	408-758-0204
41. Wilson & Geo.Meyer & Co..270 Lawrence Ave. S. San Francisco, CA 94080	415-871-1770
42. Fortan Bio Co. Inc., P.O. Box 62036, La Pérade, Quebec, Canada G1W-4Z2	
43. Home Improvements, 4944 Commerce Parkway, Cleveland, OH 44128,	800-642-2112
44. Publications, U. Calif. Agriculture & Natural Resources, 6701 San Pablo Ave, Oakland CA	510-642-2431
45. Natural Gardening Co. 217 San Anselmo Ave. San Anselmo, CA 94960	707-766-9303
46. Territorial Seed Co. 20 Palmer Ave. Cottage Grove, OR 97424	503-942-9547
47. AgAccess Book Catalog, P.O. Box 2008, Davis, CA 95617	916-756-7177
48. Ecogen, 2005 Cabot Blvd.W., Langhorne, Pa 19047-1810	800-220-2135
49. Gustafson. Inc. P.O. Box 660065, Dallas, TX 75266-0065	214-985-8877
50. Scotts-Sierra Crop Protection Co., P.O. Box 4003, Milpitas, CA 95035	800-492-8255

Bareroot fruit tree mail order nurseries

Amaryllis, Inc. P.O. Box 318, Baton Rough, LA 70821 (Potomac Pear)
Bear Creek Nursery, P.O. Box 411, Northport, WA 99157
Fowler Garden Center & Nursery, 525 Fowler Rd. Newcastle, CA 95658, 916-645-8194
Greenmantle Nursery, 3010 Ettersburg, Rd, Garberville, CA 95440, 707-986-7504
Harmony Farm Supply, 3244 Gravenstein Hwy. N., Sebastopol, CA 95472, 707-823-9125
Henry Fields, 415 N. Burnett, Shenandoah, IA 51602, 605-665-9391
Hidden Springs Nursery, 170 Hidden Springs Lane, Cookeville, NT 38501, 615-268-2592
New York State Fruit Testing Cooperative Assoc, P.O. Box 462, Geneva, NY 14456, 315-787-2205
Northwoods Nursery, 27635 S. Oglesby Rd, Canby, OR 97013, 503-266-5432
Raintree Nursery, 391 Butts Rd., Morton, WA 98356, 206-496-6400
Rocky Meadow Orchard & Nursery, 360 Rocky Meadow Rd., N.W., New Salisbury, IN 47161, 812-347-2213
Stark Bros Nurseries, Box B248CA, Louisiana, MO 63353, 314-754-4525
Southmeadow Fruit Gardens, Box SM, Lakeside, MI 49116
Van Well Nursery, P.O. Box 1339, Wenatchee, WA 98807, 509-663-8189

Suggested Literature

Books

Arnett, R. H. & R. L. Jacques, *Simon & Schuster's Guide to Insects.* Simon & Schuster. Photos of insects

Borror, D. J. & R. E.White, *A Field Guide to the Insects.* Hougton Mifflin. Colored drawings of insects

Carr, A. & W. Olkowski., *Color Handbook of Garden Insects.* Rodale. Photos of pest insects, range maps

Dreistadt, S.H., J.K. Clark, M.L. Flint, *Pests of Landscape Trees & Shrubs.* U. Cal. , Pub #3359. IPM control.

Fichter, G.S. & H.S. Zim. *Insect Pests.* Golden. Color drawings of insects, range maps

Flint, M. L., *Pests of the Garden and Small Farm.* U. Cal Pub.# 3332., Insect control based on research

Harte, J., C. Holdren, R. Schneider, & C. Shirley. *Toxics A to Z.* U. Cal. Guide to everyday pollution hazards

Johnson, W. T. & H. H. Lyon, *Insects that feed on Trees and Shrubs.* Comstock. Scientific descriptions with photos

Milne, L. & M., *The Audubon Society Field Guide to North American Insects and Spiders.* Knopf Photos

Mitchell, R.T. & H.S. Zim. *Butterflies and Moths.* Golden. Colored drawings of insects, range maps

Ogawa, J. M. & H. English, *Diseases of Temperate Zone Tree Fruit & Nut Crops.* U .Cal. Press Orchard disease control

Olkowski, W., S. Daar, & H. Olkowski, *Common-sense Pest Control.* Taunton. Research-based pest control

Powell, J.A. & C.L. Hogue, *California Insects.* U. Cal. Press Line drawings & photos, description of life cycles

Sinclair, W.Q., H. H. Lyon, & W. T. Johnson, *Diseases of trees & shrubs.* Comstock. Scientific descriptions & photos

Ware, G.W., *Complete Guide to Pest Control.* Thompson. Comprehensive treatment of insects on crops.

Zim, H.S. & C. Cottam, *A Golden Guide to Insects.* Golden. Colored drawings, range maps

Periodicals

California Agriculture, Division of Agric. & Natural Resources, Univ. Cal, 300 Lakeside Dr, 6th floor, Oakland, CA 94612-3560, Excellent coverage of new research on growing plants, including urban & small farms. Free in U.S.

Common Sense Pest Control Quarterly, Bio-integral Resource Center (BIRC), P.O. Box 7414, Berkeley, CA 94707—510-524-2567—each issue contains comprehensive information for one pest insect or disease.

IPM Practitioner, (BIRC), P.O. Box 7414, Berkeley, CA 94707—510-524-2567, updates on current research & annual update of sources of IPM products & beneficial insects

National Gardening, National Gardening Assoc., 180 Flynn Ave. Burlington, VT 05401, subscription 800-727-9097

Computer

Folio INfoBase—project summaries USDA Sustainable Agri. research. Free for formatted IPM compatable disk. Insert in IPM compatable high density drive & type SAN. In Calif: SAN Infobase, c/o Jill Auburn, Info. Group, SAREP, U.C. Davis, CA 95161. Elsewhere: Phil Rasmussen, Chari. Agri. Systems Tech. Dept. Utah State Univ, Logan, UT 84321

Internet: <telnet> <cicp.biochem.vt.edu> For info: CICP, Cornell Univ. NYAES, Geneva, NY 14456-0462

Toxics Information

Agency for Toxic Substances & Disease Registry, 1600 Clifton Rd, Atlanta, GA 30033, 404-639-0501. Packets.

EPA Public Information Center, 401 M St. S.W., Washington, D.C. 20460. 202-260-2080. Catalog

National Pesticides Telecommunications Network (NPTN) General info about pesticides. M-F, 8-6:00. 800-858-7378.

National Toxicity Program, Mail Stop A0-02, National. Inst. Environ. Health Sci., P.O. Box 12233, Research Triangle Park, NC 27709, 919-541-4482.

Pesticide Information Network (PIN) Interactive database (current & historic pesticide info) via Modem 1-703-305-5919

Useful Catalog Suppliers

A.M Leonard, Inc. P.O. Box 816 Piqua, OH 45356, 800-543-8955.

BioQuip,17803 La Salle Ave, Gardena, CA 90248-3602, 310-324-0620

Forestry Suppliers, Inc. P.O. Box 8397, Jackson, MS 39284-8397, 800-647-5368.

Gardens Alive!, 5100 Schenley Pl. Lawrenceburg, IN 47025, 812-537-8650.

Harmony Farm Supply & Nursery, P.O. Box 460, Graton, CA 95444, 707-823-9125

Necessary Trading Co, 1 Natures Way, New Castle, VA 24127, 703-864-5103

Peaceful Valley Farm Supply, P.O. 2209, Grass Valley , CA 95945, 916-272-4769.

Pest Management Supply Company, P.O. Box 938, Amherst, MA 01004, 800-272-7672.

Praxis, P.O. Box 360, Allegan, MI 49010, 616-673-2793

Rincon-Vitova, P.O. Box 95, Oak View, CA 93022, 800-643-5407

Index

core); harvest & storage of 198, 200; insect pests of (apple maggot, codling moth, leafrollers, tufted apple bud moth, spider mites, wooly apple aphid); insect-resistant varieties; interstems; rootstocks; watering 122

apple maggot *(Rhagoletis pomonella)* 11, 12, 127, 130, **131**, 133 156; history, recognition, life cycle & control

apple scab IPM 172-174, description of disease, characteristics which promote development of, control strategies; effects of fungicides on (cancer, birth defects, mite outbreaks, resistant strains); chart to record data

apricots 144-146, culture, varieties, pests, & controls; diseases of (bacterial blight, brown rot, Eutypa dieback); harvest & storage of 199, 200; insects on (earwigs, chafer beetles, plum curculio); pruning; watering 122,

AQ10* *(Ampelomyces quisqualis)* 223, powdery mildew *Podosphaera & Sphaeotheca spp)* hyperparasite

arachnids 72, 74-75, characteristics of (mites, spiders)

Armillaria root rots (shoestring rot) on ≈100 woody plants, life style & control, **180**

armyworms 15, 55, 104, 107, 118, 213; *Spodoptera or Prodenia spp.*

arsenic, arsenicals 112, 208, 226, 231; substances containing arsenic, sometimes in a compound; air pollutant

arthropods 185, 193, animals with jointed legs, segmented bodies & exoskeleton

artichokes 76, **114** culture & pest control; pests of (artichoke plume moth, brown garden snail)

artichoke plume moth *(Platyptilia carduidactyla)* 58, **114**

aromatic hydrocarbon 226, 227, 228; compounds containing hydrogen & carbon arranged in one or more benzine rings

asbestos 231, carcinogen in cigarettes (some wallboards, floor tiles, insulation materials)

ascospores, reproductive structures of certain fungi, such as scabs **171-172**, 178, 179; germination is weather related

ashes 77, 120, alkaline residues left after wood or coal burns

asparagus 111, culture & pest controls; diseases of 180, 181; insects on (asparagus aphid, asparagus beetle, spotted asparagus beetle)

asparagus aphid *(Brachycorynella asparagi)* 111

asparagus beetle *(Crioceris asparagus)* 111

aspirin 214, 218, 220, 224

Aspergillus flavus 107, fungus which synthesizes the carcinogen, alfatoxin on damp cereal grains, peanuts etc.

atrazine 11, 215; persistent pre-emergent triazine herbicide; possible carcinogen; estrogen disrupter

attractants 12, 159, 232; colors 156; food & other baits [to mix with Bt to increase pest feeding 107, (Adios*, Coax*, Entice*, Gustol*, eugenol, Slam*); cucumber beetle bait 107, 156; cucurbitacin (substances from squash or cucumbers); methyl eugenol to attract Oriental fruit flies; to attract & kill (Attractn'Kill*,Check-mate*, Nemesis*); to feed beneficial insects 106, 107, 122, 133 (Wheast*, Pred-Feed IPM*, Fruit Boost*, Soldier Bug Attracter*); yeast to attract snails 77]; see also light traps; pheromones; ultrasound, zappers

Attack*, see *Bacillus thuringiensis kurstoki,* mosquito 35

Autographa californica NPV (insect nuclear polyhedrosis virus) 85

Autographa falcifera NPV (insect nuclear polyhedrosis virus) 85

Avid*, see abamectin

avocados 55, harvest & storage of 199, 200

azadirachtin, see neem

Azatin* see neem

azinphosmethyl (Guthion*) 215, 221, OP insecticide

azoles, 217, see fungicides

Bacillus, genus of bacteria, see diseases of..........

Bacillus subtilis (MBl 600*, Quantum 4000 HB*) 223, 232, bacteria prevent growth of fungal diseases (*Verticillium spp. &Monilinia spp.* 177)

bacteria, microscopic one celled organisms which are wide spread in animals, plants, & the environment. Some cause, others prevent diseases; some are used in food or chemical synthesis, or breakdown of chemical wastes; antibiotic-resistant disease bacteria 162

bacteria, beneficial 119-120, 232, in soil [215, 218, 223 *Bacillus subtilus* (Quantum 4000HB) (against *Verticillium* wilts 107, 179, 182); in compost (against *Pythium ultimum & Enterobacter spp., & Flavobacterium balustinum)];* on leaves 107, 140, 177 *[Bacillus subtilis* prevents *Monilinia spp.* brown rot & *Aspergillus flavus; Pseudomonas fluroescens & Ersinia hervicola* interfere with fireblight]; symbiotic bacteria *Rhozobia sp.* 80, 110. 218 on roots of legumes

bacterial blight, see diseases of plants

bacterial diseases of insects 84-85 *Bacillus popuilliae* (Doom*, Milky Spore*), Japanese & other scarab beetles, 101, 218; ***Bacillus sphaericus***, mosquitoes, blackflies 35

bacterial diseases of insects, *Bacillus thuringiensis* (Bt) 16, 51, 206, 213, 118, 221, 218, 227, **232** description, life cycle, & use; biotechnology using 160-161; on beetles 41, 47, 113, *[Bt San Diego* (M-one*. M-track*) & *Bt tenebrionis* (Trident*, Novador*)]; on caterpillars 3, 8, 104, 108, 109, 115, 130, 134, 147, 148, *[Bt kurstake* (Attack*, Biobit*, Cutlass*, Dipel*, M-cap*)] & *[Bt thuringiensis* (Javelin*, Thuricide*); caffeine as additive to 104]; on fungus gnats 29, **79**, (Bt H-14, Gnatrol*); for mosquitoes & blackflies **32-33**, 35 *[Bt israelensis* (Bactimos*, Tecknar*, Vectobac*)]; on certain moths *[Bt aizawai* (Certan*, Florbac*, Centari*) 221]; in soils 80

bacterial spot, see diseases of plants

bactericides, substances which kill bacteria, see fungicides

Bactimos* briquettes 35, mosquito insecticide

Banlan*, see benefin, see herbicides

bases, substances with a neutral pH of 7, when the hydrogen ion balance is determined —taste salty

Baygon*, see propoxur 71, see also CBs

Bayleton*, see triadimefon, see also fungicides

baits, see attractants

bananas, harvest & storage of 198, 200

barriers 104, 212, 218, 232, 233; bird netting 6, 109, 110, 111; fabrics 103 [black landscape 36, 105, 170; floating row covers (Remay*) 12, 55, 58, 102, 110, 126; shade cloth; tree wraps (Sure Fire*, Tree Guard*) 148, 160]; cutworm collars 12; copper (Snail Barr*) **76-77**; Frostgard* 212; fencing 6; panty hose 71, 155; paper bags 109, 155; sticky (Stickem Special*, Tanglefoot*, Tangletrap*); inappropriate for snails 77 (ashes, glass, sand)

bats, life style & role in environment 86, houses for, 233

beans 110, as cover crop 81, 110; diseases of 180, 181; har-

borne [AIDS, hantavirus, hemorrhagic fever, myxomatosis]; transmission methods of (biological transmission, mechanical inoculation, wound contamination); for scientific names, see disease name

diseases of plants, bacterial— blights, cankers of twigs, leaves, & fruits **182-183**; blights & rots of vegetables [bacterial spot of tomato; black rot of crucifers *(Xanthomonas spp)*, corky root of lettuce *(Rhizomonas suberifaciens)* 105; soft rots & wilts of crucifers *(Erwinia spp)*]; potato scab *(Streptomyces scabies)* 112]; blights & rots of woody plants 141,142,147,148 [crown gall *(Agrobacterium tumefaciens)* on stone fruits; fireblight *(Erwinia anylovora)* 127, 128, 130, 137, 139, 140; bacterial cankers *(Pseudomonas savastanoi, Ps. syringae)* on apricots 145, cherries & peaches]; spot; root rots 120 [crown gall *(Agrobacterium tumefaciens)]*

diseases of plants, causes of 80, 116, 118, **170-171** (plant disease triangle, nutrients, disease inoculum, rainfall 177-183, resistance characteristics, water management); chart of named **177-183**; control by (antitranspirants, fungicides 216-217); prevention via 105, 108, 181, 223 [harmless antagonists *(Bacillus subtilus* competes with *Verticillium spp.* 179; *Tricoderma harzianum* competes with *Fusarium spp.* 181, 217, 219); certified disease-free plants; cross protection; mycorrhizae increase nutrient uptake; plant quarantines; resistant cultivars 6, 59, 177, 182; sanitation 177-178; solarization; suppressive soils; water management 179]

diseases of plants, fungal, on leaves [anthracnoses; blister rust *Phytophthora citrophthora* 80; chestnut blight; corky root; necrotic ringspot *(Leptosphaeria korrae)* of grasses 116-117; peach leaf curl; leaf spots **178**, 216 [*(Blumeriella jaapii, Entomosporium spp, Diplocarpon rosae, Coccomyces spp.)* of pome fruits & Rosacae; *(Guignardia bidwellii)* of horse chestnut & buckeye]; mildews [downy on (crucifers 108, grape 176, squash 109); powdery on (grapes 153, 154; legumes 110; squash 109)]; rust of vegetables 181; shot hole; white mold *(Sclerotinia spp.)* 180, 216; scabs 178 [apple, pear; *Pyrocantha*]; rusts 179

diseases of plants, fungal, on fruits, 177 brown rot, brown spoilage of citrus, bunch rot of grapes, charcoal of corn *(Sclerotium bataticol)*; see also disease name

diseases of plants, fungal, on twigs & whole plants; blights 113, **180** [club root *(Plasmodiophora brassicae)* 178; early *(Alternaria solani, Septonia lycopersici)* 216; late *(Phytophthora infestans)* 80]; cankers **179** [Black knot *(Aptosporian morbosa)*; cytospora cankers *(Cytospora spp.)*; cypress *(Seridium carinale)*; Dutch elm *(Ceratocystis ulmi)* 51; Eutypa dieback; pine pitch *(Fusarium lateritum)*]; crown rots 80, 105, 124, 125 [shoestring *(Amillaria sp.)*180; crown 80, 96, 141, 147, 178, 180 *(Phytophthora cactorum, P. cimmamomi, P. parasatic)*]; crown galls & rots 80, 177, 179 [damp-off 6 *(Rhizoctonia solani & Pythium spp.)*; *(Fusarium spp., Pythium ultimum, Scleotium rolfsii, Rhizoctonia solani)* of vegetables 104, 181, 182]; fungal wilts 80, 180,181 *(Alternaria alternata, 108, Fusarium lateritium, F. moniliforme, F. oxysporum, F. roseum, Rhizoctonia solani)*; soil-borne **178-179** *(Verticillium spp.)*]; wood rots 87, 180 Armillaria *(Armillaria spp.)*; crown *(Phytophthora spp)*; [mold, sapstain, rots (brown, dry, soft, white)]

diseases of plants, micoplasmas 183, buckskin disease of cherry

diseases of plants, unbalanced nutrients **170-171**; due to general plant stresses—causes of 177; physiological 181 [blossom end 104, 170; stresses causing 109, 177; sun scald; tuber necrosis]; physiological **127**,139 (bitter pit, corky spot, flyspeck, sooty blotch, sun scald, water core) on apples or pears; disease free cultivars 170

diseases of plants, viral 52, 53, 63, **183** [cabbage, cotton leaf crumple, infectious yellows, lettuce infectious yellows, mosaics 59, 109; silverleaf, squash leaf curl, Texas pepper, tobacco mosaics, tomato calico curl, tomato irregular, tomato mottle, tomato spotted wilt 68, walnut blackline]

Dispalure* 211, attractant pheromone of the gypsy moth

Dispatch* see microbes

Disrupt* see pheromones

diuron (Karmex*) 216, 222, 227; persistent pre-emergent substituted urea herbicide

DMP, see phthalates

DNA (deoxyribonucleic acid) 226, nucleic acid which transmits hereditary information within the cell

DNP 226, 227 dinitrophenol

dormant 226, season when crops do not grow

DOT (BoraCare*, Tim-Bor*) 214, 217, 220, 223, 228 boric acid-based wood fungicide

Douglas fir tussock moth 212, control of

Dowpon* , see DCPA

dragonflies 27, 28, see Odonata

drain care 101, biological cleaners 101

DriDie*, see silica gel

DriDie 67*, see silica gel mixtures,

Drione*, see silica gel mixtures

DSMA (Ansar*) 215, 223, organic arsenical herbicide

Dursban*, see chlorpyrifos, OPs

Dutch elm disease *(Ceratocystis ulmi)*, spread by European elm bark beetle 51, 179; see also diseases of plants

earthworms 9, 106, 117, 120 (annelid worms which live in the soil & ingest dead plant materials)

earwigs, control, life cycle & ecology of 6, **60**, 92, 120, 146 [European *(Forticula auricularia)*, ring-legged *(Euborellia annulipes)*, striped *(Labidura riparia)*]

EBDC (ethylene bidithiocarbamate) **216-217**, 226, 227, 229 broad spectrum fungicides; estrogen disrupters; potential pollutant in foods

ecdysone 14, insect molting hormone

ecdysone, natural insect hormone which affects molting

egg shell thinning 9, causes of in birds

eggs, spoiled 218, game repellent

eggplant, culture of 44, harvest & storage of 202, *Verticillium* wilt of 80, see also 179

Electrogun 91, microwave-based termite control method

elm, (American, Asian, European) see diseases of plants 179, insects on 38, 48; elm leaf beetle resistant varieties 48

encapsulated 12, 25, placed in a capsule

Encarsia formosa 52, greenhouse whitefly parasitoid

Encarsia partenopea 52, ash whitefly parasitoid

encephalitis, 186, 187; viral brain-damaging *Flavivirus spp.* diseases, transmitted by mosquitoes (California, Eastern equine, Japanese, La Crosse, St Louis, Venezuelan

Perillus bioculatus 46, two-spotted stink bug predator of Colorado potato beetle
Periplaneta spp. 92 cockroach genus
permanent wilting point 121, wilting of plant which follows a condition where water in the soil is bound so tightly that plant cannot obtain water
permethrin (Permanone*, Permethrin*) 37, 222, 233, pyrethroid insecticides are endocrine disrupters
peroxyacetyl nitrates, see PAN
persimmons 55, harvest & storage of 199, 200
persistent, substances which are long-lasting in the environment 225
pest, definition of 8
pest control agents, characteristics of urban 7, **218-220** (attractants, barriers, diseases, parasites, predators, insect growth regulators, organic pesticides, inorganic pesticides, nematicides, synergists, household chemicals)
pest control, natural 3, 7, 13 of insects by (birds & bats 86, (spiders 74, 106); of mammals by owls & hawks 163-168
pest mammals & birds, control of **141, 143, 163-168**, definition 9, imported 10, sources 10; birds (blackbirds, cowbirds European Starling, House Sparrow, Rock Dove); mammals [cats, deer, dogs, opossums, raccoons, rodents (chipmunks, mice, pocket gophers, rats, voles, squirrels); skunks, insectivores (moles, shrews)]; see natural control
pest resurgence, upsets (more pests) soon after pesticide sprays **11**, 66, 77; causes of 11 (mites 133, 135, 172; aphids 57, 58)
pesticide definitions, **204**, broad-spectrum 34, 58, 127; contact 9; measures of hazard 205 (acute, subchronic, chronic, carcinogens, lethal doses (LD_{50}, LD_{95}), teratogens); methods of exposure 205 (dermal, oral); selective 10, 13, 133; stability of 13 (non-persistent 133, persistent); types of (acaricides, bactericides, fungicides, insecticides, herbicides, picicides, plant growth regulators, repellents 7, 218; rodenticides)
pesticide, label, information on & how to read **206-208** (chemical & common names, concentration of active & 'inert' ingredients, EPA numbers, directions for use, limitations, manufacturer's name, signal words, toxicity classes, trade name of product, warning statements, weight)
pesticide use choices 3, 12, 206, 207, 208, 209 (need for? other methods? hazards of use?), extent of use at; to avoid exposure 134 (choose least toxic & least-persistent materials; dilute carefully, follow directions), use (selective application, protective clothing 22, 232, measuring & mixing 211); preventing food contamination
pesticides, all purpose killers, risks from 210; biology learned from **8-13**; classification of garden **211-217**; commonly encountered **221-225**; create secondary pests 9-10, 127, 133; effects of **8-13**, 96, 173; formulations of 207 [emulsible concentrates (EC), flowable (FL), granular, wettable powder (WP)]; introduction to **207-208**; modes of action **226-228**; more toxic to natural enemies 10; on lawns 116-118; penetration ability of 208; potential for movement in food chains & magnify in environment 9, 205; resistance to 8, 47, **52-53**, 85, 106, 133; toxicity relationships 206
pesticides, regulation of 204, Environmental Protection Agency (EPA) under Federal Insecticide, Fungicide & Rodenticide Act
pests, sources of 10-12, evolutionary changes, importation, resurgence, secondary
Petcor*, see methoprene
pH 7, 100, 116, 104, 115, 120 measure of the hydrogen ions in a solution which determine acidity or alkalinity; pH 7 is neutral, acids are ≤ pH 1-6, & alkalis are ≥ pH 8-10; as disease prevention 170
Pharorid* 17
phenothrin, 211, 229; pyrethroid insecticides are endocrine disrupters
phenylamides (**PNM**) 217, 227 control *Pythium* & *Phytophthora* fungi, see fungicides
Pherocon* 212, attractant insect pheromones
pheromones, 6, 15, 158-159, 211, 218; natural odors which attract insects; traps using 19, 128, 130, 133, 134, 156; {confusion technique (Isomate*, Luretape*, NoMate TPW*); pheromone monitoring lures [(Codlelure*, Curlure*, Dispalure*, Pherocon*)
pheylphenol (Lysol) 224, disinfectant
phosmet (Imidan*) 49, 50, 134, 213, 220; 222, 233, selective OP insecticide; use against codling moth & plum curculio
phosphorus (**P**) 115, 121, 153, mineral element that serves as a major plant nutrient, see also fertilizer
photosynthesis 227, synthesis of carbohyderates from carbon dioxide & water by plants in the presence of light
Phryganidia californica 16, California oakworm
phthalates, diethyl (**DMP**) & **diethylhexyl** (**DEHP**) 222, 225, 231 insect repellent (DMP) & plasticizers; endocrine disrupters; in contaminated air, food, & water can cause injury to liver & testicles
Phyllonorycter spp 36, leafminers on apple
Phyllotreta sp. 43, See leaf beetles (flea)
Phytophthora root rot 80, 120, 125, 180 (crown rot) infestation follows flooding during warm weather, see also diseases of plants, fungal; see also solarization 80)
Phytoselulus persimilis 76, predatory mite
picicides 209, substances which kill fish
pickleworms *(Diaphania nitidalis)* 109, caterpillars on squash
picloram 223, systemic, post-emergent herbicide. B_2 carcinogen
Pieris rapae 15, 108, imported cabbage worm
pine, diseases of 179, *Phytophthora* root rot of 80; pine pitch canker
pineapple, choosing & storage of 198, 201
piperazines 217, see fungicides
piperonyl butoxide, (Buticide*, *Ocotea cymbarium*) 224, 228; synergist to prolong pesticide activity
pistachio, *Verticillium* wilt of 80, see also 179
plague, 186, 192 (bubonic, pneumonia, septicemic) disease caused by *Yersinia pestis* bacteria, transmitted by fleas from rats to humans
planting, how to 6, 103; fruit trees **125-126**; when to 102, 106 [artichokes 114, beets, bok choy, carrots, crucifers 108 (broccoli, brussel sprouts, cabbage); corn, legumes 81, 110, lettuce, melons, okras, parsnips, peppers, potatoes, rhubarb, squash, sprouts, strawberry, sweet potatoes, tomatoes, turnips]
plants, requirements of 121 (air, nutrients, water)
Plasmodium sp 191, Malaria protozoa
plastics, plasticizers 229, 230 hazards from certain

* Trade names, Abbreviations page 226.